THE HOLT SCIENCE PROGRAM

SCIENCE, *Observation and Experiment,* by Davis, Burnett, and Gross

SCIENCE, *Experiment and Discovery,* by Davis, Burnett, and Gross

SCIENCE, *Discovery and Progress,* by Davis, Burnett, and Gross

LIFE SCIENCE, *The World of Living Things,* by Davis, Burnett, and Gross

MODERN BIOLOGY, by Moon, Otto, and Towle

MODERN CHEMISTRY, by Dull, Metcalfe, and Williams

MODERN PHYSICS, by Dull, Metcalfe, and Williams

LIVING THINGS, by Fitzpatrick and Bain

MODERN HEALTH, by Otto, Julian, and Tether

HUMAN PHYSIOLOGY, by Morrison, Cornett, and Tether

MODERN PHYSICAL SCIENCE, by Brooks and Tracy

MODERN EARTH SCIENCE, by Ramsey and Burckley

MODERN SPACE SCIENCE, by Trinklein and Huffer

MATTER, ENERGY AND CHANGE, sponsored by Manufacturing Chemists' Assoc., Inc.

SUPERSTITION TO SUPERSONICS, sponsored by Manufacturing Chemists' Assoc., Inc.

LABORATORY AND FIELD STUDIES IN BIOLOGY, sponsored by National Academy of Sciences—National Research Council

GEOLOGY AND EARTH SCIENCES SOURCEBOOK, sponsored by National Academy of Sciences—National Research Council, under the guidance of a Committee of the American Geological Institute

CHEMISTRY PROBLEMS, by Castka

SEMIMICRO CHEMISTRY, by DeBruyne, Kirk, and Beers

SCIENTIFIC EXPERIMENTS IN CHEMISTRY, sponsored by Manufacturing Chemists' Assoc., Inc.

PHYSICS PROBLEMS, by Castka and Lefler

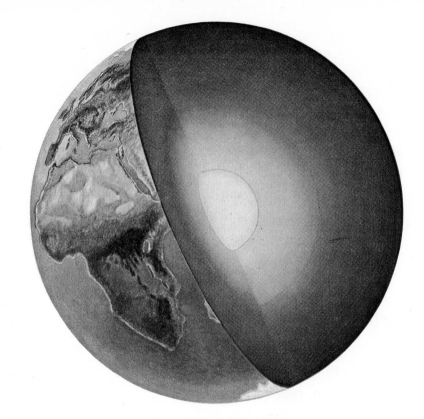

MODERN

New York

WILLIAM L. RAMSEY

RAYMOND A. BURCKLEY

EARTH
SCIENCE

Holt, Rinehart and Winston, Inc.

William L. Ramsey is Head of the Science Department of Helix High School, La Mesa, California.

Raymond A. Burckley is Chairman of the Science Department of Hicksville High School, Hicksville, New York.

The authors acknowledge with thanks the assistance of **Henri J. Floch,** Phoenix Central Schools, Phoenix, New York, who wrote the end-materials for all chapters and units in the text.

The artists of MODERN EARTH SCIENCE:

Design and format—Peter Berkeley

Art—F. R. Gruger, Jr.

Photographs—Frances L. Orkin

Certain drawings in Chapters 21 and 22, and all of the drawings in Chapter 23 have been adapted from THE FOSSIL BOOK, copyright 1958 by Carroll Lane Fenton and Mildred Adams Fenton. Used by permission of Doubleday and Company, Inc.

Unit opening photographs: **1.** Nebula in the constellation of Orion; **2.** Captain J. P. Nagel studies charts on board Esso Zurich; **3.** Sandstone outcrop in Fremont Co., Wyoming; **4.** Eruption on a volcanic peak in Katmai National Monument, Alaska; **5.** Rock arch in Monument Valley, Arizona; **6.** Reproduction of Devonian marine life; **7.** Fishing boats near Cape Ann, Massachusetts; **8.** Hurricane warnings at Hatteras, North Carolina, weather station; **9.** Jungle on the Magdalena River, Columbia. *Credits:* **1,** Copyright 1959, California Institute of Technology; **2, 3, 7, 8,** and **9,** Standard Oil Company of New Jersey; **4,** National Park Service; **5,** Union Pacific Railroad; **6,** University of Michigan.

64K6

17331–0111

PREFACE

We live in a time when growth in scientific discovery is almost explosive. In each branch of science the body of factual information increases rapidly and understanding deepens. This growth has put a difficult burden on the science student and teacher alike. The most elementary understanding of the scope of modern science requires familiarity with facts and concepts from every area of scientific thought.

A strong element in basic science education must be the study of the earth sciences. The earth and its immediate neighborhood in space form the laboratory in which all scientific experimentation must be carried on. It is the purpose of this text to provide students with a basic understanding of their home planet and its position in the universe.

The plan of the book is first to establish the position of the earth in the known universe through an introductory unit on astronomy. This is followed by a consideration of the general nature of the earth as a planet. Before the detailed study of surface features and the forces that shape them, a unit is given to consideration of the substances known to make up the earth's crust. The student is helped to recognize the role of chemistry in the earth sciences by the inclusion in this unit of a chapter on basic chemistry. Following the two units dealing with the major landforms and their origins, a unit is devoted to the earth's history as revealed by the fossil record. The concluding units deal with the liquid and gaseous portions of the earth—the water supply and the atmosphere. A final unit is concerned with a brief study of the causes and distribution of the world's climates, which are of such importance in regulating the lives of the earth's inhabitants.

The teacher who wishes to proceed immediately to the study of earth and its landforms will find it possible to reserve the introductory unit on astronomy for a later time without significant loss in the continuity. Other changes in the sequence of presentation of topics may also be made by altering the order in which the units are studied; however, Unit 3 should precede Units 4, 5, and 6, and Unit 8 should precede Unit 9. Within these limits, there is flexibility in the order in which the topics may be studied.

To assist students in mastery of technical terms associated with the discussion, each chapter opening includes a vocabulary list. Technical terms are printed in **boldface** or *italics* where they occur in the text and are clearly defined. At the end of each chapter the vocabulary is reviewed in a section which the student may use as a self-quiz to test his understanding. A complete *Glossary* also appears at the back of the book. In addition to the *Vocabulary Review* at the end of each chapter there are two groups of *Questions*. Those in *Group A* are based directly on the text and may be used as a self-quiz by the student. The questions in *Group B* are

v

more difficult and often require interpretation of the text material. At the conclusion of each unit there are *Unit Review Questions* and a group of suggestions for *Activities* and *Further Reading* to guide students who can make a broader study of the topics covered in the unit. Whenever appropriate, U. S. Geological Survey topographic sheets illustrating landforms discussed are listed at the end of a chapter. For those teachers who wish to carry farther the study of minerals and landforms, an *Appendix* includes a map showing the physiographic provinces of the United States, and a key for the identification of minerals.

The authors are sincerely grateful for the assistance of Mrs. Ethel Kurtz, Mayme S. Waggener High School, Louisville, Kentucky; Henri J. Floch, Phoenix Central School, Phoenix, New York; and Leo A. Houghton, Lakewood Senior High School, Lakewood, California, classroom teachers of earth science who read the entire manuscript and made many valuable suggestions. The authors also deeply appreciate the detailed comments of the following teachers, who read portions of the manuscript dealing with their special fields of interest: Dr. George O. Abell, Department of Astronomy, University of California, Los Angeles, California; Dr. Ralph J. Holmes, Department of Geology, Columbia University, New York, New York; Dr. Dayton E. Carritt, Department of Oceanography, The Johns Hopkins University, Baltimore, Maryland; Dr. Seymour L. Hess, Head, Department of Meteorology, The Florida State University, Tallahassee, Florida; and Dr. Victor E. Schmidt, Professor of Science, State University College of Education, Brockport, New York.

The authors were highly fortunate also in having the assistance of Dr. Benjamin Martin Shaub, Associate Professor Emeritus of Geology and Geography at Smith College, Northampton, Massachusetts. From his own collection and those of Harvard University and Amherst College, Dr. Shaub gathered and photographed in color the mineral and rock specimens in the full-page illustrations in Chapters 11 and 12.

CONTENTS

Practical Pointers in Reading MODERN EARTH SCIENCE

Read this page before you read your textbook.

1. Keep your eyes and your mind continually open. In science we base each conclusion on known facts and nothing can be taken for granted. Your eyes must be trained to observe carefully and your mind must be equally trained to reason from observations, both printed and otherwise, so as to draw logical conclusions from the observed data. With open eyes and inquiring mind you will go far in your work.

2. Get your bearings by examining the table of contents on pages vii and viii. What is the scope of this book? Are certain words in the chapter titles unfamiliar? Possibly they are now but by the time your work is completed at the end of the course, you will be familiar with all of them. This over-all glance at the subject matter content will give you a perspective necessary to understand what you will be reading.

3. After your teacher has made the assignment for which you will be responsible at the next class meeting, it's up to you to know what to do about preparing it. But first, be sure you understand exactly what is expected of you—what pages to read, what words to know, what questions, problems, projects or other activities to do, and whether the assignment is to be written or oral or both. If you are not sure, don't hesitate to ask. Write down all parts of the assignment in your notebook.

4. Skim over the assigned text material hastily to get a general idea what it is about, paying special attention to the paragraph headings in **boldface type.** These are key items in your textbook and form the basis for its organization.

5. Having obtained a general idea as to the subject matter of your assignment, go over the material carefully and give it your thorough concentration. Ask yourself repeatedly, Do I understand this? and if you cannot honestly answer yes, then read it again. As you read, study the drawings, tables, and photographs and read the captions which explain them. In the drawings, examine each label and learn the part of the drawing to which the label relates.

6. In your reading, pay special attention to the scientific words and terms printed in *boldface italic type.* These are key words and are important to a clear understanding of the text. Many of them will be unfamiliar but you must know them and be able to define each one. Science is not a difficult subject if you learn its language, but you will never succeed unless you master this essential aspect of it. Each new word or term is printed in *boldface italics* the first time it appears, but it may and probably will be used again later. If you find that you do not understand the pronunciation and meaning of a new word, look it up immediately in the *Glossary*. Similarly, if you have forgotten such a word or term and can't remember on what page you originally met it, turn to the Glossary at the back of the book and look up its definition.

7. Having read the material assigned and learned the new scientific words and terms, turn to the questions at the end of the chapter which cover the text material you have completed. Answer each one fully and, if you are unable to do so, return to that part of the text which is still unclear. Reread it with the question in mind until you have the answer.

THE age of the scientific exploration of the earth has begun. The day of lonely explorations of unknown continents and seas is all but finished; there are few lands yet to be mapped, not many mountaintops yet to be conquered. But only the surface of the earth has become known. Its interior, its atmosphere, its oceans, its history, and its future remain to challenge the scientific explorer.

A proper beginning to the scientific study of the earth is the examination of its place in the universe. Since we are closely acquainted with only this one planet on which we live, it is easy for us to forget that it is part of a vast universe and subject to the same physical laws that govern millions of more impressive objects populating the depths of space. This first unit concerns the kind of universe that surrounds the earth.

UNIT 1

THE EARTH
IN THE UNIVERSE

CHAPTER 1

THE STARS

FROM the earliest memory of mankind the spectacle of the sky has aroused fear, wonder, and curiosity. Millions of human beings have watched the stars moving steadily across the sky and the planets following their separate paths. To primitive men the night sky was a mysterious and disturbing display. Their minds could not grasp the fact that stars are distant objects independent of the earth. Superstition and ignorance filled the heavens with gods and demons whose existence was revealed to the inhabitants of the earth by the arrangement of stars in constellations and by the passage of the stars, the moon, and the sun.

As superstition gradually faded away and the study of the sky became the ancient science of astronomy, the stars and their companions were recognized as distant objects, but the earth was still believed to be the center of all. Since then, as astronomers have slowly and painstakingly pieced together their evidence, men have been forced to the conclusion that the earth is only a tiny speck in a universe that has no known limits.

The roots of the modern scientific view, which holds that the earth is a satellite of an ordinary star in a universe made up of billions of stars, go back deep into history. Each of the ancient

VOCABULARY

Refracting telescope. A telescope that uses lenses to produce images of distant objects.

Reflecting telescope. A telescope that uses a curved mirror to produce images of distant objects.

Radio telescope. An electronic device that focuses radio waves from outer space.

Spectroscope. An instrument that separates a beam of light into its various component colors.

Constellation. An apparent grouping of stars in a recognizable pattern.

Magnitude. The apparent brightness of a star in comparison with other stars.

Galaxy. An astronomical system composed of billions of stars.

Nebula (*neb*-yoo-la). A cloud of gases or dust in space.

civilizations of China, India, Babylonia, Egypt, and the Arab world developed its own science of astronomy, but the ideas of the ancient Greeks had most influence on the early development of the subject. The early Greeks believed that the earth was surrounded by a number of moving transparent spheres, one inside the other. On their separate spheres the sun, moon, planets, and stars were carried around the earth. This was an ingenious scheme to account for the obvious motions of the stars and their companions, but it had one very serious flaw. The planets were seen to move both forward and backward among the stars. If they, like everything else, revolved around the earth, their forward and backward motions required explanation. In order to preserve the basic scheme, astronomers devised for the planets a complicated system of motions about small circles whose centers, in turn, revolved about larger circles. This view of the universe was generally accepted during the medieval period.

Early in the seventeenth century, however, a Polish astronomer, Nicolaus Copernicus (koh-*per*-ni-kus) stated his belief that the sun, not the earth, was the center around which the planets revolved. Recognition of the Copernican theory was slow, but evidence to support it continued to accumulate until finally no astronomer could reasonably deny that the sun was the master of all the planets, including the earth. The foundation was established for the great advances in astronomy that have led to our present knowledge of the earth's position in the universe.

INSTRUMENTS TO EXPLORE THE UNIVERSE

Optical telescopes. The distances in the universe are so great that they cannot be measured in ordinary terms. The speed of light, about 186,000 miles per second, is the basis for the common unit of distance in astronomy; a *light-year* is the distance that light travels in one year. The largest telescopes have photographed faint patches of light from stars that are probably more than five billion light-years away. The number that would express this in miles would contain 22 zeros. Such a distance is almost unimaginable, yet the universe must extend at least this far in every direction.

The human eye unaided can see only the nearest or brightest stars in space. If there were no telescopes, the existence of billions of faint stars would be unknown, and details on even the closest planets would be invisible. The first astronomical telescope was used in the sixteenth century by an Italian scientist,

FIG. 1–1. Nicolaus Copernicus, 1473–1543, was the founder of modern astronomy. (*N. Y. Public Library*)

FIG. 1–2. The 40-inch refracting telescope at Yerkes Observatory. (*Yerkes Observatory*)

Galileo (gah-li-*lay*-oh). With his crude instrument he was the first to see and describe the moons of Jupiter, sunspots, and the mountains and craters on the moon. In the three hundred years since Galileo, astronomical telescopes have become larger and much more powerful. Large telescopes are able to detect very faint stars because of the great light-gathering power of the large lenses and mirrors. Doubling the diameter of a telescope lens increases the apparent brightness of stars four times. Actually, most astronomical telescopes are used as cameras. A photograph made through a telescope over a period of several minutes or hours will record many stars too dim to be seen by the eye directly. The photograph can then be studied as a permanent record of the observation.

There are two kinds of astronomical telescopes. The most familiar type is the *refractor*, in which light passes through lenses and is bent or refracted to give an enlarged or intensified image of the object viewed. This image can be viewed directly or photographed. The other kind of telescope is the *reflector*, which has a curved mirror that reflects light to form an image of the object viewed. The largest refracting telescope, with a lens diameter of 40 inches, is at Yerkes Observatory in Wisconsin. Forty inches is about as large as this kind of telescope can be made, because larger lenses are so heavy that they sag out of shape from their own weight. Reflecting telescopes, on the other hand, can be made much larger because the mirror can be supported from behind. The largest reflecting telescope is the famous 200-inch Hale telescope on Palomar Mountain in California.

All telescopes that depend on light have serious limitations, because the light must pass through the earth's atmosphere before reaching the telescope. The suspended materials in the atmosphere, as well as the gas molecules in the air itself, greatly interfere with the passage of the light. Also, the movements of the air distort the images. We usually see this distortion of the star images as a twinkling, which may make the heavens more interesting, but is a nuisance to astronomers. The problems that are created by the atmosphere could be compared to the problems one might face in studying airplanes from the bottom of a swimming pool. Thus astronomers are eager to set up observatories on man-made satellites circling the earth, or on the moon itself, thus avoiding atmospheric interference.

Radio telescopes. In 1931, Karl Jansky, a young engineer at Bell Telephone Laboratories, made an important discovery. He found that some of the static and background noise heard in special-

FIG. 1–3. The 200-inch reflecting telescope of the Palomar Observatory. (*Mount Wilson and Palomar Observatories*)

ized radio receivers which he had built actually came from outer space. Jansky's discovery did not arouse much interest until World War II. Then, many times during the war, radar was suddenly jammed by the same interference. Wartime research on the cause of the radar interference aroused the interest of scientists in these radio waves from deep in space, and the new science of radio astronomy was born.

The first radio telescopes were merely war surplus radar sets modified to increase their sensitivity to the desired signals. Modern radio telescopes consist of extremely sensitive receivers with very large antennas that can be pointed to any spot in the sky. The antennas usually have large bowl-shaped metallic "mirrors" to gather and focus the radio waves, just as the curved mirror collects and focuses light in a reflecting telescope. Compared to optical or light telescopes,

a radio telescope gives a less distinct image of objects in the sky because radio waves are so long compared to light waves that they cannot reveal fine details unless the antennas are extremely large. The largest radio telescope in the world is at Jodrell Bank, England. Its bowl-shaped antenna is 250 feet in diameter. With it, astronomers can track earth satellites and also observe objects billions of light years away.

Analyzing starlight. Next to the telescope, the astronomer's most important instrument is the *spectroscope.* In this device, light passing through a prism is separated into the colors of the *spectrum.* Early in the nineteenth century, it was discovered that bright and dark lines appearing in spectra are evidence of the presence of particular elements in glowing gases which give off light. With the spectroscope, or *spectrograph,* as it is called when a camera is included in the apparatus, light from any source may be analyzed. By this means, astronomers have identified about three-fourths of the known naturally occurring chemical elements in the sun. In fact, helium was dis-

FIG. 1–4. This radio telescope can be aimed at any point in the sky. It is used to study radiations from the sun and other objects in space. (*U. S. Navy*)

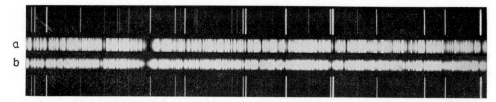

FIG. 1–5. Photographs of spectra of Arcturus (*a* and *b*), taken six months apart, show a shift in the position of the lines. This enables astronomers to measure relative velocity of the earth with respect to the star, using the Doppler effect. (*Mount Wilson and Palomar Observatories*)

covered in the sun by spectroscopic analysis before it was found on the earth. Study of the spectra of the stars reveals their composition, and other useful information as well, since the spectrum patterns are affected by such conditions as the temperature and pressure of the gases which give off the light.

The spectroscope can also be used to indicate the relative motion of the stars. This is made possible by the Doppler ef-

FIG. 1–6. The constellation Orion. Can you pick out the bright stars that are usually included in diagrams of this constellation? (*Mount Wilson and Palomar Observatories*)

fect, which applies to any wave motion, such as that of sound waves and light rays. A common example of the Doppler effect is the change in pitch of a sound, as of a locomotive horn, as its source rapidly approaches and then recedes. The pitch of the horn rises as the train approaches and then falls after the train passes. The pitch changes because the sound waves coming from the horn are pressed closer together as the train approaches and are pulled farther apart as the train recedes.

Light rays behave in the same way; they are either spread out or crowded together, depending on whether their source is moving toward or away from the earth. In a series of spectroscope observations of a star, a shift in the color bands of the spectrum may be seen. Astronomers attribute this to the Doppler effect, and can determine from it the rate at which a star is moving toward or away from the earth, and the relative motion of the earth with respect to the stars.

THE NIGHT SKY

The constellations. It is possible with the unaided eye to observe one important fact about the night sky: there are apparently permanent patterns in the scattering of the stars. From the earliest re-

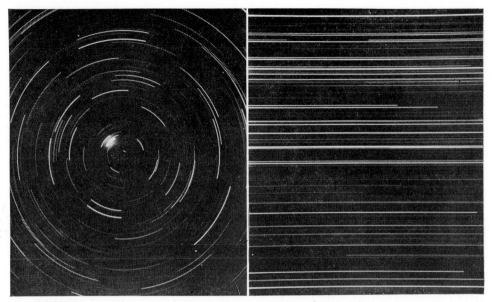

FIG. 1–7. Star streaks: left, taken with a camera pointed at the celestial north pole; right, taken with a camera at the equator. Why are the streaks curved in one photograph and straight in the other? (*Yerkes Observatory*)

corded history, names have been given to groups of stars because to some imaginative people their arrangement suggested animals, gods, and legendary heroes. Even today these star patterns are recognized as **constellations** and are identified by their ancient names, such as Ursa Major, the great bear; Cygnus (*sig-nus*), the swan; Pegasus, the winged horse; and Perseus (*per*-soos) the slayer of monsters. Although still known by the old names, constellations are now marked off by definite boundaries, just as land surfaces of the earth are divided into countries. They can thus be used as guides in the sky maps of astronomy.

Visible stars are usually named by their location in a constellation and by their degree of brightness with respect to all the stars of that particular constellation. The letters of the Greek alphabet are used to indicate rank. Thus Alpha (α) Lyrae is the brightest star in the con-stellation of Lyra, the lyre; Beta (β) Pegasae is the second brightest star in Pegasus, the winged horse, and so on. Many of the very brightest stars have individual names in addition. The five brightest stars of the northern sky, in order of their brightness, are called Sirius, Canopus (ka-*noh*-pus), Vega (*vee*-ga), Capella, and Arcturus (ahrk-*tyoo*-rus).

The motion of the earth as it turns on its axis makes the constellations seem to move through the sky as if they were on a transparent globe surrounding the earth. If the axis of the earth were extended out into space it would also form the axis of this imaginary globe on which the stars seem to be located. From the northern half of the earth, all stars seem to turn around a point in the sky, called the **celestial north pole.** A star located directly on the celestial north pole would not seem to move. The North Star, called

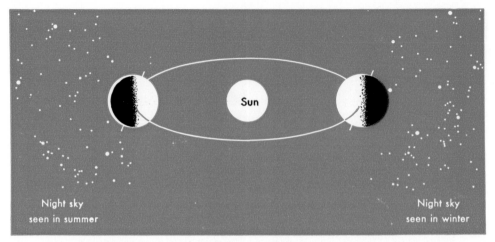

FIG. 1–8. Because the earth revolves around the sun, the appearance of the night sky changes with the seasons.

Polaris (poh-*lay*-ris), is very close to the celestial north pole and seems to move only very slightly. All other stars follow circular paths around the celestial pole, although those farther to the south are visible for only a part of their total path. These stars rise in the eastern part of the sky and set in the west as they pass out of view behind the earth. Figure 1–7 shows the motion of the stars recorded as streaks on the film during a time exposure with the camera pointed at the sky.

The movement of the earth in its orbit around the sun also causes a change in the appearance of the night sky from one part of the year to another. The reason for this is shown in Fig. 1–8.

The stars. Many of the characteristics of individual stars can be seen without the use of a telescope. For example, it is obvious that stars differ in their brightness. In considering the brightness of stars it should be noted that the brightest of the "stars" seen in the night sky are actually planets. In spite of the fact that planets only reflect the sun's light, some of them appear to be more brilliant than

most stars because they are much closer. It is usually possible to distinguish planets from bright stars because the planets ordinarily do not twinkle. Points of light from stars are more affected by the atmospheric movements that cause twinkling; thus stars twinkle while planets usually do not.

However, the stars also differ among themselves in their brilliance. The apparent brightness of a star is called its **magnitude.** The magnitude of a particular star is described by a number; a star of magnitude 2 is about two and one-half times brighter than a star of magnitude 3. The faintest star that can be seen without a telescope has a magnitude of 6. Stars as seen from the earth differ in brightness for two reasons. First, the distance between Earth and a star partially determines its magnitude, since its brightness diminishes with increasing distance. Second, the actual amount of light produced by a star affects its apparent brightness. The amount of light a star produces is determined both by its size and temperature, but mainly by its temperature. Depending on their size, stars are described as *supergiant, giant,* and *dwarf.*

By complicated methods involving observations with special instruments, the size of some of the nearer stars can be determined. The approximate actual sizes of some of these stars are compared in Fig. 1–9.

Some stars regularly expand and contract, causing their light to pulsate in periods ranging from less than one day to several hundred days. Such stars are known as *variable stars,* and one type, the cepheid (*se*-fee-id) variables, are of great importance to astronomers because the period of time between their bright and dim phases is related to their true brightness. Thus a comparison of the period and the apparent brightness of the star indicates its distance. The distance to any remote group of stars can be determined if the group contains cepheid variables.

Another way in which stars differ from each other is in their colors. Some appear white or blue-white, whereas others are red, yellow, or orange. These differences in color are related to differences in temperature at the surfaces of the stars. Like a piece of heated metal, a star is white or blue-white in color at highest temperatures, while the red, yellow, and orange colors indicate cooler surface temperatures. White and blue-white stars have temperatures of 40,000° to 60,000° F, yellow stars are about 10,000° F, orange ones about 6000° to 8000° F, and red stars about 3000° to 6000° F.

The galaxies. The ancients could not know, as they named their imaginary beasts and figures in the sky, that the stars they could see are only a tiny fraction of the billions that actually exist. A single photograph made with a modern astronomical telescope may show millions of stars too distant to be seen with

FIG. 1–9. A comparison of the actual sizes of some well-known stars.

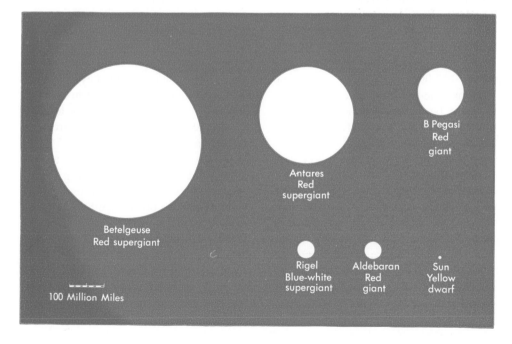

Betelgeuse
Red supergiant

Antares
Red
supergiant

B Pegasi
Red
giant

100 Million Miles

Rigel
Blue-white
supergiant

Aldebaran
Red
giant

Sun
Yellow
dwarf

FIG. 1–10. A drawing showing the probable appearance of our own Galaxy. The arrow and small circle indicate the location of the solar system.

the eye alone. All individual stars that we can see, including our nearest star, the sun, are members of a lens-shaped system composed of about 100 billion stars and called the *Galaxy* (*gal*-ak-see). The *Milky Way* we see in the sky is composed of billions of stars in the Galaxy as we look at it through its thickest part. Astronomers think that the Galaxy is about 100,000 light-years across and perhaps one-tenth as thick. Our sun seems to be an ordinary member of the Galaxy located about halfway from its center to its edge. See Fig. 1–10.

In addition to stars, the Galaxy contains a number of dust and gas clouds called *nebulae* (*neb*-yoo-lee). Photographs made with the larger telescopes show many hazy patches. It was once thought that they were all nebulae within our galaxy, but close study indicates that most of the patches are outside our galaxy. They are actually other star systems separated from us and from each other by from thousands to millions of light-years. Each one seems to contain billions of stars, just as our own galaxy does. Millions of these other galaxies can be seen with the largest telescopes, but only sixteen are within 3 million light-years of our galaxy. One of the closest, the Andromeda (an-*drom*-uh-da) galaxy, is about 2 million light-years away. It can be seen by a sharp unaided eye as a very faint and fuzzy patch of light in the constellation of Andromeda. On a good telescopic photograph, the Andromeda galaxy can be seen to have a spiral shape with curved arms projecting out from a dense nucleus of stars. See Fig. 1–11. Astronomers believe that our own galaxy would look like this if seen from another part of the universe.

The expanding universe. To astronomers, the universe now appears to be an expanse of space at least 10 billion light-years across with many millions of galaxies distributed throughout. Most galaxies are separated from their neighbors by millions of light-years. One of the most important discoveries of modern astronomy is the strong evidence that the galaxies all may be fleeing from each other at high speed. Light reaching us from the galaxies shows the *red shift.* Through the spectroscope, the lines of their spectra are seen to be shifted toward the red end of the spectrum. Many astronomers believe this can only be the result of the Doppler effect on the light, and that it indicates that the other galaxies are moving away from ours very rapidly. The more distant ones seem to be receding faster than the closer ones. At about 2 billion light-years away, which is about the maximum distance at which the red shift can be measured accurately, the galaxies seem to be moving away at well over 30,000 miles a second. It is unlikely that the galaxies are moving away

from earth as a center. However, if all space were expanding, then everything in space would seem to recede from any point in space.

The receding movement of the galaxies is an essential point to be considered in theories of the origin of the universe. If the entire universe is expanding, as the recession of the galaxies indicates, there are many ways in which the present universe might have been developed. One possibility is that all the matter now in the galaxies, with their billions of stars, was once packed tightly into a small region of space. Calculating backward from the present speed and distances of the galaxies, this would have been between 16 and 24 billion years ago. Somehow this clump of matter was torn apart in a gigantic explosion which formed the galaxies and sent them flying in all directions. Another possibility supposes that

FIG. 1–11. The spiral galaxy in the constellation of Andromeda. (*Mount Wilson and Palomar Observatories*)

FIG. 1–12. A spiral galaxy in the constellation of Ursa Major, the Big Dipper. (*Yerkes Observatory*)

as galaxies move away from each other, new galaxies are continuously being created. This is called the "steady state" or "continuous creation" theory, which assumes that the universe is infinitely old and infinitely large. A third possibility is that the galaxies move outward as the universe expands until it reaches a certain size, then draw inward as it collapses until it has shrunk to a certain size. At this point the universe expands again, and the process of expansion and contraction is repeated indefinitely.

None of these theories about the origin of the universe can be proved right or wrong on the basis of present scientific knowledge. If telescopes could see far enough into space to reveal whether or not the number of galaxies diminishes with greater distance, the basic question might be answered. If there are only a certain number of galaxies moving out in all directions, they will be farther apart and thus less numerous in deep space. On the other hand, if galaxies are being continuously created, they should be almost as numerous everywhere throughout space. Telescopes which depend upon light will probably never be able to probe deep enough into the universe to settle these questions unless observatories can be set up on artificial satellites or on the moon to avoid the problems caused by the earth's atmosphere. There is a chance that radio telescopes will be able to give an earlier answer, since they may be able to detect galaxies too far away to be seen.

STARS WITHIN GALAXIES

Kinds of galaxies. All of the galaxies within the limits of our observation can be divided into three types based on their shape. Common among the nearest galaxies are those which consist of a central round body surrounded by a flat disk. These are called *spiral galaxies,* because the disk is usually composed of arms which spiral around the center, as shown in Fig. 1–12. Spectroscopic study of these galaxies shows that they rotate on an axis passing through the central body.

Our own galaxy and the one in Andromeda are of the spiral type.

A second type of galaxy is more or less round in shape. These are called *elliptical galaxies* because they usually appear pumpkin-shaped, although the angle at which they are seen by us affects their apparent shape. Some are perfectly round. They are brightest near the center and fade out gradually; no detailed structure can be seen in them. The elliptical galaxies may be the most common of all. An example is shown in Fig. 1–13.

A third class of galaxies has no regularity of shape. These are called *irregular galaxies* and appear as hazy clouds of irregular outline. See Fig. 1–14. This group is comparatively rare, making up about 3 percent of all observed galaxies.

Star populations. Early studies of the make-up of the nearby galaxies uncovered a very puzzling feature. Even comparatively small telescopes showed that some spiral and all irregular galaxies are made up of individual stars. However, in spite of all efforts with the biggest telescopes, astronomers could not make out a single star in the center of one of the closest galaxies, the large spiral galaxy in Andromeda. Numerous individual stars were visible in the spiral arms, but the center remained only a blur. To add to the mystery, several elliptical galaxies near Andromeda also did not seem to contain a single individual star. The only reasonable conclusion was that the centers of some spiral galaxies and all elliptical galaxies are composed of stars too faint to be seen separately. This conclusion was proved correct in the early nineteen-forties when a German astronomer, Walter Baade, using the 100-inch reflecting telescope on Mount Wilson in California, succeeded in distinguishing very faint individual stars in photographs of the center of the Andromeda galaxy. Baade was able to detect these stars for the first time partly because the city lights of Los Angeles below Mount Wilson were dimmed by wartime restrictions. A more significant reason for Baade's success was his discovery that these stars in the center of Andromeda are red in color. Because the photographic film generally used by astronomers is most sensitive to blue light, the faint red stars had not

FIG. 1–13. An elliptical galaxy. Some of the individual stars in the galaxy can be distinguished around its edge. (*Yerkes Observatory*)

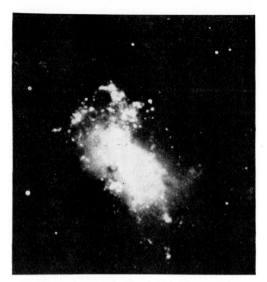

FIG. 1–14. An irregular galaxy. (*Mount Wilson and Palomar Observatories*)

registered on previous astronomical photographs. Baade's photographs were made with red-sensitive film and so picked up the weak red light. Since then, the 200-inch telescope on Palomar Mountain has been able to photograph single stars in the centers of most of the nearby spiral and elliptical galaxies, and each time the basic pattern has been the same. Spiral galaxies have mostly bright blue stars in their spiral arms and fainter red stars in their centers; elliptical galaxies are composed almost entirely of the fainter red stars. Astronomers divide these two types of stars into two main groups: Population I, which includes the brilliant blue stars, and Population II, which includes the fainter red stars.

The brilliance of the blue stars of Population I is believed to be evidence of their youthfulness, while the weak red light of the stars of Population II is considered a sign of their greater age. The discovery of the existence of the two star populations was connected with another observed fact about the galaxies. Wherever the red stars of Population II were found, there was little dust and gas in the surrounding space. Around Population I stars, clouds of dust and gas are common, but the elliptical galaxies and the centers of spiral galaxies are clear of these clouds. In the arms of the spiral galaxies and in every other location where the young blue stars of Population I are found, there are great clouds of dust and gas. This, along with other evidence, led scientists to conclude that stars are found within these clouds because it is there that the processes of star formation are actually taking place. In the neighborhood of the older red stars, the clouds of dust have been used up and no new stars are developing.

A general picture of the history of the galaxies emerges from all this evidence. Billions of years ago, millions of stars were formed in all the galaxies. The elliptical galaxies apparently used up all the dust and gas in their area. Since no material was left to form new stars, these galaxies contain only the old stars. In formation of the spiral galaxies, some dust and gas was shaped into a flat disk by the galaxy's rotation, developing spiral arms around the center cluster of stars. Within the dust in the arms of the spiral galaxies, new stars have been continually created, producing a younger star population along with the older original stars.

The birth and death of stars. Since our own galaxy, the Milky Way, is a spiral galaxy, it is possible for us to observe at close hand stars in various stages of development. Our position in the Milky Way seems to be about halfway between the center and the edge, in the midst of the gas and dust clouds from which new stars are being formed. These clouds are composed mostly of hydrogen, the lightest of chemical elements. On the earth, hydrogen is a relatively rare element, but throughout the universe it probably makes up at least three-fourths of all the matter. Most of the remaining matter in the universe is helium, the second lightest element.

Scientists believe that stars can grow out of loose clouds because the individual particles of gas and dust within the cloud have a gravitational attraction for each other. Every piece of matter, even a single atom, will attract other pieces of matter; within a cloud drifting in the depths of space this gravitational force can cause the particles to crowd together. As the cloud shrinks, its own gravitational force becomes greater and eventually causes the entire mass to contract rapidly to a billion billionths of its original size. The shrinking action causes the hydrogen atoms which make up the bulk of the original cloud to collide with one another. The collisons of hydrogen atoms eventually cause nuclear reactions to occur. (Nuclear reactions are discussed more fully in Chapter 2.) Huge amounts of energy are released by these reactions and the star first begins to produce light. The gaseous matter in the star reaches a delicate balance between the gravitational force, which tends to make the gases shrink inward, and force of expansion due to the high temperatures of nuclear reactions. In most stars, this balance continues for millions of years while the star constantly pours forth energy from its vast store of atomic fuel.

Young stars shine with a brilliant blue-white light resulting from their very high surface temperature of 40,000 to 60,000° F. As a star ages, its surface grows cooler and its color gradually fades to yellow, then to orange, and finally to red. Only the star's surface grows cooler as it grows older; its interior gets hotter. The increased heat from the inside of the aging star destroys the original balance between shrinking and expanding. The star expands, and its surface becomes cooler

because less heat reaches the outside. By the time a star reaches the red stage, its surface temperature has dropped to about 6,000° F or less and its size has increased about 100 times. An old red giant has greatly speeded up the rate at which it uses its atomic fuel. Soon it reaches a critical time when it has used too much. At this point the giant suddenly collapses and becomes a dwarf star only a fraction of its former size and brilliance. A dying star continues to grow cooler, slowly becoming fainter and fainter until finally it is no longer visible. The collapse of the star when it turns into a dwarf is extremely violent. Its atoms are crushed together so closely that a spoonful of the matter from such a star would weigh about 100 tons. It is likely that there are many such stars in the Milky Way, but only about 200 have actually been found because their light is so faint that they are virtually invisible.

It must be remembered that this story of the life and death of a star is necessarily brief and incomplete. Moreover, since it combines theories of many astronomers, it may not present the complete picture. It is given here only as a summary of the major theories that have been advanced to explain the life history of stars.

The length of time taken by a star to complete its entire sequence of changes from youthful blueness to dwarfed old age depends upon how much matter it has at the beginning. Calculations based on knowledge of the kind of atomic reactions that take place in stars indicate that approximately 13 billion years is an average lifetime for a star. Since the galaxies may have existed for only 5 to 6 billion years, it is possible that most stars have not had enough time to run the complete course from birth to death.

SUMMARY

☯

BEFORE the sixteenth century it was commonly believed that the earth was the center of the universe. The astronomer Copernicus was one of the first to support the theory that the earth, along with the other planets, revolves around the sun. Scientists now know the earth to be a small planet revolving around an ordinary star, the sun.

Modern astronomy explores the universe by means of instruments which penetrate the vast distances between the sun and other stars. Chief among the astronomical tools are several kinds of telescopes and the spectroscope. The constellations, identifiable groups of stars, are used as aids in locating positions in the sky and various individual stars. As seen from the northern hemisphere, the stars circle around the celestial north pole and the North Star. Stars vary in brightness or magnitude, in color, and in size. All observed stars are contained in galaxies, which are groups of millions of stars. Millions of galaxies are known to exist scattered throughout space. All nearby stars, including the sun, are members of a single galaxy, the Milky Way. The Milky Way also contains nebulae, clouds of dust and gases.

Study of the various types of galaxies leads to the conclusion that they contain two populations of stars. An older type of star is apparently part of the original group that formed the galaxy, but most galaxies also contain younger stars produced from dust and gas within the galaxy. Stars go through a definite cycle as they grow older. Changes in color, temperature, and size are interpreted as evidences of the age of a star.

VOCABULARY REVIEW

Match the word in the right column with the correct phrase in the left column. *Do not write in this book.*

1. Real or imagined pattern of stars
2. Apparent brightness of stars
3. Star system containing billions of stars
4. First scientist to observe sunspots
5. Stars whose brightness show periodic change
6. Instrument using lenses to observe the heavens
7. Unit of distance measurement in astronomy
8. Stars grouped according to brilliance and color
9. Stars in a late stage of development
10. Instrument for analyzing light

a. Copernicus
b. Galileo
c. refracting telescope
d. reflecting telescope
e. spectroscope
f. constellation
g. magnitude
h. variable stars
i. galaxy
j. light-year
k. star populations
l. red giants

QUESTIONS   •   GROUP A

Decide whether these statements are true or false. Reword the false statements to make them true. *Do not write in this book.*

1. The belief that the earth revolves around the sun was commonly held before the sixteenth century.
2. A radio telescope gives a somewhat distorted image of the sky.
3. The constellation patterns are useless in modern astronomy.
4. The red shift is a phenomenon observable with the spectroscope.
5. The red shift indicates that the universe may be contracting.
6. Our galaxy is spherical in shape, resembling an orange.
7. Blue stars are young and have a very high surface temperature.
8. The matter in a dwarf star is extremely heavy.
9. It is impossible even to estimate the average lifetime of a star.
10. In the universe as a whole, hydrogen is a rare element.
11. The planets appear to change their relative positions among the constellations from week to week.
12. The largest radio telescope in the world is located at the Yerkes Observatory in Wisconsin.
13. The first reflecting telescope was built by Karl Jansky.

GROUP B

1. What characteristic of the planets made some early astronomers doubt that the other planets revolved around the earth?
2. Why might Copernicus be considered the father of modern astronomy?
3. What does a light-year measure? Why must light-years be used in astronomy?
4. What is the basic difference between the two types of telescopes that depend on light?
5. How is the spectroscope used in astronomy?
6. How can a spectroscope be used to find out if a star is moving?
7. What is the difference between a nebula and a galaxy?
8. What is unusual about the Andromeda galaxy?
9. What is the chief difference between Population I and Population II stars?
10. How does the color of a star indicate its age?
11. Approximately how many miles are in a light-year?
12. Why are astronomical observatories usually located on a mountain top?
13. If the galaxies are receding, how is it possible that light from close galaxies like Andromeda occasionally shows a Doppler shift indicating that the galaxy is approaching us?
14. How is it possible for an astronomer to determine easily whether a faint patch of light is a nebula within our galaxy or another galaxy beyond our own?
15. How can we know how some parts of the universe looked a million years ago?

CHAPTER 2

THE SUN

STUDY and comparison of the stars of the visible universe indicate that the sun is only one star among millions of others very much like it. To us, however, it is different from all other stars. We are closer to the sun than to any other star and therefore have more detailed information about it. Every advance in our knowledge of the sun has a double importance, adding not only to our understanding of the greatest single influence on our planet, but also to our knowledge of stars in general.

Although the sun is comparatively close to us, it is still almost a hundred million miles away. We do not know all about the sun, but intensive study and a better basic understanding of the nature of all matter during recent years have given us a fairly accurate and detailed picture of this very complicated object.

THE STRUCTURE OF THE SUN

The parts of the sun. The sun is a huge ball of intensely hot gases, 864,000 miles in diameter. To the naked eye it appears to be a uniformly brilliant disk of light, but when seen through special telescopes it has several separate and distinct features. The main body is a sphere, darker around the edges than near the center. The darker edge, called the *limb*, indicates that the light of the

VOCABULARY

Chromosphere. The sun's surface atmosphere, made up of glowing gases.

Photosphere. A layer of brilliantly glowing gases beneath the chromosphere, source of most of the radiant energy from the sun.

Corona. A halo of faintly glowing gases outside of the chromosphere, usually visible during a solar eclipse.

Solar flare. An unusually bright cloud of gases erupting from the sun, lasting for a few hours.

Aurora. Streamers of glowing ionized gases in the earth's atmosphere.

Nuclear fusion. A nuclear reaction in which lighter-weight particles combine to form heavier nuclei.

Nova. A star which suddenly becomes many times brighter than normal.

sun must come from its interior. When we look at the center of the sun we see deeper into the sun's atmosphere toward the brilliant interior. When we look toward the edges, we look through the outer layers only, along the sun's curved surface, so that the edges of the sun appear darker. During a brief moment at a total eclipse of the sun, when the bright main body is blotted out, the sun's outer atmosphere becomes visible and provides the most impressive sight of the eclipse. A brilliant red ring, a layer of gas about 8000 miles thick on the sun's surface, flashes into view. Because of its bright red color (even though it is normally too weak to be seen), this surface atmosphere of glowing gas is called the *chromosphere* (color-sphere). Immediately beneath the chromosphere is a very thin layer of brilliantly glowing gas about 100 miles deep. Since it is the source of the greater part of the sun's light, this bright layer of gas is called the *photosphere* (light-sphere). Beneath the photosphere is the fantastically hot, dense mass of gases which compose the interior of the sun.

During a total eclipse the sun can also be seen to have a halo of faint silver-white light surrounding it. This is the *corona* (crown) which extends in all directions from the surface to a distance of a million miles or more. See Fig. 2–1. The white light of the corona is very faint compared to the intense light of the photosphere, and formerly could be seen easily only during an eclipse. Today astronomers can observe and photograph the inner part of the corona continuously during daylight hours by means of a coronagraph, a special telescope that mechanically blocks off the light from the photosphere. Thus they have learned much more about the sun's outer atmosphere than they could formerly glean from infrequent observations made only during solar eclipses. Study of the corona indicates that it is an extension of the sun's atmosphere—actually a very thin huge cloud of gas surrounding the sun and glowing with a weak light.

FIG. 2–1. The sun's corona. (*U. S. Navy*)

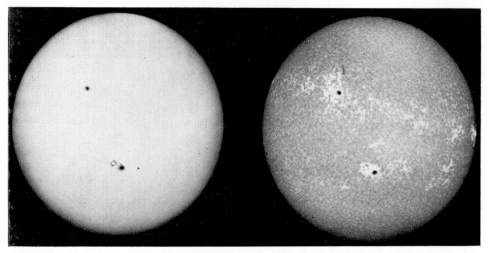

FIG. 2–2. The sun photographed directly through a telescope (left) and with a special filter that admits only the light of glowing calcium (right). (*Mount Wilson and Palomar Observatories*)

Sunspots and storms on the sun. Although the sun appears to have a smooth surface even when seen through a telescope, it shows many irregularities if examined with special instruments which record light of only one color. In the red light given off by glowing hydrogen gas, the surface looks grainy with scattered

FIG. 2–3. The sun photographed in ultraviolet light. (*U. S. Navy*)

bright spots. When seen in the violet light of glowing calcium, the surface of the sun resembles the peel of an orange, as shown in Fig. 2–2. Photographs made with ultraviolet light show bright gas clouds high in the solar atmosphere. See Fig. 2–3. All these different appearances of the sun show that the blanket of hot gases in the chromosphere and the photosphere is in constant motion. Apparently there is "weather" in the sun's atmosphere, somewhat as there is in the earth's atmosphere. The most violent disturbances in the brilliant atmosphere of the sun seem to be associated with sunspots.

In 1610 when Galileo was turning his newly constructed telescope upon various objects in the sky, he looked at the brilliant disk of the sun and discovered that its face seemed to be pitted with dark spots. Some people thought that Galileo had seen silhouettes of bodies between the earth and sun. He observed, however, that the spots moved slowly across the sun's face, and finally concluded from their motion that they were on the surface of the sun itself. On the basis of the motion of the spots, he was able to determine that the sun rotates on its axis every 27 days. Galileo had no explanation for the cause of the spots, nor did the astronomers who followed during the next 300 years. Some thought that the spots might be glimpses into the dark interior of the sun caused by some unexplained stripping away of the hot outer covering. Modern knowledge of the sun makes certain that it has no dark interior to be revealed, and although complete understanding is still lacking, modern science can give a fairly good idea of what the sunspots actually are.

A sunspot first appears as a dark area on the photosphere, usually near the middle of the sun in the vicinity of its equator. The spots look dark because the gases in them are about 1,800° F cooler than the surrounding gases of the photosphere. They range in size from about 500 miles in diameter to more than 50,-000 miles; frequently they form in pairs and occasionally in large groups. The small ones usually last only a few days but large sunspots may remain for several months. For some reason that cannot yet be explained, the sunspots follow an 11-year cycle. Approximately every 11 years the number of sunspots reaches a maximum, but this is only a very general rule and the peaks in sunspot activity have occurred at various times from as little as 7 years to as much as 17 years apart.

When the rotation of the sun carries a sunspot area around to the limb, a great shining cloud of very hot gas is sometimes seen in the vicinity of the spot. Since these streamers of bright gas extend thousands of miles upward into the sun's atmosphere, they are called *prominences*. See Fig. 2–6. Occasionally an

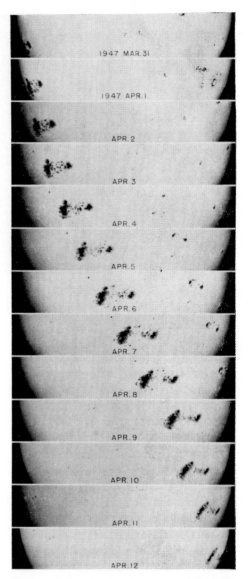

FIG. 2–4. These pictures of sunspots were taken at the same hour on 13 successive days. Note the changes in size and shape of the spots and their apparent movement across the face of the sun. (*Mount Wilson and Palomar Observatories*)

unusually bright cloud of gas appears on the surface of the sun near a sunspot. This appears as a sudden **solar flare;** an area of about 1 billion square miles of

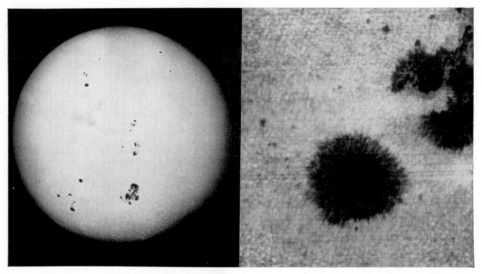

FIG. 2–5. Left, a photograph of the sun showing many large sunspots. Right, an enlargement of a group of sunpots near the center of the sun's disk. (*Yerkes Observatory*)

the sun's face that abruptly becomes 20 to 30 times brighter than other areas of the sun, then fades away within an hour or so. At the time when the flare is brightest, streamers of material can be seen shooting up into the sun's atmosphere to heights of 300,000 miles or more.

The most remarkable thing about solar flares is the direct effect they have on the earth, 93 million miles away. At the moment a flare is first seen on the sun, certain short-wave radio signals on earth are completely drowned out by a burst of static. Then, shortly after the appearance of the solar flare, the earth's upper atmosphere is bombarded with a shower of invisible atomic particles. These tiny particles, which are fragments of atoms, carry electrical charges and can produce disturbances in the upper atmosphere which greatly interfere with general radio and television transmission. Twenty to forty hours after the flare on the sun, still more effects are noticed. Brilliant

displays of the *aurora,* the northern and southern lights, occur in the region of the earth's north and south poles. Unusually big solar flares often produce displays of the aurora in the regions closer to the earth's equator, such as the United States. The auroras apparently are produced by the slower-moving heavy atomic particles ejected by the sun at the time of the flare disturbance. These particles are guided toward the poles of the earth by the magnetic field which surrounds the earth. See Fig. 2–7.

All of the evidence indicates that solar flares are actually gigantic explosions, probably connected with the sunspots. Radio waves are generated by the disturbances and reach the earth at approximately the same time that the flares are observed, since they travel with the speed of light. The streams of particles from the flares are flung out so violently by the explosion that some of the material in them leaves the sun and fans out into space. The lighter particles travel about

30,000 miles per second and are detected on the earth in about an hour. These cause the disturbances in the upper atmosphere which produce radio interference. The slower particles, which produce the auroras and magnetic disturbances, have a velocity of about 1000 miles per second and take about a day to reach the earth.

As yet, the exact cause of sunspots and the violent explosions marked by the solar flares is not known. It is obvious that sunspots are evidence of some great disturbance deep in the sun's interior, but their exact cause is still a mystery. The question raised four centuries ago, when Galileo first studied sunspots with his simple telescope, has not yet been answered.

THE ENERGY OF THE SUN

The puzzle of the sun's energy. Each of the billions of stars in the universe pours out energy on a gigantic scale. The sun, which is definitely not outstanding among the stars as an energy source, continuously produces around 500 sextillion horsepower. The earth captures only a tiny fraction of the sun's total energy output. Each square foot of the earth's surface normally receives only about 1/6 horsepower of total solar power, but the earth's small share of the sun's energy is vital. Without it, this planet would be frozen and lifeless.

One of the great puzzles since the beginning of history has been the means by which the sun continues its steady flood of power. Early attempts to explain the source of the sun's great heat were based on fire. When the sun's warmth and light disappeared at night or grew feeble in the winter, man used fire as a substitute. Thus it was only natural for ancient people to suppose that the sun itself was a constant flame in the sky. However, even the brightest of fires on earth soon dies away to embers and cold ashes, and thoughtful observers wondered how the sun could burn so fiercely day after day

FIG. 2–6. A solar prominence, estimated to be 80,000 miles high. (*Mount Wilson and Palomar Observatories*)

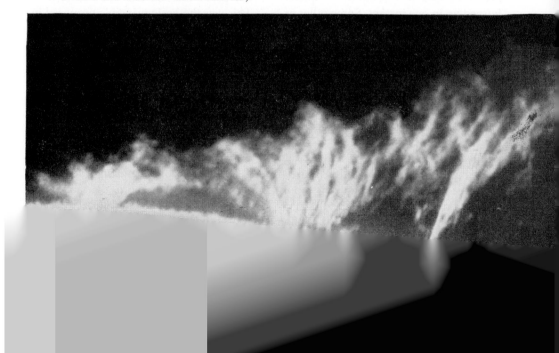

FIG. 2–7. The aurora borealis, or northern lights. (*Mike Larson*)

without exhausting its fuel. As scientists learned more about the chemistry of fire, it became obvious that the sun's energy could not be produced by ordinary burning. Simple calculations showed that the sun could not possibly give off its tremendous amounts of energy by burning, even if its substance could be completely burned up in one instant. Some other explanation was needed.

About a hundred years ago, scientists tried to explain the sun's mysterious source of energy by suggesting that the sun might be shrinking, as some stars similar to the sun are thought to be. (See page 15.) Such a gradual contraction of the sun would cause it to have less total gravitational energy and the excess could be changed to heat. Calculations proved that this process could indeed supply enough energy to account for the sun's heat, but only for the past 20 million years. The sun could not be older than 20 million years if it obtained energy mainly by contraction. Thus the contrac-

tion theory was also unsatisfactory since all other evidence indicated that the sun had been yielding its energy for at least 4 billion years. Scientists were forced to seek another solution to the problem.

Around 1925 a new idea suggested the best explanation yet for the source of energy of the sun and stars in general. This was the basic principle proposed by Albert Einstein: matter can be converted to very large amounts of energy. The principle is expressed in the famous equation $E = mc^2$, where E is energy, m is the mass of the converted matter and c is the velocity of light. It became evident that if it could be proved that a small amount of the sun's matter is continuously being changed into energy according to this equation, the enormous flood of energy lasting more than 4 billion years could be accounted for.

Another twenty years passed before a theory was developed to explain how the sun accomplishes the conversion of matter into energy. The chief clue was evidence that the sun's interior must have a temperature in the range of 18 to 36 million degrees F. Theoretical studies of the structure and behavior of atoms had shown that the fantastically high temperature within the sun could cause lighter atoms to join together, forming heavier ones. This process could conceivably convert small amounts of the matter of the atoms into energy. Continued research left little doubt that such atomic reactions do indeed take place in the sun's interior. The structure of atoms is discussed more completely in Chapter 10.

Nuclear reactions—secret of the sun's energy. Deep within the sun's body, matter is crushed together with a pressure more than one billion times the normal air pressure on earth. Atoms are crowded together so tightly that only their cores or *nuclei* remain intact. The packing is so close that the interior of the sun is a hundred times more dense than water, but the atomic nuclei in this matter still move about because of the very high temperature. Now and then two of these moving nuclei collide and *nuclear fusion* takes place. The two nuclei blend together to make a single heavier nucleus. The heavier nucleus is slightly lighter than the combined weight of the two smaller ones from which it was formed. The difference in mass is converted to energy according to the equation $E = mc^2$. This process is called a *thermonuclear reaction* since it is the fusion of atomic nuclei under very high temperatures. In a hydrogen bomb similar reactions are caused to occur for an instant to create an explosion. Within the sun, however, the process is taking place constantly.

It is known that only light atomic nuclei are capable of undergoing fusion even at the very high temperatures found

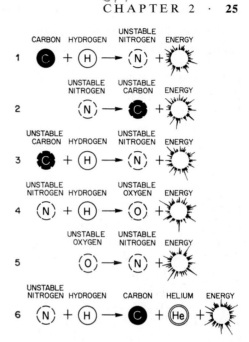

FIG. 2–8. This series of thermonuclear reactions probably furnishes most of the sun's energy. Note that although atoms of carbon, nitrogen, and oxygen are involved in the reactions, the final result is the fusion of four atoms of hydrogen to form a single atom of helium.

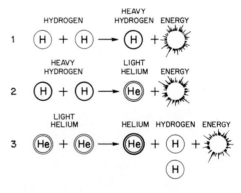

FIG. 2–9. These hydrogen-helium reactions may furnish part of the sun's energy. This series is much simpler than the one shown above in Fig. 2–8, but is essentially the same fusion reaction of hydrogen atoms to form atoms of helium.

in the sun. The lightest of all atoms is hydrogen, and since it is also the most abundant element on the sun, there is little doubt that it is the "fuel" for the thermonuclear reactions there. Research indicates that there are two probable ways for hydrogen to undergo fusion in the sun. In one, a hydrogen nucleus joins with a carbon nucleus to form an unstable nitrogen nucleus. In a series of changes, this nucleus reacts with three more hydrogen nuclei, eventually becoming carbon again and producing helium as a by-product. In the other, hydrogen nuclei may join with other hydrogen nuclei and go through a series of changes which finally produces helium and more hydrogen. These reactions are sketched in Figs. 2–8 and 2–9. In both of these reactions, hydrogen is used up and helium is finally produced along with tremendous quantities of energy. It is estimated that the sun consumes 564 million tons of its hydrogen each second and from it produces 560 million tons of helium. The difference of 4 million tons represents the change of matter to energy which is the source of the sun's immense power.

Man has always benefited indirectly from the sun's energy. However, it is only recently that scientists have designed and built devices to produce practical amounts of heat from solar radiations. Various types of solar furnaces are now being built in different areas of the earth. One type is shown in Fig. 2–10. It employs curved mirrors to focus the reflected rays on a relatively small area. Other devices to use the sun's energy employ lenses to focus the rays. In some arid regions, heat from the sun's rays is used to evaporate sea water in large structures built like greenhouses, providing fresh water for drinking, irrigation, or industrial purposes.

FIG. 2–10. The largest experimental solar furnace in the United States is at Natick, Massachusetts. The large structure at the left is made up of segments of concave mirrors which focus the sun's rays on a small area. (*U. S. Army*)

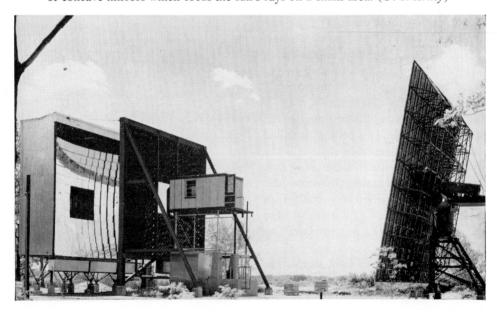

FIG. 2–11. A nova in the constellation of Hercules. The right photograph was taken on March 10, 1935. The left photograph shows the same region of the constellation on May 6, 1935. The white arrows point to the star, which had sunk to its former state. (*Lick Observatory*)

Houses have been built that can be heated during the colder seasons by solar radiations. The absorbed radiations heat gases or liquids which are then circulated through the building. Increased use of solar heat will result as scientists and engineers continue to develop new means of tapping the sun's tremendous energy.

The life expectancy of the sun. Knowledge of the means by which the sun obtains its energy makes possible a prediction of how long it can continue to supply the earth with life-giving warmth and light. All the evidence now available shows that there is sufficient hydrogen remaining in the sun to allow it to continue producing energy at the present rate for the next 5 to 10 billion years. After this, only helium will be available for the essential thermonuclear reactions in the center of the sun's interior. Helium undergoes fusion only at higher temperatures, so the sun will grow hotter and its outer parts will expand until it is many times larger than at present. Possibly the earth will be swallowed by the sun's outer layers, along with the

other planets closest to the sun. After this final outburst, the sun will finally shrink again to about one-twentieth of its present size to become a faint white dwarf star. If the earth survives at all, it will remain only as a charred cinder floating in space.

There is also the possibility that the sun will suddenly become a *nova* or exploding star. Stars are known to become thousands of times more brilliant without any prior warning. Such stars are called novas (new stars) because they suddenly become very conspicuous. See Fig. 2–11. They are not actually new stars but only appear to come into existence abruptly because of their sudden flare-up. Since no one knows the exact cause of novas, it is impossible to predict whether a given star will ever explode. If the sun did become a nova, the earth would certainly be completely destroyed. However, few novas are observed among the millions of stars in our Galaxy, and it appears that the chances of any one star such as the sun suddenly exploding are very slight.

SUMMARY

THE sun, approximate distance 93 million miles, is the star closest to the earth. It is an average-size star with a diameter of 864,000 miles, yet its volume is equal to 1 million Earths. It is composed of layers of intensely hot gases. The surface, or photosphere, is the source of most of the sun's light. Surrounding the photosphere is the chromosphere. The outermost layer, a pearly corona, may be observed during a total eclipse or with a coronagraph.

Violent storms, believed to be related to disturbances within the sun, produce sunspots. These spots are cooler than the surrounding gases and darker than the adjacent surface. Sunspots gradually increase and decrease in activity and reach maximum activity about every eleven years. Prominences and solar flares are associated with sunspots. At the time of solar flares, the earth receives electrified particles which cause magnetic and electrical phenomena such as auroras, and television or radio interference.

The sun's great energy apparently comes from the conversion of matter into energy. This is accomplished during the fusion of hydrogen into helium. The sun is expected to continue to produce energy at this rate for another 10 billion years. After this it will expand and then contract into a faint white dwarf star.

VOCABULARY REVIEW

Match the phrase in the left column with the correct word or phrase in the right column. *Do not write in this book.*

1. An exploding star
2. Brilliant display in the northern and southern skies caused by charged particles from the sun
3. Streamer of hydrogen gas
4. Center of a violent solar storm
5. Man who developed the formula $E = mc^2$
6. The union of light atoms
7. Gigantic eruptions on the sun which cause almost instant radio interference
8. Lightest element known to man
9. Surface atmosphere of glowing gases
10. Source of most of the sun's light
11. Man who determined the period of the sun's rotation
12. Core of an atom
13. Halo observed during a total solar eclipse
14. Dark edge of the sun

a. galaxy
b. limb
c. chromosphere
d. photosphere
e. corona
f. sunspot
g. prominence
h. nuclear fission
i. aurora
j. nova
k. nucleus
l. hydrogen
m. Einstein
n. solar flare
o. nuclear fusion
p. Galileo

QUESTIONS   ·   GROUP A

Decide whether these statements are true or false. Reword the false statements to make them true. *Do not write in this book.*

1. Poor television reception may occur following solar flares.
2. In 10 billion years the sun may begin to contract.
3. Sunspots are associated with violent storms on the earth.
4. A cubic foot of matter from the center of the sun would weigh less than a cubic foot from the surface.
5. The sun is considered an ordinary star.
6. If the last intense period of sunspot activity occurred in 1948, the next period of intense sunspot activity should be 1964.
7. Reactions similar to those on the sun occur during the explosion of a dynamite bomb.
8. Nuclei of heavy elements fuse most easily.
9. A spectroscope can simulate a total solar eclipse.
10. The diameter of the sun is about 12 times that of the earth.
11. An exploding star is known as a nova.
12. Most of the sun's light comes from its center.
13. Once every 24 hours the sun rotates on its axis.
14. Eventually helium will be the most abundant element on the sun.
15. The temperature in a sunspot is greater than that of the photosphere.

GROUP B

1. Explain the meaning of each of the letters and the number in the formula $E = mc^2$. What was the significance of this formula in determining the true nature of the sun's energy?
2. Using 186,000 miles per second as the speed of light, calculate the time needed for light to reach the earth from the sun.
3. Why is the sun's corona visible to the unaided eye only during a total solar eclipse?
4. What was Galileo's explanation for sunspots? What are sunspots?
5. How can sunspots help to determine the period of rotation of the sun?
6. What other events on the sun seem to be associated with sunspots?
7. Why do solar flares cause electrical and magnetic phenomena on the earth?
8. What fate is in store for the sun? How will this affect the earth?
9. Would the entire sun appear black if it were the same temperature as a sunspot? Explain the reason for your answer.
10. Calculate the number of times the sun's diameter would have to increase before the earth would be enveloped.
11. Calculate the number of square feet of the earth's surface that would collect enough energy to operate an automobile that requires 210 horsepower.
12. Why is the presence of large amounts of helium in the spectrum of a star generally considered to be a sign of age?

CHAPTER 3

THE SOLAR SYSTEM

CIRCLING around the sun in a series of complicated orbits are nine major planets and numerous smaller objects. All these bodies have at least one thing in common: they are subject to the sun's powerful gravitational pull. The sun and all the celestial objects held by its gravitational force are referred to as the *solar system.* Each member of the solar system has a definite orbit around the sun which is the result of a delicate balance between the sun's gravitational force pulling the body inward and the force of the body's own inertia tending to throw it off into space. Any such object in space that is attracted to and falls into a definite orbit around a larger body is called a *satellite,* literally, an attendant.

The earth is a satellite of the sun, revolving at a speed of about 66,600 miles per hour. This great speed keeps the earth from falling into the sun, maintaining an average distance of about 93 million miles between the earth and sun. The other members of the solar system also have their own orbits, determined by their particular speed, size, and distance from the sun. The number and variety of orbits in the solar system suggest the possibility of their crossing, thus permitting collisions to occur. In fact, this is very common. The earth collides with thousands of small members of the solar system every day. These collisions will continue and there is no guarantee that the earth will not sometime encounter an

VOCABULARY

Solar system. The sun and the celestial objects that revolve around it.

Satellite. Any celestial object that revolves around a larger object; a natural or artificial moon.

Planetesimal theory. The theory that the planets of the solar system were formed by the clumping together of smaller bodies.

Asteroid. One of the many tiny planets between the orbits of Mars and Jupiter.

Meteor. A rocklike particle in space; one of the smallest members of the solar system.

Comet. A member of the solar system, composed of rocks and frozen gases, having a very eccentric orbit.

object large enough to inflict serious damage.

The solar system as we know it today is basically an orderly arrangement of planets and smaller bodies which move around the sun with remarkable precision. But how did the sun happen to acquire its collection of satellites, our earth among them? This is a question that has always fascinated mankind. Modern science still has no definite answer, but several possibilities can be considered which are in basic agreement with most of the facts known to astronomy.

ORIGIN OF
THE SOLAR SYSTEM

Stars in collision. Stars are very far apart even within the same galaxy. The chances that two of them will collide or even come very close are very slim, but this event is still possible. A collision or near miss between the sun and another star is the basis of one of the theories of the origin of the solar system. This is generally called the *planetesimal* (little planet) *theory.* According to this theory, large masses of matter were thrown out of the sun when it experienced a glancing collision with another star. The hot material cooled to form small bodies (planetesimals) which eventually collected together and formed the planets. The theory was first proposed in 1778 by a French scientist, Georges, Comte de Buffon. Since then, the theory has appeared in several newer forms which assume that matter was drawn from the sun by the gravitational attraction of another star which came close but did not actually collide with the sun. The different versions of the planetesimal theory all have a serious weakness. All evidence indicates that matter taken from the sun or any other star would be so hot that it would quickly spread out into space as a

FIG. 3–1. In a collision of the sun with another star, the masses of material thrown out might become parts of a solar system.

gas before it could possibly cool enough to become solid material.

A companion star to the sun. A completely different explanation for the origin of the solar system has been proposed by Fred Hoyle, a modern British astronomer. He suggests that perhaps the sun once had a companion star which exploded about 3 billion years ago. Most of its material was thrown into deep space, but a cloud of gas was left behind, held by the sun's gravitation. From this cloud of gas the various bodies of the solar system were formed. This explanation is plausible, since pairs of stars, called *binary stars,* are fairly common and there seems to be no obvious reason why the sun could not once have had a companion. Also, even though exploding stars or novas are thought to be rare, it is possible that the sun's companion could have become a nova. At the present time there seems to be no basic flaw in this theory nor is there much in the way of supporting evidence.

A cloud of dust. In 1796 Laplace (la-*plas*), a French astronomer, proposed the idea that the solar system began as a vast saucer-shaped hot cloud of gas and dust slowly revolving in space. As the cloud cooled and shrank, it began to spin faster, causing rings of matter to break away from the outer edge. As the shrinkage continued, a series of rings were formed around the central mass of material. Each ring gave rise to a planet and the central mass became the sun. This dust cloud theory of Laplace gained a very large following among scientists for many years, but careful mathematical analysis eventually showed very serious flaws. It could not be shown, for example, how rings of material could ever tend to collect into globes of matter large enough to form the planets. Although Laplace's theory was not completely sound, it forms the basis for the explanation of the origin of the solar

FIG. 3–2. The explosion of a companion star of our sun might have resulted is the formation of our solar system.

FIG. 3–3. In the Laplace theory, the solar system was formed from a cloud of dust. As it cooled and shrank, it formed rings which gave rise to the planets; the central mass formed the sun.

FIG. 3–4. The solar system might have been formed from whirlpools of gas and dust. In the theory of von Weizsäcker and others, such whirlpools are believed more likely to have led to planets than the rings of Laplace.

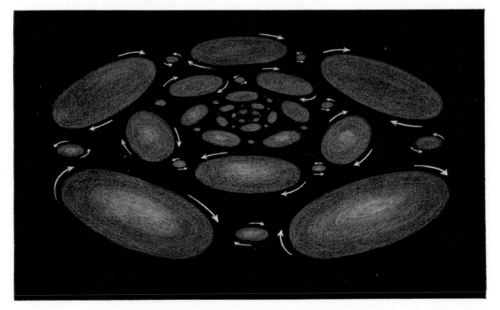

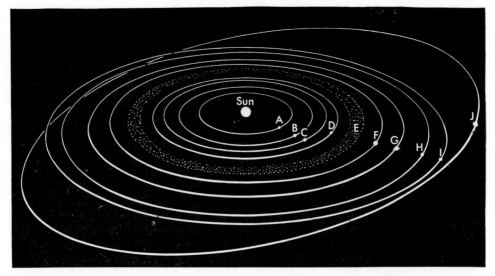

FIG. 3–5. The solar system: *A* Mercury, *B* Venus, *C* Earth, *D* Mars, *E* Asteroids, *F* Jupiter, *G* Saturn, *H* Uranus, *I* Neptune, and *J* Pluto. Sizes and distances are not proportional; the elliptical orbits are exaggerated.

system most widely accepted in modern astronomy.

The theory felt to be most in agreement with all the facts was originally put forward by a German astronomer, Carl von Weizsäcker, but was revised by several others. It is based in part on the explanation of the processes by which stars are formed from clouds of dust and gas, as described in Chapter 1. According to this theory, part of the dust cloud from which the sun was formed remained around the new star as a great, slowly rotating disk. In time, huge whirlpools developed within the disk, causing the formation of smaller globes of gas and dust. Each globe of material eventually cooled into a planet, which still revolves around the sun as a result of the original motion of the spinning disk of gas.

One interesting aspect of this theory is that it does not require that anything unusual happened to the sun to give it a group of satellites. If the theory is correct, many stars in the universe may have systems of planets and among them may be some that are similar to earth.

However, the distances to even the closest stars make it impossible to establish by any known means the existence of other solar systems.

Much more scientific labor will have to be done before the dust cloud theory of von Weizsäcker, or any other, can be accepted as a completely satisfactory explanation for the origin of the solar system. It is possible that we will never know exactly how the earth and the other satellites of the sun came into being.

THE MEMBERS OF THE SOLAR SYSTEM

The solar system in miniature. Suppose that somehow the entire solar system could be reduced in size so that the sun itself would be only about 1 foot in diameter—about the size of a basketball. Now the closest planet to the sun, *Mercury,* would be half the size of a small pea, and would be circling the basketball-size sun in an orbit about 54 feet away.

Venus, the next most distant planet, would be the size of a larger pea in an orbit about 100 feet away. Next, about 151 feet away, would be *Earth* (about the same size pea as Venus), with its BB-shot-size moon. Then would come *Mars* —a smaller pea than Earth—circling in its orbit approximately 211 feet away from the sun.

Beyond Mars in the miniature solar system, about 375 feet from the sun, a band of sand grains would represent the *asteroids.* Beyond the asteroids, the planets (except Pluto) become much larger and are much farther away. In the small scale, *Jupiter,* the next planet, would be about the size of a golf ball, one-eighth of a mile from the basketball sun. *Saturn,* surrounded by its rings, would be next, about a quarter of a mile from the sun, a little smaller than a golf ball. A half mile out would be *Uranus* (*yoo*-ra-nus), the size of a marble; then *Neptune,* also a marble at three-quarters of a mile away from the sun. Last would

be *Pluto,* no more than a small pea, separated from the sun by a full mile.

The actual size of the solar system can be estimated from the fact that Pluto is really about 3700 million miles from the sun. The actual distances and sizes of the other planets are given in the table below.

The inner planets. The four planets closest to the sun—Mercury, Venus, Earth, and Mars—are the junior members of the solar system in terms of size. (Actually, the planet most distant from the sun, Pluto, is also very small, but it is a special case and will be discussed later in this chapter.) The smallest of the four inner planets is **Mercury,** which is also closest to the sun at an average distance of 36 million miles. It is a tiny planet only 3100 miles in diameter.

Because Mercury is so close to the sun, it is not ordinarily visible to the unaided eye. It is most easily observed shortly before sunrise or shortly after sunset. Even at these times, Mercury is

FACTS ABOUT THE PLANETS

	Average Distance from the Sun (miles)	Period of Revolution	Period of Rotation	Diameter (miles)	Number of Natural Satellites
The Inner Planets					
Mercury	36,000,000	88 days	88 days	3,100	0
Venus	67,200,000	224 days	?	7,700	0
Earth	93,009,000	365¼ days	23h 56m	7,926	1
Mars	141,500,000	687 days	24h 37m	4,200	2
The Outer Planets					
Jupiter	483,000,000	11¾ years	9h 53m	88,700	12
Saturn	886,100,000	29½ years	10h 14m	75,100	9
Uranus	1,783,000,000	84 years	10h 45m	32,000	5
Neptune	2,793,000,000	164¾ years	15h 48m	27,600	2
Pluto	3,700,000,000	248 years	?	?	?

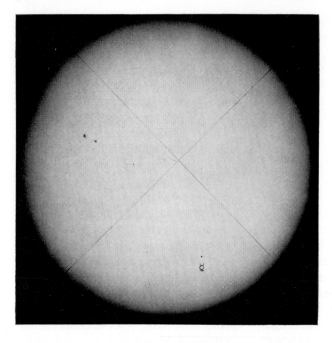

FIG. 3–6. A transit of Mercury. The planet is shown as a black dot accompanied by the ancient symbol for Mercury. The dark areas at the upper left are sunspots, and the straight black lines are crosshairs in the eyepiece of the telescope. (*Royal Observatory, Greenwich, England*)

only visible in locations where the view of the horizon is not obstructed by mountains, trees, or buildings.

Since the orbit of Mercury lies between the earth and the sun, the planet can be observed by telescope as it crosses the face of the sun. It is then visible as a circular black dot that slowly moves across the bright surface of the sun. Such a crossing, known as a *transit,* is shown in Fig. 3–6. Venus is the only other planet that makes transits of the sun.

Mercury must be one of the most desolate of all the planets. Because of its small size, it has no atmosphere, since it has little gravitation to hold any gases. Mercury also may be both the hottest and the coldest planet of the entire solar system. The same side is always turned toward the sun and must have temperatures around 700° F. The other side is always away from the sun and has continuous darkness and temperatures near the coldest possible, absolute zero, about −460° F. Even the planets most distant

from the sun do not get as cold as the dark side of Mercury, because their rotation allows all sides to receive at least a little warmth. Mercury rotates on its axis only once in 88 days, the same rate at which it revolves around the sun. This speed keeps the same side of the planet always turned toward the sun. Mercury may have fallen into this pattern of rotation because it is so close to the sun that it was deformed by the sun's strong gravitational pull in the early stages of development. When the little planet was still young and hot enough to be soft, it must have developed a bulge on the side nearest the sun. The sun's gravitation then pulled more strongly on the heavier, bulging side. As a result, Mercury fell into a period of rotation which keeps the originally heavier side always toward the sun.

Altogether, Mercury seems a very forbidding place. Its extreme temperatures and lack of atmosphere certainly eliminate any possibility of life there and make it an uninviting destination for space travelers.

On the other hand, **Venus,** the next closest planet to the sun, promises to be a prime target in future space exploration. Although Venus is relatively close to the earth and thus gives us a good opportunity to observe it, we actually know very little about it. The thick layers of clouds which completely cover the entire surface of the planet make it difficult to study Venus. Spectroscopic evidence indicates that these clouds are composed mostly of carbon dioxide, although this may be true only of the top layers. No one knows what lies beneath the blanket of clouds, but the presence of large amounts of carbon dioxide in the atmosphere of Venus makes it likely that the surface of the planet has very warm temperatures. Carbon dioxide acts as a trap for the sun's energy. Radiations from the sun pass through the carbon dioxide and heat the planet's surface, but the heat is not easily radiated back out again to be lost in space because it is stopped by the thick layers of carbon dioxide. The surface of Venus may have temperatures of as much as 660° F on the side toward the sun. Nighttime temperatures are more difficult to estimate because there is no way of knowing how rapidly Venus rotates, and the temperature on the dark side of a planet is generally determined partly by how long that side is turned away from the sun. The cloud layer on Venus prevents the observation of any surface markings which might be used to determine its period of rotation. The planet probably rotates at least several times during its 255-day trip around its orbit so that all sides receive some heat from the sun. However, it must rotate very slowly because spectroscopes can detect no Doppler effect on the light reflected from Venus. If the rotation were fast, there would be a slight Doppler shift in the light from the edge turning toward the earth and an opposite shift in the light from the edge turning away.

Recent spectroscopic studies made from instrument-carrying balloons at high altitudes show that the cloud mantle covering Venus contains small amounts of nitrogen and water vapor. In size and distance from the sun, Venus is very much like Earth and might be expected to be one member of the solar system on which life has developed

FIG. 3–7. Three phases of Venus. (*Mount Wilson and Palomar Observatories*)

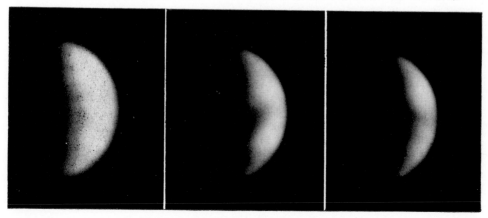

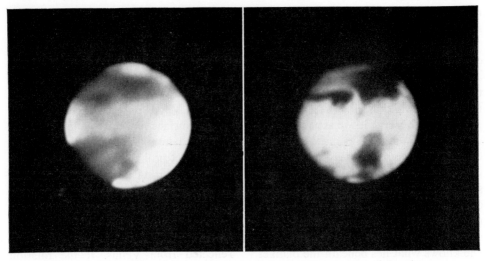

FIG. 3–8. Mars. The photograph at the left was taken in blue light; the one at the right, taken in red light, shows more detail. (*Mount Wilson and Palomar Observatories*)

somewhat as it has on Earth. If Venus has temperatures as high as indicated, it is very unlikely that any life (as we know it) exists there. However, until it is possible to launch space probes that will penetrate the cloud curtain and record data about its surface, Venus will remain a riddle.

Both Mercury and Venus appear as bright stars when viewed with the unaided eye. However, when seen through an astronomical telescope they show phases just as the moon does in its orbit around the earth. This is evident in the photographs of Venus in Fig. 3–7. These phases appear because Mercury and Venus are nearer to the sun than Earth is. (The reasons for the phases of the moon are discussed in Chapter 4.)

Next among the inner planets is *Earth,* whose characteristics as a planet are discussed in detail in Unit II. *Mars* is the last of the inner planets and is very similar to Earth in many respects. The chief difference between Earth and Mars is that Mars is smaller, being about half

the diameter of Earth and having only one-tenth of the earth's bulk. Mars has two small moons or satellites, whereas Earth has only one. Apart from our moon and Venus in its occasional near approaches, Mars is Earth's closest neighbor among the larger bodies of the solar system. Even at its closest, however, Mars is still 35 million miles from Earth, about 150 times farther away than the moon. Even with the best telescopes no more detail can be seen on Mars than can be seen on the moon with low-powered binoculars. Nevertheless, many surface features of Mars can be seen and a great deal more is known about this planet than about Venus.

About three-quarters of the surface of Mars is covered with bright reddish or yellowish patches. There seems little doubt that these are great deserts. From time to time yellow clouds which appear to be dust storms or sandstorms spread over parts of these deserts and disappear again within a few days. About one-fifth of Mars' surface is darker than the deserts and changes color with the seasons. In the Martian winter these darker areas are pale blue-green; during the summer all but a few spots turn dark brown. This change of color seems to be connected with the formation and disappearance of thin layers of ice, called icecaps, at the north and south poles. As the white areas of ice at the poles grow larger during winter, the color of the dark areas becomes lighter. When the icecaps shrink during summer, the same regions darken again. This strongly suggests that the darker areas are composed of plants which are watered by the escaping moisture from the disappearing icecaps during the Martian summer. Spectroscopic evidence shows that Mars is extremely dry and any plant life there would certainly be greatly dependent on the moisture frozen in the icecaps. Temperatures on Mars range from about 80° F to a low of about −100° F. Any plants that might exist there would have to be able to stand great extremes of temperature. Probably no definite conclusion about life on Mars can be reached until space exploration permits closer examination of the planet, although recent spectroscopic studies seem to show carbon-con-

taining compounds which might indicate the presence of some forms of life.

The miniature planets. Between Mars and Jupiter is a gap of 350 million miles. Even in the early days astronomers suspected that this space might be occupied by a small and inconspicuous planet awaiting discovery. Around 1800 a small group of German astronomers became so firmly convinced that a planet did fill this vacant orbit that they began a search for it; in 1801, a small planet, later named Ceres, was actually discovered. It appeared to be the missing planet although it was less than 500 miles in diameter. By 1815, however, four more such miniature planets were discovered in the same region between Mars and Jupiter. These tiny planets came to be known as the *asteroids.*

More asteroids have been discovered over the years, until the number known at present is greater than two thousand. Only a very few are more than 100 miles across; a few hundred are between 10 and 100 miles in diameter and the remainder are less than 10 miles in diameter. They seem to be masses of stone, perhaps mixed with metal. Some are very irregular in shape.

FIG. 3–9. Asteroid trails, marked by arrows, showing motion during 2½ hours. Because the telescope was moved to follow the apparent movement of the stars, the stars all appear as points of light while the asteroids appear as streaks. (*Lowell Observatory*)

FIG. 3–10. The planet Jupiter. The black spot in the photo at the left is the shadow of one of Jupiter's satellites as it passes across the face of the planet. In the photo on the right, taken about 50 minutes later, both the satellite (the white dot) and its shadow are seen. (*Mount Wilson and Palomar Observatories*)

The origin of the asteroids is unknown. Some astronomers believe that they are fragments of a planet which was shattered by intense gravitational forces when its orbit carried it too close to the giant Jupiter. Others suggest that the asteroids may be the pieces of two planets which collided and were both blasted into fragments. A completely different theory is that they are fragments of the solar system which never grew large enough to form an ordinary planet.

The orbits of some of the asteroids carry them across the paths of both Mars and Earth. A small asteroid known as Hermes, barely more than a mile in diameter, has come within 485,000 miles of the earth. It is very likely that the earth has collided with such asteroids in the past and will do so again in the future, although it is impossible to predict such an event very far in advance.

The outer planets. The five outer planets of the solar system—Jupiter, Saturn, Uranus, Neptune and Pluto— are very different from Earth and its neighbors. *Jupiter,* the closest of the outer planets, illustrates these differences

very well. First, Jupiter is a huge planet; it is more than eleven times the diameter of the earth. Thirteen hundred earths could be contained within the sphere of Jupiter. But its size is deceptive. It is only about 300 times as heavy as the earth, indicating that it must be much less dense. Telescopic observation confirms this, since Jupiter can be seen to be considerably flattened at the poles. Apparently its rotation makes the region around its equator bulge out, giving the whole planet the appearance of a slightly squashed orange. Like all the larger planets, Jupiter rotates very rapidly— about once every ten hours. Even with its rapid rotation such pronounced bulging at the equator could not occur unless the planet were not entirely solid.

In a telescopic view, Jupiter, like Venus, does not show solid surface features but only a sea of shifting clouds. The clouds are spread out in colored bands which constantly change their pattern and colors, indicating that the atmosphere on Jupiter must be swept by great storms. Radio telescopes record signals from Jupiter which may be the result of lightning discharges in these storms. Spectroscopic study of Jupiter's upper cloud layers shows definite presence of ammonia and methane, both poisonous gases. Hydrogen and helium are also probably present.

From all of the available astronomical evidence, Jupiter may be pictured as having only a very small solid core. The great bulk of the planet seems to consist of an atmosphere composed of dense clouds of the same gases found in the upper layers. Between the small solid core and the atmosphere there is probably a thick layer of ice and frozen gases. These conditions will probably rule out any possibility of our ever visiting Jupiter even if a way of getting there becomes available. It would be possible, however, to get a close view of this giant

of the solar system by landing on one of its twelve satellites. Four of these satellites are roughly the size of our moon and the other eight are very small. One of the larger satellites would be a much more suitable landing place than Jupiter itself and might be an excellent base from which to study the planet.

The other outer planets are very much like Jupiter. *Saturn,* Jupiter's outer neighbor, is the second largest planet of the solar system, but like Jupiter, it seems to consist of only a small solid core surrounded by an icy layer and a thick atmosphere of gases. Saturn does possess a unique feature in its famous rings, which are apparently composed of billions of small particles ranging from lumps the size of golf balls down to grains of sand. How Saturn came to have

FIG. 3–11. Saturn and its ring system, photographed with the 100-inch Mount Wilson telescope. (*Mount Wilson and Palomar Observatories*)

FIG. 3–12. A meteor trail or "shooting star." (*Yerkes Observatory*)

these rings and exactly what the particles in them are composed of are not known. Saturn also has nine satellites, one of which—Titan—is the largest known satellite of any planet. The distance between Earth and Saturn makes it difficult to measure Titan's diameter exactly, but it appears to be about 3500 miles. This puts the satellite between Mercury and Mars in size. The other eight of Saturn's satellites are much smaller, ranging from about the size of the moon down to only 150 miles in diameter.

Uranus and *Neptune* are so remote that little is known of their details. Although not so large as Jupiter or Saturn, both Uranus and Neptune are giants compared to Earth. Both are apparently made up of small solid cores surrounded by thick layers of ice and gases. Uranus has five known satellites and Neptune only two. One of Neptune's moons is very large; if it could be measured accurately it might displace Titan as the largest satellite of any planet.

Beyond Neptune, on the fringes of the solar system itself, is the orbit of the tiny planet *Pluto.* Almost nothing is known about Pluto because its great distance from Earth makes it barely visible even with powerful telescopes. Pluto's size is in doubt, but such evidence as can be gathered indicates that it is no larger than Earth and perhaps much smaller. Even Pluto's right to be considered one of the original planets is open to serious question. Its orbit around the sun has a peculiar tilt compared to the orbits of the other planets, and this, along with other peculiarities in its orbit, leads astronomers to suspect that it once may have been a satellite of Neptune. Somehow Pluto may have escaped Neptune's influence and fallen into its own orbit around the sun.

Meteors and comets. The space through which the earth passes in its orbit around the sun contains many flying rocks, which are the smallest members of the solar system. Every "shooting star" that you see at night marks the passage of one of these stray rocks through the earth's atmosphere. The particles may be extremely small, but many of them are traveling much faster than the earth and enter the earth's atmosphere with such speed that the heat generated from friction with the air vaporizes them almost immediately. The name *meteor,* given to these brief earthly visitors, comes from a Greek word meaning "something in the air." They are indeed something in the air as they plunge toward the earth at speeds that sometimes exceed 100,000 miles per hour. Usually at about 55 miles above the earth they strike dense enough air to cause them to vaporize with a brief flash of brilliantly glowing gas. It is seldom that a meteor penetrates more than 10 miles deep into the earth's atmosphere, but occasionally

FIG. 3–13. The famous Meteor Crater in Arizona. Fragments of meteorites have been excavated from the floor of the crater. (*U. S. Geological Survey*)

a large one will last until it is only a few miles above the earth's surface. It may then explode with a thunderous noise and a tremendous burst of light, scattering fragments in its vicinity.

Almost all of the billion or so meteors that collide with the earth each day are no bigger than a sand grain, but about two thousand each year are large enough to survive the trip through the atmosphere and reach the earth's surface as a solid. These are called *meteorites.* If they are big enough, they can make a large crater when they strike the earth. Meteor Crater in Arizona and probably the Chubb Crater in Canada were made sometime in the not-far-distant past by the impact of very large meteorites.

The meteors that reach the earth seem to come from two different sources. The majority are probably small fragments

FIG. 3–14. Halley's Comet. Stars in the background are visible through parts of the comet's tail. (*Yerkes Observatory*)

FIG. 3–15. The relatively eccentric orbit of a comet (in black) as compared with the orbits of the planets.

like those in the belt of asteroids between Mars and Jupiter. A second source appears to be the tails of comets. The orbits of comets seem to be cluttered with fragments of the comet that are attracted to the earth as the comet passes. Each time the earth crosses the path of a comet, swarms of meteors are seen. Several of these meteor showers occur at regular times each year. One of the most spectacular of the meteor showers is the Perseids (*per*-see-ids) which come each year in mid-August.

Edmund Halley, an English astronomer, was one of the first men to recognize that *comets* are definitely members of the solar system, since they orbit regularly around the sun. Their orbits are very eccentric, however. They swing in close to the sun, then far out again deep into space, often far beyond the solar system itself. Because they travel so far out away from the sun, most comets can be seen from Earth only after long intervals. Halley's Comet, one of the most famous, last appeared in 1910 and will not return until 1986.

As a comet comes in to take its turn around the sun, it appears to be made of a glowing, fuzzy cloud followed by a thin tail streaming out millions of miles behind. The head of the comet apparently is composed of a loose swarm of fine rock particles mixed with frozen gases that vaporize and glow when the comet nears the sun. The tail seems to be matter pushed out of the body of the comet by pressure of the energy received from the sun. As the comet approaches and circles the sun, the tail always streams away from the sun. When a comet is some distance away from the sun, it gives off very little light and is lost from sight.

SUMMARY

THE solar system is made up of meteors, comets, asteroids, and nine planets with their satellites, all revolving around the sun. Theories to explain the origin of the solar system include the planetesimal and dust cloud theory. At present the dust cloud theory is most widely accepted.

The solar system is composed of the sun; the inner planets Mercury, Venus, Earth, and Mars; the outer planets Jupiter, Saturn, Uranus, Neptune, and Pluto and a belt of asteroids that separates the two groups. With the exception of Pluto, the outer planets have greater diameters. Apparently they have dense cores surrounded by thick layers of ice and gases. The only planet that appears able to maintain life is the earth.

The belt of asteroids and the tails of comets offer an explanation for the origin of meteors. Most meteors that enter our atmosphere are vaporized by the heat of friction with the upper air. Meteors are commonly referred to as "shooting stars." If they reach the earth's surface they are called meteorites.

Comets are made up of rock fragments, ice, and gases, and have highly eccentric orbits. Only in the vicinity of the sun does a comet produce light. The tail of the comet points away from the sun.

VOCABULARY REVIEW

Match the phrase in the left column with the correct word or phrase in the right column. *Do not write in this book.*

1. The planets and other bodies revolving around the sun
2. Man who suggested the planetesimal theory
3. Small celestial bodies located in the region between Mars and Jupiter
4. The largest satellite of any planet in the solar system
5. Any small body, either natural or man-made, revolving around another body
6. Object composed of rock fragments and ice
7. Man who developed the dust cloud theory
8. A pair of companion stars
9. Man who recognized that comets are part of the solar system
10. Planet whose icecaps show seasonal changes
11. Possible former satellite of Neptune
12. Planet surrounded by rings
13. The closest planet to the sun
14. Celestial body that glows because of friction with the earth's atmosphere
15. The largest planet in the solar system

a. asteroids
b. binary star
c. Uranus
d. Comte de Buffon
e. moon
f. Laplace
g. meteor
h. satellites
i. Mercury
j. Titan
k. Halley
l. Jupiter
m. Mars
n. Saturn
o. Pluto
p. comet
q. solar system

QUESTIONS · GROUP A

In each of the following groups of terms, three are related in some way and one is not. Select the unrelated term and give a reason for your choice. *Do not write in this book.*

1. (*a*) Mars (*b*) Jupiter (*c*) Venus (*d*) Mercury
2. (*a*) comets (*b*) meteors (*c*) stars (*d*) planets
3. (*a*) Laplace (*b*) Halley (*c*) Weizsäcker (*d*) Comte de Buffon
4. (*a*) cover of dense clouds (*b*) sandstorms (*c*) shows seasonal changes (*d*) diameter 4200 miles
5. (*a*) 12 satellites (*b*) revolution 248 years (*c*) diameter 88,700 miles (*d*) weight 300 times that of the earth
6. (*a*) comet (*b*) Ceres (*c*) stone and metal (*d*) asteroid
7. (*a*) Saturn (*b*) Mars (*c*) Jupiter (*d*) Uranus
8. (*a*) rock fragments (*b*) methane gas (*c*) meteors (*d*) shooting star

Select the best term to complete the following statements. *Do not write in this book.*

9. The planet which has the least number of natural satellites is (*a*) Saturn (*b*) Mars (*c*) Mercury (*d*) Earth.
10. All the planets in the solar system (*a*) have the same surface temperature (*b*) can maintain human life (*c*) revolve around the sun (*d*) are exactly the same size.
11. The closest that Mars comes to Earth is (*a*) 35,000,000 miles (*b*) 93,000,000 miles (*c*) 240,000 miles (*d*) 186,000 miles.
12. The planet which has bright red or yellowish regions is (*a*) Jupiter (*b*) Mercury (*c*) Hermes (*d*) Mars.
13. Comets have an eccentric orbit; this means (*a*) their orbits are circular (*b*) their time of arrival is unpredictable (*c*) the sun is closer to one end of the orbit (*d*) they cannot be seen without a telescope.
14. Compared to a day on Earth, a day on Mars is (*a*) twice as long (*b*) one-half as long (*c*) about the same length (*d*) of unknown length.
15. A planet that goes through phases as our moon does is (*a*) Jupiter (*b*) Neptune (*c*) Pluto (*d*) Venus.
16. The planet with the shortest year is (*a*) Earth (*b*) Mars (*c*) Mercury (*d*) Pluto.
17. The planet farthest from the sun is (*a*) Mercury (*b*) Pluto (*c*) Titan (*d*) Jupiter.
18. The earth revolves at a speed of (*a*) 6000 miles per hour (*b*) 62,736 miles per second (*c*) 66,000 miles per hour (*d*) 606,000 miles per year.
19. The diameter of the solar system is about (*a*) 3666 million miles (*b*) 25 million miles (*c*) 9602 million miles (*d*) 7332 million miles.
20. The planet whose period of rotation is equal to its period of revolution is (*a*) Mercury (*b*) Mars (*c*) Saturn (*d*) Neptune.
21. Venus may have a daytime temperature of (*a*) 212° F (*b*) 666° F (*c*) 1000° F (*d*) −250° F.

GROUP B

1. Determine the length of time it would take a rocket, traveling at 25,000 miles per hour, to reach Mars at its closest approach to the earth.
2. Determine the approximate circumference of the earth's orbit. How could the circumference be calculated more exactly?
3. List the planets in order of diameter, starting with the smallest.
4. What is the principal weakness in the planetesimal theory of the origin of the solar system?
5. If the sun had a companion star, what probably became of it?
6. If the dust cloud theory of the origin of the solar system is correct, why is it likely that there are other solar systems in the universe?
7. Suppose you are planning a trip to Mars. List some of the things you would need to take to stay alive and give reasons why they are needed.
8. Why does Mercury probably have the lowest and highest temperatures of any planet?
9. What is the evidence that there is life on Mars?
10. What characteristics of Jupiter lead to the conclusion that it has only a small solid core?
11. Why are comets more clearly visible when they approach the sun?
12. What reason is there for thinking that the earth may be getting continuously heavier?
13. Why may Saturn's rings occasionally not show up in telescopic views of the planet?
14. Explain why meteors are more often seen late at night and usually are most numerous before dawn.

CHAPTER 4

THE MOON

FROM the earth, the most splendid object to be seen in the entire night sky is the moon. Men have worshipped it as a goddess and attributed magical properties to its light. From our study of the solar system we now know that it is a relatively insignificant body, a mere satellite of the earth, shining only by reflected sunlight. Although the moon cannot be considered a large or important body within the entire solar system, it is an unusual satellite, being very large compared with its planet: 2160 miles in diameter compared with the earth's diameter of 7926 miles. No other planet has a satellite of as large relative size. Some of the satellites of Jupiter, Saturn and Neptune are larger in diameter than the moon, but these are not large when compared with the size of the giant planets around which they revolve. Titan, the largest satellite of Saturn and believed to be the largest in the solar system, is almost as large as Mars but still is only one-twentieth of Saturn's diameter.

Because the moon and the earth are so close in size, they are more like twin planets than a planet and a satellite. At one time some astronomers thought that the moon was originally part of the earth. A huge chunk of the earth was supposed to have broken away and formed the moon, leaving a great scar on the earth's surface that became the basin of the Pacific Ocean. There is very little evidence to support this theory of

VOCABULARY

Earthshine. Illumination of the darker portion of the moon by reflection of light from the earth.

Phases of the moon. The apparent changes in the shape of the moon as it revolves around the earth.

Umbra. The darker inner part of a shadow.

Penumbra. The lighter outer part of a shadow.

Perigee (*pehr*-i-jee). The point of a satellite's orbit nearest to the object around which it revolves.

Apogee (*ap*-o-jee). The point of a satellite's orbit farthest from the object around which it revolves.

Eclipse. The cutting off of light from one celestial body by another.

the moon's origin, and most astronomers now believe that the moon was never part of the earth. The origin of the moon is not known. It is probable that the moon came into existence at the same time and in the same way as the earth. There is also the possibility that it was formed elsewhere in the solar system and later was captured by the earth.

Whatever its origin, the moon was probably once much closer to the earth than it is now. This is suggested by the fact that the moon always keeps the same side turned toward the earth. As Mercury may have developed a bulge from being close to the sun, the moon may have once been close enough to the earth to be deformed.

THE NATURE OF
THE MOON

The moon's surface. Even without a telescope the basic features on the surface of the moon are visible. The very obvious dark and light areas are rela-

tively smooth plains and mountainous regions. The plains appear dark because they do not reflect as much of the sun's light as the rougher mountainous areas. The early astronomers thought that the dark areas were oceans and the light areas were continents; some observers with vivid imaginations even thought they saw all kinds of peculiar creatures living on the moon. Modern telescopes show no oceans and no continents, but the plains regions are still called "seas" in accordance with the mistaken beliefs of the ancient observers.

Since the moon has no water and virtually no atmosphere, there are no forces of wind and water at work on the moon to wear down the jagged rocks and high peaks to the more gentle landscapes common on the earth. Lofty mountains tower above the moon's surface, some reaching heights of 30,000 feet, about as high as the highest mountains on earth. See Fig. 4–2. (How can astronomers determine the heights of mountains on a body more than 200,000 miles away? Measurements of the length of the

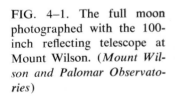

FIG. 4–1. The full moon photographed with the 100-inch reflecting telescope at Mount Wilson. (*Mount Wilson and Palomar Observatories*)

FIG. 4–2. In this detailed photograph of the moon's surface, the great lunar crater in the center is Copernicus, named after the famous astronomer. The flat areas around the craters are called seas, even though there is no water on the surface of the moon. Notice the relatively straight rays which appear to spread from the large crater out into the surrounding seas. (*Mount Wilson and Palomar Observatories*)

shadows cast by the mountain, combined with knowledge of the angle of the sun's rays, make a basis for a simple problem in trigonometry.) The mountains on the moon must be considerably rougher and more rugged than our mountains on earth because there has probably been nothing to wear them off.

The broad plains or "seas" cover about one-half of the moon's visible surface and are generally shaped like rough circles. They are not completely smooth but contain many irregularities and small mountains. Evidence based on the amount of radiation absorbed in the plains regions indicates that there is some loose covering on the surface, possibly small rocks or a layer of dust.

The most unusual feature of the moon is the thousands of craters of all sizes spread over the entire visible surface. The craters are rounded shallow depressions completely enclosed by a ring of mountains. In some craters the floor is above the general level of the rest of the moon's surface, but in most cases the floor is depressed below the surface. The craters range in size from small ones only a few hundred feet across to giants reaching 170 miles in diameter. One of the best known is Tycho (*tee*-ko) named after a Danish astronomer of the sixteenth century. Located near the moon's south pole, Tycho is about 50 miles in diameter; the mountain walls around it are about 16,000 feet high. It is one of the most conspicuous craters on the moon because a number of light streaks radiate from it in all directions. These streaks, called *rays,* are also found around a number of other craters. Since the rays cast no shadows, they must be made by some substance spread out over the moon's surface.

The origin of the craters is a mystery. Some astronomers think that they were caused by meteors colliding with the moon. Others believe that volcanic action caused huge gas pockets to push up to the surface and erupt, leaving craters as round scars. There is good evidence to support both ideas, and the question probably will not be definitely settled until the first explorers have landed on the moon and the craters have been carefully studied at first hand.

Gravity and temperature on the moon. The force of gravitation at the surface of the moon is determined by its mass and diameter. The moon's diameter can be determined from its size and distance

FIG. 4–3. The moon during its last quarter. In the photo, the rim of the moon and the craters are sharp and clear because the moon has practically no atmosphere to obscure its surface features. (*Yerkes Observatory*)

from the earth. Its mass can be determined from its effects on the movements of the earth. Calculations made from such observations show that the moon is $\frac{1}{81}$ as heavy as the earth. This mass, with its diameter, gives the moon a gravitational pull at its surface which is one-sixth of the earth's surface gravity. A 180-pound man would weigh only 30 pounds on the moon. Climbing the moon's rugged mountains would be a great deal easier than mountain climbing on earth.

The moon's relatively low gravity explains why it has no atmosphere in the ordinary sense of the word. The gases which might have been held by gravity to blanket the surface with an atmosphere were attracted so feebly that they eventually escaped into space. The atmosphere around the moon is actually about as dense as the earth's atmosphere at an altitude of more than 50 miles. It probably consists of gases from space temporarily attracted by the moon's weak gravity.

Because the moon lacks a sheltering atmosphere, its surface becomes very hot during the day and extremely cold at night. The daytime temperature goes above 200° F but drops at night to around −250° F. The great extremes of temperature have probably caused the rocks on the moon's surface to crack and break up, thus intensifying the jagged and forbidding aspect of the landscape. Since daylight on the moon lasts about two weeks and is followed by two weeks of darkness, a visit there would be decidedly uncomfortable for earth-dwellers. The possibility that life exists on the moon is extremely remote.

THE MOTIONS OF THE MOON

The moon's orbit. Since the moon is a satellite of the earth, it follows a path which carries it around the earth while the earth travels in its own orbit around the sun. The moon's orbit with respect to the earth is slightly oval-shaped, or elliptical, so that it comes a little closer to the earth on one side of its orbit than on the other. When the moon is at the

FIG. 4–4. The orbit of the moon is tilted with respect to the earth's orbit. The moon revolves around the earth in a counterclockwise direction, the same direction as the earth's revolution around the sun.

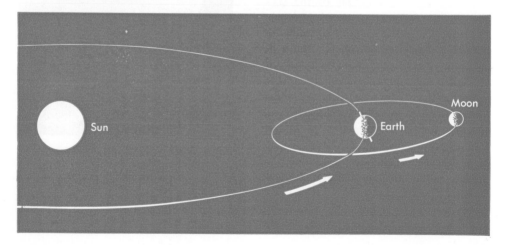

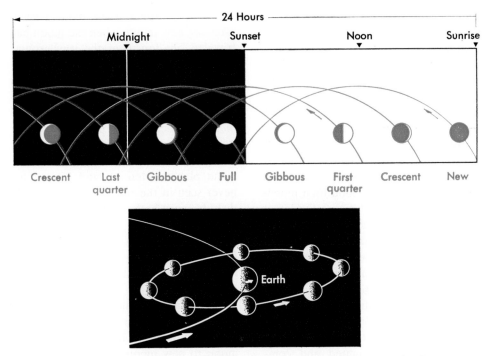

24 Hours

Midnight   Sunset   Noon   Sunrise

Crescent   Last   Gibbous   Full   Gibbous   First   Crescent   New
            quarter   quarter

Earth

FIG. 4–5. The lower diagram shows that one half of the moon is always lighted as the moon revolves around the earth. Above, the phases of the moon are shown as seen from the earth. The time scale at the top of the diagram shows how the moon rises later each day as the phases progress (from right to left), and also indicates when the moon is visible during the hours of darkness. We do not ordinarily see the moon during daylight hours (except early in the morning or late in the afternoon), because the earth's atmosphere diffuses the light from the sun.

point of its orbit closest to the earth, it is said to be at *perigee* (*pehr*-i-jee): 221,463 miles from the earth. At *apogee* (*ap*-o-jee), the farthest point in its orbit, it is 252,710 miles from the earth. Its average distance from the earth is 238,857 miles. See Fig. 4–4.

The moon moves in its orbit at a speed of about 2200 miles per hour and makes one complete revolution in 29½ days. You have no doubt noticed that the moon rises at different times on successive nights. If you have observed carefully, you also know that it always rises later than it did the previous time. This is because the moon moves in the

same direction that the earth rotates (from west to east). To anyone on the earth, the moon appears to rise over the horizon when the earth has turned far enough to allow the moon to be seen in the sky. Since the moon is moving in its orbit in the same direction as the earth rotates, the earth takes a little longer each day to turn around enough to make the moon visible in its new position farther along in its orbit. Thus the moon rises about 50 minutes later each day.

Phases of the moon. As the moon revolves around the earth, its orbit takes it first between the sun and the earth, and then to the other side of the earth away from the sun. Actually the moon seldom passes directly between the sun and earth because its orbit is tilted about 5° from the plane of the earth's orbit around the sun. When the moon is in the area between the earth and sun, the side of the moon toward us is not lighted directly by the sun. Still, the moon is faintly visible because of sunlight reflected by the earth. This light reflected by the earth, called *earthshine,* must be much brighter on the moon than moonlight ever is on earth because the larger earth is a much better reflector of light. After the moon has gone halfway around in its orbit, it is on the side of the earth away from the sun, and the face of the moon we see is fully lighted.

During one complete revolution around the earth (29½ days) the moon passes through all of the various phases between completely lighted and completely dark. When the moon is passing the point of its orbit directly between the earth and the sun, it cannot be seen: this is the dark *new moon.* A few days later, the *crescent* appears as a little of the moon's lighted side becomes visible.

FIG. 4–6. The dimly lit area of the moon is lighted by earthshine. (*Yerkes Observatory*)

The *first quarter* is seen about a week after the new moon, when the moon has traveled one-fourth of the way around the earth and appears about half lighted. As the lighted portion increases, we see the *gibbous* (humped) moon, until about two weeks after the new moon, the *full moon* is reached at a point midway in its revolution around the earth. The sun is now behind us as we face the moon. (The planets Mercury and Venus are never seen in the full phase, as a round disk, because both are on the far side of the sun during the full phase.) In the following two weeks, the moon wanes from full through gibbous, last quarter, and crescent to the dark new moon again. See Fig. 4–5.

The phases of the moon have been used since the beginning of history to measure time, since the period from new moon to new moon is a natural unit to measure lengths of time less than a year. In Chapter 8 the role of the moon in timekeeping will be discussed more fully.

Rotation of the moon. It was mentioned early in this chapter that the moon always keeps the same side turned toward the earth. In order to do this, it must rotate on its axis in about the same period of time in which it revolves around the earth. Since its period of revolution is 29½ days, its period of rotation must be approximately the same. Even though the moon does not turn its far side to us, we still have seen more than half of the moon's surface. This is possible partly because the moon does not always move in its orbit at the same speed. At perigee it moves faster than at apogee, so when the moon speeds up at perigee we see a little more of one side as we follow along. Then at apogee, when it slows down, we move ahead and see a little more of the other side. Also, because the moon's orbit is tilted slight-

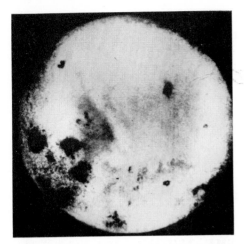

FIG. 4–7. This photograph of the far side of the moon was taken from an artificial satellite. (*Sovfoto*)

ly, we can look a little over its top and a little under its lower side as it goes around. Altogether, there is only about three-sevenths of the moon's surface that we do not see at any time.

The far side of the moon can be photographed from rockets circling the moon. Such photographs show that the hidden side apparently has fewer large craters than the side we see but in most respects it is similar to the visible portion. See Fig. 4–7.

Eclipses of the sun and moon. Any opaque object that intercepts the path of light casts a shadow. The members of the solar system all cast shadows in space, although we cannot observe the shadow of one body unless another enters the shadow area. The shadows of the moon and the earth are long cone-shaped areas extending out many thousands of miles into space. We are very much aware of the earth's shadow because we are carried around by the earth's rotation into the shadow each night. The moon's shadow is unnoticed, however, until it falls upon the earth's surface. Then all those

who happen to be in that shadow as it falls on the earth see an eclipse of the sun, one of the most spectacular sights in nature. It is also a very rare sight because three conditions must exist before we can see a total solar eclipse.

First, the moon must pass directly between the earth and the sun. This occurs at each new moon, but because of the tilt of the moon's orbit, the moon usually crosses between the earth and sun too high or too low for its shadow to fall on the earth. Therefore, the second condition is that the moon must be exactly in line between the sun and earth when it reaches the new moon phase. Still a third condition must be fulfilled if a total eclipse is to take place. Unless the moon is somewhere near perigee, the darkest part of its shadow may not reach the earth.

The shadows of the moon and the earth actually consist of two parts. The cone-shaped completely dark inner part is called the **umbra.** There is also an outer part called the **penumbra,** in which the light is only partially blocked off. See Fig. 4–7. The moon's umbra may be too short to reach the earth when the moon is in position to produce an eclipse. If the umbra does fail to reach the earth, the sun is still eclipsed, but not completely. An *annular* (ring) eclipse occurs; the sun is not completely blotted out but still shows a thin ring of light around the edges. If the umbra of the moon's shadow does fall on the earth, all those within the shadow may see a *total eclipse* in which the sun is completely covered by the moon. See Fig. 4–8.

Total eclipses of the sun are infrequent; the last one that was generally seen in the United States was in 1954 and the next will not occur until 1963. Only a small part of the world is able to see any particular eclipse because the tip of the moon's umbra never makes a shadow spot more than 167 miles across. It is only within this shadow that a total eclipse is seen. Because of the earth's rotation, the shadow sweeps across the earth's surface at several thousand miles per hour, so the total eclipse never lasts more than about 7 minutes at any location. Those in the area outside the moon's umbra, but within the penumbra, see a partial eclipse of the sun, in which a part of the sun is covered.

An *eclipse of the moon* occurs when the moon passes through the shadow cast by the earth. See Fig. 4–8. The moon frequently passes through the earth's penumbra, causing a partial eclipse of the moon. In order for the moon to be totally eclipsed, however, it must pass into the umbra, which is relatively small in the neighborhood of the moon's orbit. The moon usually misses the umbra and thus seldom undergoes a total eclipse. Still, total eclipses of the moon are more often observed than total eclipses of the sun, because on a clear night everyone on the dark side of the earth can see an eclipse of the moon. Only those few directly in the small shadow path of the moon's umbra ever see a total eclipse of the sun.

THE MOON AND THE TIDES

The moon's influence on the oceans. The earth and the moon exert a mutual gravitational force on each other. How-

FIG. 4–8. Left, an eclipse of the moon. Right, an eclipse of the sun. From what direction are the sun's rays coming in these drawings?

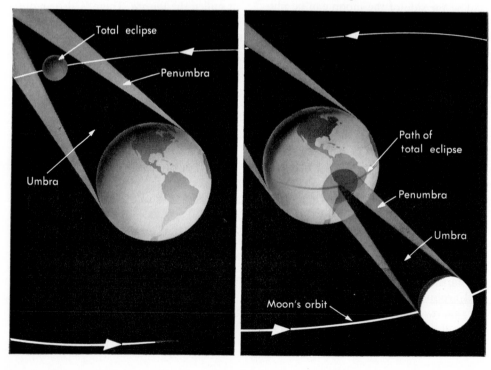

Total eclipse

Penumbra

Umbra

Path of total eclipse

Penumbra

Umbra

Moon's orbit

ever, since the earth is a larger body than the moon, the earth pulls on the moon with a stronger force than the moon exerts on the earth. Still, the moon has a strong gravitational pull of its own, and the earth is definitely affected by it. One of the best known effects of the moon's gravity is the tides which rise and fall in the oceans.

On the side of the earth toward the moon, the moon's gravity pulls out a bulge in the direction of the moon. The solid part of the earth bulges out only very slightly, a few inches at most. But the liquid part of the earth's surface, the water of the oceans, is more free to move, and the bulge produced in the oceans is quite pronounced. The oceans behave as if they were pulled away from the earth toward the moon, making a *tidal bulge* in the direction of the moon. A similar tidal bulge also develops in the oceans on the opposite side of the earth. This is because the moon's gravitational pull is less as the distance from the moon increases. The water in the oceans on the side of the earth away from the moon is attracted less than any other part of the earth since it is most distant from the moon. Thus the total effect of the moon's gravity on the opposite side of the earth is that the earth is, in a sense, pulled away from the oceans, creating a tidal bulge there also. See Fig. 4–9. The bulge on the side facing the moon is called the *direct tide* and the one on the other side is called the *opposite tide*.

If the earth did not rotate, the two tidal bulges would follow the moon around as it revolves about the earth and there would be a high tide about every two weeks as the tidal bulges passed each particular location on the ocean shores. But the earth does rotate, once each day. This means that we should expect two high tides each day as the

FIG. 4–9. The moon's gravitational attraction raises tidal bulges on the earth. In this diagram the blue arrow indicates the direction of the earth's rotation and the white arrows indicate the movement of the tidal bulges.

earth rotates and the tidal bulges pass by. However, the bulges also follow the moon's progress in its orbit and the earth's rotation has to "catch up," making the time a little longer (about 50 minutes) than one day for both high tides to pass a given spot. The rotation of the earth also tends to carry the tidal bulges forward of their position in line with the moon. As a result, the high tides do not occur for several hours after the moon is directly overhead.

Spring tides and neap tides. The sun raises tidal bulges on the earth in the same way as the moon. However, the tides caused by the sun are much weaker because of the sun's greater distance from the earth. Twice each month the sun and moon are in line with each other

FIG. 4–10. Spring tides occur when the gravitational forces of the sun and moon are in line with each other.

FIG. 4–11. Neap tides occur when the gravitational forces of the sun and moon are at right angles to each other.

(at new moon and full moon) and the tidal effects of both are added together. Tides produced at these two phases of the moon are higher than usual and are known as *spring tides*. See Fig. 4–10. (The term is not related to the spring season.) At two other points in the moon's orbit, the sun and the moon are at right angles to each other (at first and last quarter). At these two phases the tides are lower than usual because the tidal bulges of the sun and moon tend to cancel each other. These periodic lower tides are known as *neap tides*. See Fig. 4–11.

The influence of the moon on the tides also changes as the moon's distance from the earth varies. At perigee, the moon is about 30,000 miles closer than at apogee, and its gravitational pull is greater. When the moon is at perigee, the tides are even higher than normal. Therefore, when the moon is at perigee at the same time that it is in the new or full phase, when spring tides are produced, the tides can be very much higher than usual. This does not occur very often and can be predicted in advance from knowledge of the moon's motions in its orbit. Coastal regions are usually alerted to the perigee spring tides since flooding may occur, particularly if the weather is stormy. You will find a further discussion of tides in Chapter 26.

SUMMARY

OUR moon is the largest satellite in relation to its planet but not the largest in the solar system. Its period of revolution is approximately equal to its period of rotation. Therefore the same side of the moon always faces the earth.

Smooth plains, very high mountain ranges, and thousands of craters make up the terrain of the moon. Due to the lack of atmosphere and water, a minimum of weathering and no erosion occurs. Two theories for the formation of the craters are volcanic action or meteors.

Gravitational pull on the moon is only one-sixth as great as on the earth. The lack of atmosphere results in temperatures on the sunny side of the moon of up to 200° F; and as low as −250° F on the dark side.

The moon's orbit, relative to the earth, is elliptical, slightly eccentric, and tilted 5° to the plane of the earth's orbit. Each day the moon rises 50 minutes later. Although half of the moon is constantly illuminated, the portion we see of this side changes, causing phases.

A solar eclipse occurs when the earth and the moon's orbit are on the same straight line. The eclipse is total if the tip of the moon's umbra reaches the earth. An annular eclipse results if the umbra fails to reach the earth. During the full moon, a partial lunar eclipse occurs if the moon passes through the earth's penumbra. If it passes through the earth's umbra there is a total eclipse.

The gravitational attraction of the moon is the cause of tides. Great tidal ranges are produced during the new and full moon phases and are called spring tides. Neap tides, of small range, are produced during the first and last quarter phases.

VOCABULARY REVIEW

Match the phrase in the left column with the correct word or phrase in the right column. *Do not write in this book.*

1. Lightest part of a shadow
2. Tides of great range
3. Flat surfaces or plains on the moon
4. Tides of small range
5. Darkest part of a shadow
6. Changes in the appearance of the moon
7. Cuplike depressions on the moon
8. Light from the earth reflected by the moon
9. Point in the moon's orbit farthest from the earth
10. Point in the moon's orbit closest to the earth

a. craters
b. perigee
c. umbra
d. phases
e. full moon
f. eclipse
g. seas of the moon
h. neap tide
i. penumbra
j. spring tides
k. apogee
l. earthshine

QUESTIONS   •   GROUP A

Select the best term to complete the following statements. *Do not write in this book.*

1. Each day the east coast of the United States has (*a*) three high tides (*b*) no high tides (*c*) two high tides (*d*) four high tides.
2. When the earth passes into the dark part of the moon's shadow, there is (*a*) a lunar eclipse (*b*) a crescent (*c*) a solar eclipse (*d*) an annular eclipse.
3. The high tides which occur at new and full moons are called (*a*) flood tides (*b*) rays (*c*) neap tides (*d*) slack tides.
4. When the moon is in the earth's umbra, there occurs (*a*) an annular eclipse (*b*) a lunar eclipse (*c*) a new moon (*d*) a solar eclipse.
5. While traveling in space a man-made satellite is most likely to collide with (*a*) another man-made satellite (*b*) comets (*c*) meteors (*d*) planets other than the earth.
6. The moon moves in its orbit at the speed of approximately (*a*) 66,000 miles per hour (*b*) 240,000 miles per day (*c*) 2200 miles per hour (*d*) 8000 miles per month.
7. The earth rotates from (*a*) east to west (*b*) west to east (*c*) north to south (*d*) south to north.
8. The moon is said to be waning when the visible portion is (*a*) full (*b*) decreasing (*c*) increasing (*d*) eclipsed.
9. Any given point on the moon would receive continuous light for (*a*) 7 days (*b*) approximately 10 days (*c*) approximately 14 days (*d*) approximately 29 days.
10. Tides of small range occur when (*a*) the moon's gravitational attraction increases (*b*) gravitational forces of the moon and the sun oppose one another (*c*) the moon is at apogee (*d*) the earth's gravitational force increases.
11. Meteors often strike the moon's surface because (*a*) it rotates very slowly (*b*) it is very cold (*c*) it has little atmosphere (*d*) its gravitational force is stronger than the earth's.
12. The plane of the moon's orbit is (*a*) very erratic (*b*) inclined 5° to the plane of the earth's orbit (*c*) larger than the earth's orbit (*d*) parallel to the earth's orbit.
13. The phase in which we see the greatest illuminated area of the moon is (*a*) new moon (*b*) gibbous (*c*) full moon (*d*) last quarter.
14. Only one side of the moon is ever seen from the earth because (*a*) only one side reflects light (*b*) the moon does not rotate (*c*) the moon's period of rotation is equal to its period of revolution (*d*) the moon is at perigee.
15. On successive nights the moon rises about (*a*) 50 minutes earlier (*b*) 50 minutes later (*c*) the same time (*d*) 8 P.M.
16. Earthshine can best be observed during the (*a*) crescent (*b*) full moon (*c*) gibbous (*d*) first quarter.
17. Tycho is the name of a (*a*) satellite (*b*) crater (*c*) phase (*d*) ray.
18. The diameter of the tip of the moon's umbra is about (*a*) 200 miles (*b*) 300 miles (*c*) 167 miles (*d*) 800 miles.

19. On the moon, a 120-pound boy would weigh (*a*) 120 pounds (*b*) 240 pounds (*c*) nothing (*d*) 20 pounds.
20. The moon's atmosphere is about equal in density to the earth's atmosphere at an altitude of (*a*) 50 miles (*b*) 2000 miles (*c*) 7 miles (*d*) 26 miles.
21. The average distance from the earth to the moon is (*a*) 221,463 miles (*b*) 238,857 miles (*c*) 252,710 miles (*d*) 294,752 miles.
22. A total solar eclipse, at any location, never lasts more than (*a*) 3 minutes (*b*) 7 minutes (*c*) 15 minutes (*d*) 28 minutes.
23. At perigee the earth's tides (*a*) occur more quickly (*b*) are somewhat lower (*c*) are about normal (*d*) are somewhat higher.
24. If the moon were to stop rotating we would (*a*) have higher tides (*b*) see both sides of the moon (*c*) always see a full moon (*d*) have television transmission difficulties.

GROUP B

1. If you were going to the moon would it be necessary to take a raincoat? Explain your reason.
2. Would a rocket leaving the moon's surface require as great a speed or force as one leaving the earth's surface? Explain.
3. Using 186,000 miles per second as the speed of light, calculate the length of time needed for light rays from the moon to reach the earth.
4. What would be the effect on a total solar eclipse if the radius of the moon's orbit was reduced?
5. Why do we believe that the moon was closer to the earth in the past?
6. Why are the mountains on the moon more rugged than those on the earth?
7. What do photographs such as Fig. 4–7 tell us about the far side of the moon?
8. Why does the moon have light and dark areas when seen with the naked eye?
9. Why is the moon's distance from the earth continually changing?
10. Why does the moon rise later each night?
11. In what position in its orbit (with respect to the sun and the earth) is the moon at each of its quarterly phases?
12. What three conditions produce a total solar eclipse?
13. When does an annular eclipse of the sun occur?
14. If you were observing the earth from the moon, (*a*) would the earth appear to rise and set? Explain; (*b*) how would the earth appear during the full moon? new moon? first quarter? total solar eclipse?

CHAPTER 5

SPACE TRAVEL

THE earth is still mostly unexplored. Its surface is fairly familiar to us, but beneath its thin outer crust and in the depths of its oceans lie vast unknown regions. Its atmosphere surrounds us but we have only a feeble understanding of the forces that produce the patterns of weather. Even the basic questions about the very nature of the earth are still mostly unanswered. How did the planet come into existence? What has been its exact history? What is its future? Much more work will have to be done before the gaps in our knowledge of this planet are eliminated.

Every branch of science has its own contribution to make in the struggle to solve the secrets of the earth, but one new field promises to supply much new information. This is the field of *astronautics* (as-tro-*naw*-tiks): the scientific exploration of space. It is clear that many natural processes and events that take place here on earth are greatly influenced by forces beyond this small planet. The effect of sunspots on the earth is a good example. However, the relationship of the earth to what lies in space cannot be fully established until man is able to explore the unknown regions. Only by leaving the earth can we study it and fully understand it as a part of the complex pattern of the solar system and beyond.

This chapter is a brief introduction to the new science of astronautics.

GETTING INTO SPACE

The rocket. A rocket is the only kind of vehicle presently available which is able to leave the earth. In some ways a rocket motor works like an automobile engine. In both, a mixture of fuel and oxygen is burned to produce hot gases which exert pressure capable of doing work. In a rocket engine, hot gases are produced by very rapid burning of fuel in a special combustion chamber. Tre-

VOCABULARY

Astronautics. The scientific exploration of space.

Escape velocity. The speed a rocket must reach in order to leave the earth's immediate gravitational field.

Weightlessness. A condition that occurs when there is no accelerating force acting upon an object.

62

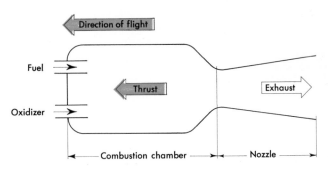

FIG. 5–1. The thrust of a rocket is produced by expansion of gases in the combustion chamber of the rocket engine.

mendous pressures push against the walls of the chamber as the gases produced from the violent burning try to expand. If the rocket's combustion chamber were completely closed off, the gas pressure would be nearly equal in all directions, but the walls of the chamber could not resist the force and the chamber would explode. However, in a rocket the combustion chamber is provided with an exhaust nozzle to permit the gases to escape to the rear. As the gases flow out of the exhaust, the pressure on the front of the combustion chamber is no longer balanced by a force in the opposite direction. The rocket then accelerates as a result of the unbalanced gas pressure pushing on the front of the combustion chamber. See Fig. 5–1. Since a rocket engine does not push against anything but itself, it operates even in the near vacuum of space.

A rocket must carry along as part of its load both the fuel and the oxygen it needs for the combustion from which it gains its accelerating force. This is an advantage in one way: it means that the rocket does not depend on getting its oxygen from the earth's atmosphere and so is able to function in space. However, it also means that a good deal of the weight to be lifted from the earth by the rocket is simply its own fuel and oxygen supply. Rockets that are intended to travel great distances in space must be

very large to carry sufficient fuel and oxygen and must be very powerful to get the entire load off the earth. Efforts are being made to perfect other systems of rocket propulsion which would require much less weight of fuel. One possibility, not yet practical, is the use of nuclear energy as a means of rocket propulsion.

Escape from the earth. To leave the earth, a rocket must achieve a certain minimum speed in order to escape the earth's immediate gravitational field. This speed, known as the *escape velocity,* is slightly more than 25,000 miles per hour if the rocket leaves from the earth's surface. If the rocket can attain the escape velocity, it will continue to move away from the earth, needing no additional force until it is affected by the gravity of another planet or some other body in the solar system.

Escaping from the earth's gravity is rather like trying to get out of a deep pit whose walls are very steep near the bottom but not nearly so steep near the top. The slope of the walls of the pit can be compared to the gravitational force tending to pull a rocket back to earth. At first, the gravity force holding the rocket back is very strong and the rocket must exert a powerful thrust to rise. As the rocket moves farther from the earth. the force of gravity diminishes; less thrust is required to keep from falling

FIG. 5–2. The launching of a satellite-carrying rocket. The satellite is enclosed in the nose cone at the top of the rocket. (*Convair/Astronautics*)

back. Finally, many thousands of miles away from the earth, the vehicle climbs out of the gravity "pit" and cannot be pulled back. In theory, the best way to launch a rocket is to give it maximum speed as soon as possible. The sooner the rocket escapes the effects of gravity, the less fuel will be spent just to keep from falling back. In actual practice the rocket cannot be launched this way. The first part of the rocket's flight must be made through the earth's atmosphere; very high speeds would cause the rocket to be battered to pieces from the impact of the relatively heavy air of the lower

atmosphere. The take-off speed is actually a compromise between going fast enough to reduce the effects of gravity before the fuel runs out, and still slow enough to avoid the effects of the atmosphere.

The problems connected with launching the rocket can be almost completely solved if the take-off point is high enough above the earth's surface to be out of the atmosphere and also high enough to have already significantly reduced the effects of gravity. The only such location is on an artificial satellite revolving around the earth in an orbit thousands of miles above the earth's surface.

Man-made satellites. If a rocket leaves the earth with less than escape velocity, it will eventually fall back to earth again. However, such a rocket can be given a sideways push with a properly timed and aimed rocket thrust just as it is somewhere near the top of its flight path. The push to the side causes it to follow a curved path as it falls back toward the earth. If the curve of the return path can be made so that it is equal to or less than the curvature of the earth, the rocket will never actually reach the earth but will keep falling continuously in an orbit around the earth. See Fig. 5–3. This is the way artificial satellites are put into earth-circling orbits.

A satellite is put into a particular orbit by firing a rocket to the altitude of the desired orbit, and then causing it to tilt so that it is parallel with the earth's surface. Then a reserve rocket motor is fired to give precisely the correct velocity that will cause it to fall in a curved path that exactly follows the earth's curvature. If everything has worked right, the rocket, or part of it, is established as a satellite. The moment when the satellite is aimed into its orbit is very critical.

FIG. 5–3. A rocket will remain in orbit if the curve of its path is equal to or less than the curvature of the earth.

If the angle is too high or the speed too great, the satellite will go into an elliptical orbit rather than a perfectly circular one. See Fig. 5–4A. If the elliptical orbit has a perigee too close to the earth, the satellite will re-enter the atmosphere and be vaporized by the heat generated from friction with the air. If the angle at which the satellite enters its orbit is too low, it will fall back to earth and disintegrate in the atmosphere. See Fig. 5–4B.

To maintain an orbit at an altitude of exactly 300 miles, a satellite must have a velocity of 18,000 miles per hour. The farther the orbit is from the earth, the slower the satellite needs to go. At a distance of 22,000 miles, a satellite would

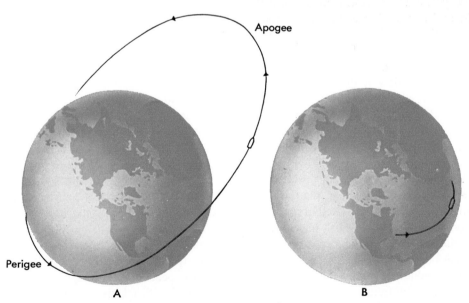

FIG. 5–4. The orbit in *A* is not circular because either the launching angle was too high or the speed of the rocket was too great. In *B* the angle of launching was too small or the speed of the rocket was not great enough to achieve an orbit.

need a velocity of 6830 miles per hour, which would take it around its orbit once every 24 hours. Such a satellite would then appear to be stationary or nearly stationary in the sky if it traveled in its orbit in the same direction as the earth rotates. Most artificial satellites follow elliptical orbits because it is difficult to launch a satellite at exactly the right angle and speed to achieve a perfectly circular orbit. However, some satellites are purposely given an elliptical orbit so that they can relay data on conditions in space both near the earth and at considerable distances away. If the satellite's approach to the earth at perigee is very close, the collision of the satellite with the gas molecules of the thin upper atmosphere slows it down. As its speed drops, the satellite curves downward. Then, as it comes closer to the earth, the earth's gravity causes it to pick up speed again and it starts to move away in a wider orbit. It may repeat the in and out motion a number of times, each time dipping further into the atmosphere. Eventually the heavier air, as it penetrates deeper into the atmosphere, will slow it down too much to maintain any kind of orbit. This means the end of the satellite, for it will plunge toward the earth and be vaporized by its contact with the heavy air of the lower atmosphere.

A satellite in a stable high orbit could be used as a launching platform for space vehicles. Such a satellite space station would circle the earth in an orbit a thousand miles or more above the earth's upper atmosphere. Rockets could be assembled at the satellite from parts carried up by freighter rockets from the earth. A space ship launched from such a satellite could start its journey virtually free of the drag of the earth's atmosphere and gravity, and could easily carry sufficient fuel to reach its destination and return.

However, the problems connected with the construction and use of such a space station are immense. For example, it would be extremely difficult to land on such an established satellite. It is impossible to overtake a satellite by chasing it in the same orbit, because each time the pursuing ship speeds up to catch up with the satellite, the ship moves into a higher orbit instead. This is in response to the basic principle that all bodies in a given orbit must have the same velocity. Changing the velocity results in establishing a different orbit. In order to land on a satellite, a space ship would have to somehow intercept it in its orbit. This requires navigation of a degree of accuracy never attempted on earth.

Aside from their potential value as launching platforms for space ships, satellites are extremely valuable research tools in themselves. They can be made to carry instruments to measure the earth's gravitational, magnetic, and electrical fields more extensively than could ever be done from close to the earth's surface. The height of the earth's atmosphere and its composition at very high altitudes can be determined by instrument-bearing satellites. Even a satellite carrying no instruments can be used to determine the shape of the earth, since irregularities in the satellite's orbit are produced by the earth's unevenness. A study of satellite orbits has already shown that the earth is not like a somewhat flattened orange, as it was previously thought to be, but is really very slightly pear- or egg-shaped. Satellites equipped with television will be able to relay information about weather, providing a better explanation of how weather is produced and also a basis for more accurate weather forecasts.

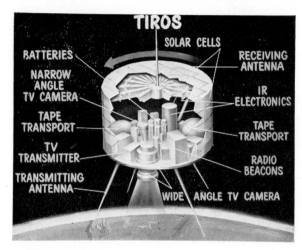

FIG. 5–5. Artificial earth satellites are useful in many ways. The Tiros satellite at the right was the first one used to transmit cloud cover pictures to use in weather prediction (*NASA photos*)

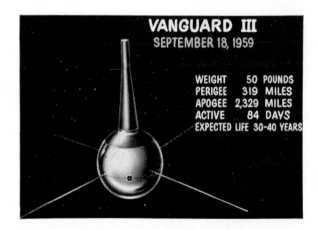

Vanguard III was used to record magnetism and other aspects of space environment.

Explorer VII was equipped to record radiations in outer space.

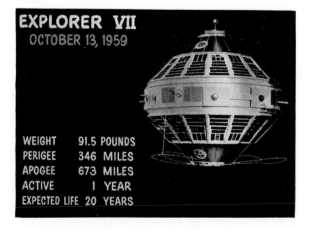

FIG. 5–6. The floating object in the foreground is a space capsule of the project Mercury, designed to carry the first American into space. The man is emerging from the capsule after it was dropped from an airplane. Astronaut Alan B. Shepard, Jr. made the first suborbital flight in such a capsule on May 5, 1961. (*NASA*)

No one knows what further explorations with artificial satellites will reveal. Although it may be some time before we become closely acquainted with the rest of the solar system, satellites have already yielded a wealth of information about the earth and the space immediately around it.

TO THE MOON AND PLANETS

Travel in the solar system. The exploration of space will be the greatest adventure in human history; yet, for the present, we must be satisfied with the modest space penetrations of the earth-satellites. Soon the moon and nearby planets will become targets, but the bold leaps to the distant planets and beyond must await new inventions. However, just to explore the interplanetary space

of the solar system in the neighborhood of the earth will probably occupy the space explorers for the next thousand years.

Travel from place to place in the solar system would be much simpler if everything were not in motion around the sun. For the same reason that it is difficult to move in a straight line on a merry-go-round, it is also difficult to travel in precise paths between the earth and other parts of the solar system. However, in some ways, the motion of the parts of the solar system is an advantage. Since all the planets revolve in the same direction around the sun, the speed of revolution will be helpful in launching a space vehicle toward the outer planets. Also, most of the planets rotate in the same direction in which they revolve around the sun. This rotational force is also very helpful in launching space vehicles. To take advantage of this motion, a ship launched from the earth will probably follow a curved path toward the east in the direction of the earth's rotation. See Fig. 5–7. It will continue to follow this curve until escape velocity is achieved; then the course will be set for the final destination. A space vehicle launched from a satellite platform can also follow the same plan but would need much less power to reach escape velocity because it would already have the speed of the satellite, and because escape velocity is less at great altitudes above the earth's surface.

Once free of the main influence of the earth's gravity, a space ship will not be held back by the strong gravitational field or the friction of the earth's atmosphere. It will be able to coast along without using any rocket power unless a change in course is necessary. To change course, small guidance rockets or jets of compressed gases can be used to bring the ship around to the proper heading.

Housekeeping in space. The problems involved in designing, building and launching a space vehicle are tremendous. Of equal difficulty are the problems in keeping the crew of the space ship fed and in good health, under many new conditions never encountered on the earth's surface.

One of the most unusual experiences in store for the space traveler will begin as soon as the rocket motors have been turned off and the ship is coasting through space without further acceleration. From that time until a landing is made on some object with significant gravity, or until the rocket engines are turned on again, the crew will experience the feeling of *weightlessness*. The crew and everything else aboard, unless held down, will float about in the interior of the ship. Ordinary motions of the crew will be complicated by the need to keep a firm grasp on some fixed object. Liquids will be particularly troublesome under weightless conditions, since it will

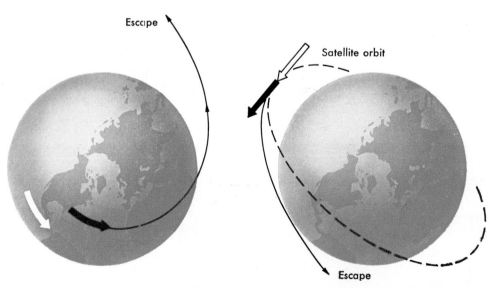

FIG. 5–7. Two possible ways to escape from the earth. At the left, the ship takes advantage of the earth's rotation (white arrow), while at the right, the velocity of an established satellite (white arrow) assists the escape.

FIG. 5–8. Some problems will be encountered in space travel. The space suit at the left is being tested under a battery of heat lamps. (*U. S. Air Force*)

This kitten is experiencing the condition of weightlessness which will be felt by men in an orbiting satellite. (*William Vandivert*)

These men are growing algae, microscopic green plants that may furnish both food and oxygen to future space travelers. (*Boeing Airplane Company*)

be impossible to pour them from a container or even to keep a liquid in an open container. A weightless liquid will not remain in an open container but will tend to float out and hang suspended in space. All liquids consumed by the crew will have to be forced directly into the mouth from some sort of closed container.

In some persons, the absence of gravity will probably disturb the sense of balance and perhaps cause dizzy spells. It is hard to predict exactly how weightlessness will affect space travelers because it is very difficult to create the condition on earth to study its effects. A weightless condition can be achieved for a few seconds on the earth by falling completely free of any restraint or by flying a precicisely plotted course in a fast airplane. The kitten shown in Fig. 5–8 was photographed during such a flight. Evidence indicates that although weightlessness may cause temporary confusion, the crew can quickly adjust themselves to it.

For the entire period of the space journey the ship will remain sealed. All food, water, oxygen, and other needs of the crew will have to be stored aboard the ship at take-off. If the journey is a long one, some provision will have to be made to reuse the original supply of water and oxygen. The oxygen supply will be a major problem. Everyone in the crew will require at least 500 quarts of oxygen every 24 hours. Only on the shortest trips will it be possible to carry enough oxygen to last the entire trip. One possible solution would be to carry along quantities of tiny water-dwelling plants called *algae* (*al*-gee). These plants would produce oxygen by photosynthesis and at the same time use up the carbon dioxide expelled by the crew. The useful little algae could also be used

as food on voyages too long to allow sufficient concentrated food to be carried. On such long voyages, the water supply problem could only be solved by recovering, purifying, and re-using all water over and over again.

Great care will have to be used to keep the cabin completely sealed. Even small punctures by collision with small meteors will allow the air inside the ship to escape explosively fast, causing the almost instant death of the occupants. Double cabin walls will probably give enough protection against this threat, and will prevent excessive loss of heat in the intense cold of space.

Outside the earth's atmosphere, sunlight is dangerously bright and shadows are inky black. The sharp contrast between light and shadow will cause problems in seeing. Some means will have to be used to help adjust the vision of the crew. Direct sunlight in space will also damage the eye, so protective filters will be necessary over observation ports.

Flight to the moon. Man's first real target in space is the moon. It is the natural first step beyond the earth because of its closeness and our great curiosity about the earth's only natural satellite. It will not be an easy target. Aside from the difficulty of building a vehicle to get there is the fact that the flight path will have to be determined by the most skillful navigation in history. The course to the moon must take into consideration the gravity of the earth, the moon, and the sun; the earth's rotation and the position of the moon in its orbit; and the tilt of the earth's axis and the tilt of the moon's orbit. Slight errors in considering the effect of any of these, plus many other factors not mentioned, will result in missing the moon completely.

Once the rocket arrives at the moon, landing will prove one of the hardest and

FIG. 5–9. A drawing showing how a rocket might land a space capsule on the moon, using the thrust of its engines to counteract the moon's gravity. (*Convair/Astronautics*)

most dangerous parts of the trip. For about nine-tenths of the distance along its flight path to the moon, a moon-rocket will be under the diminishing influence of the earth's gravity. But at about 24,000 miles from the moon, the moon's gravity takes over. The rocket will start falling toward the moon at constantly increasing speed. Unless something is done to slow the descent, the ship will shatter itself on the moon's surface. To avoid this, the rocket will have to come in for a landing tail first, using the rocket motors as a brake.

Take-off from the moon will be much easier than take-off from the earth. The moon's gravity, being only one-sixth of the earth's, will be much less of a hindrance, and the moon has no interfering atmosphere. Return to the earth will present a problem again in accomplishing a safe landing. Plunging immediately into the atmosphere would result in immediate vaporization of the ship by frictional heating. At first, the ship will simply "brush" the outer part of the atmosphere very carefully to avoid excessive heating. Then it will go back into space again on a long elliptical orbit around the earth which will bring it back into the atmosphere again briefly. On each entry the ship will be slowed down and can thus penetrate deeper into the atmosphere on the next approach. The process will be repeated five or six times until speed is reduced sufficiently to allow the final landing.

Flight to the planets. The problems of completing an interplanetary flight are basically the same as for a moon flight, except that in travel to the planets, the gravitational influence of the sun becomes much more important. A vehicle launched toward another planet can get there with the least energy if it becomes a satellite of the sun. Such a path to the planets is called a minimum energy orbit and is determined by the speed and direction of the interplanetary rocket. To reach a planet between the earth and sun, such as Venus, the rocket would be launched in the direction opposite to that in which the earth revolves around the sun. This means that after escaping the earth, the rocket would be moving slower than the earth. The sun's gravity would cause the ship to move toward the center of the solar system across the orbit of Venus. The launching would be timed so that the rocket intercepted Venus as its orbit was reached. See Fig. 5–10.

To reach Mars, whose orbit lies outside that of the earth, the rocket must take advantage of the speed of the earth's forward movement in its orbit. A Mars-bound rocket would be launched in the same direction as the earth's revolution around the sun. This would add the speed of the earth to the rocket's own speed. Since it would then be moving faster than the earth, the ship would move in an orbit away from the sun toward Mars, as in Fig. 5–10. Proper timing would allow Mars to be intercepted in its orbit. Either of these flight paths to Venus or Mars would have to be executed with extraordinarily precise timing and complete control of the ship's speed.

Landing on the planets would be generally the same process as landing on earth, using the planet's atmosphere as a brake as much as possible. Once on the planet, the space traveler could not begin the return trip until the relative positions of the planet and the earth were again favorable. The waiting period on Mars would be about 455 days, which added to the flight time would give a calculated time of about 2 years and 8 months for the round trip. For Venus, the waiting period is about 465 days, with a total of about 757 days for the round trip.

If more powerful rockets become available, it will be possible to follow more direct paths at higher speeds, thus greatly cutting down on the time necessary to travel to the planets. Direct routes will be essential to reach any planet beyond Mars in order to avoid extremely long travel times.

Beyond the solar system. None of the methods of space flight now known can make possible any thought of travel to other stars. The closest star to the sun is 4.5 light-years away and even at 223,000 miles per hour, nine times the earth's escape velocity, it would take 1200 years to get there. It is clear that man's space exploration will be confined to the solar system for a great many years to come.

FIG. 5–10. Left, a possible satellite orbit to Venus. The satellite is launched in a direction opposite to the earth's revolution. Right, a possible satellite orbit to Mars taking advantage of the speed of the earth's revolution.

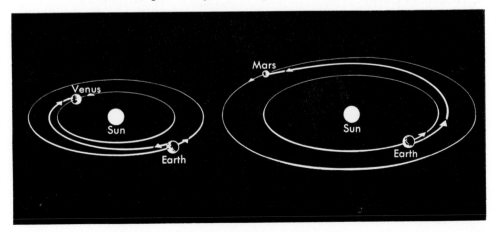

SUMMARY

THE growth of scientific knowledge about the planet Earth is being aided by the advances in the new field of astronautics, the exploration of outer space. Rockets are used in space exploration because they can function in the near vacuum beyond the earth's atmosphere. A rocket must accelerate to very high speeds to escape the earth's gravity.

With proper guidance, a rocket can become a satellite of the earth. A perfect satellite orbit around the earth would be circular, but most launchings result in elliptical orbits. It would be possible to use a satellite as a launching platform for ships to explore outer space. Satellites already have yielded much information about the earth and its atmosphere.

Space journeys within the solar system would require flight paths designed to take advantage of the earth's motions. Some of the most difficult problems in space flight are connected with the protection and care of space crews. A flight to any body in the solar system will require very accurate navigation. Flights to nearby planets could be accomplished by using orbits which would take advantage of the influence of the sun's gravity and the earth's rotation. Travel to the distant planets or to points beyond the solar system does not seem likely in the very near future.

VOCABULARY REVIEW

Match the phrase in the left column with the correct word or phrase in the right column. *Do not write in this book.*

1. Simple green plants
2. Escape velocity
3. Exploration of outer space
4. Absence of gravity
5. Process in which green plants make food and oxygen
6. Orbital velocity at 300 miles altitude

a. astronautics
b. photosynthesis
c. 18,000 miles per hour
d. weightlessness
e. rocket
f. 25,000 miles per hour
g. algae
h. respiration

QUESTIONS · GROUP A

Decide whether these statements are true or false. Reword the false statements to make them true. *Do not write in this book.*

1. Orbits of satellites indicate that the earth is somewhat egg-shaped.
2. The earth's gravitational pull increases with distance.
3. A rocket can travel in the near vacuum of outer space because it carries its own oxygen and fuel.

4. Most artificial satellites follow circular orbits.
5. At an altitude of 300 miles a satellite must maintain a speed of 6830 miles per hour to remain in orbit.
6. To take advantage of the earth's rotation, rockets are launched to the north.
7. About 24,000 miles from the moon, a moon-rocket would be mainly under the influence of the moon's gravity.
8. To reach Venus, a rocket would be launched in the same direction as the earth's revolution.
9. To land on a satellite platform, a rocket would have to increase its speed.
10. A satellite will continue to orbit if a balance is maintained between its forward motion and the earth's gravity.
11. An Atlas missile launched from the moon would require more power than the same missile launched from the earth.
12. A rocket moving faster than the earth's speed of revolution would spiral towards the sun.
13. On long space voyages algae could be used as food.
14. Rockets may safely re-enter the earth's atmosphere by following circular orbits.

GROUP B

1. Determine the total oxygen requirements of 6 men on a 23-day space voyage.
2. What is the operating principle of a rocket engine?
3. What is one future source of power for rockets?
4. How could a satellite appear stationary when viewed from the earth?
5. Discuss some of the problems of landing a rocket ship on a satellite platform.
6. At what stage in its lifetime can a satellite be compared to a meteor?
7. Why does a satellite following a north-south orbit eventually pass over all parts of the earth?
8. Traveling at the speed of 223,000 miles per hour, how long would it take a space ship to reach the Andromeda galaxy?
9. How can satellites advance our scientific knowledge?
10. How could a rocket be landed safely on the moon?
11. What happens to a rocket which rises from the earth but never attains escape velocity?
12. Why do rockets travel comparatively slowly during the first few minutes of their flight?
13. What advantages are there in launching a space vehicle from a satellite?
14. What will be the most unusual type of adjustment required of the crew of a space ship?

UNIT REVIEW QUESTIONS

1. How does a refracting telescope differ from a reflecting telescope?
2. Describe the closest galaxy to the Milky Way.
3. What is meant by the "expanding universe?"
4. How do the moon and the sun cause tides?
5. How does the spectroscope help to determine star composition?
6. Why will space crews require an extensive mathematics background?
7. What is meant by the term constellation? Name a few.
8. What are the advantages and disadvantages of using radio telescopes?
9. Why are meteors dangerous to space ships?
10. How is it possible to distinguish a planet from a star?
11. List the types of bodies found in the solar system.
12. What is meant by an elliptical orbit? An eccentric orbit?
13. What is earthshine? When can it be observed?
14. Why will space travel present unusual problems in medicine and biology?
15. Make a diagram to show a total solar eclipse.
16. Why doesn't a total lunar eclipse occur every month?
17. What was the chief contribution of Copernicus to the study of astronomy?
18. How could nuclear energy make long space trips more practical?
19. What advantages does a rocket have as a vehicle for space exploration?
20. How will the basic plan of the first space flights to nearby planets differ from the plan for the first flight to the moon?
21. What is the basic difference between stars in Population I and Population II?
22. Why does the moon go through phases?

ACTIVITIES

1. From photographs construct a model of the moon's terrain.
2. Plan a field trip to a local planetarium or local college observatory.
3. Construct models to show a total lunar eclipse or a total solar eclipse.
4. Construct a model of a radio telescope.
5. Plan an assembly program on space travel.
6. Construct models of some of the famous rockets or satellites.
7. Write a report on the physical and medical requirements of an astronaut.
8. Photograph star trails. Use a fast film in a camera with at least an f 4.5 lens. Point the camera toward Polaris and set the focus at infinity. Leave the shutter open throughout the dark period of the night, taking care to recover the camera before sunrise.
9. Construct a nonexplosive rocket. The principle of the rocket can be safely explored. Commercially designed, well-engineered toys and kits are available. Check with your instructor before starting any such project. Arrange a demonstration for the class.
10. Make scale models of the planets, showing their relative distances from the sun.
11. Make a report on the retrograde motion of the planets.
12. Make a report on Foucault's proof of the earth's rotation.

FURTHER READING

ASTRONOMY. J. S. Allen, 1945. *Bobbs-Merrill Co., Inc., Indianapolis, Ind.*

ASTRONOMY. R. H. Baker, 1959. *D. Van Nostrand Co., Inc., New York.*

INTRODUCING THE UNIVERSE. J. C. Hickey, 1951. *Dodd, Mead, and Co., New York.*

NATURE OF THE UNIVERSE. F. Hoyle, 1950. *Harper and Brothers, New York.*

A BRIEF TEXT IN ASTRONOMY. W. T. Skilling and R. S. Richardson, 1959. *Holt, Rinehart and Winston, Inc.*

★

WHEN THE STARS COME OUT. R. H. Baker, 1954. *The Viking Press, Inc., New York.*

REAL BOOK ABOUT STARS. H. Goodwin, 1954. *Garden City Books, New York.*

STARS IN THE MAKING. C. Payne-Gaposchkin, 1952. *Harvard University Press, Cambridge, Mass.*

MEN, MIRRORS, AND STARS. E. Pendray, 1946. *Harper and Brothers, New York.*

THE STARS. H. Rey, 1952. *Houghton Mifflin Company, Boston.*

YOU AMONG THE STARS. H. Schneider, 1951. *Scott, Foresman and Co., Chicago.*

AMATEUR ASTRONOMER'S HANDBOOK. J. B. Sidgwick, 1955. *The Macmillan Co., New York.*

STARS. H. S. Zim and R. H. Baker, 1956. *Simon and Schuster, Inc., New York.*

★

THE SUN. G. P. Kuiper, 1953. *University of Chicago Press, Chicago.*

SUN, MOON, AND PLANETS. R. K. Marshall, 1952. *Holt, Rinehart and Winston, Inc., New York.*

THE ORIGIN OF THE EARTH. W. M. Smart, 1953. *Cambridge University Press, New York.*

BETWEEN THE PLANETS. F. G. Watson, 1956. *Harvard University Press, Cambridge, Mass.*

★

THE EXPLORATION OF THE MOON. A. C. Clarke, 1954. *Harper and Brothers, New York.*

EXPLORING THE MOON. R. A. Gallant, 1955. *Garden City Books, New York.*

★

EXPERIMENTS IN THE PRINCIPLE OF SPACE TRAVEL. F. M. Branley, 1955. *Thomas Y. Crowell Co., New York.*

EXPLORING SPACE. Bureau of Secondary Curriculum Development, 1957. *New York State Education Department, Albany, New York.*

COMPLETE BOOK OF SPACE TRAVEL. A. T. Gaul, 1956. *World Publishing Co., Cleveland.*

EXPLORING EARTH AND SPACE; The Story of the IGY. M. O. Hyde, 1957. *McGraw-Hill Book Co., New York.*

ROCKETS, MISSILES, AND SPACE TRAVEL. W. Ley, 1957. *The Viking Press, Inc., New York.*

FIRST MEN TO THE MOON. W. von Braun, 1960. *Holt, Rinehart and Winston, Inc., New York.*

To us who dwell upon it, the earth is a very special planet. This is natural since it is our home. But what kind of planet is it actually? The question can be answered in some detail because the earth itself is the one planet of the entire solar system that is now capable of being studied at close range. In this unit the characteristics of the planet Earth will be considered as a basis for later study of its familiar surface features.

Included in the unit will be a description of some of the ways our lives are regulated by the particular planet we inhabit. It will be evident that the methods we use to locate positions and record the passage of time are determined by the nature of the earth itself. Finally, the unit on the earth as a planet considers the way we picture its distinctive surface on the flatness of paper, translating its features into the symbols of maps.

UNIT 2

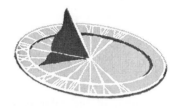

THE EARTH
AND ITS MOTIONS

CHAPTER 6

THE PLANET EARTH

AMONG the planets of the solar system, Earth is not remarkable. It is one of the smaller planets, the diameter being 7926 miles through the poles and about 27 miles greater at the equator, because the earth's rotation has caused a slight bulge there. The earth is much closer to a perfect sphere, however, than some of the larger planets such as Jupiter and Saturn. Like most of the planets, the earth is surrounded by a thick blanket of gases which form its atmosphere. The earth's atmosphere is unusual in that it contains a large amount of free (uncombined) oxygen, a gas which is not found in appreciable amounts in the atmosphere of any other planet. The earth is probably also unique in the amount of water it possesses. No other planet is known to be covered with sheets of water such as the seas which cover a large part of Earth. All of these differences are relatively minor; the one characteristic of the earth that makes it stand out among the planets is its weight compared to its size.

The weight of an object in relation to its volume is the *density* of the object. In density, the earth is distinctly unusual, having the highest density of any planet except Mercury and possibly Pluto, whose density is unknown. See Fig. 6–1. This means that the interior of the earth must be unusually heavy because the rock at the surface is much too light to account for the high density of the planet as a whole. We have no direct knowledge of the deep interior of the earth; it is still an unexplored region. Man will be able to reach other planets long before he is capable of probing the depths of the earth. The earth's interior

VOCABULARY

Density. The weight per unit volume of any material.

Shadow zone. A region on the earth's surface where a particular earthquake wave cannot easily be detected.

Crust. The outer thin layer of the solid earth.

Mantle. The thicker, more dense part of the earth beneath the crust.

Core. The very dense interior part of the earth.

Mohorovicic discontinuity (Moho). The zone of contact between the crust and the mantle.

is not, however, completely unknown. The presence of the heavy core that accounts for the earth's high density has been determined and some of its properties already discovered by indirect exploration. This chapter deals with the picture scientists have formed of the internal structure of the earth, as well as some of their theories of how the earth's history has resulted in the kind of planet we now inhabit.

EARLY HISTORY OF THE EARTH

Age of the earth. There are several ways of arriving at an estimate of the earth's age. First, it is possible to state definitely that the earth has not existed longer than a trillion years. The age of the earth can be no greater than the age of the solar system, and it is certain that the solar system cannot have existed longer than a trillion years. This maximum age limit is calculated from knowledge of the way stars are spaced in the galaxy to which the solar system belongs. The sun and its satellites move among the stars of the galaxy, and a trillion years is estimated to be the longest period of time in which a close encounter with another star could be avoided. Such an encounter would destroy or at least seriously deform the solar system.

Other evidence, however, indicates that the solar system is actually much younger than a trillion years. The age of the oldest stars in our galaxy is probably less than 20 or 30 billion years. The sun is younger and probably cannot be much older than about 10 billion years. Since it is very unlikely that the earth could have come into existence before the sun, the upper age limit for the earth can therefore be set at around 10 billion years.

More precise estimates of the age of the earth can be made through study of radioactive substances found in the earth. Radioactive elements pass through certain series of changes in fixed lengths of time regardless of outside influences. The radioactive substances present in the earth when it was formed are like clocks that have been running since the earth came into existence. Study of these natural radioactive "clocks" is one way to determine the earth's age. This method places the age of the earth at about 4.6 billion years, but this figure may be too small because it includes only the period of time since the earth solidified.

Thus, from the evidence now available, the age of the earth is thought to be not more than about 10 billion years and not less than 4.6 billion years. Somewhere between these two figures is the age of this planet.

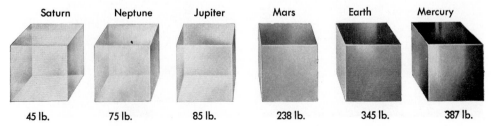

Saturn	Neptune	Jupiter	Mars	Earth	Mercury
45 lb.	75 lb.	85 lb.	238 lb.	345 lb.	387 lb.

FIG. 6–1. The average density of the earth as compared with that of some other members of the solar system.

Formation of the earth. The way in which the sun and its family of planets came into existence is still an open question. However, one of the reasons the dust cloud theory described in Chapter 3 is so seriously considered is that this seems to account best for the earth's characteristics. According to the dust cloud theory, the earth and other planets were formed within the large rotating disk of gas and dust which produced the sun at its center. In its earliest stages, the earth is pictured as a smaller disk of dust and gas rotating within the large cloud which formed the entire solar system. In time, the cloud that was to become the earth began to shrink and a solid sphere began to grow in the center.

It is possible that the moon was formed at the same time from a second center within the cloud. This theory is illustrated in Fig. 6–2.

As the cloud of dust and gas drew inward to form the body of the earth, the solid mass that was produced began to grow warm. The gases were compressed by gravitational force, and some of their energy was thus changed into heat. The release of heat energy from radioactive substances, which were abundant in the young planet, also contributed to the heating process. The newly formed earth warmed very slowly, however, and it may have taken about a billion years for the temperature to reach a point at which the earth was molten.

FIG. 6–2. The earth and moon might have looked like this in their early stages of formation. Compare this drawing with Figs. 3–2, 3–3, and 3–4.

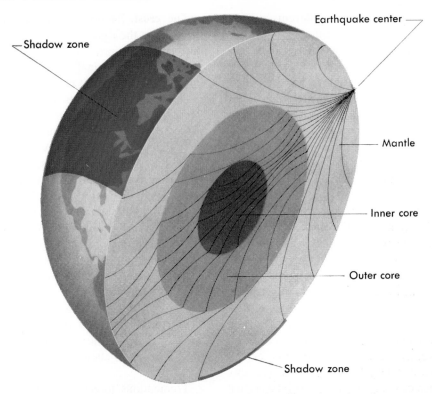

Earthquake center

Shadow zone

Mantle

Inner core

Outer core

Shadow zone

FIG. 6–3. The shadow zone results from the bending of earthquake waves as they travel through materials of different densities.

STRUCTURE OF THE EARTH

Exploring the earth's interior. The part of the earth that lies only a few miles beneath the surface is as remote from us as a star a few light-years away. By using the very best engineering skills and equipment, scientists hope to be able to drill a hole six miles into the body of the earth. (The project will be described later in this chapter.) Going any deeper seems completely beyond any possibility for many years. However, the earth itself provides a means of probing its internal structure. The earthquakes which occur constantly all over the globe and penetrate to its very center can be traced and studied.

Earthquakes are caused by sudden breaks or slipping of the rocks beneath the surface. (See Chapter 13.) The actual earthquake lasts only a few seconds, but it sets up shock waves which move out in all directions through the surrounding rock. The damage usually associated with earthquakes is caused by the waves which reach the surface in the immediate vicinity of the disturbance. The waves become weaker as they travel in all directions through the body of the earth and reach the surface at great distances from the earthquake center.

The study of waves sent out by earthquakes has been the main source of information about the internal structure of the earth. The fact that makes earthquake waves most useful to scientists is that they move at different speeds through materials of different densities. For example, in very dense rock the waves move faster than in less dense rock. Thus it is possible to get some idea of the density of the earth's interior by measuring the time a wave takes to travel from the earthquake center through the body of the earth and reach recording stations some distance away from the original disturbance.

Another aspect of the movement of earthquake waves which reveals the internal structure of the earth is the bending of the waves as they pass through materials of varying densities. One of the effects of this bending of the earthquake waves is the presence of a region called the *shadow zone*, a ringlike area around the earth at some distance from the origin or center of a particular earthquake, where the waves from that earthquake can hardly be detected. The existence of the shadow zone is interpreted as evidence that the earth has a dense liquid core. Figure 6–3 shows how such a core would bend the waves to produce a shadow zone.

Evidence gained primarily from the study of earthquake waves has led scientists to the conclusion that the earth consists of three distinct layers. Surrounding the entire globe is a thin outer *crust* of relatively light rock, with a depth of from 10 to 20 miles. Beneath the crust lies the *mantle*, a region of greater density than the crust, extending to a depth of about 1800 miles. Filling the remainder of the interior is the very dense *core*. These layers are shown in Fig. 6–4. The core appears to be divided into two layers, the *outer core*, extending from about 1800 to about 3100 miles deep and the *inner core*, which reaches from 3100 miles to the center of the earth.

The crust. Thinnest of the layers of the earth is the rigid shell that makes up the crust. The present crust is not the same as the original crust that was formed as the earth cooled from the molten condition in its early history. Through millions of years, natural earth processes (described in Units 4 and 5) have changed the surface. Volcanic activity has laid great masses of lighter rock over the original crust which now forms the foundation layer of the present crust. Great islands of rock have been raised above the general surface of the crust to form the present *continents*. Between the continental masses lie the lower parts of the crustal surface which form the *ocean basins*. The thinnest parts of the crust lie beneath the oceans. There the thickness of the crust is only about 7 miles while the crust beneath the continents is about 20 miles in thickness.

Tremendous forces are constantly at work causing the crust to bend and buckle. It is these forces that raise mountains and fracture the rocks of the crust. The source of these immense forces is not known. The oldest theories to account for them stated that the earth is shrinking, causing the crust to tear and buckle as the entire planet grows smaller in diameter. Some theories propose the continued cooling of the earth as the cause of shrinkage; others suggest that the pouring out of lava from volcanoes reduced the amount of material within the interior of the earth, causing the crust to be drawn inward. It is likely that a great deal more will have to be learned about the anatomy of the earth before a satisfactory theory to account for the movements of its crust can be developed.

The Moho. Our knowledge of the limits of the crust was confirmed by the

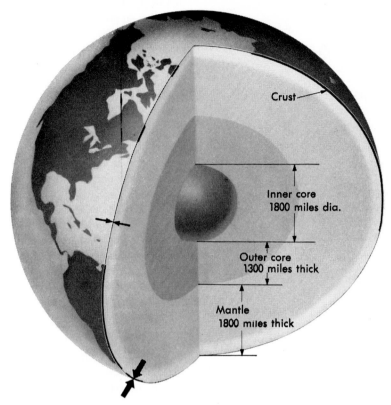

FIG. 6–4. The layers that make up the earth. The relative thickness of the crust is exaggerated. The crust is about 7 miles thick in the ocean basins (small arrows), and about 20 miles thick in continental areas (large arrows).

studies of a Yugoslav scientist, A. Mohorovicic (moh-hoh-roh-*vis*-ik), in 1909. Having noted the marked change in the way earthquake waves travel after they reach a depth of about 10 miles, Mohorovicic was able to show that this is caused by the change in density between the rocks of the crust and the rock of the mantle. This zone has come to be called the *Mohorovicic discontinuity* (boundary) and is often called the *Moho* for the sake of simplicity.

Since there is no way of obtaining samples of rock from the deep crust and mantle, no one knows exactly what the difference is between them. The Moho is evidence that there is a difference. Sci-

entists have proposed that a hole be drilled through the crust to the Moho using some of the methods by which very deep oil wells are drilled. The hole would be drilled in the ocean floor near a continental land mass since the crust is thinnest there. Figure 6–5 shows how this might be done. Such a hole would yield much valuable information about the history of the earth, the composition of the deep crust and the material that makes up the mantle. It would also add many clues to the complete history of the earth through the samples of rock taken from the drilling.

The deep interior. Until it becomes possible to drill holes into the body of

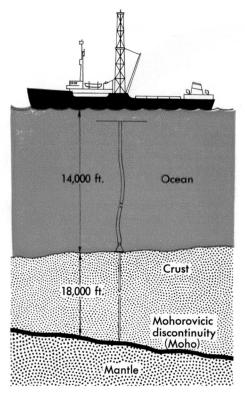

14,000 ft.   Ocean

Crust

18,000 ft.

Mohorovicic
discontinuity
(Moho)

Mantle

FIG. 6–5. The proposed method of drilling to the Moho is shown in this diagram. Geologists expect to obtain new and important information about the earth's crust and mantle from this project.

the earth much deeper than the Moho, no one can know what lies within the deep interior. All the information now available is based on indirect means of studying the interior and does not reveal the composition of the mantle and core. The best guess is that the mantle is composed of rock with a density several times greater than the average density of the rocks in the crust. Not many years ago it was believed that the earth's interior just below the crust was in the molten condition. It was thought that volcanoes were caused by breaks in the crust which allowed the molten rock to come to the surface as lava. This idea

has been discarded since it now appears that the mantle is definitely solid. Although it must be extremely hot, the mantle is actually more rigid than the crust; judging from the density measurements, it must be stronger than steel. Under the tremendous pressures at great depths, the hot material apparently does not liquefy. The old idea that the earth is soft and flexible because of its molten interior must be replaced with the picture of the earth as a relatively rigid body that cannot easily change its shape.

About halfway between the surface and the center of the earth is a sharp division between the mantle and outer core marked by a sharp increase in density. The way the material of the outer core transmits earthquake waves indicates that it may be a liquid, but the inner core seems to have some of the properties of solids. The only substance that is known to have the same general characteristics as the matter within the core is a mixture of 90 percent iron and 10 percent nickel.

The arrangement of the interior of the earth is thought to be the result of separation of the mantle and core when the earth was in the molten condition in its early history. In a molten planet, the denser metallic substances would tend to sink toward the center and the lighter rock would tend to remain near the surface. This may be the reason that the earth has what is apparently a metallic core surrounded by a thick layer of rocky material.

Another possibility is that the density changes within the earth's interior are caused not by the presence of different materials but by increase in pressure. The weight of millions of tons of rock pressing down creates extreme pressures toward the center of the earth. At the Moho the pressure is about 15,000 pounds per square inch; at the boundary between the mantle and outer core the pressure has increased to 20 million pounds per square inch and at the center of the earth it is between 40 and 60 million pounds per square inch. The very high pressures within the core may be able to crush matter together with such force that its properties are completely changed. Some theories have been proposed which attribute the high density of the earth's core entirely to the enormous pressures rather than to the presence of heavy metals such as iron and nickel. The problem cannot be settled with the knowledge of the earth's interior which is now available. Much more information must be accumulated before the composition of the core and mantle can be accurately described.

THE EARTH'S HEAT

Temperature of the earth's interior. In the lower levels of some of the very deep gold mines of South Africa the temperature of the rock is so high that it would be impossible for men to work if the mine were not air conditioned. For many years it has been well known that the temperature of the rocks within the crust rises steadily below a depth of about 50 feet. At the bottom of some deep oil wells the temperature is high enough to boil water. However, it has also been observed that the temperature increase with depth differs from one place to another. In regions of volcanic activity, pockets of molten rock are likely to be found very close to the surface. Nevertheless, in regions free of any volcanic activity the temperature also changes unevenly with increase in depth. The reason for the unpredictable variations is that different kinds of rocks con-

duct heat differently. Some layers of rocks in the crust are much warmer than others because they are able to conduct large amounts of heat upward from lower levels. On the average the temperature has been found to increase about 80° F for every mile of depth.

Although holes have been drilled to a depth of only a few miles and temperature has not been measured directly in the deep interior, the temperature at great depths can be estimated from a knowledge of the density of the mantle and core. Such estimates indicate that the temperature of the mantle probably is not greater than 4000° F. In the core the temperature must be higher but is probably not much hotter than 10,000° F.

Sources of the earth's heat. The earth has apparently lost very little of the heat it possessed when it was in the early molten stage. Only the outer parts of the planet have cooled very much; most of the original heat is still trapped within the interior. The materials of which the earth is made are mostly very poor conductors of heat. The outer regions which have cooled now act as a barrier to the escape of heat from the interior. So little heat can escape that scientists estimate that the deep interior of the earth is not likely to get much cooler.

Since so little of the heat from the interior reaches the upper layers of the earth, the heat present in the crust must come from another source. There is strong evidence that it is generated within the rocks of the crust by naturally radioactive materials. The radioactive elements radium, uranium, thorium and potassium are particularly good producers of heat. These elements are fairly plentiful in the rocks of the crust and could easily account for the heat known to be produced. It is likely that these heat-producing elements were once spread throughout the entire body of the earth and were partly responsible for the heat that caused the earth to be melted in its early stages of development. However, in the melting process, they moved upward so that they became particularly abundant in the crust. There is some evidence that these radioactive elements near the surface are now producing heat faster than it is being lost into space. This means that the earth is probably slowly growing warmer rather than cooler, although the rate of heating may be too slow to cause much change for billions of years.

SUMMARY

HIGH density and the abundance of free oxygen and water make the earth unique among the planets of the solar system.

Examination of radioactive substances gives the most accurate measurement of the age of the earth. Combining information from different scientific observations places the age of the earth between 4.6 and 10 billion years. The characteristics of the earth are best explained by the dust cloud theory of formation. Velocities of earthquake waves at different depths indicate the earth is composed of three layers: the crust, the mantle, and the core.

As the depth increases, so do the density, temperature, and pressure. Increasing internal density could be due to the accumulation of metallic materials toward the center during the molten stage of the earth. Another theory to explain increased internal density is compression of the mantle and core due to the overlying rock strata. Pressure in the core ranges from 40 to 60 million pounds per square inch. Liquefaction of the rock material is prevented by the tremendous pressure.

Interior temperatures result from heat trapped during the molten stage of the earth. Radioactive elements distributed through the crust produce surface heat. The earth's temperature is slowly increasing.

VOCABULARY REVIEW

Match the phrase in the left column with the correct word or phrase in the right column. *Do not write in this book.*

1. Mass raised above the crust surface
2. Boundary
3. Weight in relation to volume
4. Layer 10 miles in average thickness
5. Area where earthquake shocks are not easily detected.
6. Radioactive element
7. Mass composed of iron and nickel

a. density
b. crust
c. uranium
d. core
e. Mohorovicic discontinuity
f. mantle
g. continent
h. shadow zone

QUESTIONS   ·   GROUP A

Decide whether these statements are true or false. Reword the false statements to make them true. *Do not write in this book.*

1. The equatorial diameter of the earth is 7900 miles.
2. At a depth of 15 miles below the earth's surface, the temperature would be 240° F warmer than at the surface.
3. The earth is gradually getting cooler.
4. The Moho theory is the best explanation of the earth's formation.
5. The velocity of earthquake waves is greatest through dense rock.
6. The earth is made up of three concentric layers of material.
7. The age of the oldest stars in our galaxy is probably more than 10 billion years.
8. Study of radioactive substances places the age of the earth at a minimum of 6 billion years.
9. Sudden breaking or slipping of rocks below the earth's surface causes earthquakes.
10. The average thickness of the crust is about 7 miles.
11. An area where earthquake waves are not easily detected is termed a shadow zone.
12. The average thickness of the mantle is about 1300 miles.
13. The pressure at the Moho is about 15,000 pounds per square inch.
14. The core probably consists of two layers.
15. The mantle is believed to be in a molten state.
16. Earth has the smallest percentage of free oxygen of all the planets.
17. You would weigh less at the equator than at the north pole.
18. The crust is thinnest under the oceans.
19. A cubic foot of the core would weigh more than a cubic foot of the crust.
20. Since the interior of the earth was molten, it has lost much of its heat.

GROUP B

1. What would be the effect on the earth's equatorial diameter if the speed of rotation increased?
2. Draw and label a diagram to show the different layers of the earth.
3. Explain why the age of the earth is probably not more than 10 billion years.
4. How is the earth unique among the other planets?
5. What is the approximate diameter of the core of the earth?
6. Why is the age of the earth as determined from radioactive substances probably less than the true age?
7. Why are continents not considered part of the original crust?
8. At sea level the boiling point of water is 212° F. At what depth below the earth's surface would water boil? (Disregard the increase in pressure.)
9. Why is the earth's crust getting warmer?
10. Why may matter have different properties in the mantle and the core?
11. Account for the different rates of subsurface temperature increases.
12. Why do the upper layers of the earth receive little heat from the interior?

CHAPTER 7

LOCATION

To AN insect crawling on the ground the world is a jungle of pebbles, fallen leaves, grass blades, twigs, and barriers of all kinds. From the insect's level, it would be extremely difficult for anyone to grasp the idea that the earth is a huge sphere moving through space. In relation to the size of the earth, man is in about the same position as the insects. Each person sees only his small part of the earth. Thus it is natural that for centuries the earth was thought to be relatively flat, because the area that can be seen at one time does appear to be flat for the most part. But the earth is round and man is now able to see the entire planet in his mind's eye and accurately locate his position on its surface.

A great part of human history concerns the exploration of the surface of this planet. The key to the successful exploration of the earth is the method by which any position on the globe can be established. This is the result of a long process of invention and discovery beginning with the ancient Greeks. The basis for the modern system of location was established by the Greeks when they

VOCABULARY

Celestial navigation. The determination of direction and location by observation of celestial objects.

Latitude. Location measured in degrees north and south of the equator.

Meridian. An imaginary line from pole to pole, crossing the equator at a right angle.

Longitude. Location measured in degrees east or west of the prime meridian.

Great circle. Any circle drawn on the earth's surface that divides the sphere in half.

Magnetic variation or declination. The difference, measured in degrees, between true north and magnetic north.

Chronometer. An extremely accurate clock.

Dead reckoning. A method of navigation depending mainly on determination of speed and direction.

invented two imaginary lines which ran north-south and east-west, crossing in Greece since it was considered to be the center of the world. All places were located by their distances from these two lines. Later the Greek system was enlarged to seven north-south and seven east-west lines, not equally spaced but passing through the important cities of the ancient world. The Greeks knew that the earth is round and their system of lines was eventually transferred to globes so that any position on the sphere could be described.

The system of imaginary lines used in ancient times has been altered and improved with use, but it still forms the basis for the modern methods of location. Man now moves freely over the surface of the earth, and navigation, the art of determining locations accurately, has become an essential feature of modern life.

LATITUDE
AND LONGITUDE

Direction on the earth. If the earth did not spin on its axis, the task of describing any particular direction on its surface would be very difficult. The earth is very nearly a perfect sphere, and spheres have no top, bottom, or sides. Directions can only be defined if some reference point is given. Because the earth does rotate, its axis, emerging at the north and south poles, provides the reference points needed to determine direction. The four points of the compass are established according to the location of the poles: the north-south direction lies along a line connecting the two poles and the east-west direction is at right angles to this line.

From any location on the earth it is

possible to establish direction by sightings on heavenly bodies. Polaris, the star located nearly over the north pole, can be used to determine north. Other stars and constellations can be used in a similar manner if their positions in the sky are known. The sun can be used to determine east and west, since it always rises toward the east and sets toward the west. Locating direction and position by observation of heavenly bodies is called *celestial navigation* and is one of the oldest and most widely used methods of navigation.

Latitude. Suppose that a ship is sailing on a course which takes it directly along the equator. As long as the ship remains on its course along the equator it does not change its north-south position in the slightest. Its east-west position changes as its sails along, but its north-south position is clearly fixed. This would be true also for any ship sailing on a course parallel with the equator. If we knew how far north or south of the equator the ship was, then as long

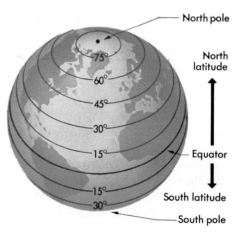

FIG. 7–1. Parallels of latitude are shown here at intervals of 15°. Note that each parallel forms a complete circle around the earth.

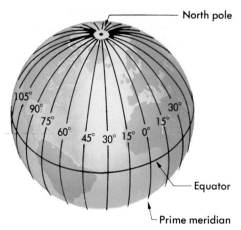

FIG. 7–2. Meridians of longitude are shown here at intervals of 15°. Longitude is measured in degrees east or west from the prime meridian (0°).

as the ship held to that course parallel with the equator, its north-south location would be clear. In describing position on the earth's surface, changes in location in a north or south direction are described by just such a system of lines parallel with the equator, called *parallels of latitude*. Figure 7–1 shows parallels of latitude drawn around the earth. The north-south location of any place on earth is called the *latitude* of that spot when it is described in terms of this system of imaginary lines.

The distance between the equator and the poles is one-quarter of the full circle around the earth, or 90° of the full circle of 360°. The location of any parallel of latitude can be accurately described if degrees are used to fix its distance from the equator, taken as 0°. Since the equator has the latitude of 0°, both the north and south poles have latitudes of 90°, and a point midway between the equator and one of the poles has the latitude of 45°. Of course, it is necessary to state whether the parallel lies north or south of the equator. *North latitude* is

used to describe all the parallels that can be drawn between the equator and the north pole; similarly, *south latitude* designates those parallels between the equator and the south pole. Washington, D. C., for example, has a latitude of approximately 39° N. This fixes its position as about 39° north of the equator.

In order to be more exact, we can divide each degree of latitude into 60 equal parts called *minutes* (symbol ′). A more precise latitude for Washington, D. C., is 38° 53′ N. Even greater exactness can be obtained by dividing minutes into 60 equal parts called *seconds* (symbol ″). In actual distance over the earth's surface, a degree of latitude is equal to about 70 miles. A minute of latitude is $7\%_{60}$ miles or $1\frac{1}{6}$ miles which is equal to one *nautical mile*. A second of latitude is equal to approximately 100 feet.

Longitude. To state the latitude of a particular place does not fix its east-west position. To do this, another set of imaginary lines, called *meridians,* are drawn from the north to the south pole so that

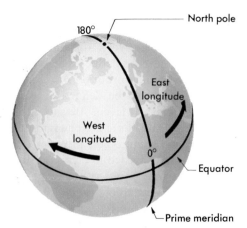

FIG. 7–3. Both east and west longitude meet at the 180° meridian, which is halfway around the earth from the prime meridian.

each one makes a half-circle around the entire earth. Figure 7–2 shows the meridians drawn on the earth. The east-west position of a place is established by stating that it lies on one of these lines; this is called the **longitude** of that location. Meridians are marked off in degrees just as parallels of latitude are. However, there is no natural starting point to be called 0° longitude. Therefore a particular meridian was designated by common agreement among all nations. The 0° longitude line, called the **prime** (first) **meridian,** was chosen as the meridian passing through Greenwich (*gren*-ich), England, which is just outside of London and was originally the location of the Royal Observatory.

Places to the east of the prime meridian are said to have *east longitude;* those to the west have *west longitude.* Naturally, east and west longitude each can extend only half-way around the earth.

The 180° meridian (directly opposite on the earth from the prime meridian) separates east and west longitude, as shown in Fig. 7–3. The longitude of Washington, D. C., is west longitude because it is west of the prime meridian; its longitude is 77° W. To fix the position of Washington very precisely, we say it is 38° 53' N and 77° 1' W.

Great circles. Another type of imaginary line on the earth's surface has become very important in navigation. A *great circle* is any circle that divides the sphere in half. The equator is a great circle, and each meridian is half a great circle, completed by its opposite meridian. However, just as a spherical object may be cut in half in any direction, any number of great circles can be drawn through any point on the globe. A path along a great circle is the shortest distance between any two points on the earth's surface.

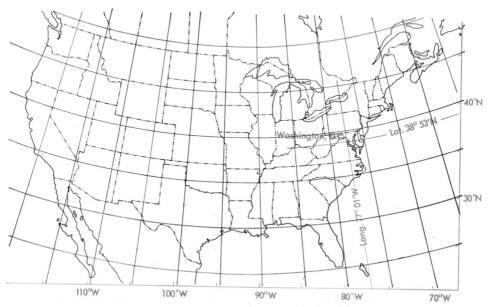

FIG. 7–4. The precise location of Washington, D. C. is shown on this map. Estimate the latitude and longitude of your county as accurately as possible. Verify your estimate, using some more precise source of information.

THE COMPASS

The magnetic compass. In navigation the most important single fact to know is the direction of travel. This can be determined by observation of the heavenly bodies, but only in good weather when the skies are clear. Another common means of finding direction is the magnetic compass, basically a magnetized needle mounted so that it can turn freely. The earth is a giant magnet. Magnetic lines of force run in a north-south direction, forming a magnetic field that extends between the poles. The magnetized needle of a compass lines itself up with the earth's magnetic field, thus causing the compass to indicate the north and south directions.

No one knows when or where the magnetic compass was invented, but it has been in use at least a thousand years. The earliest forms consisted simply of a magnetized needle floating in water, but they were accurate enough to allow sailors to venture out of sight of land without the fear of becoming hopelessly lost. However, even in the very early days of its use men observed that the magnetic needle of the compass did not always point in exactly the same direction. In some places the needle pointed a few degrees to the right of due north as determined by the stars; in other places the needle pointed a few degrees to the left. Investigation of these errors eventually revealed that the magnetic poles of the earth are not located in the same places as the true north and south poles. Since the magnetized needle of the compass points to the earth's magnetic poles, there is usually a difference between north and south as determined by the compass and true north and south. This difference is called *magnetic variation* or *magnetic declination* (dek-li-*nay*-shun).

Magnetic variation not only changes from one place to another but also from one time to another. The table below shows the variation at London, England, since 1600.

Notice that variations are given as a certain number of degrees east or west. A variation of 8° W means that a compass would point 8° too far to the west and that true north would be 8° to the east from the direction indicated by the compass. Magnetic variation has been studied for many years and thousands of measurements have been made all over the earth. As a result, charts and tables are available which give the variation for most regions of the world. Figure 7–5 shows a recent pattern of magnetic variation for the United States. The lines connecting locations of equal magnetic variation are called *isogonic* lines, while the line through areas with zero magnetic variation is known as an *agonic* line.

As yet, there is no satisfactory explanation for the cause of the earth's magnetic field. It may be the result of very slow movements of the metallic substances within the fluid inner core. A very small part of the earth's magnetism is known to be the result of bombardment by particles from disturbances on the sun.

DIRECTION OF COMPASS AT LONDON

Year	1600	1650	1700	1750	1800	1850	1900	1950
Variation	8° E	1° E	7° W	18° W	24° W	22° W	16° W	8° W

Other types of compasses. There are several other kinds of compasses which do not rely on the earth's magnetic field to indicate direction. One of the non-magnetic types commonly used is the *gyrocompass,* which is based on the principle that a spinning wheel always tends to stay in the same position and to resist efforts to change its position. The heart of the gyrocompass is a small, heavy, spinning wheel with its axis pointed true north. The wheel is mounted so that the axis can turn freely in its mounting; it is provided with a mechanism to keep it spinning. Thus the axis of the wheel continues to point true north. The gyrocompass is widely used in ships and aircraft, particularly in situations where a magnetic compass is unreliable.

Another useful type of nonmagnetic compass is the *radio compass.* A navigator can determine true north by listening to radio receivers which indicate the direction of the signals. He can chart his position by the intersection of direction lines from two or more stations whose locations are known.

NAVIGATION

Determining latitude. A navigator must be able to find his exact location in terms of latitude and longitude at any time. Generally, the latitude is found by one method and the longitude by another. The method most commonly used to find latitude is celestial navigation. Latitude can be determined from observations of the various bodies in the sky because their positions relative to the observer's horizon appear to change as the observer moves to the north or south. For example, Polaris appears almost directly overhead to someone standing at the north pole. At the north pole, the elevation of Polaris measured

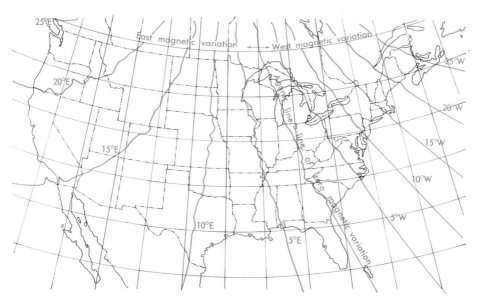

FIG. 7–5. Magnetic variation in the United States. Each line shown is an isogonic line, since it joins all locations having the same magnetic variation.

in degrees above the horizon would be approximately 90°, the latitude of the north pole. If the observer started moving south, Polaris would sink lower in the sky by 1° for every 1° change in latitude by the observer. Thus it would be possible to determine latitude by measuring the elevation of Polaris above the horizon. The latitude of the observer is approximately the same as the number of degrees that Polaris is above the horizon.

About fifty other bright stars are also commonly used for determining latitude. Since these stars are not directly over the north pole, navigators must measure their elevation above the horizon, then change this figure into the correct latitude by consulting printed astronomical tables. Latitude can be determined in the daytime by measuring the elevation of the sun at exactly noon and looking up the latitude in the appropriate table. For measuring the elevation of the stars or the sun above the horizon, an instrument called a *sextant* is used.

Determining longitude. In actual practice, longitude is usually determined by sightings on celestial bodies, but it is still often found by measuring the passage of time. We can visualize the principle on which this method of determining longitude is based by imagining a balloon suspended above the earth in some way, so that it would remain fixed in space while the earth rotated below. Such an arrangement is shown in Fig. 7–6. In 24 hours the earth would make one complete rotation beneath the balloon, and all meridians of longitude that could be drawn on the earth's surface would pass by. In that 24 hours the earth would rotate through the 360° of a full circle, or 15° each hour. If an observer in the balloon could know exactly when the prime meridian passed below, it would

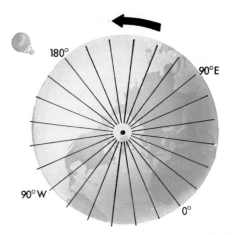

FIG. 7–6. An imaginary stationary balloon suspended above the earth would change its longitude by 15° every hour as the earth rotated beneath it.

be possible for him to determine the exact longitude of any place passing beneath him. Since the earth rotates to the east, each hour would change the longitude 15° to the west.

This principle can be used to determine the longitude of a particular location if the local time is known for that place. Each hour's difference between the local time at a particular place and the time at the prime meridian (called *Greenwich time*) is equal to 15° of longitude. Local time later than Greenwich time is east longitude; earlier local time is west longitude. If, for example, the local time is 9 P.M. when it is 12 midnight Greenwich time, the longitude of the location with that particular local time is about 45° west.

For use in calculating longitude, Greenwich time is usually determined from a very accurate clock called a *chronometer*, set on Greenwich time. Greenwich time can also be found from radio signals continuously sent out by powerful government radio stations. Local time is usually determined by sights on the sun taken at noon when the sun reaches its highest point above the horizon.

Dead reckoning. The methods of celestial navigation often cannot be used because clouds prevent the necessary observations. One of the other methods then available to the navigator is *dead reckoning.* This involves the careful recording of the speed and direction of travel. From the combined knowledge of the time spent moving in a certain direction at a known speed, the navigator is able to plot the results on a map. Calculation of position by dead reckoning is very difficult and usually gives less accurate results than other methods of navigation.

One reason for the comparative inaccuracy of dead reckoning navigation is that the navigator needs to correct for magnetic variation. He must make a correction for this variation in plotting his *course* (the path he travels over the earth's surface) as compared with his *heading* (the direction in which his plane or ship is pointing). In dead reckoning navigation, the navigator must also take into account the *drift* caused by winds or ocean currents. Corrections for wind drift are obviously more important to aerial navigation, whereas drift caused by ocean currents is a much more important factor in marine navigation.

Electronic navigation. The most widely used system of electronic navigation is called *Loran* (from the phrase *Long Range Navigation*). This system operates by means of pairs of radio stations sending out signals received by special radio equipment aboard the ships and aircraft navigating with the system. Using Loran, a navigator can locate his position with great accuracy in any kind of weather. Networks of Loran stations cover many of the principal sea

FIG. 7–7. These men are using sextants to measure the elevation of the sun above the horizon. (*Lew Merrim from Monkmeyer*)

and air lanes of the world; however, many areas are still beyond signal range of the stations.

Another type of electronic navigation is the *inertial* (in-*ur*-shal) *guidance* system. This is a complicated but very accurate combination of instruments that has the advantage of being completely self-contained. The heart of the inertial guidance system is the gyroscope. This is combined with devices that detect changes in direction of movement and an accurate clock to measure the time of travel. The information from this group of instruments is fed into an electronic computer that continuously calculates the exact position of the ship or aircraft. Before the trip begins, the computer can be given the course to be followed and the machine will automatically navigate to the destination. Although inertial guidance is practical for air and sea navigation, its use at present is limited almost entirely to guiding missiles and space rockets.

SUMMARY

ROTATION of the earth on its axis establishes the position of the poles. East-west directions are at right angles to this axis.

Latitude and logitude are measured in degrees, minutes, and seconds. Latitude is the angular distance north or south of the equator. A degree of latitude is approximately 69 miles. The altitude of Polaris can be used to determine latitude in the northern hemisphere. The instrument used to determine latitude is the sextant.

Distance measured in degrees east or west of the prime meridian, a line passing through Greenwich, England, is longitude. Maximum longitude is 180° east or west of the prime meridian. At the equator a degree of longitude is equal to about 69 miles but gradually decreases north or south of the equator. Longitude is determined by using a chronometer. Any circle that divides a sphere in half is a great circle. Great circles follow the shortest route between any two points on the earth's surface.

The magnetic poles are not in the same location as the geographic poles. In most areas the magnetic compass does not point to true north. Compass readings are adjusted to true north by using the magnetic declination or variation for the particular area. Gyrocompasses and radio compasses operate independently of the earth's magnetic field.

VOCABULARY REVIEW

Match the phrase in the left column with the correct word or phrase in the right column. *Do not write in this book.*

1. Instrument used to determine latitude
2. North-south lines on the earth
3. Navigation by astronomy
4. Method of navigating rockets and missiles
5. Correction for computing true north
6. Distance north or south of the equator
7. 0° longitude
8. Instrument used to determine longitude
9. Distance east or west of the prime meridian
10. East-west circle around the earth
11. Shortest distance between two points on the earth

a. latitude.
b. inertial guidance
c. chronometer
d. meridians
e. great circle route
f. longitude
g. nautical mile
h. parallel of latitude
i. prime meridian
j. magnetic declination
k. celestial navigation
l. sextant

QUESTIONS · GROUP A

Select the best term to complete the following statements:

1. Latitude is measured from (*a*) the prime meridian (*b*) the north pole (*c*) the equator (*d*) Greenwich, England.

2. One degree of latitude equals about (*a*) 7 miles (*b*) 15 miles (*c*) 69 miles (*d*) 108 miles.
3. The maximum longitude for any place on the earth's surface is (*a*) 15° (*b*) 90° (*c*) 180° (*d*) 360°
4. Philadelphia is about 40° north of the equator. The distance in miles from the equator to Philadelphia is approximately (*a*) 2140 (*b*) 2349 (*c*) 3920 (*d*) 2760.
5. What is the longitude of a ship when the local time is noon and the time in Greenwich, England, is 4 P.M.? (*a*) 15° W (*b*) 45° E (*c*) 60° W (*d*) 30° E.
6. A degree of latitude is equal to the same number of miles as a degree of longitude (*a*) at the equator (*b*) nowhere on earth (*c*) at the poles (*d*) midway between the equator and the prime meridian.
7. The longitude of New Orleans is approximately 90° (*a*) N (*b*) S (*c*) E (*d*) W.
8. Which of the following is part of a great circle? (*a*) Arctic Circle (*b*) prime meridian (*c*) 45th parallel (*d*) polar axis.
9. If the date in New York City is January 5 and the time is 11 P.M., the date in Greenwich is (*a*) January 4 (*b*) January 5 (*c*) January 6 (*d*) January 7.
10. When his airplane is flying under a blanket of clouds the navigator cannot use (*a*) Loran (*b*) a gyrocompass (*c*) celestial navigation (*d*) dead reckoning.
11. A primitive system of latitude and longitude was first introduced by the (*a*) Greeks (*b*) Chinese (*c*) Romans (*d*) Egyptians.
12. The rotation of the earth establishes the position of (*a*) New York City (*b*) the north and south poles (*c*) the oceans (*d*) the continents.
13. The star that is nearly over the north pole is (*a*) Polaris (*b*) the sun (*c*) Alpha Centauri (*d*) Andromeda.
14. As you move north or south from the equator, the parallels (*a*) increase in diameter (*b*) decrease in circumference (*c*) show no change in either circumference or diameter (*d*) increase, then decrease in circumference.

GROUP B

1. Could Polaris be seen from a point south of the equator? Give the reasons for your answer.
2. What are the advantages of an inertial guidance system in rockets and missiles?
3. What would be the latitude and longitude where the prime meridian crosses the equator? at the north pole? at the south pole?
4. Explain how and why Polaris is used to determine latitude.
5. What is meant by a magnetic variation of 12° E?
6. How does the rotation of the earth make possible the establishment of reference points for direction?
7. Why is knowledge of latitude and longitude more important to a ship's captain than to a bus driver?
8. Where was the prime meridian established? Explain why it was needed.
9. Give some possible causes of the earth's magnetic field.
10. Discuss the problems that might arise if each country ran the prime meridian through its capital for the purpose of making maps.

CHAPTER 8

TIME

SOME of the earliest records we have show how people used the natural rhythms of day and night, the phases of the moon, and the seasons to mark the flow of time. Today we still use the earth's ceaseless motions to keep time, although our methods of measurement are more advanced. As astronomers have slowly become better acquainted with the movements of the earth, the science of measuring time accurately has grown to a high degree of perfection.

However, we can no longer use the motions of the earth for the most exact time measurements we need. The incredibly rapid reactions of the atom and the flashing swiftness of rockets must be measured with precision never dreamed

VOCABULARY

Inclination. The tilting of a planet's axis in relation to its orbit around the sun.

Solstice. A time when the sun seems to reverse its apparent movement north or south of the equator.

Equinox. A time when the sun is directly overhead at noon on the equator.

Tropical year. The time from one vernal equinox to the next.

Sidereal (sy-*deer*-ee-al) **year.** The time required for the earth to complete one revolution with respect to the stars.

Perihelion (pehr-i-*hee*-lee-on). The point on the earth's orbit nearest the sun.

Aphelion (a-*fee*-lee-on). The point on the earth's orbit farthest from the sun.

Standard time. Time determined by division of the earth's surface into 24 time zones whose centers are approximately 15 degrees apart in longitude.

International date line. An imaginary line at about 180 degrees longitude; when it is crossed, standard time changes by 24 hours forward or backward.

of before. To measure the time that regulates our daily life, we still rely upon the earth as we have for thousands of years past, but we cannot measure the planet's movements accurately enough to meet all the demands of modern astronomers and space scientists.

HOW A YEAR IS MEASURED

The tropical year. Our year is ordinarily measured by the time the earth takes to make one complete trip around the sun. But how can we tell how long that time is? There are no signposts in space to tell when the earth has returned to its starting place. Some sort of reference point must be established to mark the beginning and end of a revolution. One of the most ancient ways of measuring this period of time is based on the regular march of the seasons. In the temperate zones, the rising warmth of the spring, the summer season of crop growth, the harvest of autumn, and the cold of winter have marked the passing of the year since man's earliest memory. This is still the common way to mark the passage of another year.

The seasons themselves occur because the earth does not rotate in an upright position, compared to the plane of its orbit around the sun. The earth's axis is tilted 23½° from this plane. This tilt is usually called the **inclination** of the planet and is not a feature of the earth exclusively. The inclination of the other planets is shown in Fig. 8–1. The earth's inclination of 23½° is about average.

As the earth revolves around the sun, the north pole is tilted first toward the sun and then away from it, because the inclination of the axis is always in the same direction. Figure 8–2 may help you understand why this is true. In June of each year the north pole is tilted most toward the sun, so the sun's rays fall most vertically on the northern hemisphere. This is the summer season for the northern half of the earth because rays which strike the earth vertically deliver most heat to each square foot. See Fig. 8–3. On about June 21 the sun is shining straight down on the *Tropic of Cancer*, an imaginary line at 23½° north latitude which marks the most northern point where the sun is ever directly overhead. At any location north of the Tropic of Cancer, which includes the entire United States (except Alaska), the sun at noon is always in the southern part of the sky. The noontime sun appears farthest north to us when it is directly over the Tropic of Cancer. Since this is the time when the northern hemisphere receives most heat from the

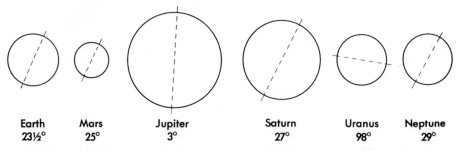

| Earth | Mars | Jupiter | Saturn | Uranus | Neptune |
| 23½° | 25° | 3° | 27° | 98° | 29° |

FIG. 8–1. Inclination of the axes of some of the planets. The inclinations of Mercury, Venus, and Pluto are not known.

sun, it is called the *summer solstice.* ("Solstice" means "sun stands still" and refers to the apparent northward and southward movement of the sun.) Actually, the hottest weather of the summer comes after the summer solstice because the heat accumulates and affects the weather most during the months of July and August.

Regions on the earth within the Arctic Circle all have 24 hours of sunlight at the time of the summer solstice, since the sun never sets on that day in these areas. This "land of the midnight sun" includes parts of Alaska (and certain other areas of North America), as well as some parts of Europe and Asia.

By September the earth is one-fourth farther around its orbit than it was in June and the north pole is no longer tilted toward the sun. See Fig. 8–2. The northern hemisphere no longer receives the sun's vertical rays and so begins to cool off. Fall begins at the time of the

autumnal equinox, about September 23, when the sun is directly over the equator. By December the earth has progressed halfway around its orbit and is directly opposite its location in June. Now the south pole is tilted toward the sun and the southern hemisphere is warmed by the sun's vertical rays. At the time of the *winter solstice,* about December 21, the sun is directly over the *Tropic of Capricorn,* which is at 23½° south latitude. When the sun is over the Tropic of Capricorn, we receive the least heat from the sun in the northern hemisphere. The full effect of the winter, however, comes after the winter solstice, due to the lag in the heating and cooling of the earth.

At the winter solstice, people in areas that experience the midnight sun in the summer do not see the sun rise at all. Conversely, the areas within the Antarctic Circle are receiving a full day of sunlight.

FIG. 8–2. The inclination of the earth's axis is always in the same direction as it revolves around the sun.

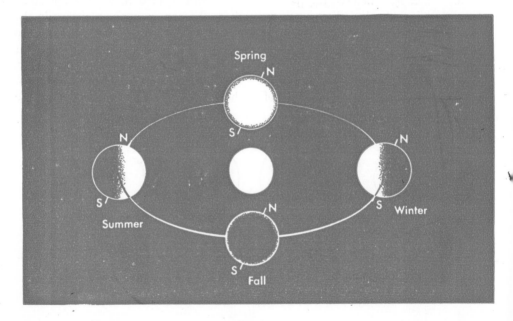

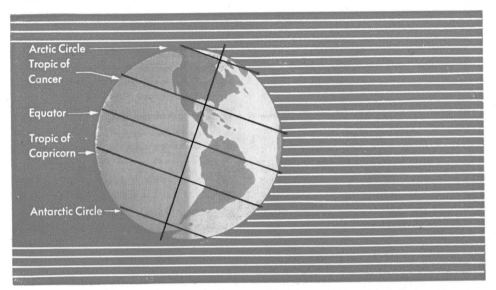

FIG. 8–3. At the summer solstice the sun's vertical rays fall on the Tropic of Cancer. At this time the northern hemisphere receives more of the sun's radiant energy than the southern hemisphere.

By March the earth has completed three-quarters of its trip around the sun. The beginning of spring, the *vernal equinox*, occurs on or about March 21 when the sun is again directly over the equator. In June the summer solstice comes again and the cycle of the seasons is complete.

With all this in mind, we can accurately define the *tropical year*. It is the length of time between two consecutive vernal equinoxes—precisely 365 days 5 hours 48 minutes and 46 seconds. Our calendar year is the same length, although we run the calendar year from January to January rather than from one vernal equinox to another.

The sidereal year. Actually, a tropical year is a little short of the length of time that it takes the earth to make a complete trip around its orbit. Mainly because of the effect of the moon's gravitation, the earth wobbles slightly as it turns on its axis. The motion, called *pre-*

cession, is like that of a spinning top; the axis of the top is not upright, but instead its upper end describes a small circle, moving much more slowly than the top rotates. See Fig. 8–4. This very

FIG. 8–4. Precession of the earth's axis is similar to the slow wobbling motion of a rapidly rotating top.

slow precessional motion causes the vertical rays of the sun to cross the equator shortly before the round trip in the orbit is completed, making the year about 20 minutes shorter than it would otherwise be.

Because of the difficulties involved in measuring a tropical year with great accuracy, astronomers sometimes use the *sidereal* (sy-*deer*-ee-al) *year.* It too is based on the length of time the earth takes to complete its orbit. However, the beginning and the end of a sidereal year are measured not by the position of the sun, but by reference points among the stars. Stars are so far away that such a thing as the earth's wobble makes little difference in their observed positions relative to the sun.

HOW A DAY IS MEASURED

Rotation of the earth. The fact that the earth spins as it moves through space has great influence on both the earth and its inhabitants. As stated in Chapter 6, the spinning affects the shape of the planet; the region around the equator bulges outward because of the force of rotation. Recent evidence gained from the artificial satellites indicates that the earth is in fact very slightly pear-shaped: the northern hemisphere is less round than the southern hemisphere.

The rotation of the earth can be demonstrated by using a Foucault pendulum, made up of a heavy weight suspended from a long rope or cable. The

FIG. 8–5. A Foucault pendulum can be used to prove that the earth rotates. (*The Franklin Institute*)

heavy weight of such a pendulum is shown in Fig. 8–5, with a model of the complete apparatus at the right of the photograph. The pendulum, once in motion, swings in a straight line. Because the earth rotates beneath the pendulum, the direction of the pendulum's swing apparently changes with respect to the circular protractor on the floor below. Actually, it is the earth's rotation that moves the protractor while the pendulum continues to swing in the same straight line.

To human beings, the important effect of the earth's rotation is the rising and setting of the sun. The sun, of course, remains the center of the solar system; it only seems to rise and set because we move with reference to it as the earth turns on its axis. Since the earth rotates toward the east, the sun seems to rise in an easterly direction and travel across the sky, setting toward the west. In the summer the sun seems to take longer to cross the sky, and the days are longer than the nights. In the winter, the reverse is true—the nights are longer than the days. The reason can be seen in Fig. 8–6. During the northern summer the north pole is tilted toward the sun, and sunlight falls on much more than half of the northern hemisphere. So, in the summer, those on the northern half of the earth spend most of their rotation time in the daylight. The longest daylight period of the year is at the time of the summer solstice, about June 21. In summer, the rotation of the earth never carries the region that is close to the north into the darkness. North of the *Arctic Circle*, the sun never sets on the summer solstice.

In winter the situation is reversed. The shortest daylight period of the year comes at the time of the winter solstice, about December 21. The south pole is

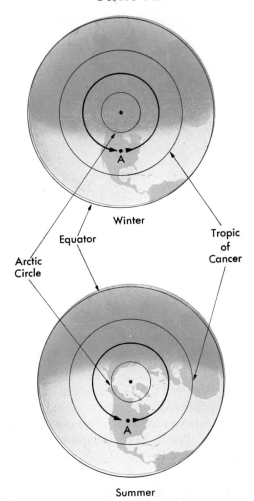

FIG. 8–6. Seasonal variation in the period of daylight is shown in this view of the northern hemisphere. The heavy arrows trace the path of point *A* as the earth rotates on its axis.

then tilted toward the sun. The northern hemisphere is more than half covered by darkness, and nights are longer than days. The south pole has continuous daylight.

On two occasions during the year, day and night are of equal length everywhere on the earth because the line that circles the earth separating night from day

FIG. 8–7. A sundial measures apparent solar time. How is this time different from standard time at the same location? (*Ewing Galloway*)

Time by the sun. Almost everyone uses the earth as a clock. The rotation of the earth makes the sun seem to move across the sky each day as the master clock that regulates our lives. One very old device for keeping time is the sundial, which tells the time of day from the position of the moving shadow cast by the sun. On a sundial, 12 o'clock noon is when the sun is at its highest position above the horizon. A day is the length of time from one noon to the next, and each day is divided into 24 equal hours. Time measured with a sundial is called *apparent solar time* because it is determined entirely by the apparent position of the sun.

It would seem that not much could go wrong with a sundial providing the sun stays out from behind the clouds. Actually, a sundial has the same trouble that some more complicated clocks have—it sometimes runs too fast or slow. The trouble comes from the fact that the earth does not always travel at the same speed in its orbit. The earth's orbit is slightly elliptical and the sun is not in the exact center, so the earth comes closer

passes directly through both the north and south poles. This occurs only when the sun is directly over the equator at the two equinoxes ("equinox" means "equal night"), that is, about September 21 and March 21.

FIG. 8–8. The distance from the earth to the sun varies because the earth's orbit is slightly elliptical. Note that the earth is nearest to the sun during our winter season.

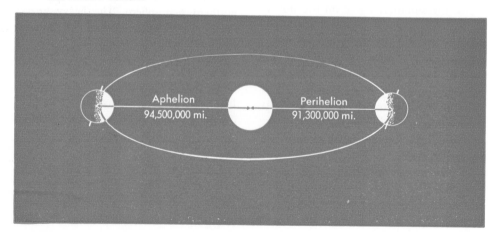

Aphelion
94,500,000 mi.

Perihelion
91,300,000 mi.

to the sun on one side of its orbit than on the other. When the earth is at the point nearest the sun, it is said to be at *perihelion* (pehr-i-*hee*-lee-on) and is 91,300,000 miles from the sun. At *aphelion* (a-*fee*-lee-on), the farthest point, the distance is 94,500,000 miles. The average distance is 92,900,000 miles. See Fig. 8–8.

At perihelion, the earth moves faster in its orbit than at aphelion. Since the speed with which the sun seems to move across the sky is determined partly by the earth's movement in its orbit, the sun seems to cross the sky slower when the earth is at perihelion in January. This is because the earth moves faster in its orbit during one rotation and has to turn longer to bring the sun back to an overhead position. As a result, a sundial will show the length of time from one noon to the next as a little more in January than in July, when the earth is at aphelion and is moving slowest in its orbit. Therefore a sundial runs too slow in the winter and too fast in the summer. Also, the apparent speed at which the sun crosses the sky is not uniform throughout the year because the eastward motion in the sky is most rapid near the solstices. Near the equinoxes, in September and March, the sun is apparently moving south or north and only part of its motion carries it eastward across the sky.

To avoid problems caused by the sun's nonuniform apparent movements across the sky, ordinary clocks are set to run on a 24-hour day which is as long as the average of the sometimes too-long and too-short days measured by the sundials. This kind of time is called *mean solar time* or average solar time. That is, clocks measure the same length of time from one noon to the next all year and so usually disagree slightly with sundials.

FIG. 8–9. An electric sidereal clock. It keeps sidereal time with a deviation of less than six seconds per year. (*Haines Scientific Instruments*)

The difference between clock time (mean solar time) and sun time (apparent solar time) is never greater than 16 minutes. The exact difference, called the *equation of time,* for any given date can be looked up in an *ephemeris* (eh-*jem*-er-is) a type of almanac. The United States Naval Observatory publishes yearly the *American Ephemeris and Nautical Almanac.*

Time by the stars. Just as the length of a day can be measured by two successive appearances of the sun overhead, a day can be measured by two successive appearances of a star overhead. The *sidereal day,* like the sidereal year, is shorter than its corresponding solar time period: a sidereal day is three minutes and fifty-six seconds shorter than a mean solar day. Clocks set on *sidereal time* therefore run a little faster than ordinary clocks. Sidereal time is used in astronomy and navigation because it is based on the actual period of rotation of the earth rather than an average figure based on the apparent motions of the sun. Location of the various stars and planets in the sky becomes easier if their time of rising and setting is given according to the sidereal clock.

Standard time. The invention of mean solar time insured that clocks would always measure days of the same length, but it did not make them agree on when the day begins. Everyone could agree that each day would begin at midnight and end 24 mean solar hours later on the following midnight, but there was not much agreement on exactly when midnight was. Each city or town could set its clocks to correspond approximately to apparent solar time so that noon would come when the sun was most nearly overhead. This was satisfactory as long as there was no need to travel. A person traveling across the country would have to reset the time to match that in every location visited.

By the 1880's in the United States the railroad timetables were so mixed up by the hundreds of different times kept by different localities that something obviously had to be done. In 1883 the railroads agreed to set up four *standard time zones* across the country. Within each zone, the time was to be uniformly that of the most important city in that zone. This was the beginning of the modern system of standard time.

Today the earth's surface is marked off into 24 standard time zones. These are based upon meridians of longitude 15 degrees apart, starting with the prime meridian. Standard time in each zone is taken as the mean solar time at the central meridian of that zone, and is one hour earlier than the zone to the east and one hour later than the zone to the west. The boundaries between zones are placed approximately midway between the central meridians of adjacent zones. See Fig. 8–10.

In the United States (excluding Alaska and Hawaii) there are four standard time zones: Eastern, Central,

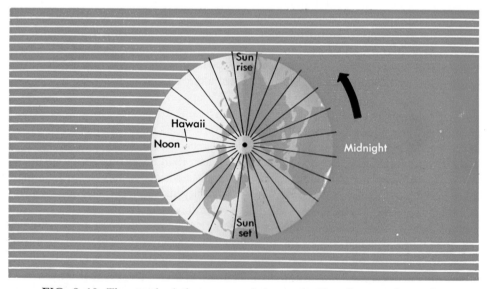

FIG. 8–10. The standard time zones of the earth. The diagram shows the situation at the equinox. When it is noon in Hawaii, it is afternoon in North America and early morning in eastern Asia.

FIG. 8–11. Standard time zones in the United States. The boundaries of time zones are not always parallel with meridians.

Mountain, and Pacific. See Fig. 8–11. The boundaries between the time zones are generally arranged so that all of each state has the same standard time.

During the summer, when the daylight hours are longer, many states and cities adopt *daylight saving time*. Clocks are set one hour ahead of standard time in April, then set back again sometime in the fall. In areas where daylight saving time is observed, people simply get up one hour earlier in the morning so as to enjoy an extra hour of daylight in the evening.

The international date line. Suppose you take off in a jet plane from San Francisco to fly around the world. Your take-off time is at sunset and you are flying toward the west over the Pacific toward the setting sun. Suppose also that the speed of the jet is great enough to

keep up with the speed of the earth's rotation. As a result, the sun never appears to set but remains suspended on the horizon. Since you are flying to the west, you keep turning your watch back as you cross each time zone boundary. Under such conditions, time would seem to stand still for you. If the jet maintained the same speed and circled the earth nonstop, the time and the day would still be the same when you finally arrived back in San Francisco as they were when you left. If you left on Friday, it would still be Friday for you when you returned, since your watch never advanced to midnight. For everybody else though, it would be Saturday.

To prevent such confusion as this, an imaginary line on the earth through the Pacific Ocean at about the 180th meridian (Fig. 7–3) has been designated as the *international date line.* To anyone passing over this line, the calendar immediately changes one day. If the line were crossed going from east to west at 6 P.M. on Friday, the time would become 6 P.M. on Saturday. Going from west to east, a day is repeated when the line is crossed. This takes care of the gain of a day when the earth is completely circled going to the west and the loss of a day when it is circled going east.

The international date line was located in the Pacific Ocean to avoid the confusion that would be created by dividing populated areas. Actually, the line does not follow the 180° meridian exactly but bends around various land areas and islands in order to avoid cutting across inhabited regions.

THE CALENDAR

The moon and the calendar. The calendar month was once based on the length of time it takes for the moon to go through all of its phases. The moon actually completes its orbit around the earth in 27⅓ days, and it might seem that the moon should complete all of its phases in this time. Actually, however, the moon takes 29½ days to come back to the same phase. The explanation for this difference is that the earth moves around the sun in the same direction as the moon moves around the earth. This means that the earth is always pulling ahead of the moon. In one revolution of the moon in its orbit, the earth has gone ahead enough so that it takes about two extra days for the moon to catch up.

Calendars would be much simpler if there just happened to be an even number of 29½-day months in a year. But a year is about 365¼ days, which cannot

1582		October			1582	
Sun.	**Mon.**	**Tue.**	**Wed.**	**Thu.**	**Fri.**	**Sat.**
	1	2	3	4	15	16
17	18	19	20	21	22	23
24	25	26	27	28	29	30
31						

FIG. 8–12. In the change to the Gregorian calendar, ten days were dropped. On this imaginary calendar page, the blue numbers are Julian dates and the black numbers Gregorian.

be evenly divided by 29½. The calendar of the ancient Romans, from which the modern calendar comes, started out with six months of 30 days and six of 29 days, but this left each calendar year about ten days short of the actual year. The Romans solved this problem by adding an extra month every few years just to catch up again. By the time of Julius Caesar, around 45 B.C., the Romans had become so confused with their calendar that Caesar ordered a complete change. The length of the months was increased to 30 or 31 days, ignoring the moon, thus getting 12 calendar months into the 365-day year. This still left one problem. A year is actually about 365¼ days long, so the new calendar, now called the Julian (after Julius Caesar) calendar, put in an extra day every four years to take care of this. Leap year, which occurs whenever the last two numbers of the year are evenly divisible by four, has this extra day.

Although it was a great improvement, the Julian calendar still did not work out quite right. The trouble was that a year is 11 minutes and 14 seconds short of being exactly 365¼ days. After the Julian calendar had been used for hundreds of years the months again got out of step with the seasons of the year. By the sixteenth century another calendar reform was needed. In 1582 Pope Gregory ordered a change to bring the date for the observance of Easter back to its proper place on the calendar. The change was accomplished by dropping out of that year the 10 days that had been gained and making every century year (1800, 1900, etc.) a leap year only if it could be evenly divided by 400. This omits 3 leap years every 400 years and satisfactorily keeps the months in agreement with the seasons. The last revision has come to be called the Gregorian calendar and has been adopted by most countries as the official calendar.

A more orderly calendar arrangement with respect to the dates and days of the week might still be devised. The chief problem is that a normal year has 52 weeks and one extra day; a leap year has 52 weeks and two extra days. Thus a date always falls one day later in the week each successive year except in a leap year, when the date leaps over a day.

Two proposed solutions are the Universal Calendar and the World Calendar. The Universal Calendar has 13 months of 28 days each. This amounts to 364 days. An extra day without a date is therefore added at the end of each year. In leap year there are two extra days. Objections have been raised to a year of 13 months because it could not be evenly divided into halves or quarters.

The World Calendar has only 12 months. The first month of each quarter (January, April, July, and October) has 31 days, all the others 30 days. This also produces a year of 364 days and requires one extra day to be added at the end of the year. The extra day is a holiday known as "World Day" and comes between December 30 and January 1. In a leap year a second "World Day" is added to the calendar between June 30 and July 1.

Changes in the calendar are not easily made. Adoption of the Gregorian calendar took several hundred years. By 1752, when England adopted it, 11 days had to be dropped. Public disturbances occurred in many countries when the change was made. Even today, many people apparently prefer the complexity of the present calendar to a more closely regulated new one.

PRECISE MEASUREMENT OF TIME

Errors from keeping time by the earth. All of the ordinary ways for measuring time are based on motions of the earth. This is completely satisfactory for most purposes because the earth is fairly dependable in its rotation and revolution around the sun. However, scientists who have to measure time with very great accuracy find that the earth's movement is not dependable enough.

The main difficulty is in determining the exact position of the earth relative to the fixed positions of the stars. So many measurements and calculations are involved in astronomical observations that there is unavoidable error in the final answer. The error is generally so small that it causes no trouble unless a long time interval must be measured very accurately.

It is also true that the earth varies slightly in the rate at which it spins on its axis. In every 1000 years it spins, the planet seems to take about 3½ seconds longer to make a complete rotation. It appears to be slowing down unevenly so

FIG. 8–13. The cesium beam atomic clock at the National Bureau of Standards. Atomic clocks are much more accurate than those which operate mechanically. (*National Bureau of Standards*)

that it rotates at different rates from time to time. Tides and winds affect the rotation slightly, and it may be that slow movements of the earth's core also affect its rotation.

Atomic clocks. The basic requirement for a very accurate clock is a movement or process that is repeated endlessly with absolute regularity. A clock that depends upon the swinging of a pendulum illustrates the measurement of time by means of some sort of constant rhythm. However, just as a pendulum is subject to many influences that can prevent it from swinging at exactly the same rate, almost any rhythmic process gives rise to inaccuracy when used as a basis for timekeeping.

Scientists have discovered that tiny vibrations are produced by atoms and molecules. All atoms or molecules of the same kind vibrate with an absolutely constant frequency. This natural property of atoms and molecules can be used to control a clock that is completely independent of the motions of the earth. The vibrations of the tiny atoms and molecules themselves cannot be made to run a clock but are used to regulate the actual clock mechanism.

Atomic clocks that have an error of one second in 300 years have been built and there seems to be no reason why greater accuracy cannot be achieved. A clock that would not gain or lose a second in 300,000 years is a definite possibility. Such superaccurate clocks are among the tools needed by scientists in their effort to bring meaning to the world of atomic structure.

SUMMARY

THE movements of the earth are used as a basis for the ordinary measurement of time. The cycle of the seasons measures the passage of an ordinary or tropical year. Seasonal changes are due to the inclination of the earth's axis, which causes first the northern, then the southern hemisphere to lean toward the sun. On June 21, the summer solstice, the sun is directly over the Tropic of Cancer and the northern hemisphere begins its summer. On December 21, the winter solstice, the sun is directly over the Tropic of Capricorn and it is winter in the northern hemisphere. On the two equinoxes, which mark the beginning of spring and fall, the sun is directly overhead at the equator. A sidereal year is based on the stars as reference points.

A day is the length of time the earth takes to make one complete rotation on its axis. Apparent solar time is measured by the position of the sun in the sky. Because the sun varies slightly in the time it takes to cross the sky, ordinary clock time or mean solar time is based on the average rate of movement of the sun in the sky. Sidereal time is measured by the position of the stars. Standard time has been established to avoid confusion resulting from the numerous small differences of local time. The international date line is an orderly means of changing the day with reference to the 24 standard one-hour time zones.

The calendar was originally based on the phases of the moon. Because of the confusion created by the uneven number of lunar months in a year, several revisions of the calendar have been carried out. At the present, the Gregorian calendar is commonly used.

VOCABULARY REVIEW

Match the phrase in the right column with the correct word or phrase in the left column. *Do not write in this book.*

1. 23½° south latitude
2. Velocity of earth's revolution decreases
3. 180th meridian
4. Uses stars as reference points
5. Parallel in the northern hemisphere
6. June 21
7. Measured with a sundial
8. Type of almanac
9. Difference that is never greater than 16 minutes
10. Calendar presently in use
11. Width 15°
12. Interval between two consecutive vernal equinoxes

a. Julian calendar
b. apparent solar time
c. aphelion
d. international date line
e. Tropic of Cancer
f. Gregorian calendar
g. tropical year
h. summer solstice
i. time zone
j. Tropic of Capricorn
k. sidereal year
l. ephemeris
m. equation of time

Decide whether these statements are true or false. Reword the false statements to make them true. *Do not write in this book.*

1. A person driving from Washington, D. C., to Los Angeles would move his watch ahead each time he entered a new time zone.
2. The sun's apparent movement is from east to west.
3. According to the Gregorian calendar, the year 2700 will be a leap year.
4. As the sun sets in San Francisco it is also setting in New York.
5. A year is actually about 364 days.
6. The equation of time is sometimes greater than 24 hours.
7. The time interval from one new moon to the next new moon is 27 days.
8. Day and night are equal in length, everywhere on the earth, on March 21 and June 21.
9. The sun's rays are never exactly vertical in Ohio.
10. Equinoxes occur around September 21 and June 21.
11. During April many communities which adopt daylight saving time set their clocks one hour ahead.
12. At 90° W it is 7 A.M. on January 23. Therefore at 165° W it must be 1 P.M. on January 22.
13. Summer days are longer than winter days because the earth's axis is parallel to the plane of its orbit.
14. The international date line is a straight line on the globe.
15. During the year the direct rays of the sun migrate a total of 23½°.
16. At noon on December 21 the direct rays of the sun are on the Tropic of Cancer.
17. If the inclination of the earth's axis were 45°, the latitude of the Tropic of Capricorn would be 45° N.
18. A sidereal day is shorter than a mean solar day.
19. During a trip around the world, a traveler would pass through 24 standard time zones.
20. There are four time zones across the United States (excluding Alaska and Hawaii).
21. The sun's direct rays cross the equator three times in one year.
22. The greatest differences in the length of day and night occur in the tropics.
23. The length of the year is determined by the period of rotation of the earth.
24. The earth is nearest the sun during winter in the northern hemisphere.
25. If the earth's axis were inclined more than 23½°, the summers in the northern hemisphere would be warmer.

GROUP B

1. If the earth rotated from east to west at one quarter its present rate how would this affect rising and setting of the sun and the length of the day?
2. If the south pole were always tilted toward the sun, how would this affect seasons on the earth?
3. What would be the disadvantage of using daylight saving time in winter?

4. Why do standard time zones usually have irregular boundaries on the land but regular boundaries over the oceans?
5. How was the Julian calendar an improvement over the older Roman calendar?
6. Explain the defects of the Julian calendar and how they were corrected in the Gregorian calendar.
7. If the earth did not revolve, how would this affect the length of time from full moon to full moon?
8. What determines the location of the Tropics of Cancer and Capricorn?
9. What is the position of the sun at the summer solstice? at the winter solstice?
10. On which date of the year would a tree cast the longest shadow? the shortest shadow? Explain the reason for your answers. Draw a labeled diagram to illustrate your explanation.
11. Describe the type of "seasons" we would have if the earth's axis were perpendicular to the plane of its orbit.
12. What would be the effect on the length of day and night if the inclination of the earth's axis were increased?
13. Why is apparent solar time too fast in January and too slow in July?
14. How is mean solar time, the time kept by ordinary clocks, related to apparent solar time?
15. Explain the need for the establishment of standard time zones in the United States.
16. Explain the advantages of daylight saving time.
17. Explain the need for the establishment of the international date line.
18. What is the purpose of leap years? How can we determine when a leap year will occur?
19. Why are atomic clocks necessary to measure time very precisely?
20. What two corrections are necessary in order to set a clock accurately from a sundial?
21. What type of seasons would occur on Mars, Jupiter, and Uranus?
22. At what season or seasons during the year are sundial time and clock time most likely to agree?
23. Why do regions of the world close to the equator have little seasonal variation during the year?

CHAPTER 9

MAPS AND MAP READING

MAPS are one of the basic tools used in the study of the earth. For the geologist, maps are a means by which the earth's surface can be brought into the laboratory and studied to gain understanding of its structure and the forces working constantly to change its surface features. To the trained eye, a map of the type used in the earth sciences not only reveals the present form of the surface but also may give clear evidence of the past events that have shaped the region.

But maps that are used for such purposes are not simple. They are necessarily more detailed than ordinary road maps or even the maps found in most atlases. The use of the accurate and detailed maps which provide much valuable information in earth science requires some special knowledge and training. The purpose of this chapter is to give a basic understanding of the methods by which maps are produced and of the general features of maps and their interpretation.

VOCABULARY

Map projection. The representation of the globe, or a portion of it, on a flat surface.

Scale. The mathematical comparison between actual distance and distance on a map.

Mercator (mur-*kay*-ter) **projection.** A map based on projection of the globe on a cylinder.

Gnomonic (noh-*mon*-ik) **projection.** A map based on projection of the globe on a plane surface.

Conic projection. A map based on projection of the globe on the surface of a cone.

Topographic map. A map showing surface features of a portion of the earth.

Relief. The irregularity in elevation of parts of the earth's surface.

Contour lines. Lines on a map joining points on the earth having the same elevation.

116

North star

FIG. 9–1. Many maps and charts are marked for magnetic declination. In the diagram, the line with the star shows the true north and the line with the arrow-point indicates the direction and degrees of declination.

MAP PROJECTIONS

Why map projections are necessary. If the earth were flat it would be a simple matter to make accurate maps on flat sheets of paper. However, the earth has a curved surface which can be represented without distortion only on another curved surface, such as a globe. Any attempt to transfer the curvature of the earth to the plane surface of a map introduces distortion of the features shown. For a map showing only a small area of the earth the distortion is slight since the earth's curvature is hardly noticeable over short distances. However, for maps of large areas the distortion becomes very great.

The various ways of transferring the curved surface of the earth onto the plane surfaces of maps are called *map projections.* There are many different map projections, each one of which has

some desirable features, but no projection can be made which avoids all distortion. Each type of projection has its own advantages and the skillful user of maps chooses the projection which best suits his need. For some purposes, a map which shows areas and shapes as correctly as possible is desirable; for other purposes, correct directions are more important than anything else. In many situations, several kinds of maps are used.

Basic map design. The user of maps is seeking many kinds of information about the earth's surface. To understand any map, he must know its relation to the compass directions. The standard method of showing the north-south and east-west directions on a map is to have the top of the map sheet as north. As one looks at the map, the right is east, the left is west, and the bottom is south. Meridians of longitude are shown as lines running from top to bottom of the map and parallels of latitude are indicated by lines running from side to side. Since the lines may be straight or curved, according to the map projection, exact direction must always be read with respect to the parallels and meridians. In certain maps, the meridians radiate from the pole as a center, and the parallels are circles.

Because of the magnetic declination, direction determined with an ordinary compass does not usually agree with true north as shown by the meridians on a map. In order to change direction shown by a compass at a certain location into true direction for the same location, an adjustment must be made for the declination. If the map covers a very large area, the declination will be different in separate parts of the map, so the declination must be looked up for each location. For smaller maps, the declination for that particular area can be given on the map. It may be given as a statement printed below the map or as a symbol on the map itself.

Once he has determined directions, the map user is generally interested in distances. All maps must have some basis for comparison between actual distance on the earth and the same distance measured on the map. This relationship is the *scale* of the map. If the map is designed to show a large area of the earth, the scale selected will be one that allows a short distance on the map to represent a great distance on the earth. For example, 1 inch may represent 100 miles. For more detailed maps of limited areas of the earth's surface a much smaller scale, such as one inch to the mile, may be used. Because of the nature of a map projection, the scale varies, due to distortion in areas away from the center. However, in maps of limited areas, the variation is not important. The scale of a map is commonly expressed by a *graphic scale*. This is a line which is divided into parts marked to represent distances on the earth. Graphic scales are very commonly shown on maps covering relatively small areas, because distances can be quickly found by direct comparison of a measurement on the map with the marked line. Another way of indicating the scale of a map is by use of a fraction such as $\frac{1}{10,000}$. This is called a *fractional scale* and means that 1 unit of measurement on the map represents 10,000 of the same units on the earth. Occasionally the map scale may be given by a statement, such as "one inch equals one mile." This is known as a *verbal* scale. In maps of large areas, the scale of various parts of the map may be given.

Projections based on a cylinder. The basic method for making all map projections is to transfer the features on the earth's curved surface onto another surface which can be laid flat without too much distortion. Most projections are the result of mathematical computations, but the method by which they are produced can be visualized if we imagine a transparent globe, lighted from within. Surface markings—for example, the meridians and parallels—are opaque and cast shadows on a piece of paper that is held against the globe. Variations in the angle and position of the paper produce varying patterns of meridians and parallels; that is, the distortion of features on the earth varies.

An example of this distortion is the map made by projecting the earth's surface onto a cylinder. Suppose that a paper cylinder is wrapped around a globe, as in Fig. 9–2, and the meridians and parallels are projected on the paper. If the cylinder were cut and unrolled the map projection obtained would appear as shown. Because the cylinder is close to the earth's surface only at the equator, such a projection accurately represents the area around the equator but greatly distorts the regions near the poles. See Fig. 9–3.

The Mercator (mur-*kay*-ter) projection, one of the most widely used of all map projections, is a type of cylindrical projection. However, the Mercator projection spaces the parallels farther apart near the poles. This gives the land near the poles the proper shape but exaggerates the size of areas in the high latitudes. The Mercator projection is most useful in navigation because directions are true. A course following a certain compass direction can be drawn as a straight line.

Projections based on a plane. If a plane surface is held so that it is tangent to a globe at a certain point, half of the globe's surface may be projected onto

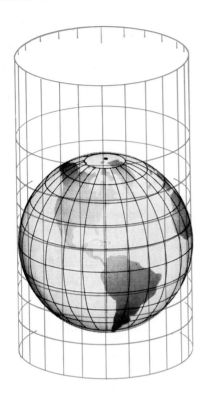

FIG. 9–2. A cylindrical map projection can be visualized as the result of wrapping a cylinder around a globe and transferring its features to the cylinder.

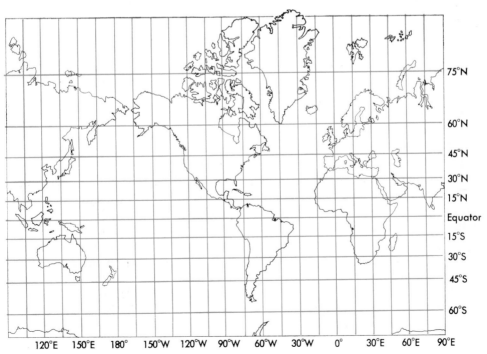

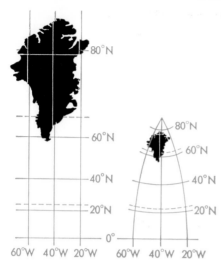

FIG. 9–3. This diagram illustrates how a Mercator projection distorts high-latitude regions.

the plane. One of the most useful variations of this method is the **gnomonic** (noh-*mon*-ik) **projection** such as that shown in Fig. 9–4. All but a very small area shown on the map is greatly distorted in size and shape. However, the gnomonic projection is useful in navigation since the great circle route, the shortest course between any two points, can be shown as a straight line. Thus a navigator may lay out the course as a straight line on a gnomonic map, then transfer the course to a Mercator map to find the correct directions. Gnomonic maps of the polar regions are called *polar projections.*

Projections based on a cone. Another possibility for transferring the features of the earth's curved surface to a surface which may be laid flat is the cone. A **conic projection** can be visualized as the result of placing a cone over a globe as shown in the upper part of Fig. 9–5. Only the region where the cone and the globe are in contact will be undistorted in the projection. However, this type of

projection is used to map relatively small areas which can be taken from the undistorted portion of the projection.

To show very limited areas, the **polyconic projection** is frequently used. This is equivalent to replacing the single cone with a series of cones, each of slightly different slope. The undistorted parts where each cone touches the globe are fitted together to form a continuous map. See Fig. 9–5, lower part.

Special types of maps. The degree and kind of information given on maps varies over a very wide range. *Political maps* show national and local boundaries clearly, and often indicate the relative size of towns and cities and their political importance. *Navigation charts* show routes and distances; *hydrographic maps* show depths of water and the topography of the sea floor. *Weather and climate maps* show these phenomena for a given period. *Geologic maps* show the distribution of rock formations, including data essential to the mining and petroleum industries.

TOPOGRAPHIC MAPS

Topography. For the earth scientist the most important features to be shown on a map are the landforms that shape the earth's surface. All the details that make up the surface features of the land are called its **topography,** and a map made especially to show these details is known as a *topographic map.* Natural features such as hills, valleys, lakes, plains, and streams are the most important details shown on these maps, but artificial features such as buildings, bridges, railroads, and roads may also be shown. Certain imaginary features such as political boundaries, parallels, and meridians may also be included.

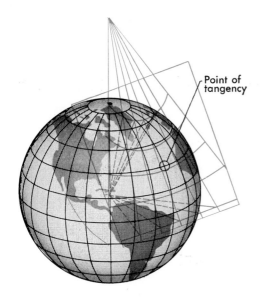

Point of tangency

FIG. 9–4. Left, the principle of gnomonic map projection. Below, an actual map produced by using this method of projection.

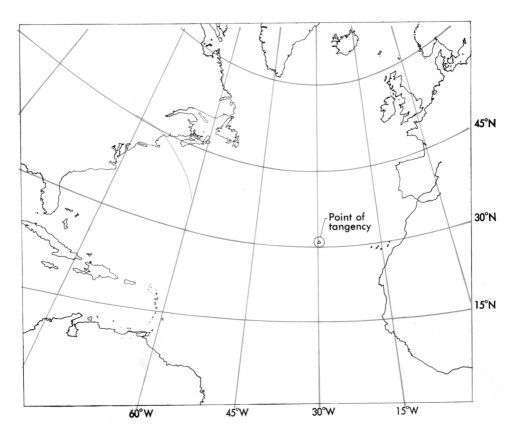

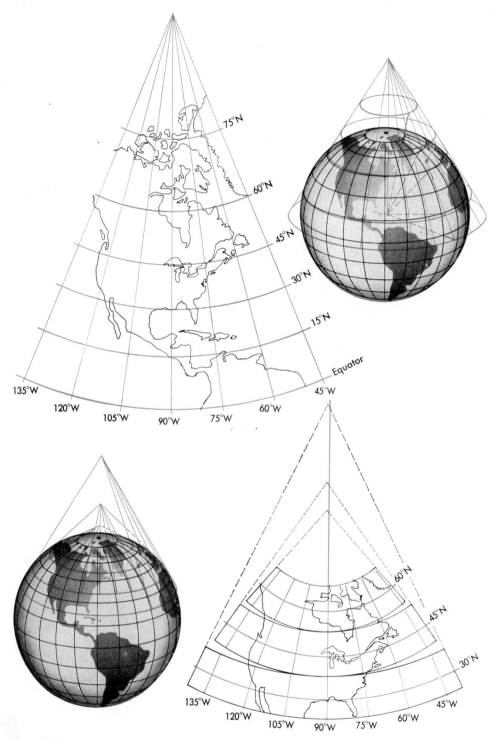

FIG. 9–5. The principle of conic map projection. Above, a simple conic projection; below, a polyconic projection.

FIG. 9–6. A relief map is one of the charts and maps used in naval operations. (*U.S. Navy*)

There are many ways of showing topography on a map, but the most useful method is one that employs symbols whose meaning is understood by those who read the map. For instance, some maps employ *hachures* (ha-*shyoorz* or *hash*-yoorz) to show mountains and hills. These are short straight lines drawn in the direction that water would take in flowing down the slopes. Often the steeper slopes are shown by heavier lines drawn close together while the gentler slopes are indicated by thin lines spaced farther apart. Color is also sometimes used to distinguish topographic features. Plains may be shown in green, low mountains in light brown, high mountains in dark brown, and bodies of water in blue. Sometimes shading is used on one side of a mountain range to give the illusion of three dimensions.

Relief. The irregularity (roughness of surface) of any area on the earth is called its *relief.* This is often expressed as a number giving the difference in elevation from the highest to the lowest points in the area. For example, the top of Mount Washington, New Hampshire, is the highest point in the state. It has an elevation of 6279 feet above sea level and rises above a plain which is itself 1200 feet above sea level. Thus its local relief is 6279 feet minus 1200 feet, or 5079 feet of relief.

The most commonly used topographic maps show the relief of an area by means of *contour lines.* Each line joins all points with the same elevation above sea level, thus giving an impression of the actual contour or shape of the land. The way contour lines show the relief of the earth's surface is illustrated in Fig.

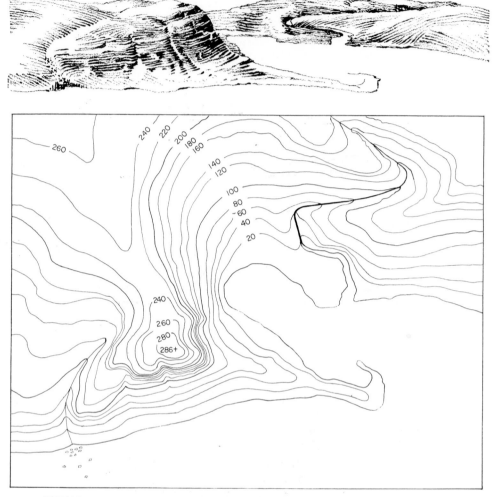

FIG. 9–7. The sketch above shows the relief of an imaginary shoreline; below is a topographic map of the area. Note that contour lines are closer on steep slopes; along river valleys they bend upstream. What is the contour interval used on this map?

9–7. The difference in elevation between neighboring contour lines is called the *contour interval;* the mapmaker chooses an interval suited to the relief of the map. A contour interval of ten or twenty feet is commonly used on topographic maps. In maps of very mountainous regions the contour interval may be as much as 50 or 100 feet in order to avoid crowding of the contour lines. In maps of flat areas it may be only one or two feet.

With a little practice it is possible to get a clear impression of the actual form of the land from a quick look at a topographic map. Where the contour lines are far apart and evenly spaced, the land is regular and slopes only slightly. If the contour lines are irregular the land is rough and if the contours are close together the slope is steep. Particular features such as hilltops, valleys, ridges, and cliffs can be recognized by their characteristic contours. Hilltops appear as a series of concentric closed curves, ridges as long parallel contours fairly close together, and cliffs as parallel contours very close together. Valleys of rivers and streams are easily identified, especially in hilly or mountainous areas, by the fact that contours bend *upstream* in crossing them.

The representation of such features as basins in plains and plateaus, or the craters at the tops of volcanic mountains may be somewhat confusing on a topographic map. The difficulty arises because these features appear as a series of concentric closed curves, just like hilltops. To avoid confusion, such areas are marked by *depression contours;* short hachures at right angles to the contours, drawn to indicate the slope of the depression. The appearance of some common landforms as represented by contour lines on a topographic map may be seen in Fig. 9–7.

United States Geological Survey maps. The governments of most countries make accurate topographic maps of their territory for military, scientific, and commercial use. The making of such maps is a slow and difficult process. Survey crews establish points of known position and elevation which are used with high-altitude airplane photographs to make the final map. In the United States, the Geological Survey has mapped more than half of the country and made the results available in the form of small-scale, detailed maps usually called *topographic sheets* or *quadrangles.* Each of these maps represents an area that covers 15 minutes of latitude and 15 min-

utes of longitude. The fractional scale for many of the topographic sheets is 1/62,500, which is very close to a scale of one inch to one mile (63,360 inches = 1 mile). Maps of the Geological Survey are all made by the method of polyconic projection.

During the past twenty years, the Geological Survey has gradually been replacing the 15-minute series of topographic sheets with a series covering only 7½ minutes of longitude and latitude. This series is published with fractional scales of 1/24,000 and 1/31,680.

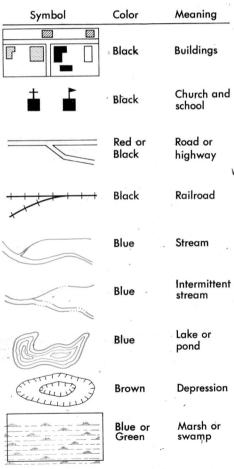

Symbol	Color	Meaning
	Black	Buildings
	Black	Church and school
	Red or Black	Road or highway
	Black	Railroad
	Blue	Stream
	Blue	Intermittent stream
	Blue	Lake or pond
	Brown	Depression
	Blue or Green	Marsh or swamp

FIG. 9–8. The symbols shown here are commonly used on topographic maps.

Other series of 30-minute maps with a scale of 1/125,000 are also published. For our western states and Alaska, one-degree quadrangles with a scale of 1/250,000 are also produced.

Many symbols are used on the topographic sheets to represent natural features and the works of man. The most commonly used symbols are shown in Fig. 9–7. The maps are printed in several colors, with the contour lines in brown. Every fifth contour, called the *index contour,* is printed slightly darker for emphasis. Water features (including snow and ice) are in blue, most of the works of man are in black, and red is used for highway classification, urban areas, and United States land lines. Areas covered with vegetation are often given a light green color.

In addition to the standard topographic maps, the Geological Survey publishes some maps in which relief is indicated by both contour lines and brown shading. The shading of the maps gives the appearance of a raised relief model of the area with the light coming from the northwest.

SUMMARY

SINCE the earth is a sphere, it is impossible to represent all or part of it on a flat surface without distortion. The smaller the area mapped, the less the distortion of shape or distance. Various map projections are employed to show the curved surface of the earth on a plane. The most common types of projections are Mercator, gnomonic, conic, and polyconic.

Directions on maps are shown in relation to parallels for east and west and meridians for north and south. On polar projections north or south is in the center. In order for navigators to use magnetic compasses to determine direction, a map must show magnetic declination so that the navigator can coordinate compass readings with map direction.

The ratio of distance on a map to the distance on the actual land surface is expressed as the map scale. This ratio may be given verbally, graphically, or by the representative fraction.

Topographic maps show the relief and physical features of a region by the use of contour lines and selected symbols. A contour line is a line drawn through points having the same elevation. The contour interval is the difference in elevation between two consecutive contour lines. On a topographic map steep terrain is indicated when contour lines are close together. Widely spaced contour lines show that the slope of the terrain is gentle. Standard symbols show topographic features other than differences in elevation.

The United States Geological Survey is the agency responsible for the topographic mapping of the United States. Principal quadrangle series are the 15- and 7½-minute series.

VOCABULARY REVIEW

Match the phrase in the left column with the correct word or phrase in the right column. *Do not write in this book.*

1. Shows ocean floor	a. scale
2. Shows rock strata	b. political map
3. Ratio of land distance to map distance	c. hydrographic map
4. Height relative to sea level	d. geologic map
5. Projection with least distortion	e. elevation
6. Shows local boundaries	f. relief
7. Irregularity of the earth's surface	g. gnomonic
8. Cylindrical projection	h. polyconic
9. Varies according to terrain	i. Mercator
	j. weather map
	k. contour interval

QUESTIONS · GROUP A

Decide whether these statements are true or false. Reword the false statements to make them true. *Do not write in this book.*

1. The only true representation of the whole earth is a globe.
2. On most maps north is at the top.
3. The Mercator projection shows great exaggeration of shape and distance at the equator.
4. Magnetic declination is used to adjust compass direction to true direction on a map.
5. The gnomonic projection shows a great circle route as a straight line.
6. If the distance between two points is 6.4 inches on a map with a scale of 1/63,360, the actual distance on the land is 12 miles 822 feet.
7. On maps of rugged, mountainous areas the contour interval selected might be 100 feet rather than 5 feet.
8. Directions east and west are indicated by parallels.
9. The greater the area mapped, the greater the distortion.
10. The Mercator projection is based on a cone.
11. On a topographic map a hilltop may be shown by a series of concentric circles.
12. Contour lines bend downstream when they cross rivers.

GROUP B

1. Using a contour interval of 20 feet and a scale of one inch to one mile, draw a contour map of an island that (*a*) is 5 miles from east to west and 4 miles from north to south (*b*) has a maximum elevation of 119 feet (*c*) is steepest on the east side (*d*) has a stream running into the ocean on the west shore, with its source at an elevation of 90 feet.

2. Tell one way in which a topographic map could be useful to each of the following: (*a*) farmer (*b*) hunter (*c*) aviator (*d*) highway engineer (*e*) army commander.
3. Make a south polar projection map showing parallels and meridians. Label the positions of north, south, east and west.
4. How many quadrangles from a 7½-minute series would represent the same area as one quadrangle from the 15-minute series? What is the advantage of the 7½-minute series?
5. What is the difference between map scale and contour interval?
6. Name five types of maps and list the features that make each useful. For what lines of work would each supply essential information?
7. Draw a graphic scale of one inch to illustrate each of the following 1/24,000, 1/31,680, 1/62,500, 1/125,000, 1/250,000. Divide each line into ½-mile sections.
8. Can contour lines cross each other? Explain the reason for your answer.
9. What are the five colors used on topographic maps of the Geological Survey? Give an example of a feature that would be shown in each one.
10. Why is a map of a small area generally more accurate than one of a large area?
11. What is meant by the term "map projection"? Give the basis for each type of projection and explain the advantages and disadvantages of each.
12. Why do certain maps show different magnetic declinations in different areas?

TOPOGRAPHIC SHEETS

Boothbay, Maine; Fort Collins, Colorado (15-minute series). *Introductory exercise in reading topographic maps.*

UNIT REVIEW QUESTIONS

1. Why do we believe that the interior of the earth is very dense?
2. How is the maximum age of the solar system estimated?
3. How long, on the average, can a star avoid an encounter with another star? How would such an encounter affect a solar system?
4. Why may radioactive determination of the age of the earth be short of the actual age?
5. Describe the most widely accepted theory to account for the formation of the solar system.
6. How do earthquakes supply information concerning the interior of the earth?
7. Discuss the meaning and value of the shadow zone.
8. Discuss in detail the three layers that compose the lithosphere of the earth.
9. What are some of the theories about the movements of the earth's crust?
10. What was the contribution of Mohorovicic to the science of geology?
11. What information could be obtained from drilling to the Moho? What would be the advantage of drilling this hole through the ocean floor?
12. Why do scientists believe that the earth's core is iron and nickel?

13. What would be the pressure at the center of the earth?
14. If the earth were to shrink, what would be the possible effect of this process on the pressure and temperature of the interior?
15. What is the length in miles of 20° of latitude?
16. What are the latitude and longitude of the following points: (*a*) north pole (*b*) south pole (*c*) intersection of the prime meridian with the equator (*d*) Tropic of Cancer (*e*) Tropic of Capricorn?
17. What is the purpose of the international date line?
18. How is longitude determined?
19. What is the agonic line? an isogonic line?
20. Why does magnetic declination vary from one point to another?
21. How is Polaris used by navigators in the northern hemisphere?
22. Why does the distance in miles between degrees of longitude decrease with distance north or south of the equator?
23. If the latitude of a point is 38° 45′ 30″ N, what is its distance from the equator? (Show all calculations.)
24. Why is a meridian not a great circle? Why can a meridian be used to calculate a great circle route?
25. Explain the possible causes for the periodic change in the magnetic declination of a particular location.
26. Why would a gyrocompass be necessary to the navigation of a nuclear submarine going under the north polar icecap?
27. Prove by calculation that 15° of longitude are equal to one hour.
28. Why does a chronometer have 24 numbers instead of 12 numbers?
29. Of what factors must a pilot be aware in order to navigate by dead reckoning?
30. What are some of the older ways of measuring the passing of time?
31. List the inclination of the various planets of the solar system.
32. If the inclination of the earth's axis were increased, how would this affect the seasons?
33. If the north end of the earth's axis always pointed away from the sun, how would the seasons be affected? How would day and night be affected?
34. Why does the warmest part of the summer come after the summer solstice?
35. How many times during the year do the vertical rays of the sun cross the equator? Explain.
36. Why is a sidereal year longer than a tropical year?
37. What have satellites shown about the shape of the earth?
38. Why is the sundial not completely reliable?
39. What is the term used to describe the difference between mean solar time and apparent solar time? Where would you find this information?
40. What are some advantages of daylight saving time?
41. What special features are shown by each of the following: (*a*) political map (*b*) contour map (*c*) weather map (*d*) hydrographic map (*e*) geologic map?
42. How is exact direction determined on a map?
43. Make a diagram to show a magnetic declination of 4° E.
44. Why might a navigator use more than one type of map projection in planning a course?

45. Distinguish between the members of the following pairs of terms: (*a*) contour line, contour interval (*b*) map scale, map distance (*c*) depression contour, index contour (*d*) elevation, topography.

46. Show how the following might appear on a contour map: (*a*) cemetery (*b*) school (*c*) church (*d*) swamp (*e*) trail (*f*) stream flowing south (*g*) orchard.

ACTIVITIES

1. (a) Make a collection of different solid objects of metal, plastic, wood, and similar materials. Make sure that they are all about the same size. Illustrate that they differ in density and specific gravity.

(b) Pour equal amounts of different liquids into separate test tubes. Show that although the volume is constant the density of the liquids varies.

2. Make a chart comparing the earth to the other planets with respect to size, density, atmosphere, rotation, revolution, etc.

3. Determine the latitude and longitude, to the nearest degree, for several major cities of the United States.

4. Construct a sundial and compare the time indicated by the sundial with standard time.

5. Sink a rod into the lawn and measure the length of the shadow three times a day for one month. Make a graph of your results and draw any conclusions possible.

6. Construct a sextant. Measure the sun's altitude every day for a month. Keep a graph to show the differences. Draw a conclusion.

7. Make models to show the positions of the sun and the earth at the solstices and the equinoxes.

8. Make a chart to show the time of sunrise and sunset for one month. Calculate the length of daylight and darkness. Draw a conclusion.

9. Using a terrestrial globe and a source of light show how the earth's movement produces night and day and the change of seasons.

10. Construct models to show the basis for different map projections.

11. Make a report on the procedure followed by the Geological Survey in making topographic maps.

12. Make clay models to show some of the major features shown on topographic maps.

13. From a topographic map of your community, make a plywood or cardboard model. Indicate the topography by varying the thickness of the material according to the contour interval.

14. From a topographic map of your community, determine the exact latitude and longitude of important buildings such as banks, churches, shopping centers, and schools.

15. Determine great circle routes from some of the major United States seaports to ports in Asia and Europe. In each case calculate the length of the trip. Do the same for air trips over the north pole.

FURTHER READING

THE PLANET EARTH. Editors of Scientific American, 1957. *Simon and Schuster, Inc., New York.*

THE EARTH. Harold Jeffreys, 1959. *Cambridge University Press, New York.*

THE EARTH WE LIVE ON. Ruth Moore, 1956. *Alfred A. Knopf, New York.*

THE EARTH BENEATH US. H. H. Swinnerton, 1956. *Little, Brown and Co., Boston.*

THE EARTH AND ITS MYSTERIES. G. W. Tyrell, 1953. *G. Bell and Sons, Ltd., London.*

★

EXPERIMENTS WITH AIRPLANE INSTRUMENTS. N. F. Beeler and F. M. Branley, 1953. *Thomas Y. Crowell Co., New York.*

THROUGH THE OVERCAST. A. Jordanoff, 1938. *Funk and Wagnalls Co., New York.*

PRIMER OF NAVIGATION. G. W. Mixter and R. O. Williams, 1952. *D. Van Nostrand Co., Inc., Princeton, N. J.*

ELEMENTS OF AERONAUTICS. F. Pope and A. S. Otis, 1941. *World Book Co., Yonkers, New York.*

AMERICAN AIR ALMANAC. Superintendent of Documents, *Washington 25, D. C.*

PRACTICAL AIR NAVIGATION. Superintendent of Documents, *Washington 25, D. C.*

PRINCIPLES OF AIR NAVIGATION. P. V. H. Weems, 1943. *McGraw-Hill Book Co., New York.*

★

OF TIME AND THE CALENDAR. E. Achelis, 1955. *Thomas Nelson and Sons, New York.*

STORY OF OUR CALENDAR. R. Brindze, 1949. *Vanguard Press, New York.*

★

THE STORY OF MAPS. L. A. Brown, 1949. *Little, Brown and Co., Boston.*

INTERPRETATION OF TOPOGRAPHIC AND GEOLOGIC MAPS. C. L. Dake and J. S. Brown, 1925. *McGraw-Hill Book Co., New York.*

WORLD MAPS AND GLOBES. I. Fisher and O. M. Miller, 1944. *Little, Brown and Co., Boston.*

THE GEOGRAPHICAL INTERPRETATION OF TOPOGRAPHICAL MAPS. A. Garnett, 1953. *George G. Harrap and Co., Ltd., London.*

ELEMENTARY TOPOGRAPHY AND MAP READING. S. L. Greitzer, 1944. *McGraw-Hill Book Co., New York.*

GENERAL CARTOGRAPHY. E. Raisz, 1948. *McGraw-Hill Book Co., New York.*

MAPPING THE WORLD: PORTRAIT OF MOTHER EARTH. E. Raisz, 1956. *Abelard-Schuman, Ltd., New York.*

ELEMENTARY MAP AND AERIAL PHOTOGRAPH READING (FM 21; 25). Superintendent of Documents, *Washington 25, D. C.*

THE evidence of modern science indicates that every object in the universe is composed of atoms; the earth is not an exception. Making up its substance are atoms of the 92 naturally-occurring chemical elements. Only a few of these elements are common, yet their combinations are many and varied. Most of these earth-making elements are also known to exist in the stars and other planets.

As yet, we know little about the composition of the stars, and even on the earth we can explore only the surface directly. Nevertheless, the chemistry of the materials close to the surface is rather precisely known to us. This unit deals first with some of the basic principles of chemistry by which the substances of the crust are formed. On this knowledge depends our understanding of the nature of minerals and rocks—the earth as we know it.

UNIT 3

THE MATERIALS OF THE EARTH'S SURFACE

CHAPTER 10

EARTH CHEMISTRY

In the two previous units we have looked at the earth as a member of the solar family, in its relations to the other occupants of space, and in its broad anatomy as a globe on whose surface men travel. Now, taking a closer look, we shall view the earth itself in more detail, as a theater where the forces of nature act to produce the conditions under which we and all other organisms must live.

But what is the earth itself? Is it the solid ground beneath our feet and the minerals we take out of the mines? Is it the water that falls as rain or snow, the rivers and oceans? Is it the air we breathe, whose movements and condi-

tion make our weather? The earth is all these things. Therefore, in describing earth processes, we frequently refer to three distinct phases of the earth's structure. Later units of this book will deal with the *hydrosphere,* the earth's envelope of water, and the *atmosphere,* its envelope of air. This unit and the three following are concerned with the *lithosphere* (stone-sphere), the solid material of the earth. These three subdivisions of the earth are actually very closely inter-related, but for convenience we shall discuss them separately.

The materials of the lithosphere are the rocks which underlie the landscape, making up the mountains, valleys,

VOCABULARY

Lithosphere. The solid part of the earth.

Element. A substance that cannot be changed by ordinary means into a simpler substance.

Atom. The smallest subdivision of an element.

Electrons. The electrically negative parts of atoms.

Protons. The electrically positive parts of atoms.

Neutrons. The electrically neutral parts of atoms.

Isotopes. Atoms of the same element which differ slightly from each other in weight.

Chemical compound. A substance formed by the combination of two or more different elements in a definite weight relationship.

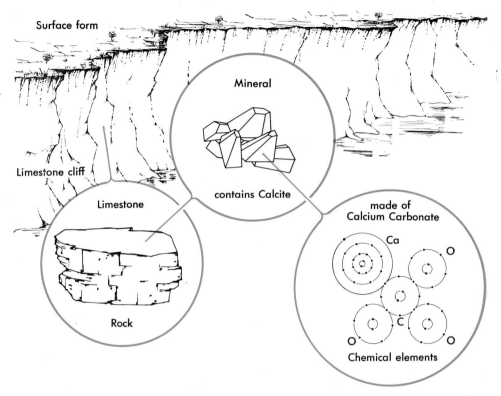

FIG. 10–1. A landform is composed of rocks, minerals, and elements.

plains, and plateaus, as well as the basins of lakes and oceans. The size and
shape of these features or *landforms* depend partly on the nature of the rocks
themselves. *Rocks* may be defined as
solid chemical and physical units covering any considerable portion of the
earth's surface. In Chapter 12 the different kinds of rocks will be described. For
the moment, let us note merely that
rocks are composed of one or more
minerals. Chapter 11 will deal with the
minerals and their properties. A close
look at the material of the lithosphere
must begin, however, with an understanding of the basic laws that govern
all matter. This chapter will discuss
some of these laws as they apply to the
various earth sciences.

ELEMENTS

The chemical elements. As rocks are
composed of minerals, so minerals, like
all matter, are composed of elements.
By definition, an *element* is a substance
that cannot be changed by ordinary
means into any other substance. The
smallest particle of an element that has
all the properties of that element is the
atom. Although they are extremely
small, the atoms of each element have a
definite mass or weight, which distinguish them from atoms of other elements. Each element is designated by a
symbol representing an atom of the element. Thus the symbol for one atom of
oxygen is O.

Although additional elements have

been created in the laboratory, 92 occur naturally on or in the earth. Of these, a few very common elements compose most of the earth's atmosphere, hydrosphere, and lithosphere. The elements, their chemical symbols, and their approximate percentages by weight are

Oxygen	O	49.5%
Silicon	Si	25.8%
Aluminum	Al	7.5%
Iron	Fe	4.7%
Calcium	Ca	3.4%
Sodium	Na	2.6%
Potassium	K	2.4%
Magnesium	Mg	1.9%
Hydrogen	H	0.9%
Titanium	Ti	0.6%

Five other elements, which account for less than half of one percent, are of great importance nevertheless because they are necessary to the existence of living organisms and through them enter into the composition of certain important rocks. They are

Carbon	C
Nitrogen	N
Sulfur	S
Phosphorus	P
Chlorine	Cl

Chemists recognize two major classes of elements, metals and nonmetals.

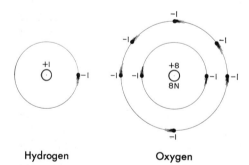

Hydrogen   Oxygen

FIG. 10–2. The atomic particles in two common elements.

Metals have a shiny luster such as that of silver. They conduct both heat and electricity readily and they reflect much of the light that comes to them. Most metals are *malleable;* they can be hammered into flat sheets. They are also *ductile;* they can be stretched into long thin wire. Some of the common metals are gold, copper, iron, aluminum, calcium, sodium, potassium, magnesium, zinc, lead, and the liquid mercury.

Nonmetals are usually poor conductors of heat and electricity and the solid ones are brittle rather than malleable or ductile. Typical examples of nonmetals are the gases oxygen, nitrogen, and chlorine, the liquid bromine and the solids carbon, sulfur, phosphorus.

A few elements have some of the properties of both the metals and the nonmetals. Arsenic and antimony are examples of this type, sometimes called the *metalloids.*

The structure of the atom. At one time, the atom, the building stone of the elements, was thought to be an indivisible body; now it is known to be composed of particles in a definite relation to each other. The particles are of several kinds. The nucleus or center of the atom has a positive electric charge, and is composed of *protons,* which are electrically positive, and *neutrons,* which have no charge. Surrounding the nucleus is a group of *electrons,* having a negative charge; these revolve around the nucleus in definite paths, or orbits. See Fig. 10–2.

All the particles in the atom have weight, and their total weight is equal to the weight of the atom. The weight of an electron, however, is so small in comparison to the weight of a proton or neutron that it can be considered zero. In speaking of the relative weights of atoms, we are usually referring to the

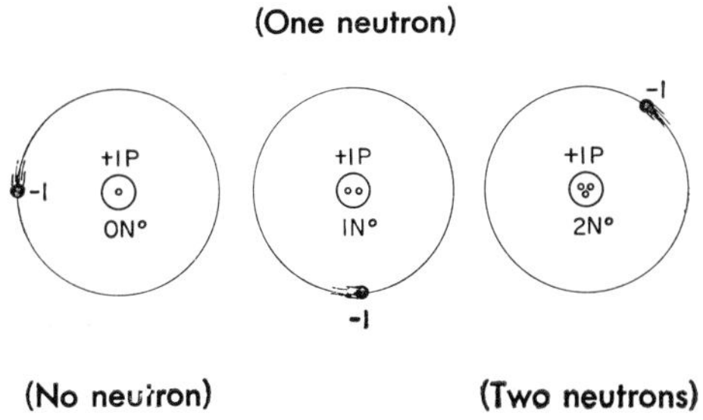

(One neutron)

+IP
ON°

+IP
IN°

+IP
2N°

-I

(No neutron)   (Two neutrons)

FIG. 10–3. The isotopes of hydrogen.

weights of the nuclei. Thus hydrogen atoms are the lightest atoms; they are exceptional in having normally one proton and no neutrons. Oxygen atoms are heavier, normally having eight protons and eight neutrons. We say "normally" because not all atoms of an element are identical; they may vary slightly in weight. These variations of an element, called *isotopes,* are atoms of the elements that have different numbers of neutrons in their nuclei. The isotopes of hydrogen are illustrated in Fig. 10–3.

In structure, the atoms shown in Fig. 10–2 are very similar. The difference

lies in the numbers of protons, neutrons, and electrons, and in the locations of the electrons in a varying number of orbits. In spite of the great variety of elements, the electrons, protons, or neutrons of one element are just like those of any other. The number of particles and their positions alone determine the different properties of the different elements, and also how they will react with one another in various combinations, as in the formation of minerals.

COMPOUNDS

The formation of chemical compounds. Elements exist under two conditions. They may be *free* or they may be united chemically in *chemical compounds.*

Free elements are chemically separate from other elements. Examples of elements often found in the free or *native* state are silver and sulfur. (See color plates, Chapter 11.) Large masses of

FIG. 10–4. Some metals are found in the free or native state. This huge mass of native copper, found in northern Michigan, weighs more than 600 pounds. (*Smithsonian Institution*)

these elements are sometimes found in earth deposits. More often, however, the free element is mixed with other substances. In a *mixture,* substances are physically mingled, just as several kinds of sand or grain may be. In such a mixture, although the individual particles may be minute, each particle may be identified within the mixture and removed from it by mechanical means.

A *solution* is a particular type of mixture, in which two or more substances are so thoroughly mixed that the particles of each substance are the smallest that can exist freely. In solutions of some chemical compounds, the particles, called *molecules,* are made up of two or more atoms of elements chemically combined in a fixed proportion by weight. Solutions of other compounds may consist of electrically charged particles, smaller than molecules, called *ions.* (Note that although the atom is the smallest unit of an element, separate atoms are rarely found in nature. The molecules of many elements consist of two atoms.) In a solution, a solid may be mixed with a liquid or a gas, a gas may be mixed with a liquid, or a solid may be mixed with another solid. There is a limit to the amount of one element or substance that may be dissolved in another under certain conditions. When this limit is reached, one of the substances escapes from the solution. Thus in carbonated beverages, gas is dissolved in liquid under pressure, during the bottling process. When the bottle cap is removed, some of the gas escapes from the liquid. Again, if sugar is dissolved in warm water, and the water is then cooled, some of the sugar may separate from the water in solid form. The sugar may also separate from the water if some of the water evaporates, since this means that the proportion of sugar to

Dissolved carbon dioxide under pressure.

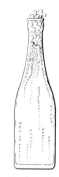

Carbon dioxide escapes when pressure is released.

Sodium nitrate dissolved in hot water.

Some of the sodium nitrate settles out when the solution is cooled.

FIG. 10–5. Changes in temperature and pressure affect the solubility of solids and gases in water.

water is changed. The behavior of solutions is an important factor in the formation of rocks and mineral deposits. For example, when the water of a lake evaporates, deposits of particular substances may form on the lake bottom; eventually these deposits may become rock.

Although many common substances are mixtures of free elements, chemical combinations form most of the materials we know. In a *chemical compound* elements are so associated, atom with atom, as to lose their individual identity. The individual elements cannot be recognized by their physical qualities, and they cannot be physically separated, like elements in a mixture. They form a new substance with entirely new properties. However, there is no change in weight during the formation of a compound. No atoms are lost. The weight of the compound is exactly equal to the sum of the weights of the elements as they were before they entered the combination.

A particular compound, wherever it is found, always consists of the same elements combined in exactly the same proportion and manner. In the compound water, the elements hydrogen and oxygen are united chemically in the proportion of two atoms of hydrogen to one atom of oxygen. See Fig. 10–6. Water is always formed when these two gases are mixed at the temperature at which hydrogen burns. At lower temperatures the gases may mingle indefinitely without chemical combination. In the pure compound water, however, neither gas can be identified by physical means. The smallest portion is still water because the two gases are united chemically.

The molecule of a compound, like the molecule of an element, is the smallest unit of the substance that can exist freely. Groups of atoms of two or more elements, chemically combined, compose a molecule of a compound. The *formula* of a compound is represented by the symbols of the atoms that make up the molecule. The number of atoms of each element is designated by a subscript numeral, as in H_2O, the formula for water. The formula does not indicate the arrangement of the atoms, although their relation to each other determines the nature of the compound. The formula does tell what elements are combined, and in what proportion.

During ordinary chemical reactions, only the electrons of atoms are involved; the nuclei are unchanged. The electrons in the outermost orbit are usually the

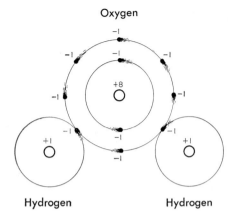

FIG. 10–6. A molecule of water is composed of two atoms of hydrogen and one atom of oxygen. The hydrogen atoms share their electrons with the oxygen atom.

only ones that take part in a chemical reaction. For example, in the formation of the compound sodium chloride, NaCl (common salt), the sodium atom loses the single electron from its outer orbit and becomes a sodium ion. At the same time the chlorine atom gains an electron in its outer orbit and becomes a chloride ion. This exchange of an electron is illustrated in Fig. 10–7. (It is important to realize that such diagrams, although helpful in the study of atomic structure and the formation of compounds, are not to be considered as true

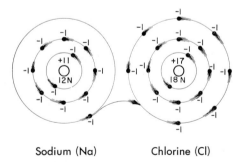

FIG. 10–7. The compound sodium chloride is formed by an electron exchange in the outer shell, as indicated by the arrow.

pictures of the actual appearance of atoms.)

Sodium chloride, as we have seen, is formed by the *exchange* of electrons. Many other compounds are formed in the same way, but this is not the only way in which atoms of elements may react to form molecules of compounds. In the case of water (H_2O), the reaction of hydrogen with oxygen results in the *sharing* of the single electrons of two hydrogen atoms with an atom of oxygen. This is shown in Fig. 10–6. Other compounds formed by the sharing of electrons between atoms include hydrogen chloride, ammonia, and methane.

Types of chemical compounds. In earth science, some types of compounds are particularly important. **Oxides,** *acids,* *bases,* and *salts* are four classes of compounds which are often met in the study of rocks and minerals.

1. Oxides are compounds which consist of an element combined with oxygen alone.

2. Acids are compounds which always contain hydrogen; their water solution turns blue litmus paper red.

3. Bases are compounds which always contain a combination of 1 atom of oxygen and 1 atom of hydrogen, called the hydroxide (OH) group; soluble hydroxides are called alkalies and turn red litmus blue.

4. Salts are compounds which contain a metal and a nonmetal or a nonmetallic group; most of them are neutral to litmus paper.

FIG. 10–8. Sulfides are another common type of compounds that occur in nature. This is a crystal of pyrite, chemically known as iron sulfide. (*American Iron and Steel Institute*)

The gas oxygen, being present in air, comes in contact with any surface to which air can penetrate, and therefore many different oxides are formed in nature. Oxidation may take place *directly*, through exposure of an element to oxygen, or *indirectly*, in the course of chemical reactions between compounds containing oxygen. The rusting of iron and the corrosion of copper are examples of direct oxidation; the oxides of nitrogen are usually by-products of reactions involving other nitrogen compounds. Some typical oxides are given in the table below.

Some elements form only one oxide, others form several. If there are two or more oxides, the number of oxygen atoms is often indicated in the name of the oxide. Thus

Carbon monoxide	CO
Carbon dioxide	CO_2
Sulfur dioxide	SO_2
Sulfur trioxide	SO_3

Most oxides which dissolve in water form either a base or an acid. The *metallic* oxides form compounds which are bases, since they contain the hydroxide group OH. Thus

$$CaO + H_2O \rightarrow Ca(OH)_2$$
Calcium hydroxide
$$MgO + H_2O \rightarrow Mg(OH)_2$$
Magnesium hydroxide
$$Na_2O + H_2O \rightarrow NaOH$$
Sodium hydroxide

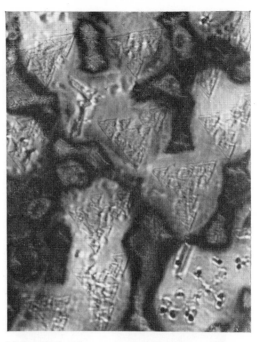

FIG. 10–9. Tiny crystals of copper oxide on the surface of a small piece of copper, magnified 1000 times. (*National Bureau of Standards*)

The *nonmetallic* oxides when dissolved in water produce acids. Thus

$$CO_2 + H_2O \rightarrow H_2CO_3 \qquad \text{carbonic acid}$$
$$SO_2 + H_2O \rightarrow H_2SO_3 \qquad \text{sulfurous acid}$$

Nonmetals may also combine with hydrogen alone to produce chemical compounds. For example, hydrogen reacts with chlorine and with sulfur, producing gases known respectively as hydrogen chloride and hydrogen sulfide.

$$H_2 + Cl_2 \rightarrow 2HCl$$
$$H_2 + S \rightarrow H_2S$$

TYPICAL OXIDES

Metallic		*Nonmetallic*	
Aluminum oxide	Al_2O_3	Silicon dioxide	SiO_2
Iron oxide	Fe_2O_3	Carbon dioxide	CO_2
Calcium oxide	CaO	Sulfur dioxide	SO_2
Sodium oxide	Na_2O	Sulfur trioxide	SO_3
Magnesium oxide	MgO	Hydrogen oxide	H_2O

FIG. 10–10. Sodium chloride is the salt most commonly found in the earth. These are the typical cubical crystals of this compound. (*Morton Salt Company*)

These gases may also be formed, in nature, by reactions of compounds containing hydrogen and chlorine or sulfur. Hydrogen chloride and hydrogen sulfide, dissolved in water, yield hydrochloric and hydrosulfuric acids, which react with some minerals, forming sulfides.

The "shorthand" statements shown here are called *chemical equations,* and are commonly used by chemists to show briefly what happens in a chemical reaction. The plus sign (+) on the left of the equation indicates that one substance reacts with another, and the arrow (→) means "produces" or "yields." If a plus sign appears on the right side of the equation it may be interpreted as "and."

Thus the equation for the reaction of calcium oxide with water

$$CaO + H_2O \rightarrow Ca(OH)_2$$

is interpreted as follows: calcium oxide reacts with water to produce calcium hydroxide. The equation for the reac-

FIG. 10–11. Crushed rock salt is moved by a conveyer belt in a salt mine deep below the surface of the earth. (*International Salt Company, Inc.*)

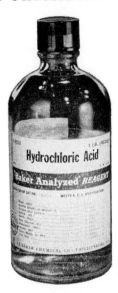

FIG. 10–12. Hydrochloric acid is one of the common acids used by chemists and geologists. (*J. T. Baker Chemical Co.*)

tion of sodium carbonate with calcium chloride

$$Na_2CO_3 + CaCl_2 \rightarrow CaCO_3 + 2NaCl$$

may be read: sodium carbonate reacts with calcium chloride, yielding calcium carbonate and sodium chloride. This explanation is necessarily brief, but it is sufficient for the chemical equations used in this book. If you wish to go further into the writing of such equations, it would be helpful to refer to a high school chemistry textbook.

In the formulas for the compounds discussed on these pages, note the hydroxide group OH in the bases and the groups CO_3 and SO_3 in the acids. These groups of atoms act as a single atom when they enter into chemical combinations. Such groups are called *radicals.* Thus, CO_3 is the carbonate radical. A radical usually remains intact throughout any series of chemical reactions in which it is involved. For example, calcium carbonate is the result of the reac-

tion of sodium carbonate and calcium chloride:

$$Na_2CO_3 + CaCl_2 \rightarrow CaCO_3 + 2NaCl$$

Other typical radicals are

ammonium	(NH_4)
sulfate	(SO_4)
phosphate	(PO_4)
bicarbonate	(HCO_3)
chlorate	(ClO_3)

When an acid and a base react with each other, a salt and water are formed. Thus

$$Ca(OH)_2 + H_2SO_4 \rightarrow 2H_2O + CaSO_4$$
calcium hydroxide · sulfuric acid · water · calcium sulfate, a salt

$$KOH + HCl \rightarrow H_2O + KCl$$
potassium hydroxide · hydrochloric acid · water · potassium chloride, a salt

Calcium sulfate contains a metal, calcium, plus the nonmetallic sulfate radical; potassium chloride contains a metal, potassium, and the nonmetal chlorine from the hydrochloric acid. In each case, the metallic element in the base has a greater attraction for the radical of the acid than for the hydroxide radical. The hydrogen of the acid combines with the OH group to form water.

Salts may also be produced directly by the action of acids upon metals, the hydrogen of the acid being set free as a gas. Thus

$$Zn + H_2SO_4 \rightarrow H_2 + ZnSO_4$$
zinc · sulfuric acid · zinc sulfate

The laws by which elements enter into certain chemical combinations rather than others are determined by the atomic structure of the individual elements. This subject is too complex to

$$2H_2 + O_2 \rightarrow 2H_2O$$

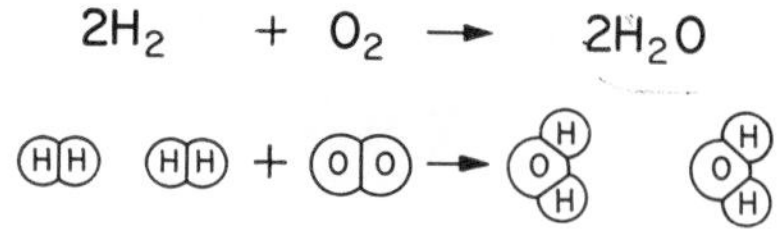

FIG. 10–14. The formation of a chemical compound by synthesis.

1. Synthesis is the formation of a compound by a combination of elements or more simple compounds. When hydrogen burns, hydrogen oxide, or water, forms. When heated, copper joins with oxygen in the air to form copper oxide, the mineral *cuprite*. Iron sulfide (FeS_2), called *pyrite,* is another example of a mineral that is a compound formed from two elements. A compound resulting from the synthesis of compounds is calcium hydroxide, or slaked lime, which is used in whitewash, plaster, and mortar. It is formed when calcium oxide (quicklime) combines with water:

$$CaO + H_2O \rightarrow Ca(OH)_2$$

2. Decomposition is the breaking down of a compound into elements or simpler compounds. Water may be decomposed into the gases hydrogen and oxygen by an electric current passed through it. By a similar process, magnesium metal is obtained from underground salt brine wells. Evaporation of the water gives dry magnesium chloride; this is decomposed to yield the free metal and chlorine gas. Thus compounds are chemically broken down into separate elements.

Decomposition of compounds into simpler compounds may also occur naturally. Unusual formations in limestone caverns are formed by the decomposition of calcium bicarbonate. This compound is produced when water containing dissolved carbon dioxide (carbonic

FIG. 10–13. Synthetic chemical reactions also occur in living things. The small knobs on the roots of these clover plants are nodules containing certain types of bacteria that can take the element nitrogen from the air and convert it into nitrogen compounds by combining it with other elements. This process enriches the soil. (*U. S. Dept. of Agriculture*)

discuss here. We are interested primarily in the general effects of chemical reactions, rather than the reasons why these reactions occur.

Types of chemical reactions. In the formation of the wide variety of minerals, totaling about 1800 different kinds, many chemical changes in the original earth crust must have taken place. Such changes are continually occurring in the course of earth processes. The elements and compounds of the earth's crust enter into chemical reactions of four common types.

$$MgCl_2 \longrightarrow Mg + Cl_2$$

$$Ca(HCO_3)_2 \rightarrow CaCO_3 + H_2O + CO_2$$

FIG. 10–15. The chemical process called decomposition.

acid) seeps through layers of carbonate rocks. When the calcium bicarbonate solution drips into a cave or cavern, the compound decomposes as the water evaporates, leaving calcium carbonate deposits in various interesting forms. The reaction during this process is given in the following chemical equation:

Decomposition is the chemical opposite of synthesis.

3. Single replacement or *substitution* is the replacement of one element by another in a compound. The valuable element bromine is obtained from sea water by a single replacement process. Chlorine gas is bubbled through the water, which contains bromine in such compounds as sodium bromide. The chlorine replaces the bromine in these compounds, liberating the bromine. The equation is

$$2NaBr + Cl_2 \rightarrow 2NaCl + Br_2$$

FIG. 10–16. Decomposition reactions have many industrial applications. In these huge ovens, soft coal is decomposed to produce coke, a form of the element carbon. (*American Iron and Steel Institute*)

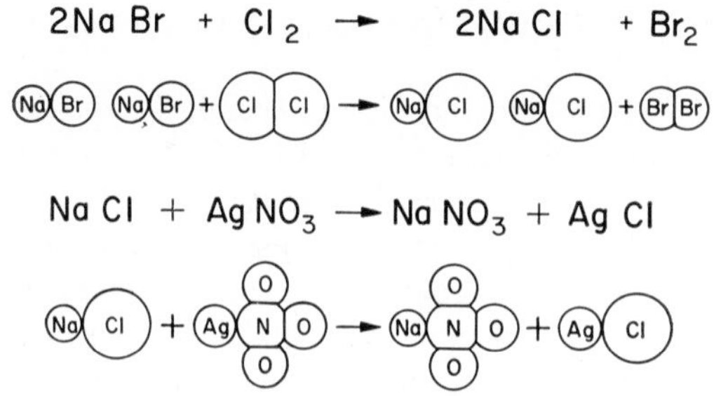

2Na Br + Cl 2 → 2Na Cl + Br2
Na Br Na Br + Cl Cl → Na Cl Na Cl + Br Br
Na Cl + Ag NO3 → Na NO3 + Ag Cl
Na Cl + Ag N O O O → Na N O O O + Ag Cl

FIG. 10–17. In simple replacement or substitution reactions, one element takes the place of another in a compound. In double replacement, there is an exchange of ions between two compounds.

When iron is placed in sulfuric acid, hydrogen gas bubbles out; the iron replaces the hydrogen, uniting with the sulfate radical to form iron sulfate.

$$Fe + H_2SO_4 \rightarrow H_2 + FeSO_4$$

4. Double replacement is the exchange of parts of two compounds to form two new compounds. Sodium chloride reacts with silver nitrate to form sodium nitrate and silver chloride.

$$NaCl + AgNO_3 \rightarrow NaNO_3 + AgCl$$

Double replacement occurs in a simple test used to identify carbonate minerals. When a drop of dilute hydrochloric acid is put on such minerals, calcium chloride and a weak acid (carbonic acid) are formed. The decomposition of the weak acid yields carbon dioxide and water.

$$CaCO_3 + 2HCl \rightarrow CaCl_2 + H_2CO_3$$
$$H_2CO_3 \rightarrow CO_2 + H_2O$$

The four types of chemical reactions occur in nature under the influence of environmental conditions, such as changes in temperature and pressure, in the amount of air and water present, and in the particular elements and compounds that come into contact. Compounds may form, then break down into others, then form new compounds that are more stable; that is, less easily broken down by changes in conditions.

FIG. 10–18. In this huge plant, bromine is obtained from sea water by bubbling chlorine through the water. This is a commercial application of a single replacement or substitution reaction. (*Dow Chemical Company*)

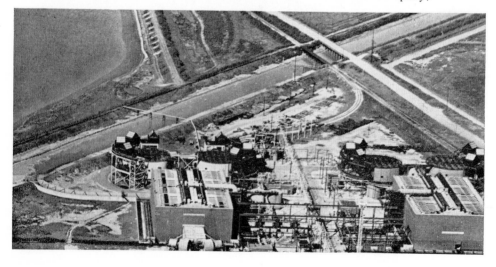

FIG. 10–19. A double replacement reaction. The white precipitate at the left is barium sulfate, formed by the reaction of barium chloride with sodium sulfate (being poured from the beaker). The formation of such a precipitate which is not soluble in hydrochloric acid is a test for sulfate compounds.

SUMMARY

THE earth is composed of the lithosphere, hydrosphere, and atmosphere. All matter is made up of elements. Ordinary chemical or physical processes cannot change elements into simpler substances. Over 100 elements are known to science but only 92 occur naturally. Most of the earth's crust is composed of eight elements, the most abundant of which are silicon and oxygen. The element's individual properties classify it as a metal, nonmetal, or metalloid.

Atoms are composed of protons, neutrons, and electrons. The chemical union of atoms forms compounds, which are generally composed of small units called molecules. A formula gives the elements in a compound and their proportions.

The sharing or exchanging of electrons between atoms forms compounds. Oxides, acids, bases, and salts are important compounds in the study of earth science.

VOCABULARY REVIEW

Match the word or phrase in the left column with the correct word in the right column. *Do not write in this book.*

1. Water
2. Air
3. Rocks and minerals
4. Mixture of minerals
5. Cannot be changed into a simpler substance by ordinary means
6. Smallest part of an element
7. Shiny luster
8. Poor conductor of heat
9. Variation in number of neutrons
10. Smallest division of a compound
11. Oxygen and one other element
12. Turns litmus red
13. (OH) group
14. Formed from an acid and a base

a. metal
b. lithosphere
c. molecule
d. nonmetal
e. isotope
f. radical
g. element
h. oxide
i. base
j. synthesis
k. salt
l. atom
m. rock
n. atmosphere
o. acid
p. hydrosphere

QUESTIONS · GROUP A

In each of the following groups of terms, three are related in some way and one is not. Select the unrelated term and give a reason why you believe it is not related. *Do not write in this book.*

1. (*a*) O (*b*) Si (*c*) Na (*d*) Cl
2. (*a*) C (*b*) N (*c*) Ca (*d*) S
3. (*a*) landforms (*b*) oceans (*c*) plains (*d*) plateaus
4. (*a*) alkali (*b*) $Ca(OH)_2$ (*c*) KCl (*d*) turns litmus blue
5. (*a*) ductile (*b*) brittle (*c*) malleable (*d*) conducts electricity
6. (*a*) O (*b*) N (*c*) Ca (*d*) S
7. (*a*) iron (*b*) arsenic (*c*) antimony (*d*) metalloid
8. (*a*) H_2S (*b*) HCl (*c*) NaOH (*d*) H_2SO_4
9. (*a*) Al_2O_3 (*b*) CO_2 (*c*) Na_2O (*d*) MgO
10. (*a*) proton (*b*) argon (*c*) electron (*d*) neutron

Decide whether these statements are true or false. Reword the false statements to make them true. *Do not write in this book.*

11. A nonmetal is rather brittle and a good conductor of heat.
12. The electron has a positive charge.
13. Soluble hydroxides are called bases.
14. Isotopes are atoms of different elements that have the same weight.
15. The particles that combine to form a compound are neutrons.

16. The weight of an atom is mainly due to the weight of the electrons and the protons.
17. The particles that are arranged in regular orbits or shells around the atomic nucleus are electrons.
18. Acids are compounds which always contain nitrogen.
19. Over 100 elements occur naturally.
20. The formula for common salt, NaCl, indicates a compound composed of a metal and a gas.
21. A solution is a type of mixture.
22. The formula H_2O means that water contains 2 atoms of oxygen and 1 atom of hydrogen.
23. The term trioxide indicates the presence of 3 atoms of oxygen in a compound.
24. An acid is produced when a metallic oxide is dissolved in water.
25. A radical usually changes in composition during a chemical reaction.

GROUP B

1. What are the properties of a salt? Why does a salt always contain a metal and a nonmetal?
2. Explain how oxidation takes place.
3. If given a series of unknown compounds, how could you classify them as acids, bases, or salts?
4. Why would chemical reactions be impossible if electrons did not exist in the outer shells of atoms?
5. How could you distinguish a metal from a nonmetal?
6. What is the chemical definition of a radical? Give the names, formulas, and elements present in four common radicals.
7. Make diagrams of four atoms, showing the neutrons, protons, and electrons.
8. How can a mixture be distinguished from a compound?
9. Dissolve water in sugar and taste it. Allow it to stand 24 hours and taste it again. Is it sweeter? Explain.
10. What is the difference in the bonding of the atoms in the compounds of sodium chloride and hydrogen chloride?
11. Describe a procedure to follow in producing calcium hydroxide from some other compound.
12. Describe a method of producing carbonic acid.
13. How is quicklime produced? What type of chemical reaction is illustrated?
14. How is limestone formed? What type of chemical reaction is illustrated?
15. How is bromine obtained? What chemical reaction is illustrated?
16. How are carbonate minerals most easily identified? What chemical reaction takes place in this chemical test?

CHAPTER 11

[handwritten notes in top margin: the type of rock formed by the solidification of magma. / Sed. / Met. / Ig. / Amphibole / A char. of Met. Rock]

MINERALS

FROM the elements and compounds described in Chapter 10 to the rocks of the lithosphere is not a long jump. Different theories of the origin of the earth suppose that the crust of the planet solidified from a whirling mass of gases, the elements in gaseous form that can now be identified in the sun and stars. Where rocks are formed from volcanic materials at the surface of the earth, we can see the solidification process going on. Although gases are present in the hot material that pours from the volcano, most of the elements and compounds have cooled to the liquid state. As the gases escape and the liquid hardens, minerals are formed from the elements and compounds contained in the molten material. These minerals, closely bound together in great masses, are rock.

Rocks that are formed from molten material originating far beneath the earth's surface are called *igneous* rocks.

VOCABULARY

Magma. Molten rock materials below the earth's surface.

Igneous rocks. Those formed by the solidification of magma.

Sedimentary rocks. Those formed in layers from materials deposited by water, wind, ice, or other agents.

Metamorphic rocks. Rocks that have been changed from their original form by great heat and pressure.

Minerals. Chemical compounds or uncombined elements found in rocks.

Specific gravity. A number that compares the density of a substance with that of water.

Quartz. A common mineral composed of silicon dioxide.

Feldspars. A group of common minerals containing aluminum, silicon, and oxygen.

Amphiboles (*am*-fi-bohlz). A group of common minerals containing silicon, calcium, magnesium, iron, and oxygen.

Micas. A group of common minerals containing the oxides of aluminum and silicon in combination with other metals.

Most often, the molten material or *magma* cools slowly under layers of rock beneath the earth's surface, forming *intrusive* igneous rocks. Sometimes the magma flows out on the surface from a volcano or from a large fracture in the earth's crust. Rocks formed by this process are called *extrusive* igneous rocks. Intrusive rocks may appear at the earth's surface when overlying layers are removed by erosion or by movements of the crust. Any igneous rock that is exposed on the surface is continuously weathered and eroded, supplying the material for **sedimentary rocks.** Most sedimentary rocks are made up of the products of disintegration and decomposition of other rocks, deposited in layers by the action of water, ice, wind, chemical changes, and the activities of living things. Once formed, both igneous and sedimentary rocks, covered by other rocks to great depth, may be changed by heat and pressure. The change may be purely physical, so that the original minerals are merely rearranged in the rock, or it may be chemical, so that new minerals are formed. Rocks that have been changed in this way, or *metamorphosed*, are **metamorphic** rocks. These rocks may themselves be further metamorphosed in later periods of heat and pressure.

The conditions of rock formation are of course the conditions of mineral formation, since the rocks are made of minerals. The differences between one mineral and another are the result of differences in chemical composition and the conditions of formation of the rock of which the mineral is a part.

COMMON MINERAL TYPES

The mineral composition of granite. The most important material on the earth's surface is the igneous rock granite, for this is the fundamental rock of the continents. Most of the continental

FIG. 11–1. A granite mass—Liberty Cap at Yosemite. (*National Park Service*)

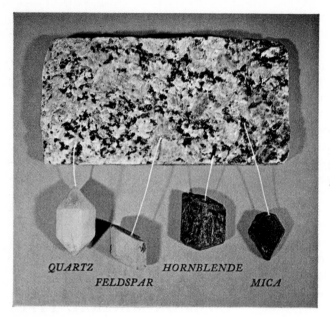

FIG. 11–2. A piece of granite is composed of minerals representing four mineral groups. (*B. M. Shaub*)

QUARTZ   HORNBLENDE
FELDSPAR   MICA

material is granite or sedimentary rocks formed from the breakdown of granite through natural processes. Minerals that contain most of the known chemical elements are scattered in small amounts through the granitic rocks.

Although granite is a very durable rock that does not yield easily to weathering or other natural processes, in time it does break down. The elements or compounds that compose it then enter into new combinations. Many of the familiar minerals and rocks were derived from granite.

The great variety of minerals, although individually important and interesting for their beauty and use to man, make up a very small proportion of the total granite mass. Granite is composed almost entirely of four mineral groups, consisting largely of the chemical elements in the list on page 136. The mineral groups are *quartz*, the *feldspars*, the *amphiboles*, and the *micas*. See Fig. 11–2. The special characteristics of these major rock-forming miner-

als will be given later in this chapter. A general description of each will serve at this point.

Quartz is the most enduring, the most nearly everlasting common substance in all nature. It is very slowly decomposed by weathering and is only slightly soluble in alkaline water. When all of the other minerals of granite have crumbled away, quartz remains in the debris as sand particles. Quartz is therefore one of the most universal minerals, found in all parts of the world.

Quartz is a compound of silicon and oxygen, SiO_2 (silicon dioxide), and is found in many forms. Crystals of quartz range in size from microscopic particles to huge blocks weighing a ton or more. It is sometimes colorless, although it may be colored by the inclusion of impurities (small amounts of other elements). *Sandstones* are sedimentary rocks which consist largely of small quartz grains; a metamorphic quartz rock is *quartzite*.

The *feldspars* are a group of related

minerals which together are far more common than quartz; however, the different types vary greatly and are considered separate minerals. Feldspars contain mostly aluminum, silicon, and oxygen. Two of them, the *orthoclase* and *microcline* feldspars, also contain potassium, while *plagioclase* (*play*-jee-oh-klase) feldspars contain sodium, calcium, or both. The feldspars occur in many colors, mostly pale or dull. They yield easily to weathering and form various clay minerals.

The *amphiboles* all contain silicon, calcium, magnesium, iron, and oxygen. The most common form, *hornblende*, also contains aluminum. It is dark green or black. Hornblende decomposes by weathering to form clays.

The *micas* occur most often in two main forms: *muscovite*, which is colorless or pale greenish or brownish, and *biotite*, which is black or dark brown. Micas are notable for the fact that they split easily into thin sheets or flakes; they are composed of oxides of aluminum and silicon, with other metals. These minerals also weather to produce clays.

In addition to the major rock-forming minerals, smaller amounts of other minerals are found in the rocks. Certain minerals are frequently found together in particular kinds of rock. This is known as mineral association, and is often an aid to the identification of particular specimens.

IDENTIFICATION OF MINERALS

Problems of identification. Before a scientist can claim to have discovered a new mineral, he must first decide whether it *is* one; that is, whether it comes under the strict classification of minerals as distinguished from other substances formed of elements and compounds. Minerals are single elements or compounds found naturally in the crust of the earth. A man-made compound, no matter how like a compound found naturally, is not a mineral. Minerals are solids; they normally have a fixed chemical composition, and are usually made up of orderly arrangements of atoms with definite crystal structure. They are inorganic (not derived from living things). A pearl, though identical in its chemical composition and structure to the mineral aragonite, is not considered

FIG. 11–3. Quartz crystals from Hot Springs, Arkansas. (*B. M. Shaub*)

a mineral because it is the product of a living organism, the oyster.

By this definition, coal is classed as a rock rather than a mineral, because it is organic, formed from plant materials. Its chemical composition also varies depending on the extent of the chemical changes it has undergone. Coal is chemically a mixture rather than a compound.

To identify the minerals in a rock specimen is not an easy task. Only rarely can a mineral be identified by a single physical or chemical property. A specimen must be examined from as many points of view as possible. Some physical properties are constant but others are variable, and great care is necessary in drawing conclusions. Intricate optical tests are among the best means of identifying some minerals, but such tests require expensive laboratory equipment operated by specialists. Simpler physical and chemical methods can be used to identify most common minerals and those of economic importance.

Visible characteristics of minerals. The first step in identification is to observe the physical characteristics of the mineral, that is, its appearance and visible structure.

1. Color is the most obvious characteristic. The color of the freshly broken surface of some minerals is a reliable clue to their identification. See the color plates in Chapter 11. The color of the surface tarnish of minerals with a metallic luster should also be taken into account. Thus pyrite, one of the iron minerals, is a pale brass-yellow on a fresh surface, and a darker yellow when tarnished. Other minerals vary considerably in color because they contain impurities. Small traces of certain elements in a colorless mineral like quartz can change its normal color dramatically to produce a variety of color types. The

colorless mineral corundum (Al_2O_3) made red by traces of chromium is known as ruby, whereas traces of iron and titanium cause it to be colored blue, in which case it is called sapphire. This color variation due to traces of impurities can be confusing to the inexperienced mineralogist.

2. Streak is the color of a thin layer of the finely powdered mineral. Rubbing the mineral against a *streak plate* of unglazed porcelain, such as the back of a tile, is the usual method of obtaining the streak. The streak of nonmetallic minerals is either colorless or very light. Metallic minerals often have a dark streak which may differ from the color of the mineral and thus be an important clue in identification. For example, the streak of pyrite is black.

3. Luster is a property determined by the ability of a mineral to reflect, refract (bend), or absorb light falling on its surface. Various terms are used to describe the general types of luster. These include *dull, pearly, resinous, silky, earthy, metallic, glassy* or *vitreous,* and *brilliant* or *adamantine* (diamondlike).

4. Crystal form is significant because it provides a clue to the internal structure of the mineral. Most minerals are *crystalline,* that is, the atoms, ions, or molecules are arranged in definite geometric patterns. As living things grow by the division of cells, nonliving things grow by the addition of molecules around a center. This is known as growth by *accretion.* Under proper conditions of formation, crystalline materials develop exceedingly beautiful geometric forms called *crystals.* Some crystals are so perfectly shaped that they seem to have been cut and polished by man rather than to have grown naturally by accretion.

Analysis shows that minerals crystal-

Garnet

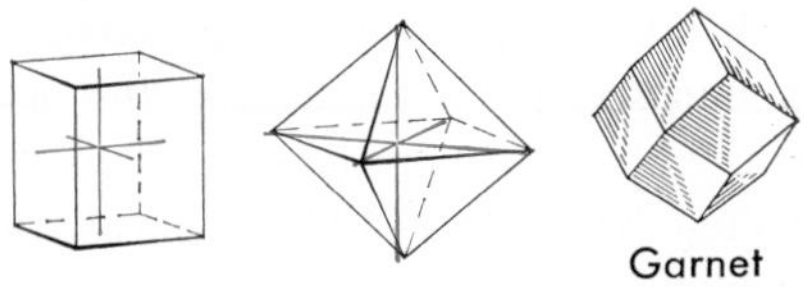

Sulfur

Isometric or Cubic System: Three axes of equal length intersect at 90° angles. Ex. galena, pyrite, halite.

Orthorhombic System: Three axes of different lengths intersect at 90° angles. Ex. olivine, topaz.

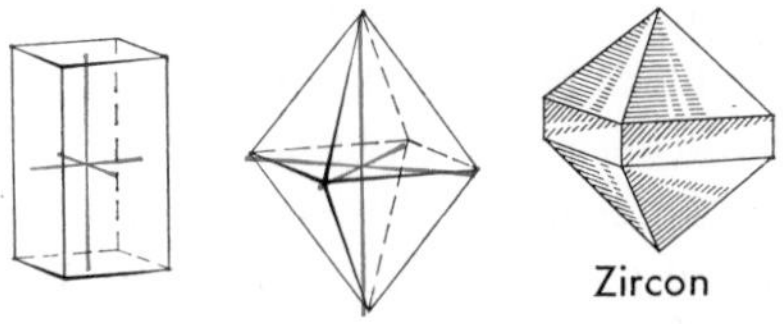

Zircon

Orthoclase   Amphibole

Tetragonal System: Three axes intersect at 90° angles. The two horizontal axes are of equal length. The vertical axis is longer or shorter than the horizontal axes. Ex. rutile, cassiterite, chalcopyrite.

Monoclinic System: Of three axes of different lengths, two intersect at 90° angles. The third axis is oblique to the others. Ex. gypsum, micas, augite, cryolite, kaolinite.

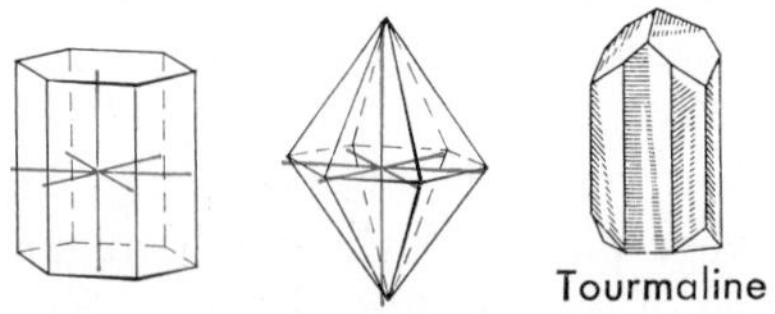

Tourmaline

Rhodonite   Chalcanthite

Hexagonal System: Of the four axes, the three horizontal axes intersect at 60° angles. The vertical axis is longer or shorter. Ex. quartz, calcite, apatite, hematite.

Triclinic System: The three axes are of unequal length and are oblique to one another. Ex. plagioclase feldspars, including albite and labradorite, turquoise.

FIG. 11–4. The six basic crystal systems.

lize according to six basic systems. As illustrated in Fig. 11–4, the systems may be outlined in terms of the arrangement of the axes, imaginary lines showing the direction in which the atoms or molecules arrange themselves. Thus, molecules aligned along two axes of equal length at right angles to each other may form a square; they may also form a double triangle if they are arranged in pyramid form. If a third axis is added, of equal length, and perpendicular to the plane of the square, the result is a solid form, either a cube or a double pyramid.

Besides the basic, simple forms shown

in Fig. 11–4, a variety of combined forms exist within each system. Since the axes are of unequal length in most systems, variations in proportion are many. Irregularities in the conditions of growth may also affect the shape of the crystal.

Crystallography, the study of crystals, is a highly specialized branch of mineralogy. The experienced mineralogist can get enough basic data from fragments of crystals to identify the crystal form with fair certainty. The variety of crystal forms is evident in the illustrations of common minerals in the color plates.

FIG. 11–5. Cleavage in minerals. Top to bottom: cubic, rhombohedral, basal.

Most minerals do not commonly occur in the form of distinct crystals. They often form complex masses of crystals which may vary from coarse-grained to submicroscopic; in some cases the crystalline nature of the mineral can only be detected with x-rays. These masses are irregular or rounded in a variety of forms resembling grapes, peas, fish-eggs, or the like, depending on their size. A few minerals are not crystalline; they have no orderly arrangement of the molecules. These minerals are described as *amorphous* or sometimes *massive*.

5. *Cleavage* and *fracture* also indicate the structure of the mineral. Some minerals, as for example the micas, split easily along certain planes, which may be crystal faces. They are said to have *poor, fair, good, perfect,* or *eminent* cleavage. The various types of cleavage are described according to the number and direction of the cleavage planes. See Fig. 11–5.

Most minerals do not break along cleavage planes, but fracture irregularly in one of several different ways. Besides revealing the true color of the mineral, these fractures may be in themselves an aid to identification. Some types of fracture are *conchoidal* (shell-like), *fibrous* or *splintery, irregular,* and *earthy*. See Fig. 11–6.

FIG. 11–6. Fracture. Left, conchoidal fracture in obsidian. Right, earthy fracture in yellow ocher, an impure form of limonite. (*American Museum of Natural History and John King*)

FIG. 11–7. Talc is the softest mineral in Mohs' scale. (*B. A. Shaub*)

Hardness. Observation of some physical qualities of minerals requires testing or measurement. We cannot determine the hardness of a mineral merely by looking at it. Because of the many possible gradations in hardness, we need a system or scale by which the hardness of a specimen can be measured. *Hardness* of a mineral is defined as its resistance to abrasion (scratching). Certain minerals are used as standards of comparison for all others. The scale of hardness, called Mohs' Scale, consists of ten minerals, given in the table below, and ranging from talc, which is one of the softest minerals, to diamond, the hardest of all minerals.

To test hardness, find out which of the minerals in the scale the unknown specimen can scratch and which it cannot scratch. For example, gypsum is harder than talc but softer than calcite. Any mineral which scratches gypsum

but does not scratch calcite has a hardness of Mohs' Scale between 2 and 3.

The following standards of hardness are useful additions to the scale:

Fingernail	2.5
Penny	3
Glass or knife blade	5.5
Steel file	6.5

Care must be used in testing hardness. A surface which is weathered, powdery, or splintery may appear to be scratched by a mineral much softer than itself. A soft mineral may make a mark on a harder one that can be mistaken for a scratch. Such a mark can be rubbed off, while a true scratch cannot. It is wise to test both ways, that is, by trying the known mineral on the unknown one, as well as the reverse.

Kyanite, an aluminum mineral, is remarkable because of its extreme variation in hardness. All minerals vary somewhat in hardness, depending on the direction in which they are scratched, but in most cases the differences are too slight to notice. Kyanite is a striking exception. It can be readily scratched with a knife parallel to the length of the elongated crystal, but the same knife blade does not mark the surface when

MOHS' SCALE

1. Talc	6. Orthoclase
2. Gypsum	7. Quartz
3. Calcite	8. Topaz
4. Fluorite	9. Corundum
5. Apatite	10. Diamond

scratched across it in other directions. Hardness is determined by the arrangement of atoms or other particles within the molecules of a substance, and is not simply dependent on the elements present. For example, diamond and graphite are both chemically pure carbon, but the former is the hardest known natural material whereas the latter is one of the softest.

Specific gravity. The relative weights of various minerals can be judged by weighing or handling pieces of roughly the same size (hefting). A more precise measurement of this property, which helps in the identification of a mineral, is the measurement of its *specific gravity.* The specific gravity of a substance is expressed as a number that tells how many times heavier a given volume of the substance is than an equal volume of water. The specific gravity of minerals can usually be determined quite simply. The specimen is first weighed carefully on a good balance. It is then suspended from the balance by a fine thread and weighed again while it is swinging freely, completely submerged in a beaker of water. If the weight in water is subtracted from the dry weight, the difference is the weight of a volume of water equal to the volume of the mineral. By dividing the weight of an equal volume of water into the dry weight (weight in air) we obtain the ratio called specific gravity.

For example, a sulfur crystal is found to weigh 4 ounces dry and 2 ounces when submerged in water. The difference in weight is 2 ounces.

Dry weight = 4 oz.
Weight in water = 2 oz.

The weight of the *displaced water* is 2 ounces, which is subtracted from 4 ounces, leaving 2 ounces. To compare the weight of the sulfur with the weight of an equal volume of water we divide the dry weight of the sulfur by the weight of the displaced water.

$$\frac{4 \text{ oz.}}{2 \text{ oz.}} = 2 = \text{specific gravity of the mineral sulfur}$$

A spiral spring balance, called the Jolly balance (Fig. 11–5), is often used to determine specific gravity. Very small differences in weights can be read directly and accurately from the scale attached to the balance.

Minerals and rocks vary widely in specific gravity, from certain types of pumice (a volcanic rock) which float on water, to gold, which has a specific gravity of 19.3 (almost 20 times heavier than water).

Special properties of minerals. There are other observable characteristics that aid in the identification of minerals.

FIG. 11–8. The Jolly balance is used to measure specific gravity accurately.

Magnetism. Some minerals are naturally magnetic. *Magnetite* and some specimens of *pyrrhotite* (*pir*-oh-tyt) both iron ores, are attracted to a magnet. *Lodestone,* a form of magnetite, acts as a magnet and attracts small pieces of iron. Its magnetic properties were known in very ancient times, and pieces of lodestone were sometimes used as magnetic compasses. Many ironbearing minerals become magnetic when heated.

Electrical properties. Certain minerals show electrical properties. When a quartz crystal is subjected to pressure, the opposite surfaces become electrically charged, showing the property of piezoelectricity. When such a crystal is properly mounted in an electric circuit, electricity flows through the circuit. The use of quartz crystals to control radio frequencies is related to this property of the mineral. Under certain conditions, plates cut from a quartz crystal can be made to vibrate at a definite rate (frequency) that depends on the crystal structure and the thickness of the plate. The thinner the crystal slab, the higher the frequency of vibration. Such plates are used to control the frequency of all radio transmitters and of many specialized radio receivers.

Sulfur and other minerals become electrically charged when rubbed. When heated, crystals of tourmaline, a silicate mineral, develop a positive electric charge at one end and a negative charge at the other.

Fluorescence and phosphorescence. The atoms in some minerals become excited when exposed to ultraviolet light (invisible light of very short wavelength). They absorb the ultraviolet light and give off visible rays of longer wavelengths. These minerals are said to be *fluorescent.* See Fig. 11–10. *Phosphorescent* minerals continue to give off light

FIG. 11–9. A lodestone, or natural magnet, is a form of magnetite. (*The Smithsonian Institution*)

after the ultraviolet light rays have been cut off. Some types of calcite, willemite (a zinc ore), and some uranium and tungsten minerals are fluorescent.

Radioactivity. Uranium and certain other elements produce invisible radiations through the spontaneous breakdown of their atomic nuclei. Minerals such as pitchblende, which contain radioactive elements, give out radiations which can be detected with a Geiger counter. The Geiger counter operates by means of a tube filled with gas that is affected electrically when exposed to radiation.

Temperature of fusion. The temperature needed to cause small splinters of a mineral to fuse (melt) in a blowpipe flame is an aid in identifying the minerals. A *scale of fusibility* is used to compare this property in different minerals.

Optical properties. Microscopic particles of a mineral can be identified by the optical effects of the mineral on a beam of polarized light, using a polarizing microscope. Such a microscope can also be used to determine the *index of refraction* of a mineral. This index is defined in terms of the refraction of light as it passes through a substance, and is different for each mineral. Because of this, the index of refraction is one of the most dependable characteristics in positively identifying a mineral. The distinctive pattern produced by the passage of x-rays through a mineral is another characteristic used in precise identification.

Other characteristics. Some minerals, such as halite (rock salt) have a distinctive taste. Others have a recognizable odor or texture. Some are noted for their brittleness or their malleability; some are

smooth or sharply angled, fibrous or granular.

Testing methods. Many specific tests have been developed for practical use in the identification of minerals. Some are very simple, while others require complex equipment and cannot easily be carried out in the field.

Simple chemical tests. The acid test identifies the mineral *calcite,* which makes up most limestone and marble deposits. Calcite is the compound $CaCO_3$, or calcium carbonate. If a drop of cold, dilute hydrochloric (muriatic) acid is placed on calcite, bubbles of carbon dioxide (CO_2) escape. That is, the

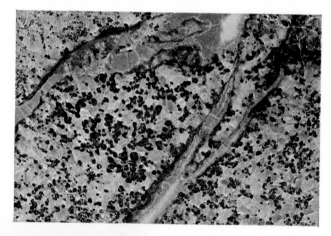

FIG. 11–10. At the right, the minerals calcite (greenish white), willemite (light brown) and franklinite (dark brown), as they appear in ordinary light. Below, under ultraviolet light, calcite and willemite fluoresce red and green, respectively. Franklinite does not fluoresce. (*B. M. Shaub*)

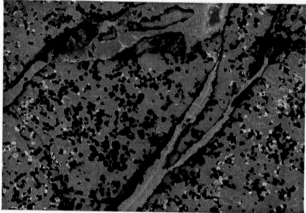

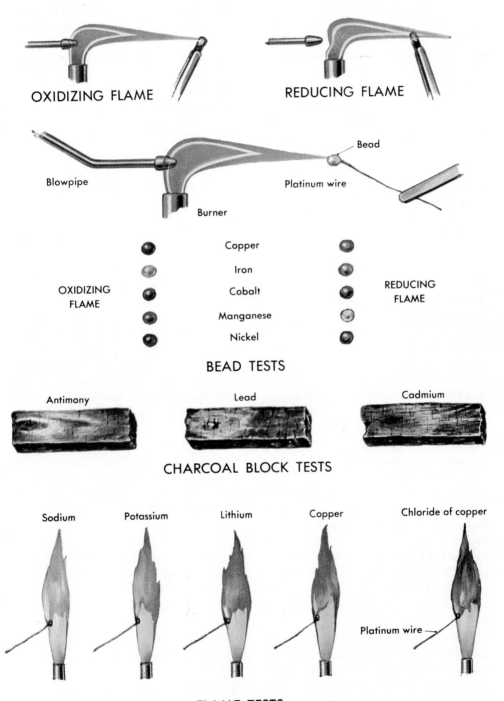

OXIDIZING FLAME   REDUCING FLAME

Bead
Blowpipe   Platinum wire
Burner

OXIDIZING FLAME   Copper   REDUCING FLAME
                         Iron
                         Cobalt
                         Manganese
                         Nickel

BEAD TESTS

Antimony   Lead   Cadmium

CHARCOAL BLOCK TESTS

Sodium   Potassium   Lithium   Copper   Chloride of copper

Platinum wire

FLAME TESTS

FIG. 11–11. These color tests are frequently used in identifying minerals.

mineral *effervesces*. Calcite is one of the few common minerals that react in this way; dolomite (a carbonate of calcium and magnesium) gives the same reaction with hot acid, but reacts slowly with cold acid.

Minerals containing phosphorus, such as *apatite*, may be identified by special tests. The mineral is dissolved in boiling concentrated nitric acid (HNO_3) and a few drops of the solution are added to a solution of ammonium molybdate. A canary yellow compound is formed if phosphorus is present.

Laboratory color tests. Several simple tests, illustrated in Fig. 11–11, depend mainly on the colors produced by the different minerals when treated in various ways. For most such tests, a *blowpipe* is used. This is a short, bent tube with a tiny outlet through which air may be blown into a flame to produce a smaller, hotter flame. According to the way in which the blowpipe is used, oxygen enters into reaction with the mineral, or hot gases are produced which take oxygen from the mineral. These flames are described respectively as *oxidizing* or *reducing* flames.

A common *blowpipe test* is to heat a small quantity of the powdered mineral on a charcoal block. Residues from the heated mineral may collect on the block; their nature and color aid in identification of the elements present in the mineral. Characteristic fumes may also be produced, and a bead of metal may remain on the charcoal block in the case of lead or silver minerals.

In the *flame test* a bit of the powdered mineral, moistened with acid and held on a clean platinum wire, is put into the flame. The resulting change in the color of the flame indicates the presence of certain elements.

In the *bead test* a clear bead of borax is formed on a loop of platinum wire. The loop is dipped into powdered borax and then held in the burner flame. The borax bead is then touched to the powdered mineral. When placed in oxidizing or reducing flames, the borax and the mineral react to produce a characteristic color determined by the elements in the mineral.

Powdered minerals can also be tested in open or closed tubes to identify colors or odors formed.

PROPERTIES OF MINERALS

The important minerals. Of the approximately 1800 minerals found in the earth's crust, some occur in comparatively large quantities and are found over wide geographical areas; others, though comparatively rare, are highly important in human activities. The following descriptions of about 50 of these important minerals will point out their uses as well as their properties.

Geologists group or *classify* minerals according to chemical composition and crystal structure. In the following pages a much simplified classification is used. The minerals containing silicon (*silicious minerals*) are treated first because they are most common and most widespread. The element silicon is never found free in nature. With the exception of quartz, which is *silica* (silicon dioxide), the silicious minerals are *silicates*, having complex molecular structures including the radical (SiO_4) and atoms of other elements such as aluminum, sodium, and potassium. Some are *hydrous silicates*, containing hydrogen either in the form of the hydroxide radical (OH) or as water combined in the crystal structure.

This group of minerals is more important than any other, because it includes about 25 percent of the known minerals and about 40 percent of the common ones.) Since they include the major minerals in granite, they form over 90 percent of the earth's crust. They are valuable as building materials, and in industrial processes.

The second group consists of certain minerals that are of major importance because of their wide occurrence as rock formers or their usefulness in industry. They include carbonates, sulfates, and other compounds, or are native elements, such as sulfur. Although these minerals contain elements that are chemically classed as metals, such as calcium, they are not sources of metals in the ordinary sense. For convenience, they will be called *nonmetallic minerals.*

The third group, *metal ore minerals,* includes the minerals which are the common metal ores. Some of the metals, like gold, platinum, silver, and copper are found in the native state. However, except for gold and platinum, they are also found in larger amounts in chemical combination with oxygen, sulfur, arsenic, carbon, and other elements. An *ore* is a mixture of a metallic mineral with waste minerals of little commercial worth, called *gangue* (gang). (Rock materials containing valuable nonmetallic substances such as sulfur are sometimes also referred to as ores.) Whether or not a material is considered ore depends on the concentration of the valuable metal in it, and economic factors such as the ease of extracting the metal and its current price on the world market, or its scarcity in a particular area. Thus certain rocks may come to be considered as ore when supplies of other rocks that contained larger percentages of the metal have been used up. New scientific discoveries create new uses for metals and minerals and create demand for those previously thought worthless.

Ores may be igneous, sedimentary, or metamorphic in origin. *Primary deposits,* (those formed first), may develop by crystallization of elements and compounds in magma, they may crystallize from water solutions in veins, or they may occur by replacement of other minerals in rocks. *Secondary deposits* are formed when ores are exposed to weathering and erosion. Ores may also be formed from recrystallization and the formation of new minerals during metamorphism. Thus metal ores may be the result of a long series of chemical and physical changes which concentrate the metal in greater proportion, making it more readily available for man's use.

The last group consists of the *gem minerals.* Some of these are semiprecious, others are considered precious stones. Most gems, such as diamonds and rubies, are cut from mineral crystals to show off their color or brilliance. The value of a gem is determined by its size, lack of flaws, beauty of color and luster, hardness (wearing quality), and perfection of crystal form. Most primary gem deposits (diamond, topaz) are found in igneous rocks; some (ruby, emerald) are formed in metamorphic rocks. Because of their durability, many gems occur in secondary deposits, having been weathered out and deposited as sedimentary material. A few gems, such as opal, are sometimes found as primary deposits in sedimentary rocks.

Note that some minerals might be placed in either of several groups. For example, *beryl* is the principal ore of the rare metal beryllium, but it has been placed in the gem category because it is better known as the mineral that forms the beautiful crystals from which the gems emerald and aquamarine are cut.

SMOKY QUARTZ   Switzerland   **CHALCEDONY**   Mexico

AGATE   **FLINT**   England

TIGER'S EYE   South Africa   **JASPER**   Vermont

ORTHOCLASE   Japan

LABRADORITE   Labrador

ANORTHITE (White)   California

MICROCLINE, Amazonite   Virginia

ALBITE   Virginia

HORNBLENDE   New York

In the descriptions of the minerals, hardness is indicated as H, specific gravity as SG and luster as L. If the chemical formula of the mineral is simple, it is given; the nature of the more complex compounds is indicated in general terms. The basic crystal system is also given for each mineral.

Many of the minerals described are included in the full color illustrations. Note that different specimens of the same mineral may vary greatly in color and physical appearance. Those pictured are representative of the more common or more attractive forms of the particular mineral.

SILICIOUS MINERALS

Quartz. SiO_2. Hexagonal, H—7, SG—2.65, L—glassy to greasy. Quartz is usually colorless or white, but may be colored by impurities in a variety of shades. It shows conchoidal fracture, and may be coarsely crystalline, forming large six-sided crystals. The varieties *rock crystal* (colorless), *amethyst* (purple), and *smoky quartz* (brown or black) are commonly found. Very finely crystalline quartz forms varieties such as *agate, onyx,* and *jasper. Chalcedony* (kal-*sed*-oh-nee) is a general name for these fine-grained varieties of quartz which have a waxy rather than a glassy luster. Other fine-grained quartz varieties are *flint* and *chert,* which are dull in appearance. Flint is usually dark gray in color, while chert is a light grayish-brown or tan. A yellowish-brown fibrous form of chalcedony of unusual interest is called *tiger's eye.* When it is cut into stones with a curved surface, the fibrous structure reflects a band of light which moves as the stone is rotated. This results in the so-called "cat's eye" effect.

Quartz, the hardest of the common minerals, is widely used in many forms. The colored crystalline varieties make beautiful ornamental or semiprecious stones. Quartz crystals are valuable in optical instruments, and because of their electrical properties, in radio and electronic equipment. Quartz sand is used in mortar and concrete and in the manufacture of glass and silica brick. In powdered form, quartz is an ingredient of porcelain, paints, and other products. Rocks formed from quartz sands (sandstones), and rocks consisting partly of quartz (granite), are important building stones.

Feldspars. *Orthoclase feldspar.* $KAlSi_3O_8$, potassium-aluminum silicate. Monoclinic, H—6, SG—2.57, L—glassy or pearly. Orthoclase may be colorless, white, gray, pink, or red. It has two good cleavages at right angles, forming blocklike fragments. *Microcline feldspar* is so similar to orthoclase in appearance that the two are often confused, but it occurs also in a green variety, amazonite, which is very distinctive.

Plagioclase feldspar. Sodium-calcium-aluminum silicate. Triclinic, H—6, SG—2.62 to 2.76, L—glassy or pearly. The plagioclase group includes a number of varieties which contain different proportions of sodium and calcium. They may be various shades of gray, sometimes white, greenish, yellowish, or bluish with an iridescent sheen. *Albite* is a white variety containing considerable amounts of sodium; *anorthite,* a rare variety containing a high percentage of calcium, is white or gray. *Labradorite* contains approximately equal amounts of sodium and calcium, and is generally gray or greenish-gray. It often shows a beautiful blue iridescence, but is not the only feldspar that does this. A sodium-bearing microcline called *anorthoclase* often shows a similar blue iridescence. It occurs in inch-square crystals in a dark gray granitelike rock, *larvikite,* found in southern Norway. Many buildings, including the base of the Chrysler Building in New York City, are made of this stone. Plagioclase feldspars have two cleavages at approximately right angles. The main cleavage surface may show fine parallel striations which are not found in orthoclase feldspars.

Feldspars are widely used in the making of porcelain, glazes, and enamel. Some varieties are cut and polished for use as ornamental stones. They are also economically important as a major component of building stones, such as granite. Most of the world's commercial clay deposits have been derived from the weathering of feldspar.

Micas. Hydrous aluminum silicates with potassium and often other metals.

Muscovite (white mica). Monoclinic, H—2 to 2½, SG—2.76 to 3.1, L—glassy to silky or pearly. Muscovite is colorless in thin sheets, light yellow, brown, green, or red in thicker blocks. It has eminent cleavage, and can be split into very thin sheets or flakes, which are flexible and elastic.

Muscovite is widely used for insulation in electrical equipment, and in wallpapers and fireproof materials.

Biotite. Monoclinic, H—2½ to 3, SG—2.8 to 3.2, L—splendent (glossy). Biotite contains magnesium and iron and is usually brown or black. Its cleavage is like that of muscovite; the thin sheets are smoky, rather than clear. Phlogopite (*flog*-oh-pyt), a relatively iron-free variety of biotite, is generally ligher in color.

Amphiboles. Complex silicates with various metals and hydrogen. Common variety: *Hornblende.* Monoclinic, H—5 to 6, SG—3.2, L—glassy, sometimes silky. Hornblende is usually dark green to black. Its two cleavage planes form rhombic fragments, and the crystals are generally long and six-sided. It is found in igneous and metamorphic rocks.

Pyroxenes. These minerals are similar to the amphiboles in composition, but lack hydrogen. Their properties are also similar to those of the amphiboles, but the crystal forms differ. Common variety: *Augite.* Monoclinic, H—5 to 6, SG—3.2 to 3.6, L—glassy to dull. Augite has four- or eight-sided crystals, and is generally dark green. It is found mainly in dark-colored igneous rocks.

Zeolites. Hydrous silicates of aluminum with other metals. Common variety: *Stilbite.* Monoclinic, H—3½ to 4, SG—2.1, L—glassy, pearly on some surfaces. Stilbite is white, occasionally yellow, brown, or red. It shows one good cleavage and forms crystals in groups, spread out at the ends like a sheaf. The zeolites are unusual in that they give off water, or "boil" when heated; the name means "boiling stone." They are found in cavities and veins in igneous rock, and are used in the Permutit process of water softening.

Chlorite. Hydrous iron-magnesium aluminum silicate. Monoclinic, H—2 to 2½, SG—2.6 to 2.9, L—glassy to pearly. Chlorite is usually some shade of green. It has eminent cleavage similar to that of the micas. The sheets are flexible but not elastic; they do not spring back as mica does. Chlorite is usually found in metamorphic rocks, but often occurs also in igneous rocks.

Olivine $(MgFe)_2SiO_4$, magnesium-iron silicate. Orthorhombic, H—6½ to 7, SG—3.27 to 3.37, L—glassy. Olivine is pale green of various shades, sometimes brown. It usually occurs in granular masses and shows conchoidal fracture. A transparent yellow-green variety is the

MUSCOVITE Maine

AUGITE Ontario

CHRYSOTILE, Asbestos Quebec

BIOTITE Maine

STILBITE New Jersey

SERPENTINE Ontario

gem *peridot*. Dark-colored igneous rocks often contain olivine.

Serpentine. $Mg_3Si_2O_5(OH)_4$, hydrous magnesium silicate. Monoclinic, H—2 to 5, SG—2.2 to 2.6, L—greasy, wax-like or silky in the fibrous variety. Serpentine is cream white through shades of green to black, often variegated or mottled in light and dark shades. Separate crystals are unknown; irregular fine-grained or fibrous masses are usual. Like chlorite, serpentine is usually the result of metamorphic alteration of other minerals, particularly olivine, pyroxenes, or amphiboles. The fibrous variety *chrysotile* (*kris*-oh-til) is the source of most *asbestos,* the rock fiber which can be woven into a thick fabric. Because it does not burn and conducts heat very slowly, it is valuable for use as fireproofing and insulation. Serpentine is an ornamental stone as marble is, but it is suitable only for interior decoration. An especially beautiful deep green form of serpentine is *verd antique marble.* It is not marble in the proper sense.

Talc. $Mg_3Si_4O_{10}(OH)_2$, hydrous magnesium silicate. Monoclinic, H—1, SG—2.7 to 2.8, L—pearly to greasy. Talc, in its several varieties, may be light green, gray, white or silvery. It is the softest of the common minerals and has a slippery, greasy feel. It has perfect cleavage, but the thin sheets are not elastic. It is found mainly in metamorphic rocks, where it has been formed from other minerals such as pyroxenes and olivine. Powdered talc is widely used in industry, for paints, ceramics, paper, and cosmetics (talcum powder). *Soapstone* is an impure talc rock, used for laboratory tables and sinks because of its resistance to most common chemicals.

Kaolinite. $Al_2Si_2O_5(OH)_4$, hydrous aluminum silicate. Monoclinic H—1 to 2.5, SG—2.2 to 2.6, L—dull. Kaolinite is the most widespread of the clay minerals. It is often colored yellow or brown by impurities, but when pure it is white. It has perfect cleavage and often occurs in microscopic flakes. Kaolinite is produced by changes in aluminum silicate minerals such as the feldspars, and is found especially in sedimentary rocks and in soil. Kaolinite deposits such as those in the famous china clay formations of England apparently resulted from the reaction of hot water on feldspars. This mineral is valuable in the manufacture of brick, tile, and pottery; purer grades of it are used in the making of fine porcelain and china, and as a filler for certain grades of paper. Paper used for printing and writing in ink contains a considerable percentage of kaolinite.

NONMETALLIC MINERALS

Calcite. $CaCO_3$, calcium carbonate. Hexagonal, H—3 on cleavage surface, SG—2.72, L—glassy to earthy. Calcite, the most abundant carbonate mineral, is usually white or colorless, but is sometimes tinted in various colors, and when

FIG. 11–12. Calcite shows double refraction. A double image of a black spot on white paper is seen through a crystal of Iceland spar. (*B. M. Shaub*)

impure, it may be brown or black. It is found in many different forms. The perfect cleavage of calcite in three directions results in its breaking into typical rhombic fragments. Crystals of many shapes, some extremely large, are common. Twin crystals are frequent. An important optical property of calcite is double refraction, the bending of light rays in such a way that each ray is broken into two, which travel through the crystal in different directions. Crystals of a clear variety called *Iceland spar,* when looked through at the proper angle, give a double image. See Fig. 11–12. Such crystals are used with microscopes to produce polarized light. (Double refraction is a property of many minerals, but can usually be detected only with special optical instruments.) Calcite effervesces strongly with cold hydrochloric acid. It is often fluorescent under ultraviolet light.

Calcite is very widespread as a rock-forming mineral. It is the main or sometimes the only mineral in limestone and marble, important building materials. It is found in many beautiful and unusual forms in caves and around the mouths of hot springs in a variety called *travertine. Chalk* is a form of calcite which is made of the microscopic shells of sea animals. The chalk cliffs of Dover, England, are famous for such deposits.

The most important use of calcite is in the manufacture of cement and mortar. Chalk is used as fertilizer and whitewash, and was the original "blackboard chalk" although this product is now made of other materials. Large quantities of limestone are used in the smelting of metals.

Dolomite. $CaMg(CO_3)_2$, calcium-magnesium carbonate. Hexagonal, H—$3\frac{1}{2}$ to 4, SG—2.85, L—glassy or pearly. Dolomite is usually white, but may also be pink or flesh-color, gray, green, brown, or black. Its cleavage is similar to that of calcite, and the crystals are usually rhombic, often with curved surfaces. Dolomite is often found with calcite. It reacts with acid, but very slowly unless the acid is heated, or the mineral is powdered. Its uses are more limited than those of calcite, but it is becoming increasingly important as a source of magnesium metal.

Sulfur. S. Orthorhombic, H—$1\frac{1}{2}$ to $2\frac{1}{2}$, SG—2.05 to 2.09, L—waxy or resinous. Sulfur is a characteristic bright yellow, which may be colored by impurities to shades of gray, green, or red. It shows conchoidal or uneven fracture, is brittle, and burns readily. It occurs both as distinct crystals and as irregular masses. Sulfur is such a poor conductor of heat that a crystal held close to your ear will be heard to crack as the heat of your hand causes the surface layers to expand while the interior is not affected. Sulfur crystals should therefore be handled as little as possible.

Sulfur is often found near the craters of volcanoes, where it is formed from the gases given off. It is also formed by changes in other minerals that contain sulfur, such as the metallic sulfides and gypsum, and occurs frequently in sedimentary rocks. It is an extremely valuable mineral used in the manufacture of sulfuric acid and other chemicals, insecticides, and fireworks, and in the making of rubber and paper.

Halite. NaCl, sodium chloride. Isometric, H—$2\frac{1}{2}$, SG—2.16, L—transparent to translucent. Halite, rock salt, is colorless or white, or with impurities may be shades of yellow, red, blue, or purple. It forms cubic crystals which may have funnel-shaped depressions on the faces; the crystals cleave easily parallel to the cubic crystal faces. It has the familiar salty taste, and dissolves easily in water.

Halite is found widely in sedimentary rocks, in large beds and masses where it has been deposited in crystal form by the gradual evaporation of sea water. It is also found dissolved in the waters of salt springs, salt lakes or seas, and the oceans. Salt has great commercial value, not merely as an essential element of diet and a food preservative, but also for the sodium and chlorine compounds made from it.

Kernite. Hydrous sodium borate. Monoclinic, H—2½ to 3, SG—1.9, L—glassy to pearly. Kernite is colorless or white and has a sweetish-alkaline taste. It breaks into long thin fibers and is fairly soluble in water. Its water solution, on evaporation, yields *borax,* which has the same basic chemical composition as kernite except that its crystals contain more than twice as much water of crystallization. Kernite is formed as a deposit from evaporation of salt lakes and is found on the surface of the earth in very dry regions, such as Death Valley, California. The borax produced from it is used extensively in the manufacture of soap, enamels, glass, and washing powders. It is also used in welding, soldering, and as an antiseptic and preservative. Its use in blowpipe tests for minerals was mentioned earlier in this chapter.

Gypsum. Hydrous calcium sulphate Monoclinic, H—2, SG—2.32, L—glassy, also pearly and silky. Gypsum is colorless, white, or gray; it may be various shades of yellow, red, or brown from impurities. Its crystals are often very long, and twinned crystals are common. The variety selenite is crystalline and usually transparent. A fibrous variety, satin spar, is also found. The mineral dissolves readily in *hot* hydrochloric acid

FIG. 11–13. Gypsum crystals take unusually beautiful forms. (*Ward's Natural Science Establishment, Inc.*)

and is slowly soluble in water. Gypsum is common in large beds of sedimentary rocks formed by the evaporation of sea water, like halite with which it is usually found. It is used mainly for plaster of Paris and other building plasters. The fine-grained variety, *alabaster,* is used for ornamental objects.

Apatite. Calcium phosphate with fluorine, chlorine, or (OH). Hexagonal, H—5, SG—3.15 to 3.20, L—glassy. Apatite is usually green or brown; it may also be blue, violet, yellow, or colorless. Its cleavage is poor, and it commonly occurs as fairly long crystals. It is found as well-formed crystals or as irregular masses in many types of rocks. Sometimes it is derived from the bones of animals, which are calcium phosphate. Apatite is used for fertilizer because of its phosphorus content. *Collophane,* sometimes called *phosphate rock,* is of about the same chemical composition as apatite, but is amorphous rather than crystalline. It is the principal mineral in the Florida phosphate beds, and is the chief source of phosphates for fertilizer.

CALCITE   Ohio

CALCITE, Travertine   Mexico

GYPSUM, Selenite   England

HALITE   Sicily

GYPSUM, Selenite   Ohio

DOLOMITE   New York

GRAPHITE   Ceylon

FLUORITE   Illinois

KERNITE   California

SULFUR   Sicily

GYPSUM, Alabaster   Italy

APATITE   Ontario

Fluorite. CaF$_2$, calcium fluoride. Isometric, H—4, SG—3.18, L—glassy. Fluorite shows many variations of color; it is most often light green, yellow, bluish green, or purple, but may be colorless, white, rose, blue, brown, or banded in different colors. It has perfect cleavage resulting in octahedral (eight-sided) forms. The crystals are generally cubic; twin crystals in which the corner of one cube seem to penetrate the face of the other are common. Some types of fluorite are fluorescent. It occurs in igneous rocks and often in limestones and dolomites. It melts at a low temperature and is used as a flux in the making of steel, and in the manufacture of glass and enamelware.

Graphite. Carbon. Hexagonal, H—1 to 2, SG—2.2, L—metallic, sometimes dull. Graphite, the "lead" of lead pencils, is black or steel-gray, and has a greasy feel. It has one perfect cleavage, forming thin flakes which are flexible but not elastic. Crystals are rare. Graphite is pure carbon, of the same chemical composition as diamond, but its properties are very different. It is found in both igneous and metamorphic rocks. Graphite is used as a lubricant, in the manufacture of crucibles for the melting of metals and alloys, and in pencils, mixed with clay. Its latest use is in the construction of nuclear reactors for the production of atomic energy.

METAL ORE MINERALS

GOLD. Au. Isometric, H—2½ to 3, SG—19.3 when pure, L-metallic. Gold forms very few compounds, and is therefore commonly found in the native state, although it is usually mixed with small amounts of other metals: silver, copper, or iron. Its color varies depending on the composition, being paler the more silver it contains. It is very malleable and ductile. It occurs most often in small particles or flakes scattered through the rock. Well-formed crystals are rare. Gold and quartz are frequently found together in veins of igneous origin. Because of its durability, gold is often found as nuggets in deposits of gravels in the beds of rivers and dried-up streams. Such gold has been weathered out of veins and other primary deposits, and transported downstream by running water. The world's greatest gold deposits are found in the Witwatersrand, also called the Rand, around Johannesburg in South Africa. Besides its common use in coins and jewelry, gold is important for dental purposes, for gold leaf, and certain industrial processes.

SILVER. **Argentite** (*ar*-jen-tyt). Ag$_2$S, silver sulfide. Isometric, H—2 to 2½, SG—7.3, L—metallic; bright on fresh surface, dull on exposure. This most important silver ore is lead-gray in color. It usually occurs in solid masses or coating other minerals, though occasionally in crystals. When used for ornamental and coinage purposes, silver is usually alloyed with copper. Native silver, in twisted, branching, or wirelike masses, is sometimes found with argentite. Native silver often occurs in veins of igneous origin.

IRON. **Hematite.** Fe$_2$O$_3$, ferric oxide. Hexagonal, H—5½ to 6½, SG—5.26 for crystals, L—metallic in crystals, dull in earthy varieties. Hematite, the most important ore of iron, ranges from reddish brown to black, depending on variations in grain size. Coarse crystals of hematite are black and shiny; a hard massive form resembles mica, and is called *specular* (mirrorlike) hematite; rounded dark shiny lumps are known as kidney ore; an earthy type is red ocher.

The streak of hematite is reddish brown, regardless of the color of the mineral. Like most iron ores, it is found in all three major types of rock. The world's largest deposits of hematite are found in the Lake Superior region of the United States.

Magnetite. Fe_3O_4. Isometric, H—6, SG—5.18, L—metallic. Magnetite is iron-black. It is distinguished from black hematite mainly by its streak, which is black. It is usually found in fine- or coarse-grained masses, but octahedral crystals are also found. Its outstanding property is its strong magnetism; the variety *lodestone* is a natural magnet.

Limonite (*ly*-muh-nyt). $2Fe_2O_3 \cdot 3H_2O$. Orthorhombic and amorphous, H—5 to 5½, SG—3.6 to 4, L—glassy. Limonite is a group name for all hydrous iron oxides. The crystallized form is called *goethite* (*goh*-thyt) after the famous German poet. It often also occurs as earthy or crustlike masses, dark brown or black in color. The streak is yellowish-brown. Limonite is always a secondary mineral, formed from other iron minerals chiefly by weathering. It is almost always present in yellow clays and soils; mixed with fine clay, it is called *yellow ocher,* and used as a pigment for paints as well as an iron ore. Most of the brown and yellow stains on rock surfaces are due to limonite.

Pyrite. FeS_2, iron disulfide. Isometric, H—6 to 6½, SG—5.02, L—metallic. Pyrite, called "fool's gold," is a brittle, pale brass-yellow mineral forming crystals which are commonly cubic or octahedral, with fine parallel striations on the surfaces. The streak is black. It also occurs in granular or rounded masses. It is the most widespread of the sulfides, and is mined for sulfur, and for the gold and copper usually found with it, rather than for the iron it contains.

FIG. 11–14. Specular hematite, an ore of iron. (*B. M. Shaub*)

Siderite (*sid*-er-yt). $FeCO_3$, ferrous carbonate. Hexagonal, H—3½ to 4, SG—3.96 when pure, L—glassy. Siderite is a light to dark brown mineral, occurring as crystals or in irregular masses. Often found in association with clay and with limestone, it is relatively low in iron content and is used as an ore in Europe but not to any great extent in the United States.

Near the hematite deposits in the Lake Superior region, there are large deposits of the low grade iron ore, *taconite*. It is a mixture of about two parts magnetite to one part hematite, and is found mixed with large quantities of worthless rock. This ore is becoming increasingly important in the production of iron and steel as higher grade ores are used up.

COPPER. **Chalcopyrite.** $CuFeS_2$, copper-iron sulfide. Tetragonal, H—3½ to 4, SG—4.1 to 4.3, L—metallic. Chalcopyrite is brittle and brass yellow. It is similar in appearance to pyrite and is also known as "fool's gold," but it is

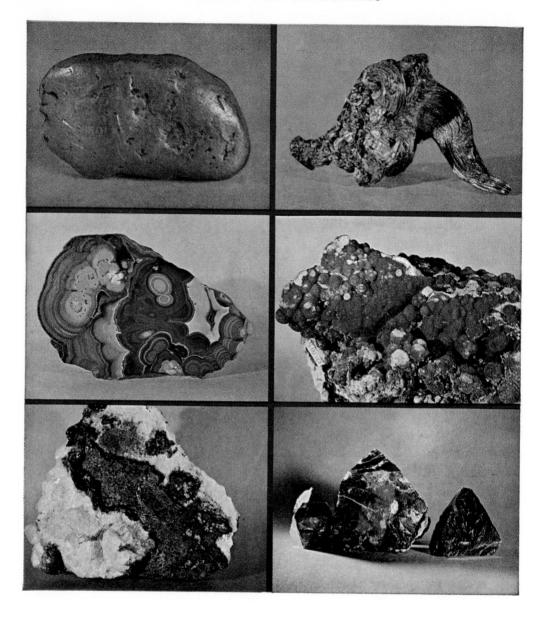

GOLD   Bolivia

SILVER   Norway

MALACHITE   Urals, U.S.S.R.

AZURITE   Arizona

CUPRITE   Arizona

SPHALERITE   Spain

HEMATITE England

LIMONITE New Hampshire

SIDERITE Austria

CINNABAR California

BAUXITE Arkansas

URANINITE (Black) India

FIG. 11–15. Cubic fragments of galena. (*B. M. Shaub*)

softer and more often in masses than in crystals. It is the most widely found copper mineral, and an important ore. Many other copper minerals are associated with it. It occurs in vein or replacement deposits, usually in igneous rocks.

Chalcocite. Cu_2S, cuprous sulfide. Orthorhombic, H—2½ to 3, SG—5.5 to 5.8, L—metallic, easily lost when tarnished. Chalcocite is lead gray; it rarely occurs in crystals. It has conchoidal fracture. Chalcocite is an important copper ore, formed mainly from chalcopyrite by complex chemical processes.

Malachite (*mal*-a-kyt) and **Azurite.** Carbonates of copper. Monoclinic, H—3½ to 4. These are copper ores of bright colors, green and blue respectively, formed by weathering from other copper minerals. Malachite, SG—3.9 to 4.03, may occur in crystals with glassy luster, but is usually in fibrous rounded masses with silky luster. Azurite, SG—3.77, is similar in its properties. It is not fibrous, but usually occurs as dark blue crystals. Both effervesce with hydrochloric acid. They are important copper ores.

Cuprite. Cu_2O. Isometric, H—3½ to 4, SG—6.1, L—sub-metallic, adamantine, amorphous, or in clear crystals.

Cuprite is red, with brownish-red streak, and occurs in cubic and 8- or 12-sided crystals as well as fine-grained masses. A special form, *chalcotrichite,* is a mass of red hairlike crystals. Cuprite is an important ore, formed by oxidation of other copper minerals.

LEAD. **Galena.** PbS, lead sulfide. Isometric, H—2½, SG—7.4 to 7.6, L—bright metallic. Galena occurs as lead-gray crystals or cleavage fragments, usually cubic. It is very common and is the major ore of lead.

ZINC. **Sphalerite.** ZnS, zinc sulfide. Isometric, H—3½ to 4, SG—3.9 to 4.1, L—resinous. Sphalerite is white when pure, but is almost always colored by iron to yellow, brown, or black, and may also be red or green. The streak is white to yellow or brown. It has good cleavage, forming complex 12-sided fragments, and is also found in rounded masses. In some sphalerite, up to 28 percent of the zinc has been replaced by iron. Its name means "the deceiver," because the iron-containing sphalerites are so lustrous and so dark that they can easily be confused with galena.

TIN. **Cassiterite.** SnO_2, tin dioxide. Tetragonal, H—6 to 7, SG—6.8 to 7.1, L—adamantine to dull. Cassiterite is usually brown or black, rarely yellow or white; the streak is white. It may be crystalline, granular, or fibrous, and is the only important tin mineral. The name is of Phoenician origin, meaning "the end of the earth," from the fact that the ancient Mediterranean people as far back as 2000 B.C. imported this tin ore from Britain.

ALUMINUM. **Bauxite** (*bawks*-yt). H—1 to 3, SG—2 to 2.55, L—dull to earthy. In strict classification, bauxite is a rock rather than a mineral, because it is a mixture of several hydrous aluminum ores, but it is generally grouped with the important mineral ores. It is normally white, but is usually stained gray, yellow, or red by impurities. It is amorphous and occurs in round grains or earthy masses. Bauxite is usually the result of weathering of aluminum-bearing rocks.

Cryolite, Na_3AlF_6, sodium-aluminum fluoride. Triclinic, H—2.5 to 3, SG—2.9 to 3, L—pearly or glassy to greasy. Cryolite was once used as a source of aluminum, and in the process of extracting aluminum from bauxite. It is now most important in the manufacture of sodium salts, and certain types of glass and porcelain.

MERCURY. **Cinnabar.** HgS, mercuric sulfide. Hexagonal, H—2½, SG—8.10, L—adamantine when pure to dull when impure. Cinnabar is vermilion-red to brownish-red, depending on its purity; mixtures of clay, iron oxide, etc. being common. It usually occurs in finely granular masses, but may form hexagonal crystals. It is the only important source of mercury, the liquid metal which has many industrial values besides its use in thermometers and barometers.

TITANIUM. **Ilmenite.** $FeTiO_3$, ferrous titanate. Hexagonal, H—5½ to 6, SG—4.7, L—metallic. Ilmenite is iron black, with black to brownish-red streak. It is found as thick flat crystals, thin plates, or compact masses, and often occurs in deposits making up part of the "black sands" found on some beaches. It is the major ore of titanium, which is used in paints and as a structural metal, since titanium alloys are comparatively light in weight but very strong. Much of what is called ilmenite is actually a mixture of ilmenite and magnetite called *titaniferous magnetite,* which looks like magnetite but is not magnetic when tested with a small magnet. The great ti-

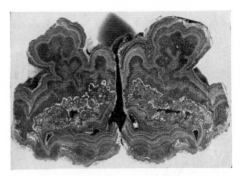

FIG. 11–16. A variety of cassiterite, called "wood tin." (*B. M. Shaub*)

tanium deposits of the Adirondack Mountains in New York State consist of this mixture.

Rutile (*roo*-teel). TiO_2, titanium oxide. Tetragonal, H—6 to 6.5, SG—4.2 to 4.3, L—metallic, adamantine. Rutile is reddish brown, blood-red, or black, with yellow or light brown streak, and may be opaque or transparent. Crystals are common; needlelike crystals are often found in quartz.

URANIUM. **Uraninite** (yoo-*ran*-ih-nyt) or **pitchblende.** UO_2, uranium dioxide. Isometric, H—5½, SG—9 to 9.7, 6.05 to 8.5 in certain varieties, L—pitchlike, dull. Uraninite, the chief source of the radioactive element uranium, is a black mineral with brownish-black streak, occurring generally in rounded masses, more or less altered by weathering. It occurs in veins (as in the Congo and at Great Bear Lake in the Canadian Northwest), and in porous sediments associated with petrified wood and other plant remains (as in the Colorado Plateau). Although the terms uraninite and pitchblende are often used interchangeably, geologists prefer to restrict the word pitchblende to the amorphous form found in veins, reserving the term uraninite for the more obviously crystalline forms found in dikes. This

OPAL Australia

TOPAZ Burma and Brazil

TOURMALINE California

GARNET Alaska and Connecticut

BERYL, Aquamarine S.W. Africa

CORUNDUM, Ruby Madagascar

FIG. 11–17. This magnificent star sapphire is a gem form of the mineral corundum. (*B. M. Shaub*)

mineral usually contains small amounts of other radioactive elements such as thorium and radium, as well as nitrogen, helium, lead, and argon. The lead and helium result from disintegration of the radioactive elements. Because the breakdown occurs at a constant rate, the amount of lead and helium can be used to estimate the time that has passed since the mineral crystallized, and the age of the rocks which contain uraninite or are associated with it can be determined in this way.

The importance of uraninite has increased tremendously since the development of methods of harnessing atomic energy. Uranium is used in atomic fission for both military and peaceful purposes. Uraninite is also a source of radium, although this element is present in only very small percentages. One of the major uranium minerals in the Colorado Plateau area is *carnotite,* a bright yellow mineral which is also a source of the metal vanadium. *Gummite* is a term for a fine-grained, yellow to orange-red alteration product of uraninite.

GEM MINERALS

Opal. $SiO_2 \cdot nH_2O$, silicon dioxide, with varying amount of water. Amorphous, H—5 to 6, SG—1.9 to 2.2, L—glassy or resinous. Opal is chemically the same as quartz, with the addition of water. It occurs in small veins or irregular masses of rounded forms, and shows excellent conchoidal fracture. Common opal may be colorless, white, pale yellow, red, brown, green, gray, or blue. *Precious opal* is white, milky blue, or yellow with the typical "opalescent" reflection of different colors within the stone. It is cut in rounded shapes, called cabochon. *Black opal,* a dark variety, and *fire opal,* with intense orange-red reflections, are also prized as gems. Another variety of opal, of great economic importance, is *diatomite* or *diatomaceous earth.* This is a white, porous, very light powdery material found in beds of sediment. It consists of the beautifully formed shells of microscopic plants

FIG. 11–18. Jade statuettes such as this are highly prized. (*B. M. Shaub*)

FIG. 11–19. Garnet crystals in rock. (*Smithsonian Institution*)

called diatoms, and is used for insulation and in refining petroleum products.

Jade. Unlike other gems, which are usually varieties of a single mineral, the gem called jade may be either a sodium aluminum silicate, *jadeite,* or a complex calcium magnesium iron silicon compound, called *nephrite.* The finest jade is usually the jadeite variety (monoclinic, H—6.5 to 7, SG—3.3 to 3.5, L—waxy or pearly). Most jade is green, but white-gray, blue-gray, violet-gray, and yellowish colors of jade are also found.

Garnet. A group of closely related minerals, silicates of various metals. (*Pyrope,* the usual deep red precious garnet used in jewelry, is mainly magnesium-aluminum silicate. *Demantoid,* a brilliant green variety resembling emerald in color, is mainly calcium-iron silicate.) Isometric, H—6½ to 7½, SG—3.5 to 4.3, depending on the composition, L—glassy to resinous. The color of garnet depends on its composition and may be red, brown, yellow, white, green, or black. The crystals usually have twelve or twenty-four sides, or combinations of the two.

Topaz. Aluminum fluorosilicate. Orthorhombic, H—8, SG—3.4 to 3.6, L—glassy. True topaz (less desirable stones are sometimes called by this name) is usually colorless, but yellow, yellow-brown, or blue-green varieties often occur in beautiful crystals which make valuable gems. The only important commercial source of the gem stones is Brazil.

Tourmaline. Complex silicate of boron and aluminum. Hexagonal, H—7 to 7½, SG—3.0 to 3.25, L—glassy to resinous. The color of tourmaline crystals varies according to their composition, since various metals substitute for one another in different varieties. As a gem stone, it may be green, pink, red, blue, or violet. Some crystals show several colors in concentric bands. The crystals are often long, and are unique in having curved triangular cross sections.

Beryl. $Be_3Al_2Si_6O_{18}$, beryllium aluminum silicate. Hexagonal, H—7½ to 8, SG—2.75 to 2.8, L—glassy. Aquamarine (pale blue-green), emerald (deep green), and rose and golden beryl are gems cut from different colored varieties of this mineral. Emeralds of fine color and perfection are more valuable than diamonds of similar quality. The six-sided crystals may be quite large. Beryl is the principal source of the metal beryllium, now used extensively in the manufacture of lightweight alloys.

Corundum. Al_2O_3, aluminum oxide. Hexagonal, H—9, SG—4.02, L—adamantine to glassy. Gem corundum occurs in several colors. Ruby is deep red, sapphire is blue; other colors such as purple, yellow, and green are known as oriental amethyst, oriental topaz, or oriental emerald, although such names are confusing. Some forms reflect light in the form of a six-rayed star and are called star sapphires or star rubies.

A variety of corundum that is closely combined with magnetite is used as an abrasive, called *emery.*

Zircon. $ZrSiO_4$, zirconium silicate. Tetragonal, H—7½, SG—4.68, L—adamantine. Transparent, colorless, brownish, or red-orange varieties of zircon are popular gem stones. Gem zircons, white and blue in color, can be produced by heat treatment of the natural stones. The crystals are combinations of four-sided and pyramidal shapes.

Diamond. Carbon. Isometric, H—10, SG—3.5, L—adamantine; uncut crystals: greasy. Diamond is usually pale yellow or colorless, but may be pale shades of red, orange, green, blue, or brown, or nearly black. The crystals are usually six-sided or eight-sided, although diamond often occurs in distorted and irregular shapes. The high index of refraction of diamond accounts for its brilliance; the "fire" of a diamond is produced by cutting the stone in such a way that light is refracted and dispersed greatly as it passes through the gem stone. The value of a gem diamond depends on its size, degree of flawlessness, and color. Pure white or blue-white diamonds are most desirable for gems, although the term "blue-white diamond" is sometimes misused by jewelers to describe stones of inferior quality.

Most of the world's diamonds are not of gem quality, but are widely used in industry for abrasive purposes. Very small diamonds are now produced synthetically for industrial uses. They are more uniform in quality than natural stones, although somewhat more expensive to produce. Thus far no synthetic diamonds large enough to be called gems have been made.

SUMMARY

IGNEOUS, sedimentary, and metamorphic rocks are mixtures of minerals. A mineral is a naturally occurring solid substance with definite chemical and physical properties. Most minerals are compounds; some are single elements.

Approximately 1800 different minerals are known but only a few of these make up most of the rocks of the earth's crust. Feldspar, quartz, and mica are examples of the most common mineral compounds, all of which contain silicon. Carbonates, oxides, and sulfides are other common groups of compounds found in minerals. Many metals are extracted from carbonates, oxides, and sulfides of metallic elements. Some metals can exist in a free or uncombined state.

Composition, origin, and arrangement of atoms determine mineral properties, such as color, luster, hardness, cleavage, fracture, streak, specific gravity, crystal shape, and reaction to acid. Minerals are identified by their properties. Detailed chemical or optical analysis may be required for the final identification of certain specimens.

Minerals may be grouped as silicious and nonmetallic minerals, metal ores, and gems. Silicious minerals include quartz, chlorite, and serpentine; nonmetallic minerals include calcite and apatite. Typical ore minerals are hematite and malachite; typical gems, opal and corundum.

VOCABULARY REVIEW

Match the word or phrase in the left column with the correct word or phrase in the right column. *Do not write in this book.*

1. Changed rock	*m*	**a.** fracture
2. Deposits in water	*f*	**b.** streak
3. Magma		**c.** sedimentary
4. Powder of a mineral	*b*	**d.** borax
5. Relative weight	*x*	**e.** crystal form
6. Plane surface	*h*	**f.** igneous
7. Molecular structure	*e*	**g.** hardness
8. Mohs' scale	*g*	**h.** cleavage
9. Ultraviolet light	*k*	**i.** specific gravity
10. Bead test	*d*	**j.** luster
11. Silicon dioxide	*l*	**k.** fluorescent
		l. quartz
		m. metamorphic

QUESTIONS · GROUP A

Give the name of the mineral described in each of the following groups of phrases. *Do not write in this book.*

1. Decomposed feldspars, white in pure form, hydrous aluminum silicate, very soft.
2. L—metallic, pure carbon, used in "lead" pencils, used as a lubricant, crystals are rare.
3. Conchoidal fracture, granular masses, glassy, magnesium-iron silicate.
4. SiO_2, six-sided crystal, hardest common mineral, conchoidal fracture.
5. Double refraction, reacts with cold dilute HCl, cleavage results in rhombic fragments, $CaCO_3$.
6. Sea green, cosmetics, greasy feel, softest common mineral.
7. One perfect cleavage, soluble in water, deposits result from evaporation, sweetish alkaline taste.
8. $KAlSi_3O_8$, blocky fragments, L—glassy or pearly, H—6.
9. Greasy feel, metamorphic alteration of other minerals, fibrous variety source of asbestos, hydrous magnesium silicate.
10. SG—3.2, wedge-shaped fragments, 6-sided crystals, contains hydrogen.
11. Green, thin sheets, found in metamorphic rocks, flexible but not elastic.
12. Dissolves in hot HCl, common in sedimentary rocks, twinned crystals are common, L—glassy, pearly or silky.
13. Bright yellow, burns easily, H—1½ to 2½, waxy feel.
14. Green, poor cleavage, used for fertilizer, long crystals common.
15. NaCl, colorless or white, cubic crystals, found widely in sedimentary rocks.
16. Gives off water when heated, H—3½ to 4, hydrous silicates of aluminum with other metals, one good cleavage.

17. Some types fluorescent, cleavage results in octahedral forms, H—4, crystals generally cubic.
18. Thin sheets, flexible and elastic, H—2½ to 3, contains magnesium and iron.

G R O U P B

1. Give the principal mineral source and its hardness, streak, luster, specific gravity, chemical formula, and special properties, for the following metals: iron, silver, copper, aluminum, tin, zinc, lead, mercury, and titanium.
2. Explain why it is difficult to identify a mineral by its color.
3. Kaolinite and chalk look very much alike. Explain how you could differentiate one from the other.
4. Calcite, fluorite, quartz, and halite look very much alike. If you were given four specimens, what procedure would you follow to identify each mineral?
5. List the materials that you could use in the field as convenient standards of hardness.
6. If the dry weight of a mineral specimen is 9.8 ounces, but the weight in water is 5.7 ounces, what is its specific gravity?
7. Explain the difference between fluorescence and phosphorescence. Give several examples of minerals that possess these properties.
8. Describe three experiments that would illustrate the electrical properties of certain minerals.
9. Name a mineral that is a natural magnet. Name several minerals that become magnetic when heated.
10. What is meant by the index of refraction of a mineral? What is the cause of varying indexes of refraction?
11. Describe the procedure you would follow in conducting a series of bead tests.
12. Describe the procedure you would follow in conducting a series of flame tests.
13. Discuss the difference between primary and secondary ore deposits.
14. Explain why lead is associated with uraninite deposits. Why is uraninite of greater importance today than it was 25 years ago?

CHAPTER 12

ROCKS

WHAT is a rock? We are accustomed to thinking of rocks as small pieces of a hard substance that varies widely in color and texture. The definition given in Chapter 10, however, makes clear that in earth science the word applies to great masses of material that cover large areas of the earth. The smaller rocks we know are merely fragments broken from large masses that may extend for many miles. Although such fragments are important clues to the nature of the rock mass, no one sample can tell the whole story. The study of rocks, or *petrology*, has developed from observation of hundreds of thousands of rock samples found in all parts of the world. From these samples, scientists have tried to find out how rocks were formed, and what determines their variation in composition and structure.

The first problem of the petrologist was description and classification. He had to find out which of the likenesses and differences among separate samples of rock are meaningful. Only after rocks had been grouped into broad categories could their full story begin to emerge. Rocks are classified in several ways: by their origin, their mineral composition, their texture, and their color. The last three properties may be determined directly by examination of rock samples. Origin can be determined indirectly according to theories developed from the experience and observation of geologists,

VOCABULARY

Petrology. The scientific study of rocks.

Stratified rocks. Rocks which occur in parallel layers.

Massive rocks. Rocks which are unstratified.

Extrusive rocks. Igneous rocks formed when magma flows out over the earth's surface.

Intrusive rocks. Igneous rocks formed when magma solidifies among other rocks below the earth's surface.

Fossils. Preserved evidences of ancient life on the earth.

Placer deposits. Deposits of minerals in the gravels of stream beds.

Foliation. Arrangement of minerals within a rock in bands or layers.

186

FIG. 12–1. Massive rock structures are exposed in many areas of the earth's surface. This is the Great White Throne in Zion National Park. (*Union Pacific Railroad*)

over the years, and from the evidence of the rocks themselves and the circumstances in which they were found.

IGNEOUS ROCKS

Rock origins. The composition of rocks reveals much about their origin. Most rocks are mixtures of the minerals discussed in Chapter 11; some rocks, such as coal, are of organic origin. As we have seen, the rock-forming minerals are relatively few, but the number of possible mixtures are many, and make classification difficult. One type of rock grades into another by small degrees; the colors, textures, and other properties of the minerals cause great variety of appearance. Nevertheless, certain features of the rocks provide clues to the circumstances under which the rock masses were formed; that is, whether the rocks are igneous, sedimentary, or metamorphic. Sometimes it is obvious that metamorphic rocks were formerly either igneous or sedimentary types; some metamorphic rocks, however, may be so changed that their origin cannot be determined.

The formation of igneous rocks. The hot liquid mineral mass, or magma, which is the source of igneous rock, comes from deep within the earth. As

PINK GRANITE   Maine   **HORNBLENDE SYENITE**   Vermont

· ·

COMMON IGNEOUS ROCKS

Predominant Minerals	Coarse-grained ────────────────→			Fine-grained →	Glassy
		Porphyritic			
Quartz Orthoclase Plagioclase	Granite			Rhyolite	Obsidian Pumice
Biotite or Hornblende	Syenite			Trachyte	Pitchstone
Plagioclase Hornblende or Biotite	Diorite	Granite, Syenite, Diorite,	Rhyolite Trachyte, Andesite, and Basalt Porphyries	Andesite	
Plagioclase Pyroxene	Gabbro	Gabbro, Pyroxenite, Peridotite, and Dunite Porphyries		Basalt	Tachylite
Pyroxene Plagioclase Olivine	Pyroxenite				
Olivine Pyroxene	Peridotite				
Olivine	Dunite				

Acidic to Basic   *Light Color to Dark Color*

Increase in Cooling Rate ────→ Decrease in Grain Size ────→

PYROXENITE   Ontario

ANDESITE PORPHYRY   Nevada

RHYOLITE BRECCIA   Mexico

TRACHYTE TUFF   West Germany

VESICULAR BASALT   Colorado

RED OBSIDIAN   Oregon

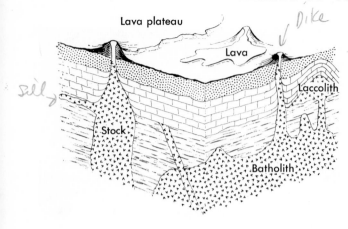

FIG. 12-2. Intrusive and extrusive igneous rock structures.

stated in Chapter 6, scientists believe that the material below the earth's surface, though very hot, is kept in a rigid state by the great pressures in the depths. If the pressure is lessened at any place, the material becomes liquid, and a body of magma forms. The magma may work its way upward through the overlying layers of rock. The heat and pressure of the magma may cause the rocks above to move or break up, making room for the magma to rise. The process is probably hastened by melting of the overlying rock. The hot magma may then break through cracks in the earth's surface so that the molten rock or *lava* is allowed to spread over wide areas of the land. A small cone or large mountain of rock may form at the opening. The term *volcano* is used for both the opening and the accumulation of material. Magma that reaches the surface cools to form *extrusive* rocks—rocks that have been "pushed out." Such rocks are usually glassy or finely crystalline in texture; large crystals have not had time to develop. If the rock that overlies the mass of magma prevents it from reaching the surface, however, the magma cools slowly to form *intrusive* or *plutonic* rocks. These have a coarser texture, be-

ing composed of a mass of larger crystalline grains of varying sizes. Intrusive rocks are exposed to view by erosion of the overlying rocks.

Igneous rocks differ according to their mineral content. They generally contain minerals such as micas, olivine, hornblende, and pyroxene, with orthoclase and plagioclase feldspars and quartz. Those rocks that have least of the iron-magnesium minerals (such as amphiboles and pyroxenes), are light in color and relatively light in weight (SG—2 to 3). These are acidic or silicious rocks, containing a high proportion of silica. The rocks that are richer in iron and magnesium are darker and heavier (SG —3) and are called basic. The table on page 188 shows the relation of these properties to the color and composition of igneous rocks. Some of these rocks are pictured in the color photographs on pages 188 and 189.

Igneous rocks are also classified according to their texture. Differences in the rate of cooling produce gradations of crystal size from very large to very small. The table shows the relationship of some important igneous rocks with respect to texture and composition. Thus *granite* is an acidic, light-colored rock composed mainly of quartz and ortho-clase feldspar; it is coarsely granular. *Syenite, diorite, gabbro,* and *peridotite* are other coarse-grained intrusive rocks; they contain the darker-colored minerals in varying proportions. Under some con-ditions, both extrusive and intrusive rocks may cool slowly at first, and then more rapidly. This process produces the *porphyries,* of which several are shown in the table. In a porphyry, fairly large mineral crystals are set in a mass of very fine crystals. *Rhyolite* and *basalt* are lavas; *obsidian* and *tachylite* are glasses formed when extruded magma cools very quickly.

Some other igneous rocks of special interest are *pegmatite,* a very coarse-grained variety of granite; and *pumice,* a rhyolitic lava that cools so quickly that the gases do not escape before the rock hardens. Pumice has a spongelike struc-ture because of the trapped gas bubbles. Some samples of pumice are light enough to float in water.

Igneous intrusions. Because the man-ner in which the magma cools affects the texture of the rock, it is important to know the various forms in which intru-sions occur. The typical intrusive forma-tions are shown in Fig. 12–2.

1. Batholiths. A large mass of intru-sive igneous rock, whose lower limit is indefinite, is called a **batholith.** Such structures commonly form the cores of mountain ranges. They are uncovered as erosion strips off the overlying rock, and their extent can only be determined by the area that is exposed. Batholiths are chiefly composed of granite and related rocks, because the slow cooling of huge masses of magma at great depth results in the formation of large crystals. Rock found at the center of a batholith tends to be coarser-grained than that at the edges, since the center of the mass cools even more slowly than the outer areas. A batholith of relatively small extent may be called a *stock.*

2. Laccoliths. Magma that has been intruded between layers of sedimentary rocks, causing them to arch upward, forms a *laccolith.* The magma spreads out between the layers and forces them up to a height that may reach 1000 feet over an area of 100 square miles. Unlike a batholith or stock, a laccolith has a definite floor, which is revealed when erosion reaches the rock layers beneath the intrusion. The rocks of a laccolith are similar to those of a batholith, but vary in texture with the size of the mass.

3. Sills. A sheetlike mass of more fluid magma that flows between the layers of existing rock, lifting them just enough to make room for itself, forms a *sill.* The walls of a sill are more or less parallel with the enclosing layers, in con-trast to those of a laccolith. Cooling of the magma in a sill is more rapid than in a batholith or laccolith, and the mag-ma cools faster along the contact with the surrounding rock than in the middle. Therefore the outer zones of a sill may differ greatly in structure and composi-tion from the center area.

4. Dikes. A mass of magma that fills a crack or fissure in existing rocks is called a *dike.* Dikes are often outgrowths from a batholith. They normally cut across the rock structures. Cooling of the magma in a dike is similar to that in a sill. Sometimes the rocks of a dike may show very large crystals, however. These develop because magma containing large amounts of gases and water vapor re-mains fluid for an unusually long time. Thus crystals of quartz, feldspar, and mica several feet in diameter have been found in some dikes.

Intrusive bodies such as dikes and sills are often associated with extrusive rocks, as around a volcano. When a volcano becomes extinct, the magma that fills the passageway does not reach the surface, and cools slowly, forming a *volcanic neck* made up of rocks similar to those in dikes.

Extrusive rock masses. The lavas that are the result of extrusive, or volcanic, activity are generally fine-grained. However, in large masses of lava, the center part of the magma may cool relatively slowly, and large crystals may form. Sometimes the upper layers of a lava flow contain many gas bubbles. When cool, the rock shows many irregular smooth-walled holes. This rock, which is usually of the dark-colored type, such as basalt, is called *scoria*. The dust, ash, and fragments of rocks thrown out by volcanoes harden to form *tuff* and *breccia*.

FIG. 12–3. This miner is drilling to expose a gold-bearing quartz vein in a South Dakota gold mine. (*Bureau of Mines, U. S. Dept. of the Interior*)

Extrusive rocks of long-extinct volcanoes are sometimes found buried under later sedimentary rocks. In some parts of the world recent lavas are visible on the surface, and can be seen flowing from active volcanoes. Thus geologists have actual evidence of the kinds of rock formed by various types of volcanic activity. Volcanism and its characteristic features are discussed in Chapter 16.

Metallic ores in igneous rocks. The ores of metals valuable to man are often associated with igneous rocks. Such ore deposits occur mainly in and around intrusive masses. In magma, atoms and ions of metals are mixed with those of other elements. As the magma works its way upward toward the surface, the composition of the mixture changes, due to changes in temperature and pressure. Some of the mineral is no longer soluble in the magma, and is precipitated in any cracks or crevices of the cooling igneous rock or the surrounding rock layers. A mass of such material is called a *vein*. Veins are usually definitely distinguishable from the surrounding rock; sometimes small quantities of the mineral are present in the rocks around the vein. A system of veins that is rich enough in mineral ores to be profitably mined is called a *lode*.

SEDIMENTARY ROCKS

Types of sedimentary rocks. The second major group of rocks, the sedimentary rocks, may be formed in two ways. Some are *fragmental* sedimentaries, made up of fragments of other rocks that have been carried away from their source by water, wind, or ice and deposited. By means of the pressure of layer after layer of material and the cementing action of certain substances among the rock materials, the fragments become hardened into rock. The shells of small organisms that drift down to the bottom of a body of water may also become cemented to form rock. The *chemical* sedimentary rocks, such as those containing calcite and gypsum, are formed from materials precipitated from solution in water. A number of typical sedimentary rocks are shown on page 196.

The fragmental rocks are grouped according to the size of the fragments they contain; the chemical sedimentaries are grouped according to their composition. Thus in the table below, *conglomerate* is classified as a coarse-grained rock formed from gravel, which is understood here to include large fragments, even boulders, as well as small pebbles; these may be of one or several kinds of rock. *Sandstones* consist of cemented grains of quartz sand. Because some sandstones are porous, liquids easily move through them, and such sandstones are commonly reservoirs for oil and water. *Shale* is clay that has become rock, mainly by pressure. Clay consists of flaky particles of various minerals, and the flakes tend to become pressed into parallel layers. Thus shales have a typical fracture, tending to split into relatively flat pieces. Their texture is usually too fine for the individual particles to be visible to the unaided eye.

Limestones vary in their texture according to their composition, and may be very fine-grained or contain visible fragments of shells. The shells may be mixed with very fine precipitated material. *Dolomite* is similar to limestone but differs somewhat in its chemical composition. Limestone is essentially calcium carbonate; dolomite contains more magnesium.

COMMON SEDIMENTARY ROCKS

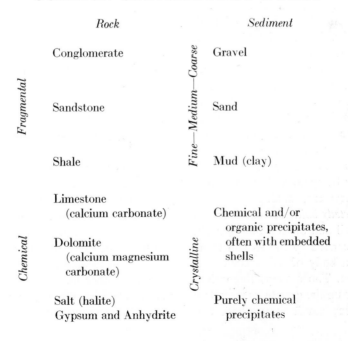

	Rock		*Sediment*
Fragmental	Conglomerate	*Fine—Medium—Coarse*	Gravel
	Sandstone		Sand
	Shale		Mud (clay)
Chemical	Limestone (calcium carbonate)	*Crystalline*	Chemical and/or organic precipitates, often with embedded shells
	Dolomite (calcium magnesium carbonate)		
	Salt (halite) Gypsum and Anhydrite		Purely chemical precipitates

| Mouth of river | Boulders, stones and pebbles solidify to form conglomerate | Sand and silt solidify to form sandstone and siltstone | Clay is compacted to form shale |

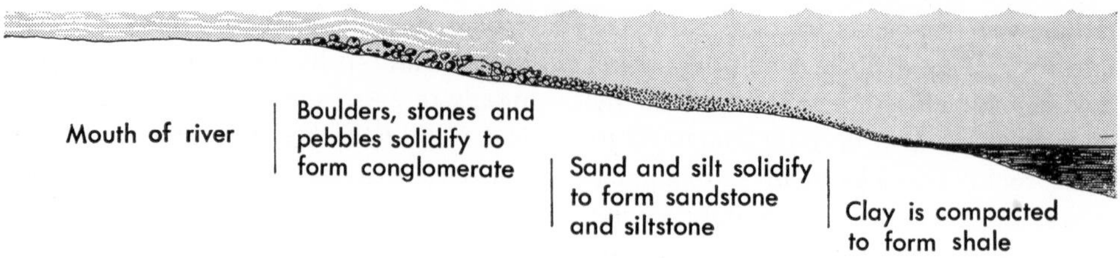

FIG. 12–4. Gradation of fragments in the formation of sedimentary rocks:

Boulder	over 256 mm (10.1 in.)	Sand	2–0.2 mm (0.08–0.008 in.)
Stone	256–64 mm (10.1–2.5 in.)	Silt	0.2–0.02 mm (0.008–0.0008 in.)
Gravel	64–2 mm (2.5–0.08 in.)	Clay	less than 0.02 mm (0.0008 in.)

A special feature of sedimentary rocks is the fossil remains they often contain. *Fossils* are evidences of animals or plants that were buried when the sediment was deposited. Fossils are of immense importance, because they show the types of life found on the earth at different periods of past ages. Unit 6 is concerned with the story revealed by fossils, and the time scale for the history of the earth which geologists have been able to construct.

The formation of sedimentary rocks. The weathering of granite illustrates the general process of formation of sedimentary rocks. First, a large mass of granite may be exposed when the overlying rocks are weathered and carried away by streams. Gradually, wind and weather, by processes that will be described in detail in Unit 5, break up the surface of granite. Some of this decomposed rock waste remains on the surface to form part of the *residual soil;* some of it is carried away by wind and streams and deposited elsewhere, making up part of the *transported soil.* A considerable amount of soil and broken bits of rock, however, is carried by the stream to its destination, a body of water such as a lake or ocean. The streams themselves help to break up the granite as they flow over its surface, carving out a bed. The

faster a stream flows, the more it can carry away.

Thus the materials going to the sea consist of solid fragments of both decomposed and undecomposed debris (clays, sands, pebbles, and boulders) and of materials in solution derived from chemical decomposition of minerals (carbonates of potassium, sodium, magnesium, calcium, iron, etc., together with sulfates and chlorides of the above elements).

When the solid materials enter a sea or lake, an assorting, or grading of the debris takes place. In this respect the sea may be likened to a series of graded sieves. As a stream enters the sea, its speed of flow, and therefore its ability to transport solid material, is lessened. This causes the stream to drop the coarsest materials of its load, which, if left undisturbed, may later form conglomerate. As the stream proceeds, its speed becomes less and less, and correspondingly finer and finer materials are deposited, ranging from coarse sand to very fine sand, the materials that will become sandstone. Finally, the force of the stream being entirely spent, there remain suspended in the sea exceedingly small particles of clay and other finely divided materials. These particles often give the ocean a muddy appearance near the mouth of a river, especially in times of heavy rains over the lands drained by the river. The particles drift out to deep water, where they eventually settle in layers to form shale. See Fig. 12–4.

The amount and quality of the rock waste entering the sea varies with weather changes and other conditions from very large amounts to practically nothing. Also, the current entering the sea is at times much stronger than at others, and as a result zones of sedimentation are farther out at some times than at others. Therefore deposition is subject to continual variations, overlappings, and interruptions. These variations cause the layers of sediments to stand out more or less distinctly, that is, to show bedding planes or sedimentation lines which are often conspicuous in sandstones and shales.

As time goes on these sediments are converted into coherent rocks. The sands are slowly cemented together by small amounts of substances, usually dissolved from the sands themselves. These cementing substances are redeposited upon and between the sand particles, gradually filling the spaces between the grains of sand. The main cementing substances are silicon dioxide, calcium carbonate and ferric oxide.

The origin of limestone. The same waters that wash the solid rock waste into the sea carry with them, in solution, the carbonates and other soluble substances found in this waste. Of these dissolved substances, calcium carbonate is by far the most important from a geological point of view.

Calcium carbonate is removed in solution from the rock waste by means of the ever-present carbon dioxide in the water permeating the mantle rock, for calcium carbonate is soluble in water containing carbon dioxide, though hardly

soluble at all in pure water. The calcium carbonate is usually not precipitated (separated from the solution) immediately on entering the ocean, because there is ordinarily sufficient carbon dioxide in the sea to prevent precipitation of this substance.

However, differences in temperature and other conditions in some oceans affect the ability of the water to hold the calcium carbonate in solution. Then precipitation may occur in certain areas, forming layers of calcium carbonate which later may harden into beds of limestone. A more common source of limestone is the plant and animal life of the seas, which takes the calcium carbonate from the water and uses it to form shells or skeletal structures. As the organisms live and die, generation upon generation, the deposits accumulate to form vast beds of limestone.

The conditions of life required by the various types of organisms largely determine the nature of the limestone. Corals and simple marine plants thrive in clear, relatively shallow water, usually at temperatures above 68°, and in areas of open water, free of sand and silt. Limestones formed under such conditions are almost purely calcareous (consisting of calcium carbonate). On the other hand, some marine animals such as clams and mussels usually live in mud and sand. Accordingly, limestone formed from the shells of these animals or their ancient relatives may contain sand and clay in small or large proportion.

A soft, porous variety of limestone is called *chalk*. Scattered sometimes through the chalk deposits are masses of a very different material, *flint*, a variety of fine-grained quartz. These flint nodules are derived from microscopic marine animals and plants whose shells are silicious (consisting of silica) rather

CONGLOMERATE   Colorado   SANDSTONE   New York

SHALE   Texas   ROCK SALT   New York

LIMESTONE   Massachusetts   DOLOMITE   Minnesota

SLATE   Pennsylvania

QUARTZITE   South Dakota

MICA SCHIST   Vermont

MARBLE   Georgia

PHYLLITE   Massachusetts

GNEISS   Massachusetts

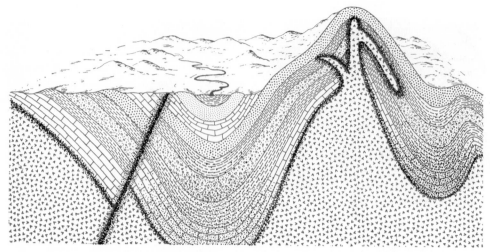

FIG. 12–5. Rocks may be metamorphosed by folding, by contact with intrusions, and by heat of friction where rock layers have slipped along a crack.

than calcareous. Flint is very hard and has been used for centuries to strike fire.

Metallic ores in sedimentary rocks. Deposits of metallic ores sometimes accumulate as sediments and are found associated with sedimentary rocks. The process of weathering may alter the minerals in the rocks or separate them out and concentrate them in stream beds. Thus gold is sometimes found in *placer deposits,* where it has been deposited in stream gravels.

Iron ores are the most important metallic ores occurrring in sedimentary rocks. Oxides of iron are found in nearly every type of sedimentary rock, having been produced by the weathering of iron-bearing minerals. However, the iron ore is present in very small concentration, and is not usually commercially valuable. Important iron ore deposits are generally the result of concentration of the iron by weathering. The iron minerals, which are insoluble, remain behind as the products of weathering are carried away, enriching the ore.

When iron oxide is weathered out of the rock in humid areas, such as swamps or bogs, it may be further oxidized through bacterial action. The mineral then formed is *limonite,* hydrous ferric oxide. Limonite deposits may be buried by later sediments and subjected to heat, which distils off some or all of the water, forming the mineral *hematite* (Fe_2O_3). The lack of oxygen in swamps and bogs, and the presence of carbonic acid, may result in formation of ferrous carbonate ($FeCO_3$) or *siderite.*

METAMORPHIC ROCKS

Types of metamorphic rocks. The effects of the forces that shape the surface of the earth are far-reaching. As will be shown in Unit 4, the rocks of the crust are warped, folded, and compressed by tremendous heat and pressure in the course of broad adjustments of the crust to igneous intrusion, the weight of accumulated sedimentary rocks, and earth movements due to various other causes. Since heat and pressure bring about both physical and chemical changes in the rock-forming minerals, the rocks may be very much altered by these factors. The heat at the contact areas of intrusions may cause recrystallization of the minerals in the surrounding rocks. Beds of sedimentary rocks may be folded so sharply that there is tearing, stretching, and mashing of the minerals. Gases and liquids escaping from the magma of intrusions may penetrate the surrounding rocks, so that new minerals are formed. Chemical reactions between already existing minerals may produce large crystals of garnet or other common metamorphic minerals. When rocks are buried deeply, the heat of the depths of the earth also brings about chemical changes.

The most noticeable effect of metamorphism on a rock is *foliation,* and this characteristic serves to divide these rocks into two groups. In foliated rocks, the minerals are drawn out, flattened, and arranged in parallel layers or bands. Rocks that contain mica or iron-magnesium minerals show foliation because these minerals tend to form flakes or needles, growing larger in certain directions only. This tendency is increased by pressure that squeezes and mashes the grains as they form. Rocks containing quartz or feldspar do not become foliated metamorphic rocks, because crystals of these minerals, even under pressure, tend to grow larger in all directions. The foliated rocks tend to split parallel to the banding. Unfoliated rocks fracture without definite pattern.

The simpler metamorphic rocks are formed directly from sedimentary rocks. The changes are largely due to recrystallization of existing minerals in the rock, and very few new minerals are formed. For example, *slate* commonly forms from shale. It is very fine-grained and usually does not show banding, but splits very easily into thin slabs. The flat surfaces that result from splitting of slate make this rock valuable for roofing, for slate sidewalks, and for "blackboards."

Marble is recrystallized limestone. Under heat and pressure, the fine crystalline particles of limestone are recrystallized as much larger crystals. Organic materials that may have darkened the original limestone are driven off, so that the resulting marble is white except in cases where it contains mineral impurities. Then it may show colored veins, bands, and other patterns.

Quartzite is usually a quartz sandstone that has been compacted and either recrystallized or cemented so that the pores of the original sandstone are closed. This rock fractures through the quartz grains rather than through the cementing material, as sandstone does. Quartzite is extremely hard and durable. Because it is so resistant, it forms the bulk of many hills and mountains from which weaker rocks have been eroded.

Serpentinite, largely the mineral serpentine, is the result of metamorphism of rocks such as pyroxenite, peridotite, and dunite.

Phyllites and *schists* are more highly metamorphosed rocks. Phyllites are formed from shale under greater pressure than that which forms slate. They have a higher luster than slate and may be silky in luster due to the presence of fine grains of mica. Schists are coarser than phyllites and are formed from slate under still higher pressure. They are foliated rocks with fairly distinct bands of different minerals, and usually split very easily along the bands. Schist is classified according to the most prominent mineral in the rock. Thus we have mica schist, hornblende schist, chlorite schist, and quartz schist.

FIG. 12–6. Crumpled dark green gneiss, banded by coarse white granite. (*U. S. Geological Survey*)

Gneiss (nice) is still more highly metamorphosed. It may be derived from granite, from complex rocks of igneous or sedimentary origin, or from a mixture of metamorphic rocks that have been invaded by igneous materials. Because of these variations in composition, it is very difficult to define. Gneiss is a coarse-textured rock with parallel streaks and bands of minerals, resembling schist except that it does not split nearly as readily. Like schist, it is also classified by its most conspicuous mineral, although it may sometimes be named according to its structure or origin. Thus we may speak of a mica gneiss or a hornblende gneiss, or of an injection gneiss, or a granite gneiss.

When rock undergoes successive periods of heat and pressure, separated by long spaces of quiet, one type of metamorphic rock may be changed into another. Usually slates tend to form schists, and schists to form gneiss. Quartzite that contains impurities is sometimes metamorphosed again to form quartz schist.

COMMON METAMORPHIC ROCKS

Metamorphic Form	Characteristics	Original Form
Slate	Fine grain, without banding Near-perfect cleavage	Shale
Marble	Crystalline, usually coarse Foliation revealed only by streaks of impurities	Limestone Dolomite
Quartzite and Quartzite Conglomerate	Compact, massive	Sandstone or Conglomerate
Anthracite		Bituminous Coal
Graphite		Anthracite
Serpentinite	Massive	Peridotite Pyroxenite
Schist and Phyllite	Fine banding Pronounced foliation	Rhyolite, Andesite, and Basalt Shale and Shaly Limestone
Gneiss	Coarse banding Imperfect foliation	Granite and other coarse-grained rock Shale, Shaly Limestone, Conglomerate

Quartz and muscovite (white mica) give this schist its characteristic light color.

The important metamorphic rocks of each group are shown in the table on page 200; they are illustrated on page 197.

Coal. Metamorphism is essential in the formation of a highly important natural resource, coal. In the production of coal, the remains of plants that accumulate in a swamp or bog are changed by heat and pressure that drive out moisture, gases and other matter, leaving carbon in varying amounts. The necessary conditions for a coal bed are that the swamp is stagnant, and that it is slowly sinking. The stagnant water prevents oxygen from reaching the plant material, so that decomposition is stopped after a short or long interval, depending on conditions. The sinking of the swamp-land allows layer after layer of plant remains to accumulate. This partly decomposed matter is called *peat,* and is used in some parts of the world as a fuel. Most coal beds have their origin in swamps relatively near the sea. When the sea inundates the swamp the coal bed is covered over with later sediments. The sediments, including the coal bed, may then be folded during mountain-making movements. Once the plant debris is buried, the heat and pressure drives off the moisture and gases to some extent, and coal is formed. *Lignite,* a brownish, woody-appearing substance, is coal that still contains 30 to 40 per-cent of water. Though it seems dry, it loses water on exposure and crumbles to pieces. **Bituminous** or **soft coal** is more strongly compacted; the proportion of carbon is higher. When bituminous coal

FIG. 12–7. Outcrops of bituminous coal near Fairbanks, Alaska. (*Bureau of Mines, U. S. Dept. of the Interior*)

FIG. 12–8. Thin-bedded sandstone in Guadalupe County, New Mexico. Notice the well-defined bedding planes. (*U. S. Geological Survey*)

is strongly folded and heated, it becomes *anthracite* or *hard coal,* with a high carbon content. Under intense metamorphism, practically all the volatile materials are driven out of the anthracite. The resulting product, graphitic anthracite, is almost worthless as a fuel. The ultimate product of metamorphism of anthracite is pure carbon in the form of graphite.

ROCK STRUCTURES

Stratification. Igneous, sedimentary, and metamorphic rocks, considered as broad masses, tend to occur in characteristic structures. Some rocks are in definite layers, roughly parallel to each other. These layers are called beds or *strata,* and the rocks in which they are found are called *stratified* rocks. Others show no apparent strata, and are said to be *massive* or unstratified.

Sedimentary rocks are almost always stratified. The different strata are recognizable by differences in color, composition, or texture from the adjacent beds. The strata part readily along their surfaces or bedding planes. Igneous rocks usually occur in massive formations, although lava flows may show stratification, with beds of volcanic dust or fragments lying between the layers of lava. Metamorphic rocks may be either stratified or massive, depending on their composition and on the conditions under which they were formed.

Jointing. A characteristic of all three kinds of rocks is the presence of cracks or *joints* in fairly regular patterns. These joints are due to various causes. In igneous rock, they are probably formed during the cooling process. Such joints develop at right angles to the cooling surface. Thus in a level intrusion, such as a sill, or in a lava flow, the joints run vertically, while in a vertical dike they are horizontal. Jointing in fine-grained igneous rock may result in columnar structure, creating unusual steplike features such as the Giant's Causeway in

Ireland and the Devil's Postpile in California. See Fig. 12–7.

In sedimentary rocks, jointing may be the result of contraction during drying of the beds, or of strains put on the rocks when the beds are uplifted or bent by warping or folding. The joints are at right angles to the bedding planes, and may form systems which divide the rock into clearly defined blocks. These often determine the shape of the cliffs formed by these rocks.

Jointing in metamorphic rocks is the result of the great stress and high temperatures to which they are subjected. Some types of metamorphic rocks, such as gneiss, may show joints similar to those in igneous rocks, whereas others, such as slates, may have joints similar to those in the sedimentary rocks from which they originate.

FIG. 12–9. Jointing in fine-grained igneous rock formed the Devil's Postpile, Devil's Postpile National Monument. The columnar structure is revealed by weathering. (*National Park Service*)

SUMMARY

ROCKS may be mixtures of minerals in almost any proportion, or may be composed mainly of one mineral. Rocks have no fixed chemical formula, and are classified in three groups mainly on the basis of origin.

Igneous rocks are formed from the solidification of magma. Intrusive or plutonic rocks are those that hardened beneath the surface of the earth. Extrusive or eruptive rocks are those that cooled above the surface. Volcanoes are the visible result of extrusive activity. Batholiths, laccoliths, sills, and dikes result from igneous intrusions. Intrusive rocks are generally coarser in texture than extrusive rocks.

Sedimentary rocks result from the hardening, compressing, or cementing of rock fragments, organic remains, or the products of chemical precipitation. Fossils and metal ore deposits are often associated with sedimentary formations.

Metamorphic rocks are composed of previously existing rocks that have been changed by the heat and pressure that accompany crustal movements or intrusions of igneous magmas. Changes may be too small to detect or so great that it is impossible to determine the original rock. Metamorphism may result in a new crystalline structure, coarsening of texture, foliation, and the formation of new minerals.

VOCABULARY REVIEW

Match the phrase in the left column with the correct term in the right column. *Do not write in this book.*

1. Evidence of pre-existing plant or animal
2. Flowing molten rock above the surface of the earth
3. Rock waste that remains where it was formed
4. Spongy exterior
5. Hard coal
6. Igneous intrusion between layers of existing rock
7. Partially decomposed plant remains
8. Concentration of minerals in stream bed
9. Study of rocks
10. Soft coal
11. Formed from animals with silicious skeletons
12. Parallel layers or bands
13. Large crystals in mass of fine crystals
14. System of metallic ore veins

a. placer deposit
b. anthracite
c. porphyry
d. residual soil
e. batholith
f. fossil
g. foliated
h. bituminous
i. pumice
j. sill
k. petrology
l. precipitated
m. lode
n. lava
o. peat
p. flint

QUESTIONS · GROUP A

In each of the following groups of terms, three are related in some way and one is not. Select the unrelated term and give a reason for your choice.

1. (*a*) granite (*b*) syenite (*c*) obsidian (*d*) gabbro
2. (*a*) gneiss (*b*) slate (*c*) phyllite (*d*) schist
3. (*a*) anthracite (*b*) graphite (*c*) peat (*d*) bituminous
4. (*a*) limonite (*b*) hematite (*c*) pyrite (*d*) siderite
5. (*a*) basalt (*b*) diorite (*c*) trachyte (*d*) rhyolite
6. (*a*) limestone (*b*) marble (*c*) gneiss (*d*) shells
7. (*a*) lava (*b*) foliation (*c*) volcano (*d*) extrusive
8. (*a*) quartz (*b*) sandstone (*c*) quartzite (*d*) shale
9. (*a*) limestone (*b*) trachyte (*c*) conglomerate (*d*) dolomite
10. (*a*) granite (*b*) diorite (*c*) gabbro (*d*) peridotite
11. (*a*) scoria (*b*) schist (*c*) tuff (*d*) breccia

Select the best term to complete the following statements. *Do not write in this book.*

12. Fossils may be found in (*a*) granite (*b*) obsidian (*c*) shale (*d*) marble.
13. The main mineral in limestone is (*a*) garnet (*b*) peat (*c*) calcite (*d*) limonite.
14. The rock made up of cemented quartz grains is (*a*) conglomerate (*b*) marl (*c*) gabbro (*d*) sandstone.
15. A rock of organic origin is (*a*) coal (*b*) obsidian (*c*) phyllite (*d*) pegmatite.

16. A rock that may float on water is (*a*) syenite (*b*) pumice (*c*) granite (*d*) sandstone.
17. A mass of intrusive igneous rock whose depth is uncertain is called a (*a*) sill (*b*) dike (*c*) rhyolite (*d*) batholith.
18. Simple marine animals that live in water at temperatures above 68 degrees are called (*a*) fossils (*b*) clams (*c*) sharks (*d*) corals.
19. A form of coal that contains 30 to 40 percent water is (*a*) bituminous (*b*) anthracite (*c*) graphite (*d*) lignite.
20. A volcanic neck contains rocks similar to those found in a (*a*) vein (*b*) placer deposit (*c*) dike (*d*) lode.

GROUP B

1. Discuss several ways that you could distinguish white marble, white quartzite, chalk, and white coral.
2. What determines the size of crystals formed in igneous rocks?
3. Why are fossils not found in igneous and metamorphic rocks?
4. Discuss the processes involved during the formation of hematite, limonite, and siderite.
5. Discuss the process involved in the four major types of igneous intrusions. Describe each type.
6. Discuss the characteristics of schists and gneisses. How are they classified?
7. Define magma. Explain and give examples of the difference between extrusive and intrusive rocks.
8. Discuss how rock fragments carried by a stream are sorted when the stream enters a larger body of water.
9. Explain the following statement: Of the three classes of rocks, igneous rocks are oldest.
10. In what respects do metamorphic rocks differ from the original rock?
11. What is the difference between acidic and basic rocks?

UNIT REVIEW QUESTIONS

1. What are isotopes? Name the isotopes of the element hydrogen.
2. What determines the different properties of elements?
3. Tell the difference between an atom and a molecule; between a mixture and a compound.
4. What information can be determined from a chemical formula?
5. Compare the relative weights of the particles that make up an atom.
6. List the various properties of acids, salts, bases, and oxides.
7. What procedure might be used to obtain calcium sulfate? potassium chloride? Write a chemical equation for each of the reactions.
8. What procedure could be followed for the preparation of hydrogen? Write a chemical equation to illustrate the reaction.

9. Name two substances that result from the reaction between sodium carbonate and calcium chloride. Write a chemical equation to show the reaction.
10. Name all the elements found in each of the following: bicarbonate radical, sulfuric acid, sodium nitrate, iron sulfate, magnesium hydroxide, carbonic acid, sulfur trioxide, ammonium radical.
11. How might you decide whether a given substance is a mineral?
12. What minerals are commonly found in granite? Of these minerals, which is the most resistant to weathering? What is the eventual fate of the other minerals in granite?
13. What is the usual method of obtaining the streak of a mineral?
14. List the six basic crystal systems. Draw a diagram for each system showing the axes and their relationship to one another. Give an example of a mineral for each crystal system.
15. Differentiate between the terms cleavage and fracture.
16. Describe how Mohs' scale can be used to determine the hardness of an unknown mineral.
17. What chemical test could be used to identify a mineral that contains phosphorus?
18. Without resorting to chemical analysis, how might you differentiate plagioclase feldspar from orthoclase feldspar?
19. Muscovite, biotite, phlogopite, and chlorite are somewhat similar in appearance. What properties would enable you to identify each mineral?
20. Two dark green minerals are augite and hornblende. How could you tell one from the other?
21. How were kernite, halite, and gypsum formed?
22. What determines whether a certain mineral is classified as a gem?
23. What are the differences between the following: batholith, sill, dike, and laccolith? Make a labeled diagram of a cross-section of the earth's crust illustrating each of these igneous intrusions.

ACTIVITIES

1. Make a collection of local rocks and minerals. Identify each specimen.
2. Make a series of models out of wood, plastic, cardboard, or other material to illustrate the basic systems of crystals. Exhibit these with minerals from each of the systems.
3. Set up an experiment to grow different types of crystals. Solutions of salt, sugar, potassium permanganate, sulfur, alum, or copper sulfate will grow good crystals. Consult your instructor or refer to a high school chemistry book for procedure.
4. Set up a display of sediments and the rocks that they form.
5. Obtain or draw a map of the continental United States and label the location of important mineral deposits.
6. Make a collection of metal ores and exhibit them with an example of the extracted metal.

7. Consult your instructor or refer to a high school chemistry book and do several borax bead tests, flame tests, or blowpipe tests.

8. Using litmus paper, determine whether common household substances such as fruit or vegetable juices, ammonia, and bleach are acids or bases. Wet the litmus paper with distilled water and test solid substances to see whether they have acidic or basic properties.

9. Make a report on the extraction of aluminum. Obtain samples of the materials involved.

10. Make a circle graph to show the relative quantities of the major elements in the earth's crust.

11. Try to arrange a talk by a local lapidary or "rockhound."

12. Form a class committee to arrange a field trip to a local quarry, museum, or fossil formation in your area.

13. Put a mixture of different sediments such as gravel, clay, and sand into a tall vessel of water. Stir and let it stand. Record the times required for the deposition of each type of sediment.

14. Using a magnifying glass, try to determine the common minerals in dry sand.

15. Arrange collections of rocks to show different features such as chemical families, fossils, precipitates, and organic origin.

16. Collect samples of soils in your school area. Classify them as acidic or basic. Find out what pH means.

17. Fill a sandbox or aquarium with a mixture of sand, gravel, and clay. Slope the material so that it resembles a hill. Run water over the "hill" and observe the materials that are eroded and the place of deposition. Change the volume and velocity of the stream of water and observe the effect.

18. Make a report on the importance of conservation of our mineral resources.

FURTHER READING

MODERN CHEMISTRY. C. E. Dull, H. C. Metcalfe, and J. E. Williams, 1958. *Holt, Rinehart and Winston, Inc., New York.*

ALL ABOUT THE WONDERS OF CHEMISTRY. I. M. Freeman, 1954. *Random House, New York.*

★

GEOLOGY MERIT BADGE HANDBOOK. Boy Scouts of America, *New Brunswick, N. J.*

TEXT-BOOK OF MINERALOGY. E. S. Dana and W. E. Ford, 1954. *John Wiley and Sons, Inc., New York.*

MINERALOGY. E. H. Kraus, W. F. Hunt, and L. S. Ramsdell, 1959. *McGraw-Hill Book Co., New York.*

GEM HUNTER'S GUIDE. R. P. McFall, 1951. *Science and Mechanics Publishing Company, Chicago.*

ROCKS AND MINERALS. R. M. Pearl, 1956. *Barnes and Noble, Inc., New York.*

HOW TO KNOW THE MINERALS AND ROCKS. R. M. Pearl, 1955. *McGraw-Hill Book Co., New York.*

FIELD GUIDE TO ROCKS AND MINERALS. F. H. Pough, 1953. *Houghton Mifflin Co., Boston.*

THE crust of the earth is not a simple shell enclosing the body of the planet, like the rind enclosing an orange. The picture we have of activity deep within the earth, of forces that work to shape the surface, is completely at odds with any such concept. From areas of the crust that are exposed to close examination, we have pieced together a history of constant and widespread change throughout long ages.

There is no complete explanation for the forces that raise mountains and crumple great sections of the outer crust. The origin and working of these forces is among the most baffling problems in the study of the earth, but their surface effects are well known. In this unit the major landforms created by massive crustal movements are examined, and theories of the origin of landforms and of the forces themselves are considered.

UNIT 4

THE FORCES THAT SHAPE THE EARTH'S SURFACE

CHAPTER 13

DIASTROPHISM

DURING the millions of years of earth history, there have been great and widespread changes in the crust of the earth. We know that the earth's surface has not always been exactly as it is now, with oceans, continents, plains, and mountains in their present locations. Even in ancient times, men were puzzled by evidence that land areas had risen above the water or sunk beneath it. They wondered why they found seashells buried in the rocks on the tops of high inland mountains.

The science of geology hardly existed until the end of the eighteenth century, but early writers on natural history knew that great earthquakes could open cracks in the surface, and that lava and ashes from volcanoes could cover up whole towns and villages. Some of these writers believed that only such great and violent events could bring about changes at the earth's surface. They explained everything, even river valleys, as the result of sudden catastrophes that split open the earth or pushed up the mountains. Other

VOCABULARY

Constructional landforms. Landforms that have been built up by forces acting beneath the earth's surface.

Diastrophism. Movement of solid parts of the earth.

Thrust. Horizontal movement of the earth's crust.

Subsidence. Sinking of the earth's crust.

Isostasy. The state of balance of the earth's crust.

Anticline. The crest or upfold of a rock fold.

Syncline. The trough or downfold of a rock fold.

Joint. A fracture in a rock surface.

Fissure. An open fracture in a rock surface.

Fault. A fracture in a rock surface along which there is displacement of the broken surfaces.

Seismograph. An instrument to detect, measure, and record movements of the earth's crust.

writers, however, developed a different explanation for many of the landforms they observed. These men believed that a slow, gradual, unending process of building up by earth movement and wearing down by erosion is responsible for most of the landforms. In this view, vast stretches of time were needed for the development of the landscape as we see it today. Evidence can be found that our landscape is still changing in the same ways.

The modern approach to geology was clearly expressed by James Hutton, a Scottish geologist. In 1785, before the Royal Society of Edinburgh, he explained his theory that the present is the key to the past. Since then, working on this basis, geologists have formed theories concerning the development of the landforms found all over the world, classifying and describing them according to their origin, rather than their appearance. Although most of these theories are generally accepted as fact, we should remember that geologists differ in their interpretation of individual observations, and that appearances, in the study of landforms, as in many things, can be deceiving.

THE LANGUAGE OF LANDFORMS

Description of surface features. To take a journey across the United States by any route is a fascinating experience. The scene constantly changes, as we cross valleys and mountains, plains and plateaus. Starting at New York City, we might travel up the Hudson Valley, then through the Great Lakes region to Chicago. From there, we might cross the Great Plains to Denver, the mile-high city in the foothills of the Rockies. Trav-

FIG. 13–1. James Hutton, the Scottish geologist, formulated the basic principles of modern geology. He strongly influenced the development of this science in the nineteenth century. (*Brown Brothers*)

eling southwest across the Colorado Plateau which extends through parts of Utah, Arizona, and New Mexico, we might reach the Grand Canyon. Then, crossing the mountain ranges of the Pacific Coast, we would arrive at the shores of that ocean. Along the way, how many hundreds of different points of beauty and interest we would have passed! You undoubtedly know of such places near your home.

When we describe these familiar features of the landscape, we may use general terms that tell how each looks to us. We may say that a mountain is steep or gently sloping, or that in a certain plains area there are many flat-topped hills. However, such descriptions do not tell how a region "got that way" or why it resembles or differs from other regions of similar appearance. Once we view the landscape in relation to its geological history, it has a new fascination.

Physiography, the branch of geology that deals with the earth's surface features, has a language that makes precise description possible. When the physiographer speaks of *landforms,* the terms he uses tell something of their origin and past history.

Constructional and destructional features. To the geologist, all landforms may be thought of as the result of a combination of processes that continually work against each other. Constructive processes build up the landforms by earth movements that shape the surface; destructive processes sculpture the surface by erosion. Some landforms, therefore, are classed as *constructional;* these are mountains, plains, and plateaus. *Destructional* features are those which have been carved out or deposited on the surface by weathering and by agents of erosion: streams, ice, winds, and waves. These landforms include valleys, caves and cliffs, river deltas, sand bars, and dunes. Often it is hard to separate the constructional from the destructional features. Any large landform is a product of both processes operating at the same time. Nevertheless, we can study the operation of these processes more clearly if we separate them mentally, using geological terms for the features of the landscape to indicate the processes that have occurred and the visible effects they have produced. This unit deals mainly with constructional processes: movements of the earth's crust.

RISE AND FALL OF THE EARTH'S CRUST

The evidence of earth movements. Evidence that earth movements have occurred in the distant or recent past can be observed in many places. Mount Robson, in the Canadian Rockies, towers more than 13,000 feet above the present sea level. Yet fossils of marine animals, such as shark's teeth, found in the topmost rock layers tell us that these layers were pushed up from under the waters of the ocean.

Those who have studied the fossil remains in the rocks of the world agree that at one time in the geologic past a land bridge extended from Asia to North America in the area of the present-day Aleutians. Dry land also extended from Iceland through the British Isles and to continental Europe. Large parts of the continent of North America were repeatedly covered by seas. North and South America were not always connected by the Isthmus of Panama. From studies of rock structure as shown in surface outcrops over wide areas, geologists have reconstructed the history of most of the earth's surface through great stretches of time. What was once the floor of a shallow sea may have been covered with sediments, lifted up, folded and cracked, worn down to a level, and again covered by the sea, then lifted again, to be again worn down. The earth's crust has apparently been thrust up and forced down or pushed sideways not once but many times in the past. Careful observations show us that these processes are still going on.

More sudden and violent earth movements, usually affecting more limited areas, can be observed in our own lifetime and are described in recent historical accounts. On June 7, 1692, the streets of the famous pirate city of Port Royal, Jamaica, suddenly quivered and shook. Huge waves swept in from the ocean, and in a few minutes most of the city sank into the sea. This is the only recorded case of an inhabited city being swallowed by the ocean as a result of a violent earthquake. Recently, divers investigating the sunken city found many of the cracked buildings intact after two and a half centuries. In the past hundred years, earthquakes in California, Japan, and elsewhere have made slight changes in the face of the earth. More will be said of these later in this chapter.

Diastrophism. All the movements of the solid parts of the earth are included in the term *diastrophism* (dy-*as*-truh-fiz'm). The movements of the earth's magma are included in the process of *volcanism*, which will be discussed more fully in Chapter 16. Diastrophism and volcanism are very closely related. Thus, many of the features described in this chapter as the results of diastrophism are also found associated with volcanic features.

Earth movements may be described according to the direction of motion. *Uplift* is either a local or a widespread rising of the crust. Often islands arise in the deep seas of the Pacific. In the course of earth history, large areas of continents have been raised to higher elevations by diastrophic processes. In the Scandinavian region, former shorelines can be detected high above the present sea level, showing that parts of Sweden and Finland have been raised as much as 900 feet.

Subsidence occurs when the earth's crust sinks. Islands in the Pacific have disappeared beneath the water from time to time in the historic past. Large continental areas have subsided, resulting in invasion by shallow seas. The present shoreline of Maine shows many "drowned" valleys where the sea has invaded the land, forming bays. In other places former hills in the land surface have become islands.

Changes in elevation are noticeable inland as well as on the seacoast. Lake

FIG. 13–2. Marine fossils are found in the strata visible in the mountain peaks of Mount Robson, British Columbia. (*Canadian National Railways*)

shores, as in the Great Lakes region, show that the lake basins have been tilted and lifted several feet higher since they were first formed in past ages.

Thrust is a horizontal (sideways) motion of the crust, by which large masses of rock slide against one another into new positions. In 1906, movement of rock that caused the San Francisco earthquake cut across roads and fences, leaving remarkable evidence of the extent of the movement.

CAUSES OF DIASTROPHISM

The theory of isostasy. From their study of rock structures, geologists have found that the earth's surface features have varied greatly in past ages. However, they conclude that the general relation of mountain region to plain, and ocean deep to continental mass, has remained fairly constant. That is, there is no evidence that continents once existed in what are now the great ocean basins, or that seas which covered parts of the continents were as deep as the present ocean depths. In fact, the oceans and continents seem to be underlain by different types of igneous rocks. There is good evidence that the foundation rock of the continents is largely granite, while that of the ocean basins is basalt, a much denser rock. From precise measurements of the pull of gravity in mountains as compared with plains, geologists have also concluded that the rocks underlying mountain areas are lighter than those beneath plains areas.

All these observations have led to the theory that continents and ocean basins, as well as mountains and plains, are in a state of balance, and that they maintain this balance by slowly adjusting themselves vertically. As rock from a higher region is removed by erosion and deposited on a lower region, the higher region slowly rises while the lower region becomes heavier and slowly sinks. This theory of *isostasy* (from the Greek meaning "equal standing") helps to explain why the wearing down of the mountains and the filling up of the ocean basins have not resulted in a level surface over the whole earth.

To visualize the theory of isostasy, we may think of the earth's crust as consisting of lighter and heavier sections. These sections rest on a base which yields to changes in pressure from above by flowing. As stated in Chapter 6, the material of the earth beneath the cooler, upper part of the crust is not usually liquid. However, geologists have found in laboratory tests that even solid rock is somewhat plastic under certain conditions; it changes shape or flows when

subjected to great pressure. See Fig. 13–3. Of course, the balanced earth sections are not really separate; one blends into the other gradually, but the total effect of isostasy may be diagrammed as in Fig. 13–4.

The continual slow subsidence of an area while sediments are being piled on it helps to explain why sedimentary beds laid down in shallow seas or near the shore may reach enormous thickness. If the ocean floor did not subside, the sediments would fill the ocean basin so that deposition would cease. The beds would then be limited to the depth of the basin.

Studies of the effects of glaciation bear out the theory of isostasy. In the recent geologic past, just as now, enormous amounts of water were withdrawn from the oceans by evaporation. However, instead of being returned to the

FIG. 13–3. Solid rock is plastic under intense pressure. The limestone cylinder on the left was distorted into the form at the right by a vertical pressure of 125,100 pounds per square inch while a pressure of 22,100 pounds per square inch was applied laterally. (*Dept. of the Interior, Bureau of Reclamation*)

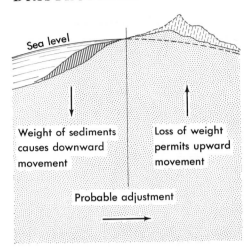

FIG. 13–4. The theory of isostasy is one explanation for diastrophism.

oceans by the rivers, the water piled up on northern North America and Europe in the form of great ice sheets. The weight of the ice seems to have caused a marked subsidence of the ice-burdened lands and a corresponding general uplift of the remainder of the earth's surface. The uplift, being spread over a much greater area, is not easily traceable. The depression of the lands, however, affecting a comparatively small area, was very pronounced in some places. The land in Quebec, Canada, was depressed about 1000 feet. When the ice melted, the depressed areas began to rise again. They are probably still rising, as shown by emerged shorelines of lakes and rivers along the coastal areas, as in the Great Lakes and the Hudson-Champlain Valley. These show that the area has been uplifted and tilted.

The theory of isostasy alone, however, is not enough to explain the great folding and thrusting movements of the crust. Geologists can only form theories about the basic causes of such movements, which are among the great mysteries of science. We do not know enough about the way rock materials behave far below the earth's crust to be certain about the truth of any one theory, or how important one factor is compared to others. Several of the various theories that have been suggested are helpful as possible explanations of the cause of mountain-making forces.

The contraction theory. It is generally accepted that the earth is gradually shrinking, either because it is cooling, or because great pressures squeeze parts of it into a smaller volume, causing a continuous increase in density. Because of this shrinking, the interior is always becoming a little too small for the exterior. This "misfit" would bring about a continual tendency toward readjustment. Gravity draws the crust inward as the shrinkage occurs. The crust, however, being rigid, cannot just settle down upon the smaller interior as an unruffled layer, and so it undergoes thrusting and buckling. The stronger and heavier blocks of the crust sink, while the weaker strata, crowded and squeezed, are thrust upward to form the great mountain ranges. Great blocks of rock have been uplifted and thrust horizontally over the earth's surface. Some blocks have been elevated without crushing or folding to form the ridges called block mountains. In the Northern Rocky Mountains, breaks of this type occurred over a wide area. In one case, a mass of rock 10,000 feet thick was pushed eastward for about 18 miles over the bedrock below. This movement, which alone shortened the earth's crust by 18 miles, illustrates the type of evidence that supports the concept of the shrinking earth.

In speaking of the movements by which the adjustments of the crust occur, we must distinguish between forces of two types. The stress on rocks may be one of *compression,* a pushing or squeezing together of the rock masses, or it may be one of *tension,* a pulling apart of the rock masses. Compression usually results in the shortening of the surface area. As we have seen, if the crust is adjusting to a smaller interior, such shortening is essential. However, since the compression may be greater in some areas than in others, the total adjustment process is not likely to operate smoothly and evenly. Where one rock mass is pushed together, others may be pulled apart. Since rock is less resistant to tension than to compression, breaks are more likely to occur in regions where the rocks are under tension. The tensional stress lengthens the surface area, as the rock masses slide against each other along the break.

The contraction theory accounts for the mountain zones which are common along the edges of the continents. In the course of adjustments due to shrinking, the continental sections of the crust, being lighter, are pushed up by the heavier ocean sections as they sink. Because the continental areas are lifted up, the shallow inland seas recede from them, and more land emerges. The pushing or wedging action at the edges of the continents, as ocean floors sink, compresses the rocks and folds them. These rocks are relatively weak, being mostly sediments in the coastal areas. Melting of rocks from the heat of friction may be responsible for the volcanoes which are common in regions of folding.

The convection theory. Another theory which would account for the pushing up and folding of the rocks, especially those in the great mountain chains that border the continents (see Chapter 14), is the *convection theory.* Convection currents are set up in liquids (and also in gases) by heating. The cooler portion

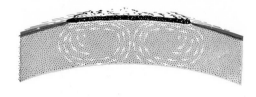

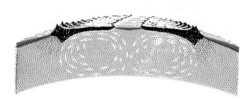

FIG. 13–5. Convection may occur on a large scale in the rocks below the earth's crust.

of a liquid, being more dense than the heated portion, sinks. This pushes up the heated portion. The rising liquid loses heat at the surface and then moves down again. Thus circulating currents are set up which continue as long as heat is applied.

The theory has been advanced that convection currents are set up under the crust, the source of heat being radioactive elements such as uranium. The heat accumulates because the rocks conduct heat slowly, and the resulting expansion causes plastic flow upward. This process, occurring under the continental mass, might result in the situation illustrated in Fig. 13–5.

Continental drift. A further attempt to account for diastrophic movement and for the folding and faulting that occur most strongly along the edges of the continents is the *continental drift theory.* The theory supposes that originally only one large continent was formed when the earth's crust cooled. This single continent was composed mainly of granite, which, being lighter than the underlying materials, "floated" on them.

In time, the single continent broke up and the various sections drifted apart. It is claimed, for example, that northward movement of Africa created pressure against Europe, forming the Alps and neighboring mountains, and that the western mountain ranges of North and South America are the result of "piling up" as the continents drifted westward against the basin of the Pacific.

It is hard to imagine what force might bring about the drifting, but the theory is supported by some geological evidence. A glance at a globe will help to make this theory clear. If the maps of North and South America were moved eastward against Europe and Africa, the continental shapes would match well. Some old mountain belts in America would appear continuous with belts of similar geologic age in the eastern continental masses.

EFFECTS OF EARTH MOVEMENT

The deformation of the rocks. The effects of diastrophism may be seen in various ways at the earth's surface. The uplifted shorelines described on page 211, and erosional features such as the position of stream valleys, which will be discussed later in Unit 5, are evidence of movement. More useful, however, are the rock structures as they are revealed at the surface in outcrops. These often help geologists to discover what processes have been at work to produce the landscape features.

Sedimentary rocks are especially good indicators of diastrophism, since any deformation of them is clearly shown by tilts, bends or breaks in the layers. In some areas, rock layers which were deposited in a horizontal position are now slanted at considerable angles, giving evidence that they were tilted after deposition. In other areas, the beds show folds, indicating that tremendous sidewise forces acted on the rocks and caused them to bend and wrinkle. In addition, there has often been fracturing of the rocks, with shifting of the layers along the breaks so they no longer match. Sometimes the layers have simply been pushed up or down without disturbance of their horizontal arrangement; then other types of evidence, such as uplifted shorelines, may be needed to indicate the movement. By more pronounced and long-continued pressure, the beds of rock may be pushed into wavelike folds. As we have seen, solid rock is plastic under great heat and pressure. The folding of rock under these conditions is called *plastic deformation.*

The rock folds may be small, each one measurable in inches or feet, or so large that they are measured in miles and are responsible for great mountain ridges. With the folding, there may also be cracking or fracturing rather than bending of the rock. Where they yield to stress by breaking, the rock layers may slide over one another along the break. Such movement or *faulting* is shown in Fig. 13–6. The story of folding and faulting in some regions may be easily reconstructed from simple observation of the rock outcrops. In other areas, the story may be almost incredibly complex, only decipherable after careful study of a wide area. *Structural geology,* as the

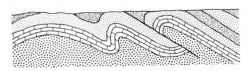

FIG. 13–6. A fault may result from folding and fracturing of rock layers.

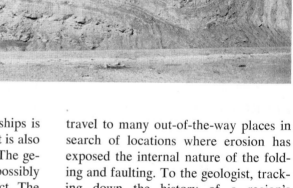

FIG. 13–7. Folding shortens the earth's crust, forming anticlines and synclines. (*U. S. Forest Service* and *U. S. Geological Survey*)

study of rocks and their relationships is called, may be complicated, but it is also highly important in modern life. The geologist must learn all that he possibly can about this phase of his subject. The finding of valuable ore deposits or large fields of petroleum depends on an understanding of such complexities. The details of structure may be complicated, and much of the "evidence" may have been destroyed by erosion of the rock layers, or buried under soil and later sediments. Still, there are usually enough remnants of folds to allow the geologist to reconstruct the original conditions. Certain layers may be easily distinguishable from others, and thus serve as clues. When the geologist studies an area he hunts for surface outcrops of rocks such as those revealed by railroad cuts or other man-made excavations. He may

travel to many out-of-the-way places in search of locations where erosion has exposed the internal nature of the folding and faulting. To the geologist, tracking down the history of a region's development may be as exciting a "detective" hunt as any in fiction. The following pages will give some idea of the turns and twists in the story of rock structure.

Folds. If a region of horizontal sedimentary beds laid down under the ocean waters were to be lifted up without deformation or erosion, the surface would not tell us much about the structure beneath, because only the top layer would be visible. Any lower layers would not appear until streams had cut deep into the beds. In actual fact, however, there is almost always some bending or *warping* of the sedimentary beds into broad, low, domes and shallow basins. These may extend for many hundreds of miles, as in the Colorado Plateau. Because the beds are thus tilted in places, the lower layers show up along the stream beds and in other outcrops.

When the layers are more strongly folded, and the beds sharply tilted, the deeper structure can be pieced together even more easily. Then the geologist can reconstruct, in imagination, the outlines of the folds. Folds, in their simplest form, may be compared to waves on the ocean. Each has a crest or upfold, and a trough, or downfold. The crest of a rock fold is called an *anticline;* the trough is a *syncline.* For very broad folds covering hundreds of miles, the terms *geanticline* and *geosyncline* are used. See Fig. 13–7.

If we could see a region that had been recently folded, and on which no erosion had taken place, the anticlines would be ridges; the synclines would be valleys. Erosion begins, however, as soon as the

folds are lifted above the water and continues as the uplift goes on. Thus deep erosional valleys may cut across the anticlines, or in fact, the erosion process may be so extensive as to carry away entire groups of anticlines. In some cases, the synclines which might have been valleys finally become the tops of mountains after the removal of surrounding rock material in a later period of erosion. See Fig. 13–8.

Remember that in speaking of anticlines and synclines, we refer to structure and not to surface appearance. Thus there are synclinal mountains and anticlinal valleys, formed when erosion has worn away the weaker rocks and left the stronger ones to stand out as mountains or ridges in the landscape. In the Appalachians, a region of strongly folded strata, such ridges are common.

Dip and strike. In deciphering the structure of an area of folded rock, the geologist uses various methods. Careful measurements of the degree of tilt of individual outcrops are made, and the type of rock is determined as closely as possible. The results of these observations are mapped so that their relation to each other can be studied. A geologic map or diagram shows the tilt of a rock bed in terms of its *dip* and *strike.*

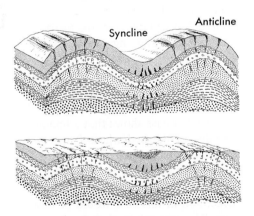

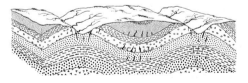

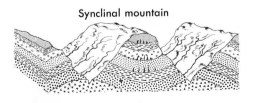

FIG. 13–8. Synclinal mountains develop as weaker beds are eroded. Above, erosion levels the initial anticlines and synclines, exposing weak beds in the anticlines. Right, uplift brings about further erosion and the resistant rocks of the syncline remain as a ridge.

FIG. 13–9. A Brunton pocket transit. The compass is used to determine strike, and the dip is measured in degrees around the graduated circle after the instrument has been leveled. The instrument is also used to determine accurately the location of a rock outcrop for preliminary mapping in the field. (*Wm. Ainsworth and Sons, Inc.*)

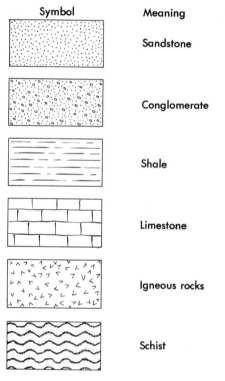

Symbol	Meaning
	Sandstone
	Conglomerate
	Shale
	Limestone
	Igneous rocks
	Schist

FIG. 13–10. Variations of symbols such as these are generally used in geological diagrams to indicate the different types of rocks. Note that the symbols are based on rock features such as the strong cleavage of shale and the jointing of limestone.

To find the dip and strike of a rock bed, the geologist must first find a flat rock surface that can be identified as a bedding plane. With an instrument called the Brunton pocket transit, he measures the direction and angle of inclination of the bed. The instrument combines a compass and a *clinometer*. The latter uses a pendulum or a mounted level to show the degree of tilt from the horizontal when the instrument is placed on a slanting surface. See Fig. 13–9.

Suppose that a certain bed slants at an angle of 30° from the horizontal. This is the angle of *dip*. Suppose also that the compass shows that a line along the edge of the bed where it meets the horizontal plane extends north and south. This direction is the *strike*. The direction of dip is at right angles to the strike, and in this case would be east or west. The bed might thus be described as dipping 30° E. The relation of dip to strike is shown in Fig. 13–11.

Pitching folds. Once the dip and strike of the beds have been determined over a wide enough area, the pattern of the folds begins to emerge. An imaginary

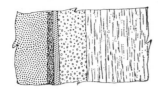

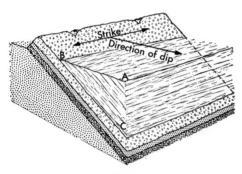

FIG. 13–11. The strike of dipping sedimentary beds is at right angles to the dip. The sketch at the top shows the relation of the beds on the surface.

line running along the top of an anticline or along the bottom of a syncline is called the *axis of the fold*. If the axis is horizontal, or nearly so, the ridges produced by resistant beds after erosion will be more or less parallel. A fold cannot continue indefinitely, however.

Many anticlines are cigar-shaped; their axes slant downward at each end. These are called pitching folds. The angle between the axis and the horizontal is the *pitch*. On a map or aerial photograph of an eroded pitching fold, the resistant beds wrap around the ends of the folds. See Figs. 13–12 and 13–13.

Joints and fissures. The process of folding, as we know, is the result of plastic deformation of solid rock. But does this process operate without cracking or pulling apart of the rocks? Deep within the earth the great pressures caused by the weight of thousands of feet of heavy rock materials above compress the lower layers tightly so that it is impossible for a crack to appear. Any space that tends to develop is filled with flowing rock. Near the surface, however, the confining pressures are less and permit the rocks to yield by fracturing instead of flowing. Therefore fissures and joints form at and near the surface. In a series of folded rocks, geologists find that the deeper the strata, the smaller the cracks, until finally there are no cracks in the lower layers.

Because the top of the anticline and the bottom of the syncline are under the

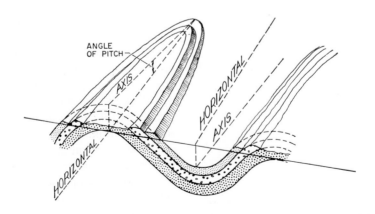

FIG. 13–12. Rock relationships in a pitching fold.

FIG. 13–13. Sheep Mountain, Wyoming, shows dramatically how resistant beds outcrop in an eroded pitching fold. (*Barnum Brown*)

greatest tension during the folding, it is here that the cracks develop. Anticlinal cracks open upward and collect water which freezes and speeds the disintegration of the anticline. On the other hand, many mountains are the remains of synclines. Because synclinal cracks open downward, these structures present a resistant surface to erosion. The typical occurrence of fissures is shown in Fig. 13–14.

If there is little separation between the rock walls, a fracture is classed as a *joint.* If, on the other hand, the crack is

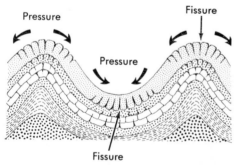

FIG. 13–14. In folded rock layers fissures are formed where pressure builds up tension.

an actual gap, it is called a *fissure.* These cracks should not be confused with the joints formed in some igneous rocks as they cool. Such joints always develop at right angles to the cooling surface. Joints and fissures due to other causes are also found in sedimentary and metamorphic rocks (see Chapter 12), but those due to folding can be distinguished by their relation to the dip of the rocks.

Faulting. Joints and fissures are terms for fractures along which there has been little or no movement of the rocks on either side. If there is any slippage along the fissure or joint, the fracture is called a *fault.* The *fault surface* is the more or less vertical surface along which a movement of the rock beds takes place.

Vertical faulting occurs when an entire block of rock is raised evenly so that the layers remain in their original horizontal position. In this type of faulting the rock layers on one side of the fault will be displaced or *offset,* so that they are no longer continuous. Sometimes a cliff called a *fault scarp* is formed at the surface. *Horizontal faulting* does not displace the rock layers vertically along the fault, but can be observed at the surface, where streams and other features are offset. The movement along a horizontal fault is not usually very great; whereas vertical faulting may cover thousands of feet, and in some cases the rocks may shift many miles.

Types of faults. Vertical faults are of several kinds. The type shown in Fig. 13–6, which occurs in folded strata, is called a *thrust fault.* Under conditions where the rock is not sufficiently plastic to bend into sharp folds, the rocks break as shown. Thrust faults are the result of compression, and produce a shortening of the crust where they occur.

Faults may also occur in unfolded strata, or in areas where the rock masses are only gently deformed. Usually many faults occur, in an area called the *fault zone.* The amount and kind of faulting, like folding, must be determined from rock outcrops and other evidence; very seldom is an actual recent fault surface visible. In reconstructing the fault movement, geologists distinguish two types of faults, normal and reverse, according to the apparent movement on one side or the other. Often it is hard to tell whether

one side has moved down or the other up, or whether there has been movement on both sides.

The two types of faults are shown in Fig. 13–15. Notice the terms used to describe the various features of faults. The strike of a fault, like that of a tilted rock bed, is the direction along the line of the break. The dip of the fault is the angle between the fault surface and the horizontal. The *hanging wall* and the *foot wall* are taken from the names used by miners for these parts. If you imagine yourself descending along the fault, as in a tunnel, you will see that the hanging wall in both types of fault would be above you, while you would be walking on the foot wall.

In normal faults, also called *gravity faults,* the hanging wall has dropped down in relation to the foot wall. This type of fault is a result of tension, rather than compression, and its effect is to lengthen the surface area of the crust at that point.

In reverse faults, the result of compression, the hanging wall has been pushed up over the foot wall and there is surface shortening. The thrust fault

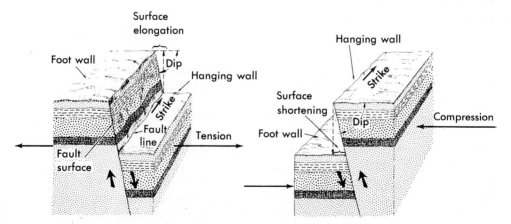

FIG. 13–15. The relationships of the rocks on a normal fault (left) and a reverse fault (right).

FIG. 13–16. Sandstone beds are offset in this fault. (*U. S. Geological Survey*)

described earlier is actually a type of reverse fault in which the angle of dip is very low.

It is important in mining operations to know the type of fault movement that has occurred. Only the geologist can tell whether coal beds, for example, will probably be found at certain depths, due to offset of beds by faulting. Ore deposits are often found along fault lines, and the direction of dip of the fault is therefore significant. Both normal and reverse faults produce fault scarps of similar appearance, because in a reverse fault, the weight of the overhanging rock causes it to fall or yield quickly to erosion. The geologist observes the rock relationships at the surface; these allow him to determine in which direction to continue his search for ore deposits related to the fault system.

In a few places on the earth huge parallel faults have developed which have allowed the blocks of rock between them to sink. This results in the formation of broad valleys flanked on each side by steep fault scarps. Such a valley is called a *rift valley* or *graben,* a German word meaning "trough." The Dead Sea occupies just such a rift valley. Another famous example is the upper Rhine Valley. In some cases the land between the two parallel faults is pushed up from below to form an elevated area called a *horst.* See Fig. 13–17.

The fault types described here are of course only the simpler, basic types. Faults may occur along the strike of the beds, along the line of the dip, or at an angle to either of these. The resulting offset of the strata may be very complex when erosion has leveled the fault surfaces. It is the geologist's task to untangle the story by any means he can find. Fault blocks that are large enough to form mountains are the result of repeated movement over long periods of time. Erosion progresses during the entire time the scarp is being created; therefore the tops of even "recent" fault blocks may be considerably eroded.

EARTHQUAKES

Some famous earthquakes. Geologists class faulting as a constructional process because it results in the formation of many landforms. To mankind in general, however, the earth tremors that accompany faulting are among the most destructive of all natural processes. Man fears them even more than the eruptions of volcanoes because earthquake shocks rock the ground, which, from childhood, he has thought of as a firm and stable foundation.

References to earthquakes appear in the writings of the ancients as well as in more recent historical records. From these it has been estimated that in the last 4000 years more than 13 million people have lost their lives in earthquakes.

In the past 1500 years Japan has experienced 225 destructive earthquakes. The greatest shock was in 1891, when 20,000 buildings were destroyed, 7000 people killed and another 17,000 injured. Railroads were disrupted, and flimsily constructed buildings collapsed, trapping or crushing thousands under the debris.

In 1923 the earthquake at Sagami

Bay destroyed Yokohoma and a large part of Tokyo. The shocks overturned stoves and light fixtures, causing fires which spread rapidly. Because water mains were broken, the fires could not be extinguished, and a high wind sweeping over the city caused over a million persons to lose their homes in a few hours. The loss of life from fire and falling masonry was well over 100,000. Soundings taken in Sagami Bay before and after the earthquake showed movements of the sea bottom, mostly downward, amounting in some places to hundreds of feet, caused probably by the shifting of sediments on the bottom of the bay.

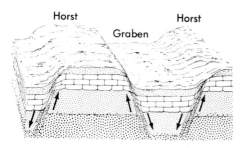

FIG. 13–17. A rift valley or graben is formed by faulting, as shown in the diagram. Below, the Crag Lake graben in Idaho. (*U. S. Geological Survey*)

Not all large earthquakes have occurred in Japan, however. On December 16, 1811, a major earth tremor shook the region of New Madrid, Missouri. This was followed by a series of aftershocks which continued for days. In 1812 two more severe shocks occurred, the last of which was the most severe of all. In three months' time, 1874 shocks were recorded in Louisville, Kentucky, 200 miles away; 400 miles away chimneys toppled at Cincinnati, Ohio. The tremors were felt from the Rocky Mountains to the Atlantic Coast and from Canada to the Gulf of Mexico. This is probably the greatest earthquake on record in the United States. It had many interesting geologic effects, such as landslides, changes in river courses, and the creation of lakes and swamps.

The San Francisco earthquake which occurred early in the morning on April 18, 1906 caused 452 deaths and destroyed over 28,000 buildings. This destruction was due more to the resulting fires than to the quake itself. Broken gas mains caused fires to start and these spread rapidly, especially in the downtown business and residential parts of the city. Dynamite was finally used to stop the fires but damage to homes, stores, schools, churches, and business buildings ran to more than 200 million dollars.

A devastating earthquake hit Agadir, Morocco, on March 1, 1960. The quake occurred west of the city, in an area at the southwestern end of the earthquake belt that extends through Italy, Greece, and Turkey. It was the first sizable

FIG. 13–18. Views of the Hotel Saada before and after the Agadir earthquake give dramatic evidence of the power of the shock. (*Associated Newspapers, Ltd. and Pierre Boulat—courtesy* LIFE © *1960, Time Inc.*)

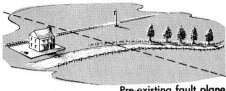

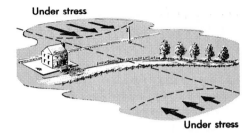

Pre-existing fault plane

Under stress

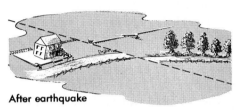

Under stress

After earthquake

FIG. 13–19. According to the elastic rebound theory of earthquakes, stress builds up slowly and is then suddenly released.

earthquake shock ever recorded in this part of Africa. See Fig. 13–18.

It is interesting to note that despite the destruction they cause, earthquakes are not of great importance as geologic agents. Their effects are largely local. The movement of great rock masses is the cause, not the result, of earthquakes.

The mechanism of earthquakes. Most earthquakes are the result of movement along an existing fracture in the deep rock beds. The walls of a fault are usually very closely pressed together. Before rock beds that are under stress finally move along a fracture, they undergo many years of slowly increasing pressures. Finally the stress exceeds the strength of the rock. Then a sudden movement occurs along the fault, caus-

ing the earthquake vibrations. According to the *elastic rebound theory* of earthquakes, pressure is exerted on two adjacent rock areas from opposite directions for long periods of time. The pressure may be upward, downward, or sideways, and as it increases, the rocks bend slowly. Eventually the strain becomes so great that the rocks split apart, either vertically or horizontally, along a fault line that may continue for many miles.

FIG. 13–20. Along the San Andreas fault in California, repeated movement on the fault line has sharply offset the river courses. (*U. S. Forest Service*)

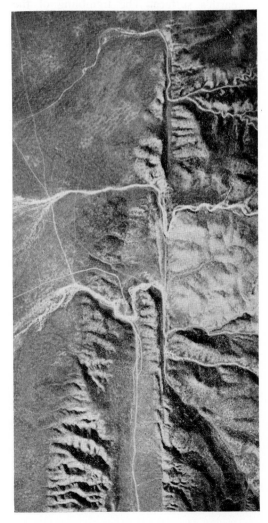

The San Andreas fault, along which movement occurred to cause the California earthquake in 1906, can be traced over a distance of 270 miles. The chief movement along the fault was horizontal, the southwest side shifting toward the north in relation to the opposite side. In some places the horizontal displacement was 21 feet. The southwest block was lifted a maximum of 3 feet, indicating a possible twisting movement.

There are thousands of known faults all over the earth, but few of them seem to be the sources of earthquakes. Most earthquakes, therefore, must probably have their source in faults below the earth's surface. The trembling of the solid rock immediately after faulting sets up the earthquake shocks, which may be strong enough to affect an entire continent or may be so slight that sensitive instruments are needed to record their presence.

Earthquakes that are the result of crustal movements, such as faulting, are classed as *tectonic*. These are the larger quakes, and originate in the outer 25 to 100 miles of the lithosphere. Earthquakes are also often associated with volcanic activity. The *volcanic* types are due either to explosive volcanic activity or to the flow of magma below the crust. Sometimes earthquakes may trigger a volcanic eruption. Earthquakes caused by volcanic activity are always relatively feeble compared with the more violent, tectonic earthquakes; however, they may be the cause of greater local damage.

Landslides occurring over a wide area may result in earthquakes of lesser intensity than those associated with faulting or volcanism. *Landslips,* as such landslides are called, usually occur in regions of rugged relief, or on the sea floor near the margins of the submerged continental shelves.

Earthquakes of tectonic, volcanic, or landslip origin may also occur under the ocean. Their most noticeable effect is the production of seismic sea waves, or *tsunamis* (tsoo-*nah*-meez). The destruction caused by these waves is almost beyond belief. The tsunami that accompanied the earthquake at Lisbon, Portugal, in 1755 was responsible for the deaths of most of the 60,000 people who lost their lives in a matter of minutes. The peculiar characteristics of tsunamis will be discussed in Chapter 26.

Earthquake regions. Although earthquakes occur over the entire earth, they are most frequent and noticeable along two great belts. The shaded areas on the map, Fig. 13–21, show the locations of greatest activity and intensity of earthquakes. These belts are areas of crustal weakness where the effects of diastrophism are most evident. One belt circles the Pacific, extending from Chile on through Peru, Central America, Mexico, California, and Puget Sound. Northward it goes through the Aleutian Islands, to Japan, the Philippines, Indonesia, New Zealand and certain Pacific Island groups. Over 90 percent of the large earthquakes occur in the area of the Pacific belt. The second large belt includes the Alpine regions of Europe, and the Mediterranean area, including North Africa and a section across Asia.

The two earthquake belts do not coincide exactly with the areas of volcanic activity, but both are related to the regions of active deformation. Their areas do, of course, overlap to a great extent. These active zones are regions whose mountains are of recent formation, with steep slopes and many faults.

The areas outside the earthquake belts are not entirely free from tremors. Some have been known to occur in places which are outside the region of present-day mountain formation and volcanic activity. Such tremors are few and far between but may cause considerable damage when they do occur. The Charleston, South Carolina quake in 1886 is an example. Some minor quakes occur in areas of deposition, possibly caused by overloading of sections of the earth's crust. Others, like those in New England, may have been caused by adjustments to the loss of weight due to melting ice after the last glacial age.

Detecting earthquakes. When an earthquake occurs, vibrations go out in all directions from its center, traveling as waves through the earth. Usually the center is a line, rather than a point, since most earthquakes occur along fault lines. The effects of the tremor are felt more strongly at the surface in areas of loose or water-soaked sediments than in bedrock. (Think of a bowl of jelly, hit sharply with the handle of a knife. The bowl does not shake visibly, but the jelly does.)

The center or source of the shock is called the *focus.* The point or line on the surface directly above the focus is the *epicenter.* The surface effects of the earthquake usually increase and then diminish radially from the epicenter. The *seismograph* (*syz*-muh-graf), shown in Fig. 13–22, is an instrument which detects and records earthquake vibrations. Analysis of the record, or *seismogram,* aids in locating the earthquake focus. Most earthquakes occur from 5 to 15 miles below the surface, but the foci of some earthquakes have been located at 420 miles down. The wave motions traveling from the focus are of three kinds, each having its own characteristic known speed. The greater the distance from the focus an earth tremor is recorded on the seismograph, the longer the time lapse between the

FIG. 13–21. The shaded areas on this map show the belts of greatest earthquake activity. (Compare with Fig. 16–12.)

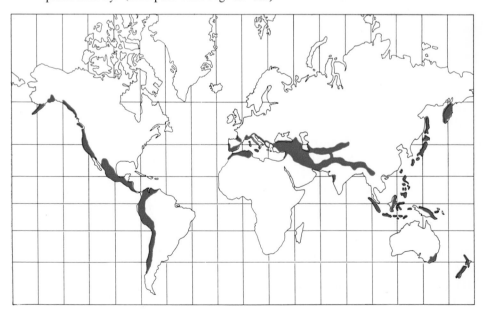

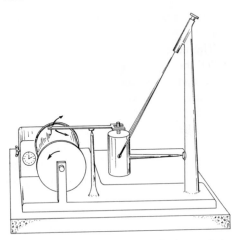

FIG. 13–22. A seismograph is used to detect and record vibrations of the earth's crust.

fastest and the slowest waves appearing on the seismogram. It is much like a race between a fast horse and a slow one. The slow one will fall farther and farther behind as the distance increases. Thus the distance of the focus from the recording station can be calculated. The seismogram also indicates how intense the earthquake is and how long it lasts.

To determine the epicenter, records from several seismographic stations are compared. Circles are then drawn for at least three stations with the station as the center and a radius of the distance to the focus indicated at that station. The focus is the point where the three circles meet. See Fig. 13–23.

The intensity of an earthquake is measured in terms of its effects on man, its damage to structures such as buildings and bridges, and changes in the earth's surface. In the scale used in the United States, a series of numbers indicates degrees of intensity. The scale starts with number I intensity, described as so slight as to be barely felt. The numbers go up to XII, which denotes total destruction, objects on the surface being thrown upward into the air. On a map, the intensity of a shock is indicated by lines drawn around the epicenter, each connecting areas of the same intensity. These are called *isoseismals* (ey-soh-*syz*-muls), meaning "equal shaking." See Fig. 13–24.

Although it is useful for comparison, the scale of intensity is not precise enough for engineers to use in constructing buildings to withstand earthquake shock. For this purpose special instruments have been devised to measure intensity.

The seismogram is a record of earthquake vibrations written by the vibrations themselves and tells much about the nature of the waves that produce it. In the seismogram, Fig. 13–25A, the three types of waves are shown. The straight line is the normal recording during periods of no disturbance. Note that this line suddenly takes on a wavy appearance at the letter *p* and that at letter *s* the wave changes and continues to letter *l* where it changes again. The first

FIG. 13–23. The focus of an earthquake can be located by means of seismograph recordings taken by at least three different stations.

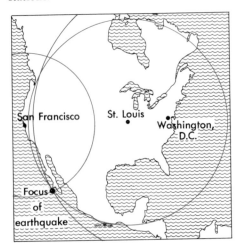

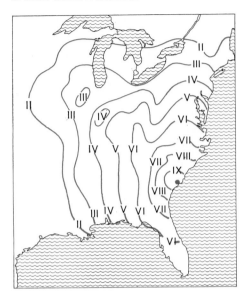

FIG. 13–24. Isoseismals drawn for the Charleston, South Carolina earthquake of 1886. The brown dot indicates the focus of this earthquake.

wave is called the *primary wave,* the second is the *secondary wave,* and the third is the *long wave.*

The primary and secondary waves travel from the focus beneath the surface of the earth, as shown in the diagram, Fig. 13–25B. They are called *body waves,* because they travel through the body of the earth. The primary waves are similar in nature to *sound waves;* the particles of the medium through which the wave passes vibrate to and fro (longitudinally) in the direction the wave travels. The secondary waves are like those that travel over the surface of water when it is disturbed; the particles vibrate with an up-and-down motion (transversely) perpendicular to the direction the wave travels. The longitudinal waves are set up when the body waves reach the surface at the epicenter. They travel along near the surface.

The speed of the three types of waves is as follows:

primary waves
        3.4 to 8.5 miles per second

secondary waves
        2   to 4.5   "   "   "

long waves
        about 2   "   "   "

The primary and secondary waves, where they reach the surface, are reflected, as shown in the diagram. The record of the shock is complicated by these reflections, received by the seismograph after the first long waves are recorded.

As indicated in Chapter 6, the body waves also indicate differences in density beneath the crust. The speed of the waves and their path through the earth change in ways which can be interpreted by seismologists to give valuable information about conditions and structures

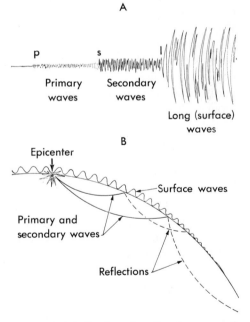

FIG. 13–25. Earthquake vibrations are of several kinds. They are shown in diagram A as they appear in a seismograph; in diagram B, as they travel through the earth.

within the earth. Artificial earthquakes of low intensity are used to locate oil. Interpretation of the record of the reflected waves gives the depth and slope of the rock layers.

Precautions against earthquakes. In regions within the earthquake belts the possibility of predicting earthquakes has been studied. We know that earthquakes recur, but even when we know that a particular region is accumulating elastic strain which approaches the point of fracture, we still cannot predict the hour or day or even the year when the rocks will snap and move. Evidence shows that the period of full moon, high tides, heavy rainfall, changes in barometric pressure, and earth vibrations tend to set off earthquakes, but we are unable to make practical predictions of the time these will occur.

The fact that shocks and tremors occur frequently in certain areas points to the importance of preparing for them by making use of the information gained by experience. The amount of damage done to buildings in an earthquake is partly determined by the nature of the ground, the strength of the foundations of the structures and the way in which they are built. The type of materials used, as well as the intensity of the waves, and their velocity and duration are also factors to be considered.

There is little we can do about the waves themselves, but we can take precautions against them. Builders can avoid building on loose, unconsolidated sediment, especially if it is not well drained. They can avoid weak construction and the use of poor materials. In the major earthquake belts, they can avoid the construction of buildings that are too tall and bridges that have too high a center of gravity. Perhaps building codes should be set up in earthquake

zones to prevent construction of buildings that lack reenforcement, or that are encumbered with heavy ornaments and parapet walls. Structures using brick veneer and dry brick laid in old lime mortar with unanchored or untrussed roofs or unreenforced chimneys should be outlawed. Houses could be constructed of lightweight, strong, fireproof materials, with one-piece rafter construction from ridgepole to floor sills. Elevator shafts, stair wells, water towers, bridges, and water, gas, and electric conduits should be reenforced and trussed, supported or anchored so that ruptures will not add to the damage.

CONSTRUCTIONAL LANDFORMS

The characteristics of constructional landforms. The processes of diastrophism and volcanism are responsible for the major constructional features of the landscape: mountains, plains, and plateaus. How can we distinguish between these landforms in anything more than a vague and general way?

Most people think of a plateau as a region of high elevation with a flat surface of considerable extent, and a plain as an extensive flat area of low elevation; mountains are thought of as high areas of rugged topography. In modern earth science, however, the physiographer classifies mountains, plains, and plateaus according to their structure as well as their topography. Plains and plateaus are composed of rock layers that are generally in the same horizontal position in which they were formed originally from deposited materials. Plateaus usually have greater relief than plains because of their greater elevation. A *plain* is a region of horizontal rock structure

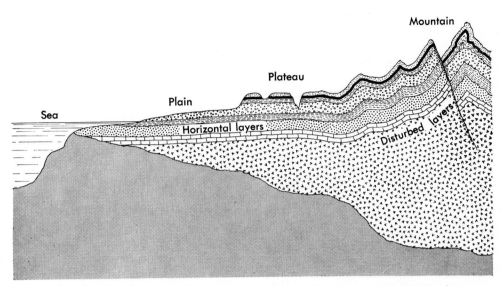

FIG. 13–26. The typical structure of plains, plateaus, and mountains is shown here in diagrammatic form.

with low relief; a *plateau* is a region of horizontal rock structure with high relief. The maximum relief of a plain measures a few hundred feet, whereas in a plateau, the relief is more than a thousand feet. In a plateau, because of its higher elevation, the streams fall a greater distance, thus developing greater speed that enables them to carry larger quantities of rock fragments. Therefore the streams cut into a plateau rapidly, forming deep valleys with steep sides which in time widen during the course of erosion. The lower elevation of a plain accounts for its slower moving streams. In the late stages of plain erosion, gently rolling areas of lower relief are formed, rather than the spectacular scenery of plateaus.

Mountains, as distinguished from plains and plateaus, are landforms with a relief greater than 2000 feet and a rugged summit of relatively small area. All true mountains are composed of rock masses in a nonhorizontal or *disturbed*

position. Mountains may be made of rocks which are tilted, folded, or domed, or built up from volcanic materials.

The life history of landforms. Because, as we have said, constructional processes are constantly opposed by destructional (erosional) processes, constructional landforms are almost never seen in their initial, unchanged state. Ideally, they may be considered to pass through three stages of development as destructional forces modify their surfaces; these are *youth, maturity,* and *old age.* Together they make up the *life history* of the landform. The life history varies according to atmospheric conditions. Thus, a mature plateau in an arid region presents quite a different picture from a mature plateau in a humid region. Moreover, landforms do not always complete the life cycle; a mature plain may be uplifted long before it has reached old age, entering instead into the youthful stage again.

In youth, a landscape has rugged

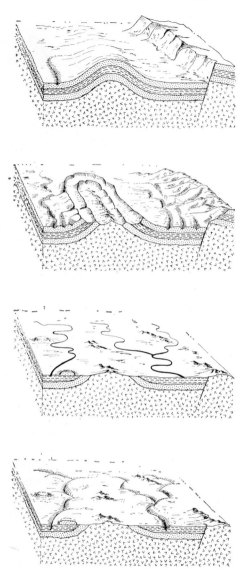

topography with steep slopes and deep narrow valleys. In maturity, the surface is much cut up, and shows a great variety of features. In old age, the landscape is worn down, and the varied features are destroyed. The flat surface that results is called a *peneplane* (almost a plane). When uplift rejuvenates a peneplane, the resulting topography is determined by the nature of the rocks that originally formed the surface.

Sometimes tilted sedimentary beds are covered by horizontal beds which cut across them. This results in an **unconformity,** and indicates that an interval of erosion wore down the tilted beds to form a flat surface. The area was then depressed, so that sediments were deposited on it. Such structural relationships are very useful clues to the history of a region. See Chapter 21.

The physiographic provinces. The topography of the United States, in spite of its great variety, can nevertheless be classified systematically. The broad areas of mountains, plains, or plateaus are in themselves natural subdivisions of the whole. These are the *physiographic provinces,* or *regions.* They have been defined and described, with their characteristic features, in great detail. Study of the physiographic provinces helps people to appreciate the scenic beauty of our country and to understand the influence topography has had on our history and economy. The appendix of this book includes a brief account of the provinces, with a map showing their relief. Such a description serves merely as a starting point for further investigation. In the following chapters, references will be made to particular topographic features of the United States. It will be helpful to you to locate these on the map and note their relation to the surrounding areas.

FIG. 13–27. The stages of youth, maturity, old age, and rejuvenation in typical landforms. Note that in the youthful stage the gentle anticline forms a low hill; the fault scarp shows narrow steep valleys. These features are further developed in maturity; as erosion proceeds, weak and strong rocks produce a variety of forms. In old age the area is a peneplane. Rejuvenation allows the streams to develop new landforms partly determined by the nature of the rocks.

SUMMARY

EXCEPT in regions of earthquakes or volcanoes, the earth's crust is relatively stable. To the geologist there is much evidence that movement has taken place in many areas of the world and still continues. Marine fossils in the Canadian Rockies, drowned valleys of the coast of Maine, and the shorelines of Finland and Sweden are evidence of the processes that are changing the face of the earth.

The topography of the earth's surface results from two conflicting processes: constructional and destructional. Over long periods of time constructional processes build or raise portions of the earth's crust only to have the destructional processes of weathering and erosion wear them down.

Diastrophism refers to any movement of the earth's solid parts. Isostasy, contraction, convection, and continental drift are theories advanced to explain these movements.

The study of the arrangement and relative position of the rock masses of the earth's crust is structural geology. This science enables the geologist to reconstruct original conditions by analysis of the remnants of previous landforms. The discovery of valuable ore deposits or large fields of petroleum depends on a knowledge of the architecture of the earth.

VOCABULARY REVIEW

Match the phrase or word in the left column with the correct phrase or word in the right column. *Do not write in this book.*

1. Crest of rock fold
2. Pulling apart of rock masses
3. Any movement of the solid part of the earth's crust
4. Horizontal rock structure with high relief
5. Folding of rocks under great heat and pressure
6. Mountain
7. Sinking of the earth's crust
8. Horizontal motion of the crust
9. Slippage along a fissure or joint
10. Currents in a heated gas or liquid
11. Seismic sea wave
12. Trough of rock fold
13. Weathering
14. Point on the earth's surface above focus
15. Horizontal rock structure with low relief

a. diastrophism
b. isostasy
c. subsidence
d. continental drift
e. constructional landform
f. anticline
g. syncline
h. fault
i. plateau
j. destructional force
k. tsunami
l. plain
m. epicenter
n. tension
o. convection
p. plastic deformation
q. thrust

QUESTIONS · GROUP A

Decide whether these statements are true or false. Reword the false statements to make them true. *Do not write in this book.*

1. The source of an earthquake shock is called the isoseismal.
2. The axis of a fold is an imaginary line running along the bottom of a fault.
3. The longitudinal waves set up by an earthquake would take about 28 minutes to reach a point 20 miles from the epicenter.
4. The coastline of Maine shows evidence of subsidence.
5. The earth is gradually expanding.
6. The cooler portions of a liquid are more dense than the heated portions.
7. The foundation rock of the ocean basins is largely basalt.
8. Faulting occurs when rock layers slide over one another.
9. A geanticline is a broad trough covering hundreds of miles.
10. The study of structural geology gives clues to the past.
11. The Rhine Valley is an example of a thrust fault.
12. Earthquakes that result from crustal movements are classed as tectonic.
13. Over 90 percent of the large earthquakes occur in a belt that surrounds the Atlantic Ocean.
14. One of the most important factors in classifying landforms is the surface topography.
15. A peneplane is characteristic of a landscape during old age.
16. Disturbed strata are characteristic of a mountainous region.
17. The area within a physiographic province has the same general rock structure.
18. A plateau is always composed of horizontal rock.
19. Geology as a science came into existence at the end of the 15th century.
20. Dip is measured with a clinometer.
21. A joint is a crack in rock beds with little displacement of the rock masses.
22. In a gravity fault the foot wall has dropped in relation to the hanging wall.
23. The San Francisco earthquake of 1906 was caused by movement along the San Andreas fault.
24. Oil geologists use barometers to interpret rock structure beneath the earth's surface.

GROUP B

1. What is included under the subject of structural geology?
2. Illustrate and define strike and dip as applied to folded sedimentary rocks.
3. Discuss the geographical belts of earthquakes and their relationship to areas of volcanic activity.
4. What are the characteristics and significance of an unconformity?
5. What is a physiographic province?
6. Explain warping of the earth's crust. What are some possible causes? What are the results?
7. What are the principal causes of earthquakes?

8. Account for the presence of marine fossils in areas of plains, plateaus, and mountains.
9. Discuss the significance of the theory of isostasy. Make a labeled diagram to illustrate your explanation.
10. Explain the continental drift theory. What evidences support this theory?
11. How is the Brunton pocket transit used?
12. What are the differences between faults, fissures, and joints?
13. How could you differentiate between an anticline and a syncline?
14. Illustrate and define: vertical faulting, horizontal faulting, thrust fault, gravity fault, horst, and graben.
15. Illustrate and define the elastic rebound theory.
16. What are some events that may precede earthquakes? What precautions may be taken to avoid loss of life from earthquakes?
17. Why is surface topography of questionable value in the classification of landforms?

CHAPTER 14

MOUNTAINS

FROM the earliest historical times, mountains have been an inspiration to man. Perhaps no other landform displays such varied and beautiful scenery. Mountains are the highest solid part of the earth. Most of those which are high enough to be glaciated have nearly vertical walls of rock which may be thousands of feet high. They have sharp peaks and narrow, deep valleys that cradle the snows which keep alive the cascading mountain streams. Not all mountains, however, are so steep. Actually, the average slope is about 20° except near the top. Mountains give an impression of extreme steepness because the incline is not a continuous rise, but is broken up by steplike areas that have very steep slopes. In ascending a mountain, we notice the steep slopes but not the long intervals of gentle rise between them.

Mountains are more massive and more rugged than hills, and true mountains have a complicated relief of over 2000 feet. Many areas of rough surface which are locally called mountains are really only hills because the relief is less than 2000 feet. Mount Everest in the Asian Himalayas is the highest mountain in the world, with an elevation of 29,141 feet. In the Pacific Ocean, the Marianas Trench goes down 35,640 feet below the surface of the sea. The vertical distance from the top of the highest mountain to the deepest part of the

VOCABULARY

Mountain system. A group of similar mountain ranges.

Cordillera. A belt of mountain systems.

Block mountains. Mountains that result from faulting.

Folded mountains. Mountains that result from folding of rocks.

Complex mountains. Mountains that result from a combination of faulting, folding, and volcanic action.

Talus. A mass of rock debris at the base of a steep mountain or cliff.

Water gap. A valley cutting across a mountain ridge, through which the stream still flows.

Wind gap. An abandoned stream valley cutting across a ridge.

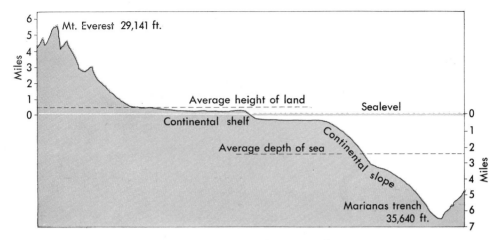

FIG. 14–1. The earth's total relief.

oceans is thus about 12 miles. This is called the *total relief* of the earth. It seems very impressive until it is compared with the earth's diameter. On the common classroom globe of the earth, this relief cannot be shown in true scale because it is so small in relation to the earth's size. See Fig. 14–1.

MOUNTAINS OF THE WORLD

Mountain groups. Mountains are of many shapes and sizes, and are arranged in many different combinations. To describe them, specific terms are used. A single more or less isolated summit is a *peak*, as, for example, Pikes Peak in Colorado. Some volcanic peaks are far distant from any other mountains. *Ridges*, such as those in the Harrisburg, Pennsylvania area, are much longer than they are wide. A mountain *range* is a great ridge or continuous group of peaks and valleys. A *chain* of mountains is a group of ridges that run in a somewhat parallel pattern. A group of mountain ranges that are similar in form and struc-

ture make up a mountain system. A belt of mountain systems of great extent is called a **cordillera** (kawr-dil-*yair*-a).

Almost all of the great mountains of the world are included in the four great cordilleran regions shown in Fig. 14–2. Notice that these are generally near and parallel to the borders of the continents, and in regions of crustal weakness described in Chapter 13. The North American Cordillera includes the Rocky Mountain system, the Sierra Nevadas, the Cascade Ranges, the Basin Ranges, and the United States—Alaska–British Columbia Coastal Mountains. The Andes of Western South America are a continuation of the North American Cordillera. The Southern European Cordillera is composed of the Carpathians, the Alps, the Pyrenees, and the mountains of Spain, as well as the Atlas Mountains of North Africa. The Asiatic Cordillera includes the Caucasus, the Himalayas, the Kunlun, Tien Shan, Hindu Kush, and the Pamirs, together with some other smaller ranges.

Mountains of diastrophic origin. Many mountain ranges are the result of the diastrophic processes described in

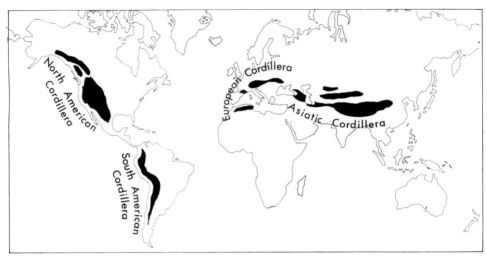

FIG. 14–2. The major cordilleran regions of the earth. Compare this map with Figs. 13–21 and 16–13.

Chapter 13. According to their structure, they are divided into two main types: *block mountains* and *folded mountains.*

Mountains that are the result of faulting are known as block mountains be-cause of their basic form, although erosion may cut deeply into the surface, forming a varied skyline of peaks. The Sierra Nevada of California is carved from a block 400 miles long and 50 to 80 miles wide. This was uplifted by

FIG. 14–3. The Sierra Nevadas were formed from a great fault scarp. This photograph

complex faulting and slopes to the west. The fault scarp faces east, rising 2 miles high in places. On the west side, the block slopes gently. In this area, erosion by water and glaciation has created some of the most magnificent scenery in the world. There are deep valleys such as Yosemite, Tuolumne, and Kings, imposing peaks such as Mount Whitney, as well as many beautiful mountain lakes.

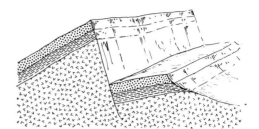

FIG. 14–4. The basic structure of typical block mountains.

In the Great Basin, east of the Sierra Nevada, a large number of smaller mountain ranges rise from 3000 to 5000 feet above the basin floor. Many of these are block mountains also. They run generally north and south, and some show crooked fault lines along their bases, with many smaller faults intersecting the main faults. The Wasatch Range south of Salt Lake City is a group of block mountains showing complex faulting with grabens and many small fault scarps. Faulting is still going on here.

Mountains resulting from folding of sedimentary or lava beds may be of many types. As we have seen in Chapter 13, the ridges may be anticlinal, the result of the actual upfolding, or they may result from variable resistance to erosion. In the dipping strata of the folds, weak beds are eroded first, leaving resistant beds as *synclinal* or *monoclinal* ridges (Fig. 13–8).

The Jura Mountains of France and Switzerland are a series of simple folds of sedimentary rocks containing marine fossils. Study of these mountains shows that only the uppermost layers of the ridges have been worn down by erosion,

shows the deeply carved, steep eastern slope of the range. (*U. S. Geological Survey*)

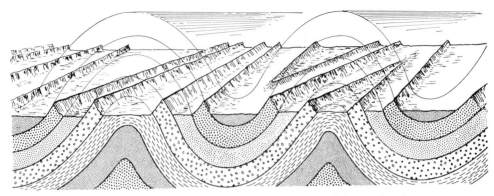

FIG. 14–5. The basic structure of fold mountains and the typical forms resulting from erosion of sedimentary beds.

and that most of the eroded material has been deposited on the valley floors. These are young folded mountains, and their ridges are mostly anticlinal.

The folded or Newer Appalachians, in Pennsylvania and Virginia, are a region of very old sedimentary rocks probably formed from a geosyncline extending from Newfoundland to the Gulf of Mexico. The folded rocks were uplifted several times at long intervals. The result is a region of long ridges, called by the early settlers the "Endless Mountains," because they curve back and forth on each other, following the resistant folded beds. At the tops of the ridges are the even surfaces of former peneplanes. The mountains of this area rise about 2000 feet above the nearby lowlands. Cigar-shaped mountains, zigzag ridges, and canoelike synclinal ridges are typical of this region. See Fig. 14–5.

Volcanic cones and domes. Mountains that owe their existence to extrusive volcanism are volcanic cones and lava domes. Lassen Peak in California (the only active volcano in the continental United States outside of Alaska), Vesuvius in Italy, Fujiyama in Japan, Popocatopetl in Mexico, and Aconcagua in Chile, are all excellent examples of volcanic cone mountains. Each of these gigantic peaks was formed by the gradual building up of its slopes, mainly by accumulation of volcanic fragments and lava from successive eruptions. Molten rock, hurled into the air, cools rapidly and solidifies. The resulting particles are irregular in shape, so that they readily build up very steep sides around the central opening, or crater. The great volcanic mountains of Hawaii result chiefly from lava flows. They are less steep in slope, although they rise as high as 30,-000 feet above the floor of the Pacific Ocean. Their circumference at sea level is about 100 miles. These vast mountains were built up gradually as the flowing lava spread out over a considerable area before it became cool enough to solidify.

Within volcanoes, the lava often solidifies in the main vents instead of flowing out. These cylindrical masses, called

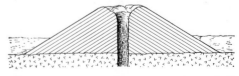

FIG. 14–6. The basic structure of a typical volcanic cone mountain.

plugs or *necks,* often remain after the less resistant volcanic debris enclosing them has been eroded. They often rise as much as 2000 feet above the surrounding countryside. In Arizona and New Mexico there are more than 150 plugs to mark the sites of former volcanoes.

In some places on the earth, volcanism has been so extensive that entire mountain ranges have formed from the volcanic deposits. Volcanic activity in the Aleutian Islands is now building a mountain range on the bottom of the ocean along an arc extending about a thousand miles. A mountainous area of about the same extent is also developing today on a line running northwest to southeast, centering in the Hawaiian Is-

lands. The Cascade Range, extending from California into British Columbia, is made up largely of volcanic formations.

The development of volcanic cones, domes, and other features is discussed more fully in Chapter 16.

Dome mountains. Sedimentary beds may be uplifted into broad domes. Mountain regions that result from erosion of dome structures usually have an underlying core of resistant igneous or metamorphic rocks. Erosion of the broad dome of sedimentary beds results in circular ridges around the central area, and eventually in irregular mountainous topography in the igneous rock as it is sculptured by water and glaciation. See Figs. 14–7 and 14–8.

The Henry Mountains in southern

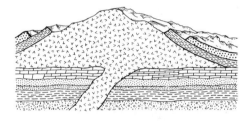

FIG. 14–7. At the right, the basic structure of a laccolithic dome mountain. Below, Bear Butte, near Sturgis, South Dakota. This is an exposed laccolith, showing outcrops of the upturned sedimentary rocks around its base. (*U. S. Geological Survey*)

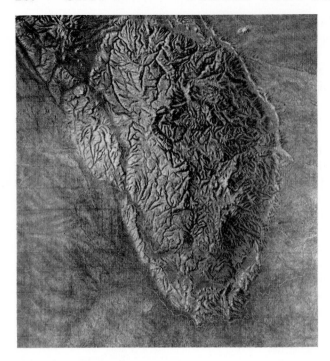

FIG. 14–8. On this relief map of the Black Hills of South Dakota, note the roughly circular valley and the broad plateau surrounding the rugged center of the dome. (*U. S. Geological Survey*)

Utah are formed from a group of laccoliths, extending like thick leaves from a trunklike stock, which pushed up the sedimentary beds. The igneous rocks have been exposed in most cases, and the sedimentary beds form ridges around them.

The Black Hills of South Dakota have a very broad dome core which is an extension of the roots of the Rocky Mountains. The exposed central area, largely granite and pegmatite, rises 4000 feet above the plain which surrounds the dome. A limestone platform rims the core, rising higher than most of the central summits. The inner edge of the limestone bed, which forms a plateau on the west side of the dome, is 800 feet above the valleys of the core area. Deep canyons have been cut in the limestone beds. A wide valley separates the limestone from the outer ridge of the dome. Because of its bright red earth, this is called the Red Valley; few trees grow there, and it was known to the Indians as the Racetrack. Mount Rushmore National Memorial is carved in a peak of the central Black Hills.

The Adirondack Mountains are a high-arched dome of complicated structure, with many faults around the edges. The extensive central area has been

FIG. 14–9. The basic structure of complex mountains.

eroded by water and glaciers and shows the remains of several peneplanes formed in the course of long history of repeated uplift and erosion.

Mountains of combined origin. Mountains which show the results of a combination of mountain-making forces are called *complex mountains.* Folding, faulting, volcanic eruption, and intrusion, and dome formation have all taken a part in the building of these complex mountain groups. The Rocky Mountains and the Andes of South America give evidence of all these kinds of mountain building processes. Some other complex mountains include the White Mountains of New Hampshire, the Ramapos of New York, the Blue Ridge Mountains of eastern United States and the Laurentians of eastern Canada.

The Alps in France and Switzerland, and the Himalayas in southern Asia, were formed from a highly complicated series of folds that have been overturned and thrust-faulted. Thick beds of limestone and shale, and, in some areas, slate and schist, make up the folds. The contorted rocks, eroded by streams and glaciers, have produced a great variety of interesting forms, and these mountains are famous for their scenic beauty.

Mountains of erosional origin. Some landforms that are commonly called mountains do not conform to the geologist's definition, because they are actually regions of horizontal structure that have been deeply eroded or *dissected* (cut up). A high plateau, especially one that has been uplifted after some erosion has occurred, may become an area of steep gorges and high summits. The Catskill Mountains of New York are a dissected plateau, with ridges several thousand feet high (Fig. 15–10).

Isolated remains of resistant rock materials are often called mountains, although they may be horizontal, undisturbed strata, such as the flat-topped buttes of the western plateau region. Many such remains are true mountains, however, having originally been a part of an igneous intrusion or a strongly disturbed rock mass. These mountains are called *monadnocks,* after Mount Monadnock in New Hampshire, which is 3000 feet high and rises above a peneplane which itself is 1200 feet above sea level. Pikes Peak in Colorado is also a monadnock.

LIFE HISTORY OF MOUNTAINS

Youth. During the stage of early youth, mountains are still growing, either by the accumulation of materials from eruptions, or by slow uplift of their rocks. Erosion alters the surface as it is built up. The building-up process is a very gradual one, taking place over exceedingly long periods of time and accompanied by occasional earthquakes. During this building process, the mountain surfaces are constantly being attacked by weather, stream erosion, and glaciation. Young mountains, such as the Alps, the Himalayas, and the Rockies, are thus both very high and very steep, with sharp or even needlelike peaks and deep, narrow valleys. Young mountains very often rise well above the snow line and so they support glaciers during the entire year. (The effects of glaciers will be described in Chapter 19.)

Because of their great height, many young mountains are crowned with perpetual snows, even in equatorial regions. Snow avalanches and landslides commonly occur on the steep slopes of young mountains, especially where there are frequent earthquakes. At the bases of the bare rock cliffs that tower many thousands of feet, rock debris, or *talus*, collects in sloping piles. Mountain streams are vigorous and cut narrow and deep ravines or V-shaped gorges, with numerous waterfalls where the water plunges hundreds or even thousands of feet. Glacial lakes are also quite common. In some places a broader valley suddenly narrows, forming a canyon as the stream passes through resistant rocks. This spot provides an excellent site for the construction of a high dam to impound large volumes of water for community water systems, for irrigation, and for the economical generation of electric power.

During the period of youth, these streams have not had the time necessary to carry away most of the rock layers that cover the igneous cores of dome mountains. But even in the youngest of mountains the uppermost layers are already worn away because the agents of erosion start their work as soon as mountain growth begins. In young folded mountains, the original anticlines are still hills and the synclines are still the valleys. In young block mountains, fault scarps are still prominent, with notches where stream valleys were cut off by movement along the fault.

Maturity. In maturity mountain growth has stopped. The rugged scenery has been worn down to form the rounded tops of lower summits and the gentler slopes are fringed by talus covered with finer particles or with topsoil. In lower and middle latitudes, the timber line usually reaches to the summits.

Avalanches and glaciers are rare in mature mountains except for those located in very high latitudes, where the cold climate keeps the slopes bare. In temperate regions, the mountain elevations in maturity are often too low to maintain enough snow and ice for glaciers and the degree of slope is usually not great enough to enable gravity to move the earth or snow. Earthquakes seldom originate in mature mountains because faulting, the primary cause of tremors, has ceased.

In these areas the streams also are mature. They flow more slowly than the roaring streams of the higher, young mountain areas. Their valleys are wider, with gentler slopes, and the uplands between the valleys are narrowed down to form divides that are more rounded than jagged.

In some mature mountains, the streams are even older than the mountains themselves, having become established before the land was uplifted. As the surface rose, the streams cut deeper, keeping pace with the rise. In mountain ridges and scarps, these rivers develop valleys called *water gaps* that cut across the mountain masses. If the waters in the gap drain off, because the increase in altitude exceeds the rate of erosion, or because of changes in the total stream pattern, a *wind gap* remains. Water and wind gaps are common in the Appalachian mountain regions. They served as passes for the early pioneers traveling to settle in new sections of our country to the west. These gaps were very often of strategic importance in the colonial wars because they were relatively easy to defend and were the only practical means of access to the valleys and plains beyond the mountains.

In the Appalachian Mountains, as in other mature, folded mountains, there are many examples of synclinal and monoclinal peaks and ridges. In mature block mountains, the fault scarps have been completely dissected by streams. Triangular faces, the remains of the fault surface, may remain between the valley

FIG. 14–10. The topography of mountain regions differs according to structure and stage of erosional development. At the right, a range in the Colorado Rockies shows features of complex mountains in the youthful stage. Below, ridges along the Susquehanna River in Pennsylvania illustrate a mature stage of erosion in fold mountains. (*Chuck Abbott from Rapho-Guillumette; Carl Mansfield from Shostal*)

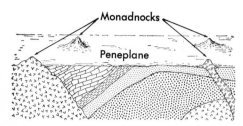

FIG. 14–11. Monadnocks in a peneplane developed on a mountain region are remnants of folded and faulted underlying rock formations.

openings, but are disappearing. Lakes may appear between blocks. The slopes on the two sides of the block are more nearly alike. Mature dome mountains show the features already described in the Black Hills.

Other examples of mature mountains include the White Mountains of New

FIG. 14–12. In summer, sheep graze close to the jagged summits of the French Alps. They are driven to lower slopes during the colder seasons. (*Yvon*)

Hampshire, the Green Mountains of Vermont, and the Adirondacks of New York.

Old age. Erosion continues steadily as long as the land slopes sufficiently and erosional agents are active. There is no clear line of division between maturity and old age. Over exceedingly long periods of time, the mountains are worn down until they are almost level. This late period of the mountain cycle is called old age. The final surface feature is a peneplane, with low rolling hills and an occasional monadnock. Remember that the peneplane is not a true plain because it usually lacks the horizontal layers of true plains. Instead, it hides under its flat surface the folded, twisted, or tilted rocks that are the identifying marks of true mountains. Southern New England is a raised peneplane with typical monadnocks in New Hampshire and Massachusetts. The regions around Manhattan Island and Westchester County in southern New York State are in the southern fringe of this very old mountain region. In many places the peneplane surfaces have been eroded or covered by glacial deposits, but they can be identified in some areas by ridges of nearly uniform elevation.

The rivers of old mountain regions are very slow moving, with few tributaries and low banks. They commonly bend in large loops or *meanders* along a wide flat bed. The water is not as clear as that of streams in younger mountains, because the region is deeply covered with weathered rock and soil deposits. During the long, long periods of erosion that lead to old age, it is almost a certainty that diastrophic forces will uplift the region, setting up a new cycle of erosion. The rivers are then *rejuvenated* by the increase in slope, and begin to cut down through the erosion surface in new beds.

The Piedmont Upland, with the monadnock Stone Mountain in Georgia, is a typical example of a rejuvenated old mountain region.

The economic value of mountains. The scarcity of soil, the steep slopes, the narrow valleys, and the cold climate of mountains generally make them poor farming areas. Nevertheless, mountains are valuable to man in many ways. Their humid slopes often provide lush grasses for grazing. Their rushing streams provide water for irrigation and electric power. They frequently contain rich deposits of valuable mineral ores. Such deposits are relatively easy to find in mountains because the numerous streams

expose the strata containing rich veins. In a plains region, on the other hand, the ore-bearing strata may be buried hundreds of feet beneath the surface.

Large quantities of the precious metals gold, silver, copper, zinc, lead, and iron are taken from mountains. We obtain much of our building stones, such as granite, marble, slate, and sandstone, from mountain quarries. Some mountain areas produce large quantities of coal, rock, salt, sulfur, and phosphates. The lower mountain slopes usually supply valuable timber. In addition, the cooler climate at higher elevations provides comfortable and beautiful vacationlands in tropical regions.

SUMMARY

THE term mountain is applied to massive rugged landforms with a relief of over 2000 feet. Mountains vary in their origin and rock structure. Block mountains, folded mountains, and volcanic mountains are the three principal types. Sedimentary beds raised by igneous intrusions may form dome mountains.

Most of the earth's mountains are the result of bending of the crust accompanied by fracturing of the rocks, This process results in block mountains. The Sierra Nevada is a single tilted block while the Great Basin of Nevada is composed of many tilted blocks. The Sierras represent young mountains that are still growing.

Folding of sedimentary or lava beds results in a series of parallel ridges. When erosion has cut deeply into the folds, complex patterns of curving ridges may develop as a result of differences in rock resistance. The Jura Mountains and the newer Appalachians are examples of fold mountains in varying stages of erosion.

Domes, necks, and volcanic cones are easily recognizable features of mountains of volcanic origin. Lassen Peak, Fujiyama, and Aconcagua are examples of mountains resulting from accumulation of products of volcanic activity.

Mountains occur as isolated peaks, irregular groups, parallel ridges or ranges, complex systems, and cordilleras. Weathering and erosion produce various characteristics that enable the mountains to be classed as young, mature, or old.

VOCABULARY REVIEW

Match the phrase in the left column with the correct word or phrase in the right column. *Do not write in this book.*

1. Belt of mountain systems
2. Loop in stream
3. Folded mountains
4. Valley that cuts across mountain mass
5. Remains of former volcano
6. Isolated summit
7. Deeply eroded
8. Combination of mountain-building forces
9. Rock fragments

a. monadnock
b. talus
c. meander
d. peak
e. cordillera
f. monoclinal ridges
g. plug
h. dissected
i. water gap
j. rejuvenated
k. complex mountains

QUESTIONS · GROUP A

Decide whether these statements are true or false. Reword the false statements to make them true. *Do not write in this book.* *Why?*

1. The extension of the North American Cordillera is the Cordillera of the Caucasus.
2. Most of the active volcanoes in the continental United States are located in Alaska.
3. The Andes of South America are complex mountains.
4. The summits of young mountains are usually well below the snow line.
5. Wind gaps are common in the mature Appalachians.
6. Rivers are rejuvenated by the action of diastrophism.
7. The highest mountain has an elevation greater than the depth of the deepest part of the ocean.
8. Volcanic action is building a mountain range on the bottom of the ocean in the area of the Aleutian Islands.
9. The Henry Mountains and the Black Hills of South Dakota are examples of domed mountains.
10. The Catskills are composed of complex folds.
11. Young mountains have many U-shaped gorges.
12. Avalanches are common in mature mountains.
13. Manhattan Island is part of the southern fringe of a raised peneplane.
14. Mountains supply large quantities of metallic ores.
15. Mountains have an average slope of about 35°.
16. The total relief of the earth is about 12 miles.
17. The Sierra Nevada is composed of a single block.
18. A characteristic of a peneplane is the occurrence of monadnocks.
19. Cones made up of volcanic debris are more resistant than volcanic necks.
20. Pikes Peak is an example of a butte.

GROUP B

1. How is the total relief of the earth calculated?
2. Illustrate and explain the principal methods of mountain building.
3. Name and give the location of the principal cordilleran regions.
4. Name and locate the only active volcano in the continental United States, outside of Alaska.
5. Discuss the relationship of the timber line to the age of the mountain.
6. Discuss several ways in which mountains are of value to man.
7. Why are the Catskills not included in the geologist's definition of mountains?
8. Describe the characteristics of young mountains. Give examples.
9. Describe the characteristics of mature mountains. Give examples.
10. Describe the characteristics of old mountains. Give examples.

TOPOGRAPHIC SHEETS

Harrisburg, Pennsylvania. *Folded mountain.*
Henry Mountain, Utah. *Dome mountain.*
Yosemite Valley, California (special). *Block mountain.*
Crater Lake, Oregon (special). *Volcanic activity.*
Worcester, Massachusetts. *Peneplane.*
Fayetteville, West Virginia. *Rejuvenation.*
Mammoth Cave, Kentucky. *Dissected plateau.*
Fort Collins, Colorado (Rocky Mountains). *Complex mountains.*

All of the above are in the 15-minute series.

CHAPTER 15

PLAINS AND PLATEAUS

THE westward movement in America, as the settlers pushed the frontier ever farther and farther toward the Pacific, is an exciting story. The adventures of the pioneers and the hardships they encountered have become familiar to all of us through books and films. We can picture the pioneers on horseback and in their covered wagons, seeking a place to establish a home in the wilderness. In the early part of the nineteenth century, the settlements spread westward through the Appalachians and steadily on through the prairie lands of Ohio, Indiana, Illinois, Iowa, and the surrounding states. The fertile farmland, the woods, and the easily navigable rivers attracted many settlers in spite of the difficulties and dangers of an unexplored country and hostile Indians. Beyond this region, however, progress was slow. The Great Plains, stretching west to the foot of the Rockies, were grasslands, with few navigable rivers and without enough water for the only farming methods the pioneers knew. Attempts to settle the land were doomed to failure until a much later period. Meanwhile the settlers and the gold-seekers of 1849 moved on to the Pacific Coast, some by the difficult land journey, others by water, traveling around Cape Horn by ship.

By the 1870's, however, cattle-grazing had become profitable in the plains, and new methods of irrigation and farming with machinery made some farming possible. The railroads had made transportation easier. Then the Great Plains too were settled, and by the end of the 1880's the frontier had practically disappeared. The history of this region includes the era of the cowboy, who was truly a figure of courage and endurance, with his own way of speech, dress, and

VOCABULARY

Alluvial plain. A plain formed by the deposition of materials from rivers and streams.

Outwash plain. A plain formed by the deposition of materials washed out from the edges of a glacier.

Continental shelf. Relatively shallow ocean floor bordering a continental sea coast.

Fall line. Region where coastal plain adjoins the oldland, characterized by numerous waterfalls.

252

behavior. The long conflict between the cattlemen and the farmers developed, and is perhaps not yet really settled.

The plains of America, in the conditions they imposed on the settlers, have had much to do with our national character. So too, have the plains lands of Europe and Asia helped to determine the progress of civilization.

Origin of plains and plateaus. Plains and plateaus, as pointed out in Chapter 13, are composed of layered rocks in a more or less horizontal position. Except for lava beds, such rocks are sedimentary, and therefore the result of deposition following erosion. However, many of the plains and plateaus of the world are considered constructional features, because they have emerged as landforms through diastrophism. Flat-lying beds

covered by seas or lakes become plains or plateaus when they are lifted up or when the water level is lowered. A very slight lowering of the water level or rise in the land exposes a broad extent of flat rock beds. These form the *coastal plains* and the *interior marine* and *lake plains.* *Lava plains* and plateaus, being the result of volcanism, are also constructional features.

On the other hand, some plains are the direct result of destructional agents. These are the *alluvial* (a-*loo*-vee-ul) *plains* formed by streams as they deepen their valleys, transport rock fragments, and deposit them along the river bed, at the river mouth, or at the bases of mountains where the slope of the stream bed changes. Streams flowing out from the edges of a glacier also carry debris and

FIG. 15–1. The wagon trains found passage slow and difficult over the Great Plains region. (*Culver Service*)

later deposit it to form an *outwash plain.*
The glacier itself deposits masses of debris called *till* that it has picked up and
transported. Till plains are sometimes of
vast extent in areas where glaciers covered parts of a continent. The building
up of glacial and alluvial plains, and their
characteristic features, are described in
Unit 5.

A peneplane is sometimes thought of
as a plain, but more precisely, it is an
erosion surface, since the underlying
rocks are not necessarily horizontal.

PLAINS

Coastal plains. Coastal plains are
composed of fragments eroded from the
rocks along the shore by ocean waves or
carried into the sea by rivers. The wave
motion of the sea spreads out the rock
debris until a smooth flat surface is developed. This extends seaward sometimes hundreds of miles under the water,
forming the *continental shelf.* On emergence, all or part of the shelf becomes a
coastal plain.

Coastal plains range from very narrow
to very broad. They vary in their surface
features for several reasons: the structure of the rock beds, the nature and degree of uplift, and the type of oldland on
which the coastal plain rests. Thus, in a
certain coastal plain region, the sea may
have advanced and retreated several
times in the geologic past. This would
give the beds in these plains a complicated structure, since periods of erosion
at the surface would have alternated
with periods of deposition. Again, the
uplift in a particular region may have
been a simple rise in level, or may have
included warping into low domes and
basins. The oldland may be quite flat, or
may be irregular, so that hills of the old-

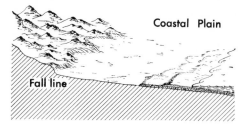

FIG. 15–2. The Atlantic Coastal Plain,
showing the location of the fall line and
related features.

land rock rise above the coastal plain
sediments. All of these conditions affect
the coastal plain surface in its early
stages, as well as in its later development
through erosion.

The Atlantic Coastal Plain and its extension, the Gulf Coastal Plain, stretching from New York to Florida and on to
Texas and Mexico, has an interesting
history. Deposits hundreds of feet thick,
consisting of loose beds of sand, lime,
and clay, were laid down on the oldland
of ancient metamorphic rock which also
forms the older Appalachians. When the
beds were laid down, the ocean margin
stood about at the edge of the Piedmont
Upland. At this line the coastal plain sediments adjoin the oldland. It is called the
fall line, because of the waterfalls that
mark the change in slope of the streams
that pass from the oldland down into the
plain. Many major cities are located
along the fall line, such as Trenton, Philadelphia, Baltimore, Richmond, and Augusta. These cities grew up from the villages established where water power was
available from the falls and where travelers were obliged to take land trails
after having gone up the navigable rivers
of the coastal plain.

After the deposition of sediments, the
area was greatly uplifted, so that the
shoreline extended farther into the ocean
and rivers began to cut their valleys

across the new plain. Measurement of the ocean bottom deposits above the continental shelf show that much of the area now under water must have been exposed in the past, and that the shoreline advanced and retreated from time to time. Deep troughs of uncertain origin that resemble stream gorges are found along the outer margin of the continental shelf. One extends seaward from the mouth of the Hudson River to a depth of 7000 feet at the seaward end, more than a hundred miles from the present mouth of the river.

The latest submergence of the land gave the shoreline its present position. The Atlantic Coastal Plain is narrow in the north and widens as it extends southward. Submergence caused the drowning of river valleys to form the deep harbors of New York and Delaware, and the bays and estuaries of Virginia and North Carolina. The edges of gently dipping

resistant beds in the coastal plain form ridges that can be traced in many places, and these have been identified under the waters off New England. The great fishing banks such as the Grand Banks of Newfoundland are believed to be northern extensions of the coastal plain ridges.

The Atlantic and Gulf Coastal Plains have the typically monotonous topography of a region of horizontal rocks that were recently part of the sea floor. Broad areas of flat land are broken only by occasional groups of low hills. Some of these hilly regions, as in the north, are due to glacial deposits. Others, like the ridges of New Jersey and the Alabama-Mississippi-Texas region, mark resistant beds in the plain. These result in a belted coastal plain, with lowland areas between the ridges. The Black Belt of the south, famous for its fertile black soil, used mainly for cotton growing, is in a limestone belt between more resistant

FIG. 15–3. The Florida Everglades. (*Florida State News Bureau*)

beds which form uplands. The hilly section in central Florida is due to underground erosion in limestone, resulting in numerous sinkholes or depressions which later filled with water to become lakes.

Along the eastern seacoast, the coastal plain shows all the many features of wave and wind action, such as cliffs, sand bars, and sand dunes. Swamps and marshes are common, particularly in Florida. Here swamps such as the Everglades occupy nearly 6000 of the 7000 square miles of southern Florida. Millions of water-loving birds make their homes here, and the swampland supports other wildlife of great interest and variety.

The Gulf Coastal Plain merges into the plain of the Mississippi River, which stretches up into Illinois. On its broad floor, the river swings back and forth, carrying a million tons of soil each day to the sea. Some of this deposited soil builds up the land at the delta of the river, extending the area of Louisiana. The rivers of the Atlantic Coastal Plain do not form deltas because the waves and currents of the ocean carry off the sediment and distribute it along the coast or on the continental shelf.

Coastal plains in other parts of the world are those of southeastern England and northern France (actually the same plain, cut by the English Channel), and that of northern and western Siberia. The latter is by far the most extensive

FIG. 15–4. The Central Lowland in Illinois is an almost level prairie. (*U. S. Dept. of Agriculture*)

FIG. 15–5. The badlands of South Dakota, a part of the Great Plains, are the result of extensive erosion in a semiarid region. (*American Museum of Natural History*)

coastal plain in the world, being over 1000 miles wide.

Interior marine plains. As indicated in Chapter 13, vast inland continental areas were once covered by shallow water. Sediments laid down in these regions built up roughly level deposits which now form interior marine plains. These are usually quite flat, with occasional low domes and few streams, which move slowly and meander in broad valleys. After erosion has progressed, the plains area may show low rolling hills. The interior plains area of the United States is a vast region that includes the Central Lowland (the prairie land of Iowa, Illinois, and the surrounding states), and the Great Plains to the west.

In some of the northern parts, glacial till has covered the rolling hills and left a level surface, or one which shows mainly features of glacial origin. Well borings and other indications of the rocks present under the till reveal the buried landscape. In the Great Plains, the monotony of the flat lands is broken in some parts by sand dunes and extensive areas of badlands, where erosion under semiarid conditions has carved the surface into fantastically rugged shapes. A few small mountain areas, related in origin to the Rocky Mountains, also interrupt the flat surface.

Interior plains in other parts of the world include the Argentine pampas, a remarkably flat plain covering about

250,000 square miles. Great stretches of grasslands are dotted with occasional farms and settlements. Most of Russia and Northern Siberia and adjacent countries around the Baltic and North Seas are true plains areas. Like the interior plains region of North America, this land was under water for long geological ages.

Lake plains. Lake or *lacustrine* plains are formed by the emergence of a lake floor. Sometimes there is uplift of the lake sediments, but more often the emergence results from the drainage of large lakes.

The largest lake plain of North America extends for 100,000 square miles in Minnesota, North Dakota and the provinces of Saskatchewan and Manitoba in Canada. This fertile farming area was once the floor of a great lake which geologists have named Lake Agassiz. During the last great ice age, Lake Agassiz was formed when ice dammed the streams that drained to the north. The final melting of the ice caused the drainage of the lake bed. Today the black muck soil of the former lake bottom is highly valuable for wheat farming.

The ancient Lake Bonneville in Utah was at one time as large as Lake Huron. Evaporation has reduced it to the present Great Salt Lake, leaving lacustrine plains. Former shorelines of this ancient lake can be identified in valleys between mountain ranges that were once islands.

Life history of a plain. A young plain is an extensive level area with very few, widely separated, shallow river valleys containing slow-moving water. Drainage is poor and often there are lakes and swamps. The coastal plain of Florida and the plains of the Russian Ukraine are typical young plains.

In maturity, the streams have acquired new tributaries and have widened and deepened their valleys to produce an area of gently rolling surface with good drainage. The prairies, described earlier, are mature plains.

In old age, the plains are worn level once more, and are often thickly covered

FIG. 15–6. Wheat harvesting in North Dakota, in a portion of the large fertile plain left by the great glacial Lake Agassiz. (*U. S. Dept. of Agriculture*)

FIG. 15–7. From the South Rim of the Grand Canyon, the Colorado River is seen winding through the gorge it has carved in the plateau. (*David Muench*)

with deposits of soil and silt. The few rivers meander over their wide flat beds.

The economic importance of plains. Plains make excellent sites for airports, roadways, railroad beds, and canals because of their flat surfaces. The most productive, large scale agricultural regions of the world are to be found in the Interior and Great Plains areas of the United States and the Great Central Plains of Europe and Russia. The deep deposits of fertile soil assure bumper crops that are easily cultivated by machinery. Temperate zone plains, because of their low elevations, are warm and have long growing seasons. These are the most densely populated areas of our globe. In the torrid zones plains produce tropical vegetation in magnificent profusion, but in the frigid zones agricultural production is meager.

Alluvial plains have soil of exceptional fertility and fine texture, easy to plow and cultivate.

PLATEAUS

Types of plateaus. The elevation of most plateaus of the world exceeds 2000 feet. Height above sea level, however, is not the sole factor in classifying a landform as a plateau. The Appalachian Plateau has an elevation of 3000 feet, but

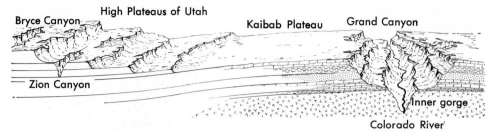

FIG. 15–8. The basic rock structure of the Colorado Plateau in the region of the Grand Canyon.

the Great Plains, near the Rocky Mountains, have a maximum elevation of 6000 feet. They are called plains because they are very much lower than the neighboring mountains, which reach altitudes exceeding 14,000 feet. The *relative* elevation of a region is more important than its actual elevation. However, a more precise distinction between a plain and a plateau is the difference in relief. A plateau has high relief and a plain low relief. A plateau forms a steep escarpment at least on one side, marking the change to a region of lower elevation. Usually the scarp is deeply carved by streams.

True plateaus may be classified according to their origin. Most plateau regions are the result of diastrophism, by which broad areas were uplifted, usually with some slight folding or warping, and often with faulting. A high region of horizontal rocks in which much faulting has accompanied the uplifting process may be called a fault plateau. Some plateau regions are the result of volcanism, through the outpouring of lava from fissures. The lava, spreading over a vast area, covered the former land surface and produced a level region of layered volcanic rocks. Often there are erosion surfaces between the layers, showing that streams began to cut into the lava beds in the long periods of quiet between the lava flows.

A fault plateau. The Colorado Plateau, occupying an area of the southwest covering 130,000 square miles, is the result of broad uplift, followed in later ages by vertical faulting, especially in the southwest or Grand Canyon section. The rock beds of the plateau are a thick series of limestones, sandstones, and shales, laid down through many ages. Repeated uplift and erosion have resulted in a region where the streams have cut deep canyons into the most ancient sediments. Where the Colorado River has created the spectacular Grand Canyon, the plateau is from 7500 to 9300 feet above sea level.

Fault lines break up the Grand Canyon region into a series of plateaus with scarps like giant steps that face west. These have retreated steadily eastward as their faces have been eroded. The displacement along the fault at the edge of the westernmost plateau is 6000 to 7000 feet; farther east at Hurricane Ledge the displacement is 6000 feet. The present scarps are not the actual fault scarps, however, but the result of erosion along the fault line. Resistant beds in the higher block have come to stand up against the weaker ones in the lower block. Hurricane Ledge has a height of 1000–1800 feet.

A lava plateau. West of the Rocky Mountains of Idaho is the Columbia and

Snake River Plateau, one of the most extensive lava plateaus in the world. It includes parts of Washington, Oregon, California, and Idaho. Basaltic lava flows, spreading from fissures, covered at least 200,000 square miles of an area of old mountains. The greatest thickness of these flows is at least 5000 feet. The Blue Mountains were surrounded and partly buried by the lava. In the valleys of the Snake River some of the buried parts of these old mountains have been exposed. In some places, the lava beds have been raised into low anticlinal folds, creating long ridges, such as Saddle Mountain, through which the Columbia River has cut a deep gorge. The canyon cut in the lava by the Snake River for many miles is as deep as the Grand Canyon of the Colorado, but lacks the contrasting colors of the sedimentary beds.

Along the course of the Columbia River are several vast abandoned gorges. The largest is the Grand Coulee, between 800 and 900 feet deep and from 1½ to 4½ miles wide. These gorges are believed to mark former courses of the river during glacial periods when ice blocked the main river channel. The Grand Coulee dam serves to irrigate this part of the plateau.

The steep walls of the river gorges in the plateau are due to the columnar jointing of the lava beds. Large, powerful streams can tear away the blocks of lava, whereas the small streams make little impression on the lava surface.

Life history of plateaus. The appearance of a plateau at different stages of

FIG. 15–9. A deeply eroded portion of a great lava plateau, the Columbia Plateau in Washington. (*U. S. Geological Survey*)

erosion depends on whether the conditions are dry or humid, and also on the type of rock that is being cut into by the streams. A *young* plateau in a semiarid region, like the Colorado Plateau, shows striking scenery. At Grand Canyon, the Colorado River has cut down 6000 feet, in a valley whose width varies from 5 to 15 miles. The sedimentary layers of the plateau show a series of steps, the more resistant layers forming cliffs and the softer ones gentle slopes or terraces. As seen from the edge of the canyon, the river, 300 to 400 feet wide and about 40 feet deep, looks like a thin ribbon. The great steps descend from the rim in a magnificent display of colors that change subtly with the passing light and shadow. At the top, the resistant blue-gray Aubrey limestone forms steep cliffs. A short distance beneath it is the bright band of the Coconino sandstone, a white resistant bed. The Supai sandstones below this are soft; they give their red color to the limestone cliffs beneath them. These,

known as the Redwall limestones, are a resistant bluish-white formation, actually, but water dripping over the surface has stained it. Soft shale formations form the Tonto Platform, a terrace that varies in width as it runs along the canyon walls. Cliffs at the edge of the inner gorge, where the river cuts into ancient metamorphic rocks, are a resistant sandstone. There is little soil or talus on the surface of the canyon; most of the debris is washed away by the infrequent rains into the muddy water of the river.

In less arid regions, young plateaus show more rounded surfaces and gentler slopes, with soil covering and some talus. Streams are few, however, and cut deep into the rocks.

Mature plateaus are generally called mountains, since they are rugged areas. Numerous streams have cut wide valleys through the broad surfaces of the original plateau. In the Catskill "Mountains," a maturely dissected plateau, the summits are relatively flat-topped and there

FIG. 15–10. The Catskills of New York are the remains of a mature plateau. The ridges are relatively flat-topped and have horizontal terraces along their slopes. (*Fairchild Aerial Surveys, Inc.*)

FIG. 15–11. Buttes (below), a mesa (right), and their typical rock structures. (*Union Pacific Railroad and U. S. Geological Survey*)

are terraces or benches along the mountainsides to reveal the generally horizontal structure of the original rocks.

Plateaus in *old age* are worn almost level, with mere remnants of the original plateau standing out here and there. In arid regions these are steep walled with flat upper surfaces. If they have broad tops they are called *mesas*. The smaller ones with narrow tops are called *buttes*. See Fig. 15–10. Mesas and buttes are found in large numbers in New Mexico and Arizona and buttes are the common landform of the Dakotas, Montana, and Wyoming. In humid regions the last remnants of old-age plateaus are more rounded.

The economic importance of plateaus. The canyons that are typical of plateaus are not favorable to transportation. They are so wide and so numerous that bridg-

ing is impractical and the bottoms are so narrow that there is little or no room for roadways or railroad beds. The streams are rapid and the water level changes suddenly and frequently as the volume of water in them changes. The many waterfalls, dangerous rapids, and giant boulders discourage travel by boat. It is little wonder that vast areas of plateaus are inaccessible. But the streams have cut into the rock layers so deeply that vast cross sections are exposed to observation and sometimes rich ore deposits are revealed. The Mexican plateau is rich in silver ore with some deposits of gold.

Perhaps the greatest economic value of plateau canyons is that they can be dammed to impound the water in large reservoirs for irrigation and for the generation of electricity.

SUMMARY

PLATEAUS and plains are composed of layers of sedimentary rock or lava flows, generally in a horizontal position. Although sedimentary beds are the result of deposition of material transported by destructional forces, plains and plateaus of this kind are considered constructional features because their emergence is due to diastrophism. The distinction between a plateau and a plain depends on the relative elevation and the extent of the relief.

Plains may be classified according to place of origin or manner of origin, for example, coastal plain, lava plain. Most plateaus are the result of diastrophism by which areas are warped or faulted, such as the Colorado Plateau. A few are the result of volcanism, such as the Columbia Plateau.

Economically, plains are the most productive agricultural regions of the world. They make excellent sites for airports, railroad beds, canals and roadways. The greatest value of plateaus is the fast moving rivers which may be dammed for the generation of electricity or to provide water for irrigation.

VOCABULARY REVIEW

Match the phrase in the left column with the correct word or phrase in the right column. *Do not write in this book.*

1. Grand Canyon
2. Deposit of running water
3. Coastal plain
4. Lava plateau
5. Edge of Piedmont Upland
6. Interior marine plain
7. Lake plain
8. Unstratified glacial debris

a. till
b. fall line
c. lacustrine plain
d. alluvial plain
e. emergence
f. peneplane
g. Russian Ukraine
h. Argentine pampas
i. Colorado Plateau
j. Columbia Plateau

QUESTIONS · GROUP A

Decide whether these statements are true or false. Reword the false statements to make them true. *Do not write in this book.*

1. Most plains are considered constructional features.
2. The Atlantic Coastal Plain was once part of the continental shelf.
3. The Black Belt rests upon bedrock composed of basalt.
4. The largest lake plain in North America was the floor of a lake formed by the glacial damming of rivers.

5. The highest parts of the Great Plains have a lower elevation than the Appalachian Plateau.
6. The Blue Mountains were partly covered by till.
7. Buttes are characteristic of an old-age plateau in arid regions.
8. The underlying rocks of plains and plateaus are always sedimentary.
9. An outwash plain is formed when a river overflows its banks.
10. The most extensive coastal plain in the world is the Gulf Coastal Plain.
11. Great Salt Lake is all that remains of the former Lake Bonneville.
12. Plateaus are very fertile farming areas.
13. Mesas are characterized by their broad tops.

GROUP B

1. In outline form compare the life cycles of plains and plateaus. Use diagrams to show topography and rock structure.
2. Account for the formation of Lake Agassiz.
3. What conditions usually result in the formation of canyons?
4. How do buttes differ from mesas?
5. Why is a peneplane not a true plain?
6. What are the indications that the Atlantic Coastal Plain was once submerged?
7. Account for the fact that the northern Great Plains are rolling rather than flat.
8. What is the cause of badlands?
9. What are fault plateaus?

TOPOGRAPHIC SHEETS

Antelope Peak, Arizona. *Alluvial plain, desert plain.*
Phillip, Mississippi. *Alluvial plain.*
Mobile, Alabama. *Coastal plain.*
Bright Angel, Arizona (special). *Canyon, butte, plateau, dissected plateau, rock terrace.* (History and description of Grand Canyon on back.)
Junita Arch, Colorado. *Mesa.*
Fayetteville, West Virginia. *Dissected plateau, erosional remnants, gorge.*
Renova West, Pennsylvania (Allegheny Mountain region of Appalachian Plateau). *Plateau.*
Chemult, Oregon. *Lava plateau.*

All of the above are in the 15-minute series.

CHAPTER 16

VOLCANISM

VOLCANISM is a term which covers all kinds of volcanic activity. It includes the processes that give rise to magma and cause its movement in the earth and its expulsion as gases, lava, and solid debris from openings in the crust.

Volcanism, unlike diastrophism, builds up surface forms by a rapid and dramatic process. We cannot easily observe the slow movement of the earth, and are usually directly aware of it only through earthquake shocks. On the other hand, the great heat within the earth, and the outpourings of lava, by which a mountain may be built in a few months, have captured the imagination of mankind since the earliest times. Many myths and legends center around the evidence of volcanism. Vulcanus, or Vulcan, was the Roman god of fire, and a volcanic island in the Mediterranean was thought to be his home.

In recent years, volcanism has been studied carefully, and much has been learned about the processes of rock formation and the conditions that prevail under the surface of the earth.

Magma. In the discussion of igneous rocks (Chapter 12), magma was described as a hot liquid rock mass. The origin of the heat of magma and the reasons for its rise to the surface are not

VOCABULARY

Volcanism. A general term including all types of activity due to movement of magma.

Fumaroles. Fissures or holes in volcanic regions from which steam or other gases are emitted.

Caldera. A basinlike depression formed by the complete destruction of a volcanic cone.

Dike. Solidified magma in vertical cracks or fissures.

Sill. Solidified magma in horizontal formations.

Laccolith. A domed mass of igneous rock formed by intrusion beneath other rocks.

Batholith. A very large mass of intrusive igneous rock whose lower limits are unknown.

fully understood. As we have seen (Chapter 6), the temperature of the crust increases with depth, to the extent that we can measure it. Most of this heat may be "left over" from the original molten state of the earth. Some of it is probably due to radioactivity, and this may be sufficient to create convection currents. Also, evidence indicates that the material beneath the surface, though hot, is solid, the great pressures apparently preventing it from melting.

What, then, does cause a mass of rock material to melt? Probably increased heat in a limited area from radioactivity, with a release of pressure from above, as by faulting, causes the solid material to liquefy. The liquid magma is lighter than the surrounding rocks, and works its way upward, melting other rocks in its path. As pressures from above decrease, gases develop, making the magma lighter and aiding it in its upward journey. Near the surface the magma is then a very hot fluid, composed largely of silicates with oxides, sulfides, and steam and other gases held in solution by pressure. If it actually reaches the surface, the gases and easily-evaporated materials escape, and the minerals solidify in the form of lava. If overlying rocks contain cracks and fissures beneath the surface, into which the magma can flow, it may cool and solidify more slowly there.

EXTRUSIVE VOLCANISM

Volcanoes. What is a volcano? We have recent experience to tell us what it is. On February 20, 1943, a Mexican farmer was plowing his cornfield about 200 miles west of Mexico City. He heard a deep growling noise, and then saw a cloud of smoke come out of a small hole in the ground. He hurried to the nearby village of Parícutin (pah-*ree*-koo-teen) to spread the news, and when the villagers returned they saw the beginnings of a volcano. It was born amid a series

FIG. 16–1. This recent eruption of Kapoho, a volcano on the lower slope of Mauna Loa in Hawaii, is striking evidence of the forces at work beneath the earth's crust. (*Werner Stoy from Camera Hawaii*)

of small earthquake shocks which continued for weeks.

Blasts of hot gases escaped into the air, followed by a series of explosions that hurled chunks of rock sky-high together with dust and bits of rock. The expanding magma broke open the earth's surface and from several openings lava flowed forth in large quantities. On its first birthday Parícutin was more than 1500 feet high, the nearby village was abandoned, the pine trees for miles around were dead, and the ground was buried under many feet of debris. In 1944 great lava flows reached five miles to bury a village, leaving only the top of the church steeple to mark the spot. In 1952 the volcano was pouring out 200,-000 tons of lava each day. Now volcanic activity is at a standstill, but Parícutin may awaken again at any time.

A volcano, then, is a mountain or hill formed around a vent in the earth's crust through which hot materials are expelled. As these solids accumulate around the opening, they build up a variety of types of *cones,* the type depending upon the chemical and physical nature of the ejected matter. Lava that is of the dark, basalt type, containing little silica, is not very viscous; it flows rapidly for great distances before it hardens. This kind of lava spreads out to form a cone with a very broad base and a gentle slope. Light-colored lava, rich in silica, is very viscous; it does not flow readily. Cones built up by this thicker lava have steep sides because the lava hardens before it has a chance to spread. Chimborazo, a great volcanic peak in the Andes Mountains, has a steep-sided lava cone of this type.

If solid, angular fragments are ejected in large quantities, very steep cones are built up because of the tendency of the particles to interlock.

TYPES OF ERUPTIONS

Quiet volcanoes. In Hawaii the volcanoes discharge large quantities of very hot, relatively fluid lava which gives off its gases readily. This fluid lava spreads out quickly to form a broad cone with gentle slopes. Such a volcano is called the *oozing* or *quiet* type. It is nonexplosive, but sends fountains of lava hundreds of feet into the air in spectacular scarlet tongues. When the boiling lava overflows its containing crater, it flows swiftly toward the lower levels, where it destroys vegetation and buries everything in its path. The speed of flow from Mauna Loa (*mow*-nah-*loh*-ah), on the island of Hawaii, has been clocked at 12 miles an hour. During its eruption in November, 1959, its neighbor, Kilauea (kee-lou-*ay*-ah), sent lava fountains 1950 feet into the air.

Explosive volcanoes. Some volcanoes explode with unbelievable violence. The eruption is often preceded by loud rumblings and earthquakes which open up the ground, forming great fissures, draining lakes, and developing hot springs. When Tambora on Soembawa (soom-*bah*-wah) Island, in the East Indies, erupted in 1815, the rumblings were heard for a thousand miles in all directions. They were caused by the movement of magma and gases held under tremendous pressures. Finally the greatest eruption ever recorded by man occurred. An estimated 38 cubic miles of extremely hot gases, lava, and shattered rocks were blasted into the air.

Intermediate volcanoes. A type of volcano intermediate between the *quiet* and the *explosive* kinds is one which is sometimes quiet, sometimes explosive or a combination of both. Stromboli (*strom*-boh-lee), located north of Sicily in the Mediterranean Sea, is a volcano of this

FIG. 16–2. Kilauea volcano in eruption. This photograph, taken at night, shows a hot lava flow and the lava fountains characteristic of the quiet type of volcanoes. (*National Park Service*)

type. It erupts every fifteen minutes or so with minor explosions which hurl fragments of partially solidified lava into the air, as well as clouds of steam which reflect the light from the glowing lava below, providing a visible beacon at night for navigators. Stromboli has thus come to be known as the "lighthouse of the Mediterranean."

Fissure eruptions. A form of extrusive activity which does not build cones is that of *fissure flows*. Floods of very fluid lava have been extruded from fissures at great distances from volcanic cones. These include the great lava plains and plateaus of the world. The Columbia Plateau described in Chapter 15, and the Deccan Plateau in India are known to have been built up by a series of fissure flows. In Iceland, extensive fissure flows have occurred in modern times and the total quantity of lava produced there during all time exceeds the amount produced in the entire central Pacific.

PRODUCTS OF ERUPTIONS

Gases and vapors. Steam is by far the the most abundant vapor that escapes from most volcanoes. Fissures or holes from which steam and other gases escape are called *fumaroles.* There are many fumaroles in the Valley of Ten Thousand Smokes, northwest of Katmai Volcano, Alaska, as well as in the crater itself. Gases emitted by fumaroles are usually more than 90 percent steam, at temperatures ranging from 100° to 650° C. Some of this steam is formed when ground water seeps down into areas heated by magma; but much of it probably comes from water vapor that is dissolved in the magma itself. Hydrochloric and hydrofluoric acids, sulfur, and boron compounds rise with the steam. The steam and other vapors also carry up with them gaseous metals in large quantities. These include iron, copper, zinc, tin, silver, antimony, lead, arsenic, and molybdenum, whose compounds are deposited as incrustations along the fissures from which the gases rise. Other hot gases that commonly issue from vents include carbon dioxide, carbon monoxide, methane, hydrogen, nitrogen, ammonia, oxygen, helium, and argon. Fumaroles are common in areas of active volcanoes and also in areas where most surface activity has stopped.

Volcanic gases may have injurious effects. Carbon monoxide, sulfur dioxide, and hydrogen sulfide are poisonous, and carbon dioxide can kill by suffocation. The high temperature of the gases can burn the lungs or the entire body. Where gases collect in valleys, wild life may be killed. Many animal bones are found in such a valley on the island of Java.

Fragmental materials. The solid material hurled from volcanoes varies in size from large chunks or *blocks* to the tiniest of particles. Large, thick, rounded masses, often with ends that twist in a spiral, are called *volcanic bombs.* Smaller intermediate fragments of similar shape are called *lapilli* or *cinders,* whereas the finest particles are ash and dust. (Note that cinders and ash are not *burned*

FIG. 16–3. This volcanic bomb of unusual size was markedly twisted in its passage through the air. (*U. S. Geological Survey*)

material, but solidified rock particles.) Some of the fragmental material is still liquid when it is hurled upward; the twisted shape of volcanic bombs shows that it solidified while in motion. Gas bubbles in the lava expand as the fragments travel through the air, so that the material is often full of small holes.

Volcanic blocks are sometimes exceedingly large: Stromboli has thrown blocks weighing over two tons for a distance exceeding two miles. When ground water poured into the pit of Halemaumau in Hawaii during an earthquake that caused the pit walls to collapse, a steam explosion occurred with such violence that a block weighing 14 tons was sent 2500 feet into the air.

Other fragments and most of the ash fall near the vent and help to build up the cone. Dust is carried by the winds for hundreds of miles, and is very destructive to vegetation. The rocks formed from fragmental material are volcanic breccia, from coarse fragments, and tuff, soft consolidated ash and dust.

Lava. Lava issuing from a volcano sometimes pours over the rim of the crater, but in many cases it breaks through a weak spot in the wall or goes through fissures in the sides of the cone. When it first appears, it is often red- or white-hot, but its surface cools quickly and it becomes darker. The cooled lava takes many forms. It may cool rapidly on the surface, while the under part is still very hot. Then the crusted lava on the top breaks into jagged chunks which are stirred up as the liquid portion flows slowly on. This type of lava flow is called *block lava*, or in Hawaii, *aa* (*ah*-ah). Often, however, the lava solidifies with a smooth surface, having a ropy or billowy appearance. This is called *pahoehoe* (pah-*hoh*-ay-*hoh*-ay). When basaltic lava flows into water, it develops a pe-

FIG. 16–4. A great dust cloud accompanied the eruption of Mont Pelée. (*American Museum of Natural History*)

culiar structure resembling a pile of pillows; such flows are called *pillow lava.* When they are found between sedimentary strata, they indicate the underwater origin of the beds. The rapid cooling of the pillow surface forms a glassy rind of tachylite.

Sometimes the top and bottom of the flow cool rapidly, while the portion in the interior is still liquid. This liquid material may flow out, leaving tunnels in the solid lava. In 1935 when lava from Mauna Loa threatened the city of Hilo, Hawaii, the Army Air Corps bombed the source tunnel of the lava. Cool air rushed into the new holes and the flow solidified to form an effective plug diverting the lava from the city.

The temperatures of the lavas from Kilauea, Vesuvius, and Etna are about

FIG. 16–5. Lava forms. Above, a close-up of lava tunnels. The pencil in the middle of the photo indicates the size of the tunnels. Below, cascades in pahoehoe. (*John A. Shimer; U. S. Geological Survey*)

1000° C. (1830° F.) When cool, such lavas show pronounced jointing, in definite systems at right angles to the cooling surfaces.

Condensed water sometimes mixes with the volcanic ash and dust to produce thick streams of mud, resembling lava, that flow down the sides of the volcano. These are called *mud torrents*.

Economic importance of volcanism. In some regions of the world, fumarole fields are being used for the generation of electric power. Holes drilled hundreds of feet below the surface tap underground sources of superheated steam which is led by large pipes into steam turbines that run electric generators. Large power plants using steam from volcanic sources are operating today in Larderello, north of Rome in Italy, and in the Coast Ranges of California north of San Francisco. The fumarole gases used for generating electric power are approximately 94 percent steam, mixed with varying amounts of carbon dioxide, sulfur dioxide, ammonia, methane, and helium. Separation of the latter gases from the steam yields by-products of considerable value. Sulfur dioxide is used in the manufacture of sulfuric acid, ammonia in the making of fertilizers, and methane as a fuel gas. Helium, an inert gas, finds increasing use in the smelting and metallurgy of light metals that react readily with the oxygen in the air. It is also used as the lifting gas in balloons and dirigibles because it is lighter than air, and will not ignite when mixed with air.

In Italy, ammonium carbonate, sodium carbonate, and boric acid are extracted from the steam and hot water in volcanic areas. Hydrogen sulfide gas oxidizes in air to form water and sulfur, which is deposited in commercial quantities. Such deposits are found in Italy, Mexico, and Japan. The sulfur is formed by the action of air on hydrogen sulfide as follows:

$$2H_2S \;+\; O_2 \;\rightarrow\; 2H_2O \;+\; 2S$$
hydrogen   oxygen   water   sulfur
sulfide   in air

Other chemical products of commercial value obtained from volcanoes include alum and borax. *Traprock* is a general term for various volcanic rocks useful for building roads. Pumice is valuable for grinding and polishing. Tuff, which becomes durable upon exposure to air, is quarried for use as a building stone.

Lava, volcanic ash, and dust eventually form very fertile soil which supports productive farms.

VOLCANIC FEATURES

Cones. Three main types of volcanic cones are recognized. *Shield cones* or *lava cones* are broad at the base with gentle gradients composed of successive layers of dark lava. Classic examples are the Hawaiian cones formed by eruptions of the quiet type. *Cinder cones* are formed by the explosive type of eruption. They have fairly narrow bases and steep, symmetrical slopes of interlocking, angular cinders. Mont Pelée (puh-*lay*) and Krakatao (krah-kah-*tow*) are examples of cinder cones. *Composite cones* are built of alternate layers of cinders and lava. These composite cones are intermediate in steepness between the lava cones and the cinder cones. The presence of both solid fragments and lava shows that at times explosions have thrown out cinders and at other times internal pressures, aided by gases, have discharged lava. The fragments ejected

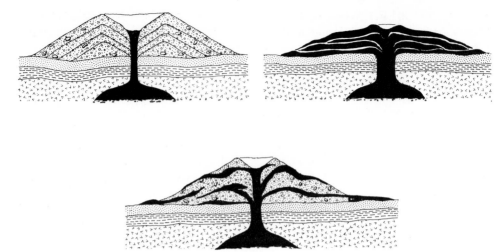

FIG. 16–6. The major types of volcanic cones. Top left, cinder cone; right, shield cone; bottom, composite cone or stratovolcano.

at different periods of time often form successive layers of varicolored deposits between layers of lava. Volcanoes with this stratified structure are called *strato-volcanoes*. Fujiyama in Japan, Mayon in the Philippines, and Mounts Rainier, Hood, and Shasta in the United States are good examples of this type of volcanic cone.

Openings commonly develop in cones at a point some distance below the main vent, and materials flowing from these build up smaller, subordinate volcanoes called *parasitic cones.* Other types of cones which rarely exceed 20 feet in height are called *spatter cones.* These form in the lava fields away from the main vent. As the lava cools, a crust is formed, and hot gases force out lava in spattering fountains through openings that develop in the crust.

Craters and calderas. The funnel-shaped pit at the top of the volcanic cone is known as the *crater.* The crater widens as material is ejected since the very hot magma melts and breaks up the crater walls. The rim also collapses by destruction of the funnel sides from explosions. Often a smaller cone is built up on the crater floor by materials erupted from the vent.

A *caldera* is a great basinlike depression formed when explosions completely destroy the upper part of a volcanic cone, or when the cone collapses. Collapse may be due to subsidence along a circular fracture, or to recession of the magma feeding the volcano. The term was taken from an immense pit called La Caldera (the Caldron) in the Canary Islands. It is almost 3000 feet deep, with a diameter of 3 miles. The tremendous calderas at the summits of Kilauea and Mauna Loa in Hawaii were formed by the collapse of the tops of their shield cones. This resulted from the withdrawal of the supporting magma, either by eruptions onto the surface or by lowering of the lava as it moved down into the earth.

The calderas of some extinct volcanoes fill with rain water or melted snow. Crater Lake in Oregon occupies a caldera with a diameter of 5 to 6 miles and

FIG. 16–7. Above, the wide dome of Haleakala, on the island of Maui, Hawaii, is the largest extinct crater in the world. Below, Mayon, in the Philippines, is an outstanding example of a composite cone. (*Josef Muench; Eric Pavel*)

walls that rise over 2000 feet above the surface of the lake. The caldera is the remains of the ancient volcano Mount Mazama. Its walls are made up of alternating beds of lavas, pumice, and breccia, with glacial till. A small recent cone forms Wizard Island. The deep blue of the water and the beautiful form of the crater make this a famous scenic feature of the northwest. (See page 278.)

Nonvolcanic craters. Some craters in the earth's surface were formed by the impact of huge meteorites. *Meteor Crater* in Arizona is a depression 500 feet deep with a diameter of nearly one mile. Most geologists believe that it is of meteorite origin. Because the underlying strata are not disturbed, it is obviously not volcanic in origin. Chubb Crater, in the province of Quebec, Canada, is also

thought to be due to the impact of a very large meteorite. It is 11,500 feet in diameter and 1800 feet deep. Five billion tons of granite were apparently smashed by one falling body in producing this depression. A lake two miles wide now fills a part of the crater bowl.

VOLCANIC ACTIVITY IN HISTORIC TIMES

There are almost 500 active volcanoes known today. We can assume that hundreds of others must have been active in recent geologic times because their cones show little erosion.

Any volcano that is erupting, or that has recently erupted, is said to be *active.* If its activity ceases for a considerable

FIG. 16–8. The walls and pavement of this Pompeiian street were buried for centuries under volcanic debris. (*Trans World Airlines*)

time it is called *dormant;* but if there is evidence to suggest that it will not erupt again, we say that it is *extinct*. However, nobody can be absolutely sure that an extinct volcano is not just dormant.

Vesuvius. Vesuvius (veh-*soo*-vee-us) stands on the site of an older volcano, Monte Somma, which the early Romans thought to be extinct. Its cone was covered with a thick layer of rich soil which supported a luxuriant growth of green trees. In 79 A.D., however, it erupted for the first time on record, and buried the cities of Herculaneum, Stabiae, and Pompeii under hot ashes and mud. Excavations carried on since the middle of the eighteenth century have uncovered these cities, including the remains of victims, most of whom were caught huddled in basements where they had sought protection. Pompeii was covered by a blanket of deadly gases and lapilli, cinders, and ashes; but the port of Herculaneum, to the west of Vesuvius, was engulfed by layers of the same substances drenched with water. This semiliquid material hardened to form a deposit that reaches a depth of 65 feet in places. It is composed of two distinct layers which together average about 20 feet in thickness. The lower layer is composed of cinders and lapilli; the upper one is of fine white ash consolidated by water. Molds of human bodies, buildings, and other evidences of ancient Roman culture are preserved in these deposits.

Again in the year 1631, a violent eruption killed many people, sent streams of hot lava to the sea, and shot dust so far into the air that it was carried to Constantinople 800 miles away.

Etna. Mount Etna is on the east shore of densely populated Sicily. In the year 1169 its violent eruption destroyed Catania, and it has been very active ever since. Its crater is 1500 feet deep. The

FIG. 16–9. This great rock plug rose during the 1902 eruption of Mont Pelée. (*American Museum of Natural History*)

volcano covers an area of 460 square miles, and its summit rises dramatically 10,758 feet above the neighboring sea.

Mont Pelée. Mont Pelée, in the West Indies, had been inactive since 1851. Suddenly, in 1902, it blew off the top of its crater, sending a black cloud of dust and hot gases down its sides, and destroying the city of St. Pierre, on the north end of the Island of Martinique. About 30,000 people lost their lives by breathing the hot dust and gases. At the same time an immense needlelike spine arose from the depths of the crater and towered 5276 feet above sea level. Pushed up by pressures from below, this gigantic rock plug slowly rose a thousand feet above the rim of the broken crater. Its weak rock soon crumbled, however.

Krakatao is a small volcanic island located in Sunda Strait, between Sumatra and Java in the East Indies. In

FIG. 16–10. The waters of Crater Lake fill the caldera of ancient Mount Mazama. The circular form of the crater and the symmetry of the recent cone, Wizard Island, are well shown in this view. (*Ray Atkeson from Shostal*)

August of 1883 an eruption began throwing out dust and pumice following a period of earthquakes. Tremendous explosions continued for three days. Most of the island was blasted away, and a hole 1000 feet below the level of the sea was blown out. Fragments were blown 17 miles upward and airborne dust from the volcano encircled the earth, causing colorful sunsets for many months before it finally settled. In the vicinity of the explosion, the dust was so thick that sunlight was blotted out. In Batavia, a hundred miles away, lamps were needed during the daylight hours. Tidal waves 100 feet high were generated by the explosions. These spread out in all directions destroying many seaside villages and drowning 36,000 people.

Lassen Peak. The only volcano in the continental United States (excluding Alaska) that has erupted since the beginning of the twentieth century is Las-sen Peak in northern California. The volcano started to erupt in May 1914, and has erupted on several occasions since that time, throwing out gases, cinders, and ashes. Several explosions took place in 1915. This mountain is included in Lassen Volcanic National Park.

Katmai (*kat*-my). The volcano Katmai is located where the Alaskan Peninsula joins the mainland. Fortunately only a few people live near this volcano; its site is a National Monument. On June 6, 1912, a violent explosion occurred which was heard at Juneau, 750 miles away, and even at Fairbanks, across the Alaskan Mountains.

It has been determined that almost five cubic miles of ash and dust were hurled out and deposited over a wide area. Twelve miles away the ashes were three feet deep, and 100 miles away Kodiak was covered with almost a foot of dust.

Hawaii. Hawaii is the largest of a series of marine volcanic mountains about 2000 miles southwest of California. It has two high lava cones—Mauna Kea (13,780 feet), and Mauna Loa (13,680 feet), and the lower Kilauea (4050 feet) with its lake of liquid lava. Mauna Loa and Kilauea are active; they are included in Hawaii National Park. Lava flowing from Mauna Loa sometimes forms streams as much as one mile wide and 40 miles long. These often flow into the ocean with great hissing and boiling of the water.

The 1959 eruption of Kilauea gave scientists a great opportunity to study the volcanic process. A series of earthquakes heralded the eruption. In one week, in May, over 2500 small quakes were recorded. On November 14, there were 2200 in 24 hours, and that night the eruption began. In the preceding weeks, instruments recorded the swelling of the volcanic dome. The staff of the observatory, run by the United States Geological Survey, were able to take samples of the lava as it poured from the crater, before it touched the rocks outside.

Distribution of volcanoes. Volcanoes may form in mountain regions, on plains or plateaus, or on the sea floor. Almost all of the volcanoes of the world are found in two major belts which cover much the same regions as the earthquake belts pictured in Fig. 13–21. These are roughly the zones of fracture in the earth's crust.

The Pacific Ocean is bordered by a circular volcanic belt, sometimes called the "ring of fire." The other large belt stretches across the Mediterranean eastward through Asia Minor and Persia to Baluchistan, crossing the Pacific belt in the East Indies and extending through the Hawaiian Islands, the West Indies and the Azores. See Figure 16–12.

In the region of the Aleutian Islands a huge volcanic mountain chain is being built. Violent undersea eruptions commonly occur here, and occasionally cones are built up hundreds of feet above the surface of the sea only to be destroyed rapidly by the action of ocean waves. Submarine volcanoes of very great size have been built up in the Central Pacific. Many of these have since undergone a series of changes involving

FIG. 16–11. An old engraving shows the island of Krakatao before the eruption of 1883. It has the tall, steep cinder cone typical of the explosive type of volcano. (*Culver Service*)

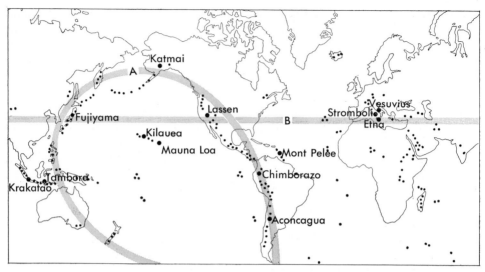

FIG. 16–12. The major volcanic belts of the earth.

the formation of calderas and cinder cones, followed by erosion and a gradual sinking of the rock mass very slowly below the surface of the sea. Coral reefs have been built up around many of these cones, forming *atolls* (See Chapter 20).

Life history of a volcano. When a volcano becomes extinct, so that no further material is added to the cone, the agents of weathering and erosion continue their work of wearing it down and carrying it away. Finally the entire mountain is leveled.

During *youth,* however, the active volcano continues to build up its cone during intervals of eruption much faster than the destructive forces can erode it during its intervals of dormancy. Many times during its history it fills valleys of erosion with new lava deposits, tending to maintain the symmetrical form characteristic of youth. The stage of *maturity* is reached only after a long, steady period of erosion of the cone. This can only occur when the volcano is extinct. The mature stage of erosion is marked by gullies and valleys cut deeply into the

slopes. Wave erosion acts on extinct island volcanoes. On land, erosion of composite cones eventually leaves the hard central neck or volcanic plug standing as an isolated shaft of rock long after the softer layers have been worn down and carried away in *old age*. Dikes of igneous rock sometimes remain radiating from the central plug and masses of volcanic material may be left in concentric circles around it. In the final stages of old age these are removed. Then intrusive masses such as laccoliths, which are usually associated with the original source of the lava, may be observed at the surface.

INTRUSIVE VOLCANISM

Intrusive forms. As we have seen in Chapter 12, intrusive igneous rocks are found as batholiths, laccoliths, sills, and dikes. These intrusions, once they are exposed, show various relationships to the rocks around them, depending on the way the magma rose from its deep

FIG. 16–13. A volcano in old age, Shiprock near Farmington, New Mexico. The neck and radiating dikes, exposed by erosion, are all that remain of this ancient volcano. (*Spence Air Photo*)

FIG. 16–14. A great dike near West Spanish Peak in Colorado. The horizontal lines in the dike are the marks of the bedding planes of the sedimentary strata into which the dike was intruded. (*U. S. Geological Survey*)

source. Many of the smaller intrusions are directly associated with volcanoes. Others are offshoots of deep batholiths which underlie vast areas. Intrusive bodies are usually found together, with dikes leading into sills and laccoliths, and laccoliths thinning out to form sills or dikes.

Dikes. The *vertical* cracks or fissures which magma enters to form dikes may cut across the bedding planes of sedimentary rocks. The magma may also invade massive igneous or metamorphic rocks that show little definite structure. Some dikes are harder than the rocks they penetrate; others are softer. If they are harder than the surrounding rocks, they usually remain projecting above the surface after erosion has removed the softer bedrock. Dikes vary in width from less than an inch to many feet and in length from a few feet to many miles. The Great Dike in Rhodesia is 300 miles long and is more than 5 miles wide in some places. Most dikes form in pre-existing cracks. In some cases the magma pushes apart the walls, enlarging the space, and may thus produce new fractures which it fills.

Sills. Sills are similar to dikes except that the magma wedges itself in between the sedimentary rock layers *horizontally* over a wide area. Thus it has the form of a thin sheet.

Perhaps the best-known sill in the United States is that which forms the Palisades of the Hudson. In the sedimentary strata of the region forming the western shores of the river, beds of very resistant dark-colored rock appear. Several of these, which were poured out on the surface as lava flows, form the ridges of the Watchung Mountains of New Jersey. One, however, was forced in between the sedimentary layers as a sill, and later tilted. Uncovered by erosion, it is exposed along the river from Jersey City as far north as Haverstraw, forming a picturesque series of steep cliffs. The columnar jointing from which the Palisades takes its name results in the occasional breaking off of large masses of the traprock.

Laccoliths. The large domed mass of igneous rock called a laccolith is an indication of how magma pushes up the overlying rock. The magma for this mass

FIG. 16–15. The Palisades of the Hudson River Valley are the result of tilting of a sill. (*Ewing Galloway*)

FIG. 16–16. The Sawtooth Mountains are formed from a part of the Idaho batholith. (*U. S. Forest Service*)

is supplied through a small, more or less vertical fissure, so that the mass above has a flat floor, resting on the sedimentary strata. The laccoliths of the Henry Mountains, described in Chapter 14, were among the first to be studied. An intrusion cannot be positively identified as a laccolith until erosion exposes the underlying rocks at some point, but the presence of a laccolith is suggested by a typical domelike hill.

Batholiths. Batholiths, which are the parent source of many other intrusive and extrusive masses, extend deep into the earth. They are distinguished from laccoliths by their great size and by the fact that they extend downward indefinitely. Batholiths form the roots of mountain ranges and the bases of continents. Some are known to be 100 miles wide and 1000 miles long. The Idaho batholith, which is exposed in the Sawtooth Mountains of Idaho and underlies

part of the Northern Rockies, extends over an area of 16,000 square miles. The great fault block of the Sierra Nevada is part of a gray or white granite batholith; the domes and cliffs of Yosemite and the adjacent canyons are formed of this granite. Batholiths often contain gold-bearing quartz veins, whose later erosion results in stream placer deposits. Batholiths which were intruded during crustal revolutions are usually made up of granite gneiss, in which the biotite and some other minerals show strong banding.

Stocks. A stock is an intrusive body differing from a batholith only in size. Ordinarily, an intrusion less than 40 square miles in area is called a stock. Stocks may be simply rounded projections from a batholith. It is often difficult to distinguish a stock from a volcanic neck, when overlying rocks have been removed by erosion.

SUMMARY

Volcanos are conical hills or mountains developed around an opening in the earth's surface from which gases, rock fragments, lava, ashes, and cinders are expelled. Volcanos are destructive from our point of view but are considered geologically constructive because they build up the surface of the earth. They may be classified as active, dormant, or extinct. Mauna Loa is an active volcano, Vesuvius is dormant, and Mount Mazama, now the site of Crater Lake, is extinct.

The gradual accumulation of hot gases under great pressure due to underlying liquid magma is the principal cause of volcanic eruptions. The types of eruptions are quiet, explosive, or intermediate. Volcanic eruptions sometimes result in great loss of life and tremendous destruction of property.

Even when not active, volcanos often emit water vapor, sulfur dioxide, hydrogen sulfide, and ammonia from small local vents called fumaroles. Fumaroles are used to furnish heat for industrial purposes, and valuable by-products are obtained from the gases they emit.

Depending on its mineral content and resulting viscosity, lava may form such features as block lava, pahoehoe, and pillow lava. Sills, dikes, and laccoliths are due to subsurface magma intrusions. Many interesting topographic features are the direct result of subsurface magma intrusions which are later revealed by faulting or erosion.

VOCABULARY REVIEW

Match the phrase in the left column with the correct word or phrase in the right column. *Do not write in this book.*

1. Explosive type
2. Stratified structure
3. Subordinate volcano
4. Liquid mineral mass
5. Rounded masses, often with spiral ends
6. Intermediate type
7. Vents through which gases escape
8. Consolidated ash and dust
9. Funnel-shaped pit
10. Roman god of fire
11. Billowy appearance
12. Fissure flow
13. Quiet type
14. Basinlike depression

a. Columbia Plateau
b. volcanic bombs
c. caldera
d. Mauna Loa
e. fumaroles
f. block lava
g. magma
h. cones
i. pahoehoe
j. Stromboli
k. crater
l. Tambora
m. breccia
n. parasitic cone
o. Vulcan
p. stratovolcano

QUESTIONS   ·   GROUP A

Decide whether the following statements are true or false. Reword the false statements to make them true. *Do not write in this book.*

1. A recently-born volcano in Mexico is Parícutin.
2. An explosive volcano in the East Indies is Pelée.
3. La Caldera is located in the Canary Islands.
4. Mount Mazama is an example of a quiet volcano.
5. The "ring of fire" borders the Pacific Ocean.
6. Sills are vertical intrusions.
7. The Henry Mountains resulted from a series of domelike batholiths.
8. Lava of a high silica content is very viscous.
9. Vesuvius is known as the lighthouse of the Mediterranean.
10. The most extensive fissure flows may be studied in Iceland.
11. Lava will eventually weather to form fertile soil.
12. The volcanic cones of the Hawaiian Islands are classified as shield cones.
13. Chubb Crater is an example of a caldera.
14. The Palisades of the Hudson are formed by a sill.
15. Chimborazo is made up of lava with a low silica content.

GROUP B

1. What is included in the term volcanism?
2. What causes the melting of rock masses below the surface of the earth?
3. Discuss the characteristics of the various types of lava.
4. Trace the life history of a volcano.
5. List some of the useful materials that may be produced by a volcano.
6. List two examples of the power generated by the force of an exploding volcano.
7. How was the city of Hilo, Hawaii, saved during the 1935 eruption of Mauna Loa?
8. List the characteristics of each of the following: shield cone, cinder cone, composite cone or stratovolcano, parasitic cone, spatter cone.
9. What is the probable origin of Chubb Crater? Why do geologists believe that Meteor Crater is not of volcanic origin?
10. How is extrusive volcanism different from intrusive volcanism? Describe the topographic features that may result from each type of volcanism.

TOPOGRAPHIC SHEETS

Crater Lake National Park, Oregon (special). *Extinct volcano.*
Lassen Volcanic National Park, California. *Young volcano.*
Shasta, California. *Mature volcano.*
Shiprock, New Mexico. *Volcanic neck.*

All of the above are in the 15-minute series.

UNIT REVIEW QUESTIONS

1. Discuss fully the cause and effect of the San Francisco earthquake of 1906.
2. What are the characteristics of plateaus, plains, and mountains?
3. Discuss the importance of the type of building construction used in earthquake areas.
4. How does the study of glaciation bear out the isostatic theory?
5. Illustrate and explain how the convection theory could account for the great mountain chains along the coastlines of continents.
6. What is the significance of a rock outcrop to a geologist?
7. Why is surface topography not sufficient evidence to classify an area as a syncline or anticline?
8. Illustrate and explain the terms dip and strike.
9. Illustrate and explain a pitching fold.
10. Illustrate, label, and explain two different types of faults.
11. Illustrate and explain how the epicenter of an earthquake can be located.
12. What are the two principal causes of earthquakes?
13. Describe the cause and effect of the Lisbon, Portugal, earthquake in 1755.
14. What may be the cause of earthquakes in the New England area?
15. Illustrate and describe the three types of waves that accompany earthquakes.
16. Discuss conditions under which a landform may never complete its life cycle.
17. Compare the following areas in relation to rock type, rock structure, and topography. (*a*) Sierra Nevada and the Great Basin (*b*) Jura Mountains and the Newer Appalachians (*c*) Vesuvius and the Cascade Range (*d*) the Black Hills and the Henry Mountains (*e*) the Andes and the Adirondacks (*f*) the Alps and the Catskills.
18. Discuss how a water gap may become a wind gap.
19. Why are earthquakes extremely infrequent in mature mountains?
20. Explain and illustrate by a labeled diagram the difference between a synclinal and a monoclinal ridge.
21. Why are suitable power-plant sites more frequent in young mountains than in those that are mature or old?
22. Discuss the formation of the volcanic mountains of Hawaii.
23. What indications are there that the Hudson River originally had a much longer course?
24. Why are deltas not found along the Atlantic coast?
25. Why are many plains and plateaus considered constructional features rather than destructional features?
26. Compare the characteristics of a lake plain with those of a coastal plain.
27. Compare the characteristics of the Piedmont Upland with the Atlantic Coastal Plain. What is the fall line? Account for the location of major cities on the fall line.
28. What are estuaries? Locate some important estuaries.
29. What are some common features of the seacoast along a coastal plain?
30. What indication is there that southeastern England and northern France were once an unbroken stretch of land?

31. Why may salt-water fossils be discovered in the interior lowlands?
32. Trace the history of Lake Agassiz.
33. What features indicate that Great Salt Lake was at one time a much larger lake?
34. Why are plains more suitable to agriculture than plateaus?
35. What is the evidence that Wizard Island was formed after the destruction of Mount Mazama?
36. How is a laccolith formed?
37. Discuss the classification of volcanoes as quiet, explosive, and intermediate. Give an example of each.
38. When was the first recorded eruption of Vesuvius? What evidence shows that Herculaneum and Pompeii were covered with different materials?
39. Briefly discuss the most recent volcanic eruptions of each of the following: Parícutin, Kilauea, Katmai, Etna, Krakatao.
40. Write a balanced equation to show the reaction of hydrogen sulfide with oxygen. Discuss the values of volcanic products.
41. Discuss the difference between a sill and a dike. Give examples of each.
42. What is the relationship of an atoll to a volcano?
43. What is a fumarole? Name some of the products emitted by a fumarole.
44. Discuss the relative importance of diastrophism and volcanism in the production of earthquakes.
45. Explain why some rock formations that are commonly called mountains are not really considered to be mountains by geologists.
46. Distinguish between the four major types of magma intrusions. Describe some topographic features that may result from such intrusions.
47. Explain the formation of such features as the Giant's Causeway and the Devil's Postpile.

ACTIVITIES

1. Prepare a bulletin board display of pictures illustrating recent and past earthquakes.
2. Make models in clay, plaster, plywood, or papier maché to illustrate folding and faulting. Paint the various rock layers.
3. Draw a map of the world and print the names and dates of disastrous earthquakes in the proper places.
4. On a map of the United States locate and outline the major physiographic provinces.
5. Make models to illustrate some of the major physiographic provinces of the United States.
6. Collect photographs of typical topography, scenery, industry, etc., in the physiographic provinces of the United States. Most state tourist bureaus are glad to supply these pictures.

7. Make a model to illustrate the theory of isostasy.
8. Make a relief model of the Harrisburg, Pennsylvania, region. Use the Harrisburg 15-minute quadrangle for reference.
9. On an outline map of the world locate and label 12 important mountain systems.
10. Make a labeled wall chart to illustrate the relationship of the Mindanao Deep and Mount Everest.
11. Make models to illustrate mountains in the different stages of their life cycles. Include such characteristics as ruggedness, streams, snow line and glaciers, timberline, etc.
12. Make models to illustrate the difference between peaks, ridges, chains, systems, and cordilleras.
13. Make a report on national parks that feature mountains.
14. Make models to illustrate a batholith, laccolith, sill, and dike.
15. Prepare a report on the formation of the Palisades of the Hudson.
16. Consult a topographic map of Crater Lake and make a model of the area as it is today. Exhibit this project along with a description and a model of the area before the formation of Crater Lake. Historical and geological information useful in this project is given on the back of the Crater Lake National Park topographic map.
17. Make a report on the result of excavations that have been made in the area of Mount Vesuvius.
18. Build dioramas to illustrate the features of a plain or plateau in various stages of its life cycle. Tourist bureaus are a good source of photographs to supply the idea to work from.
19. Obtain a geologic map of your area and draw a profile to show the arrangement of its rock strata.
20. Prepare a report to show how landforms have influenced the history or development of some particular geographic area.
21. Write an essay on how changes in communication and transportation have helped man to become relatively independent of the influence of various landforms.
22. Make relief maps or models to show the surface of the sea bottom under the Atlantic or Pacific Ocean. Identify diastrophic and volcanic features on the map.
23. Make a rough topographic map of the area in which you live and identify on it any of the topographic features about which you have studied in this unit.
24. Use layers of clay, foam rubber, or wet paper to demonstrate the changes that occur during folding and faulting of rock layers.
25. Make a report on how engineers can demonstrate that plastic deformation of rocks actually occurs.
26. Consult biological references to prepare a report on how land bridges in the past affected the spread of animal species to the different parts of the world.
27. Make clay models of each of the major types of volcanic cones.
28. Prepare a report on the methods by which man-made seismic waves are used in the exploration for petroleum.

FURTHER READING

GEOLOGY. W. H. Emmons, G. A. Thiel, and I. S. Allison, 1955. *McGraw-Hill Book Co., New York.*

GEOMORPHOLOGY. A. K. Lobeck, 1939. *McGraw-Hill Book Co., New York.*

INTRODUCTION TO PHYSICAL GEOLOGY. C. R. Longwell and R. F. Flint, 1955. *John Wiley and Sons, Inc., New York.*

★

THE WORLD WE LIVE IN. L. Barnett, 1955. *Time Inc., New York.*

DOWN TO EARTH: AN INTRODUCTION TO GEOLOGY. C. G. Croneis and W. C. Krumbein, 1936. *University of Chicago Press, Chicago.*

CAUSES OF CATASTROPHE. L. D. Leet, 1948. *Whittlesey House, New York.*

THE EARTH WE LIVE ON. Ruth Moore, 1956. *Alfred A. Knopf, New York.*

THE CRUST OF THE EARTH. S. Rapport and H. Wright, 1955. *New American Library, New York.*

★

STORY OF MOUNTAINS. F. C. Lane, 1950. *Doubleday and Co., Inc., Garden City, New York.*

HIGH CONQUEST. J. R. Ullman, 1941. *J. B. Lippincott Co., Philadelphia.*

★

VOLCANOS, NEW AND OLD. S. N. Coleman, 1946. *John Day Co., New York.*

ALL ABOUT VOLCANOS AND EARTHQUAKES. F. H. Pough, 1953. *Random House, New York.*

CONSTANT change is found in all of nature. A sapling gradually becomes a giant tree; a flightless caterpillar turns into a butterfly. Such changes in the world of living things are well known because they take place within the lifetime of a man. Changes in the rocks that form the landscape of the earth's surface are less easily seen. They occur so slowly that no one person lives long enough to see for himself the changes that occur in the apparently everlasting mountains, plains, and valleys.

Each feature on the earth's surface is a product of one of the forces that build landforms. At the same time, each feature was subject to change from the moment it was exposed to the destructional agents—sun, water, wind, and ice. This unit is an introduction to the processes that produce continuous changes on the surface of the earth.

UNIT 5

THE FORCES THAT SCULPTURE THE EARTH'S SURFACE

CHAPTER 17

WEATHERING AND EROSION

THE seemingly solid and permanent earth is in fact a scene of constant change. Earthquakes, volcanic eruptions, and the rise of mountains are evidences of the unsettled interior of the planet, and the permanence and solidity of the rock of the crust are only an illusion, since it is subject to decay. Anyone who has attempted to make out the fading inscription on an old tombstone or observed the crumbling exteriors of old stone buildings has seen evidence of the slow breakdown of rock. Given enough time, all of the rocks of the earth's surface, tombstones and mountains alike, undergo slow disintegration and removal.

Chiefly responsible for these attacks on the rock is the atmosphere working through the agencies of weather and climate: heat from the sun, moisture, frost, and wind. Taken together, the destructive processes that slowly crumble the rock into little pieces are called *weathering.* Weathering is actually a process of adjustment to changes in conditions. As rocks become exposed, they are subjected to conditions different from those under which they were originally formed. They are affected by atmospheric gases, and by variations in temperature and moisture which produce characteristic changes depending on the rock's resist-

VOCABULARY

Weathering. The natural disintegration and decomposition of rocks and minerals.

Erosion. The removal of soil and rock fragments by natural agents.

Exfoliation (eks-foh-lee-*ay*-shun). The splitting off of scales or flakes of rock as a result of weathering.

Carbonation. The chemical combination of substances with carbon dioxide.

Oxidation. The chemical combination of substances with oxygen.

Hydration. The chemical combination of substances with water.

Mantle rock. The layers of loose weathered rock lying over solid bedrock.

Humus. The organic matter in soil, produced by decomposition of plant and animal materials.

ance to the various agents of weathering. An important product of weathering is the soil, the basis of human existence. The soil is the loose rock debris mixed with organic matter.

Weathering breaks up rock, but the sculpture of the land is not accomplished until the forces of *erosion* carry away the products of weathering. Weathering operates over the entire surface of the earth and prepares the rocks for erosion by streams, glaciers, wind, and waves.

Weathering and erosion are constantly at work wearing down the land surfaces. However, the landforms thus worn down are continuously replaced due to diastrophism and volcanism. Thus the geologic role of these opposing forces is to shape the earth's surface, producing beautiful, interesting forms at each stage of the erosional cycle.

WEATHERING

Mechanical weathering. The effects of weathering may be seen wherever rock is exposed. Small chips of rock may be loose or easily pulled off the surface; some of these may crumble at a touch. When the rock is broken with tools, the inner parts are found to be firm and may

be different in color from the surface. In cracks and crevices, however, where air and water have been able to penetrate, the exposed rock has been stained and softened.

The process that produces such changes is twofold: *mechanical* and *chemical.* These phases of weathering operate simultaneously. When rock is broken down into small pieces without undergoing any change in its mineral composition, the process is said to be mechanical weathering. One of the most important means of mechanical weathering is temperature. More specifically, low temperatures that cause water to freeze are responsible for much of the mechanical weathering. When water freezes, it expands by about 10 percent of its volume. If water seeps into cracks in rock and then freezes, the pressure exerted by its expansion is capable of splitting the rock. This *frost wedging* can pry off great blocks from masses of rock, as shown in Fig. 17–1. However its greatest effect as an agent of weathering is through the constant chipping off of small grains of rock as water seeps into tiny crevices and freezes there.

Another process of mechanical weathering causes thin flakes or curved scales to peel off the exposed rock surfaces.

FIG. 17–1. Frost wedging causes large rock masses to break into smaller blocks. (*U. S. Geological Survey*)

The cliffs or boulders are thus given the typical layered appearance shown in Fig. 17–2. This is *exfoliation.* It was once thought to be caused by strains produced in the rock as a result of unequal expansion between the outer surface and the interior when the temperature changed from day to night. It has been observed, however, that exfoliation is most common in humid climates and not in the deserts where temperature changes are greatest between day and night. This has led to the conclusion that exfoliation is caused by the combination of temperature changes and the expansion of certain minerals in the rock which combine chemically with water seeping into the rock through tiny cracks.

In some places, such as the Yosemite Valley and the Nubian Desert, great domes have been formed by exfoliation of shells of granite as much as 10 feet thick. In these cases, relief of internal pressure following erosion of material from the surface is believed to be an additional factor in the exfoliation process.

Another important means of mechanical weathering is the activity of plants and animals. As they grow, the roots of trees and shrubs work their way into small cracks and wedge the rock apart. See Fig. 17–3. Burrowing animals, such as gophers and prairie dogs, are also a factor in weathering, since their digging activities constantly expose new rock surfaces to be weathered. Earthworms play a major role in weathering by bringing fine rock particles to the surface where they are exposed to the atmosphere and its weathering action, and by making burrows which allow water and air to penetrate the soil more easily.

Chemical weathering. Working hand in hand with mechanical weathering are the chemical changes that cause rock to disintegrate. In chemical weathering, reactions between minerals in the rock and carbon dioxide, oxygen, and water alter the composition of the rock minerals.

FIG. 17–2. Exfoliation results in the peeling and flaking of rock surfaces, as shown in these granite outcrops. The picture was taken at the summit of the Sierra Nevada in California. (*U. S. Geological Survey*)

The products of mechanical weathering are merely smaller fragments of the original rock, whereas the products of chemical weathering are different substances from the original rock. This is illustrated by the action of carbon dioxide. Although dry carbon dioxide has no effect on rock, many minerals react with carbonic acid, which is formed when carbon dioxide from the air dissolves in moisture. Minerals containing compounds of iron, calcium, magnesium, sodium, or potassium, when attacked by carbonic acid, form carbonate compounds. This process is called *carbonation.* Carbonate compounds are generally more soluble in water and are therefore more easily removed and carried away. The various minerals containing the elements mentioned differ considerably in their resistance to carbonation. One of the most susceptible is calcite; rocks containing this mineral (such as limestone and marble) weather very rapidly, particularly in moist climates. Most rocks contain at least one mineral which is affected by carbonation, and the removal of that mineral exposes the more resistant minerals to other forms of weathering. For example, feldspars react with water and carbon dioxide according to the following equation:

$$2KAlSi_3O_8 + 2H_2O + CO_2 \rightarrow$$
$$Al_2Si_2O_5(OH)_4 + 4SiO_2 + K_2CO_3$$

Since the potassium carbonate is readily soluble, this reaction tends to break up any rocks containing feldspar, leaving kaolinite (clay) and silicon dioxide (sand).

Like carbon dioxide, oxygen is most effective as an agent of chemical weathering when it is dissolved in water. Nevertheless, some moisture is present in almost any environment, and rocks are

FIG. 17–3. Mechanical weathering: a glacial boulder is being split by the growth of the birch tree's roots. (*U. S. Geological Survey*)

usually subject to attack by oxygen, or *oxidation.* Iron-bearing minerals, especially, combine with dissolved oxygen to form reddish-brown iron oxide. The reddish color of rocks and certain soils is almost always due to the presence of iron oxide. Other compounds of iron, like the mineral pyrite, may be oxidized to form soluble compounds, as the following equation shows:

$$2FeS_2 + 2H_2O + 7O_2 \rightarrow 2FeSO_4 + 2H_2SO_4$$

Rocks containing pyrite will thus slowly disintegrate by oxidation, since the resulting chemical compounds are readily carried away dissolved in water.

Besides aiding the action of carbon dioxide and oxygen, water is able to alter some minerals by chemically combining with them in a process known as *hydration*. The reaction between water and the minerals results in the formation of new mineral substances. Thus hydration is the process by which limonite is formed from hematite, as in the following equation:

$$2Fe_2O_3 + 3H_2O \rightarrow 2Fe_2O_3 \cdot 3H_2O$$

The chief weathering effect of hydration is actually mechanical rather than chemical: the swelling of the minerals during hydration. This creates many tiny cracks in the rock that promote further weathering. Exfoliation is probably due, at least in part, to this effect of hydration.

Water alone also dissolves minerals from the rocks, thus aiding the disintegration process. A few minerals, such as halite, dissolve easily in water; others dissolve more slowly. Minerals in solution are not chemically changed, and may be redeposited when the water evaporates or conditions change.

The continued removal of minerals from the soil and rock by solution as water seeps down from the surface is called *leaching*. In leaching, minerals may be transferred from the upper layers of the soil and rock to lower parts, thus creating enriched deposits of much greater value than the less concentrated deposits nearer the surface. Important ores of iron, copper, and other metals have frequently been enriched by leaching.

Among other agents of chemical weathering are the acids produced by some plants as they grow. Lichens, for example, cling to rocks, and besides exerting mechanical pressure, help to decompose the rock through the secretions by which the plant obtains minerals. The acids formed when plant and animal matter decays also play a part in chemical weathering.

The results of weathering. The various processes of mechanical and chemical weathering already described are relatively slow. However, over hundreds of thousands and millions of years their combined effects cause the breaking up and decomposition of almost all rocks on or near the earth's surface. This is why the land surfaces of the earth have accumulated a layer of more or less detached rock fragments of various sizes ranging from tiny grains to giant boulders. This covering layer is referred to as *mantle rock*. The depth of the layer varies greatly from one location to another. In some places it is completely lacking because the rock fragments have been carried away by erosion as fast as they were formed by weathering. Beneath the mantle rock lies the unweathered solid *bedrock* of the earth's crust.

Sometimes the smaller fragments produced by weathering are carried away, leaving large boulders on the surface. Such *residual boulders* may rest precariously on the bedrock, or seem to be piled one on top of the other. The boulders often form in jointed rocks, where weathering removes the material around the joints, rounding off the surfaces of the blocks. In some areas, the effects of weathering create fantastic shapes, especially where the rock consists of layers of differing resistance, and where weathering is aided by wind action.

As long as the mantle rock remains over the bedrock, weathering is confined mostly to the exposed upper parts of the mantle rock. But erosion is constantly removing the mantle rock and exposing fresh bedrock to the mechanical and chemical forces of weathering. The speed at which the bedrock is weathered and the type of weathering that is most active is determined by several factors:

1. The nature of the rock. Rocks are subject to weathering according to their composition. Igneous rocks are, in general, resistant to mechanical weathering, and are affected mainly by chemical processes. Although their decomposition is slow, they are eventually crumbled as the alteration of the minerals (feldspar, for example, which forms kaolinite) causes the grains to separate. The swelling action of hydration is particularly effective in breaking up igneous rocks. As we have seen, quartz is least susceptible to weathering and the quartz grains endure as sand. Rocks that are mainly quartz, such as the metamorphic rock quartzite, are among the most enduring.

Of the sedimentary rocks, limestone is affected mainly by carbonation and by water, which dissolves the products of carbonation, leaving behind any sand or other insoluble minerals contained in the rock. The other sedimentary rocks are subject mainly to mechanical weathering; the rate of weathering depends mainly on the composition of the material that holds the grains together. Shales and sandstones that are not firmly cemented gradually return to their original condition of separate particles of clay and sand. On the other hand, conglomerates and sandstones that are strongly cemented by silica last even longer than most igneous rocks, and often make up the prominent features of many weathered landscapes.

Rocks that are strongly jointed and fissured are more subject to weathering than rocks which contain few cracks.

2. Climate. In dry climates, weathering tends to be relatively slow and to involve mechanical rather than chemical methods. The same is true of very cold

FIG. 17–4. Balanced Rock, in the Garden of the Gods, is a weathered residual boulder of red sandstone. (*Colorado Springs Chamber of Commerce*)

climates, since chemical weathering requires both warmth and moisture. In humid, warm climates, weathering is relatively rapid. Some rocks are more resistant in dry climates than in humid ones. Limestone is a very durable rock in arid regions. In parts of Nevada and surrounding states, limestone forms the highest ridges and peaks. In a changeable climate, weathering usually proceeds more rapidly than in a more constant one, since changes of temperature encourage mechanical weathering. The contrast in scenery between the eastern and the southwestern portions of the United States is partly due to the differing effects of weathering in a humid and a semiarid climate. Typical landscapes in each region are shown in Fig. 17–5.

3. Topographic conditions. Altitude, slope of the land, and exposure to sun and rain all influence weathering. Temperature decreases and rainfall increases with height. Steep slopes allow removal of rock debris, so that new surfaces are more quickly exposed to the action of weathering.

Soil formation. Once a layer of mantle rock has been created by weathering, the upper exposed rock fragments continue to be decomposed by weathering while the lower parts are partially protected. The continued weathering of the exposed mantle rock eventually results in the creation of a layer of soil at the surface.

Soil first comes into existence as an accumulation of grains of mineral matter from decomposed mantle rock. The minerals in the original soil are the minerals present in the rocks whose weathering produced it. The various feldspars, the most abundant of the rock-forming minerals, upon decomposing yield fine grains of a group of compounds: the hydrated aluminum silicates. Other minerals containing aluminum also may produce such compounds when they decay. Together, these materials are called *clay.* Granite and other rocks containing abundant quartz tend to form *sandy soils,* the grains of relatively unaffected quartz being left after the other minerals in the rock have decomposed. In addition, soil generally contains a number of particles of rock and minerals which in size lie between the microscopic clay particles and the larger sand grains. These particles are classified as *silt.*

The weathered mineral and rock grains that originally form soil very often

FIG. 17–5. The differing effects of weathering are evident in these photographs. Above, a humid climate; left, a semiarid climate. (*U. S. Dept. of Agriculture; Santa Fe Railroad*)

do not remain in the same location as the bedrock from which they came. The agents of erosion may transport them to other locations, depositing them on rock that is quite different from their source. Thus soil in a particular location may be classified as either *residual soil* or *transported soil.*

Residual soils rest on the bedrock from which they were derived, and show a gradual transition downward into the subsoil. They grade into rotted rock which crumbles readily when it is exposed on the surface. Transported soils, on the other hand, have been carried to their present position by the action of winds, running water, or glaciers. Their texture may vary considerably, depending on the transporting agent, and they generally lack the gradual downward transition of residual soils. There is usually a definite boundary between transported soil and the bedrock on which it is found.

The weathering of rock is only the first step in the formation of soil. The second step is begun when plants gain a foothold in the young soil and add organic matter. Plants, in turn, foster the growth of animals. As the plants and animals die, their remains become a part of the growing soil structure in the form of *humus,* a dark organic material which is a part of fully mature soils. The additional weathering and deposition of organic material necessary to produce fertile soil take place only near the surface of the original soil layer. Thus the upper six or eight inches of the beginning soil layer of weathered rock becomes the rich and productive *topsoil;* beneath is the less fertile *subsoil* which is lacking mainly in the vital humus needed in a rich soil. See Fig. 17–6.

About half of the total volume of a fully developed topsoil consists of min-

FIG. 17–6. A soil profile. Note how the dark topsoil at the top merges into the lighter-colored subsoil lying on limestone bedrock. (*U. S. Dept. of Agriculture*)

eral and rock particles. The remaining volume is accounted for by humus and the tiny spaces between the soil particles, filled with either air or water. From this mixture of mineral matter, organic remains, water, and air, plants are able to extract the nutrients vital to their growth.

The rate at which topsoil is formed depends on variables such as climate and the nature of the weathered rock, but an average figure would probably be about one inch each 500 years. There is no way to speed up the slow process during which the rock decomposes and thousands of generations of plants and animals run their life cycles to supply the organic matter in the soil. Once soil has been swept away by erosion, no amount of knowledge or work can repair the

FIG. 17–7. Talus slopes at the base of a large mountain. The weathered talus at the base of the slopes has begun to support vegetation. (*U. S. Geological Survey*)

damage quickly. It is mainly for this reason that loss of soil through careless and unwise use of the land is a problem of national concern. Soil is an irreplaceable natural resource. Its care is our responsibility, for our lives depend on the fertility of the soil.

EROSION

The agents of erosion. Having been reduced to small particles by weathering, rock is subject to removal to other locations by the processes of erosion. The means by which erosion is accomplished depends to a large extent upon the climate of the locality. In dry climates, the wind is most effective in picking up the rock grains and moving them, often for great distances. The windborne rock grains also abrade unweathered rock; thus wind is an agent of both erosion and weathering. It is this dual capacity for both wearing away and carrying away the rock on the earth's surface that makes the wind so effective in sculpturing the land. In Chapter 20 the work of the wind will be considered in detail.

In most climates, the most important agent of erosion is moving water. The work of waves and currents is effective along shores of oceans and lakes, and will be considered in Chapter 20. More important, however, are the streams of water running over the earth's surface, visibly eroding the products of rock weathering. Rock particles suspended in running water may further wear away the solid rock. Water is also a powerful agent of erosion in the form of glacial ice. Moving ice transports large rock fragments which act as sharp cutting tools to scour the solid bedrock as the glacier moves. At this point we need only mention running water and glaciers as important erosional forces. A far more complete explanation of the way they work is given in Chapters 18 and 19.

There is another agent of erosion that works in a much less obvious way than those already mentioned. This is gravity, which is constantly present on the earth and surprisingly effective in eroding the weathered rock. The erosional processes which are controlled directly by gravity are sometimes grouped under the term *mass-wasting*.

Gravity and erosion. When rock fragments are separated from a mass of solid rock by weathering processes, they fall to the lowest part of the surrounding surface. If the weathering rock is on a steep slope or on the face of a cliff, the rock fragments tumble down until they reach the base of the slope. The result is the accumulation of a pile of various sizes of rock fragments, called *talus,* at the bases of most cliffs and steeper slopes. On gentle slopes the rock fragments move down so slowly that the lower part of the talus has weathered sufficiently to form soil and is covered with vegetation. See Fig. 17–7.

Accumulation of talus is only one of the obvious ways in which gravity brings about erosion. Gravity operates less conspicuously when soil and the general mantle covering a slope is very slowly carried downhill by its own weight. This process is called *soil creep,* and is usually

so slow that it may be unnoticed unless buildings, fences, or other conspicuous objects on the moving surface are displaced. Soil creep is generally faster when the soil and mantle are thoroughly wet, because water lubricates the particles and allows them to move more freely over one another.

Movements of the mantle down slopes may be much more sudden and dramatic than the slow motion associated with creep. Masses of loose rock and soil on a slope may abruptly slide downhill in a landslide. At the beginning the landslide may consist of only a small amount of loose rock debris which breaks from the top of a slope. As the material progresses down the slope it gathers momentum, dislodging more of the mantle resting on the slope until it ends as an avalanche of boulders, rocks, and soil.

FIG. 17–8. This landslide occurred in the Montana earthquake of 1959. The source area of the landslide is evident on the slope in the background. (*U. S. Geological Survey*)

FIG. 17–9. A rock glacier, sometimes called a talus glacier, in the Silver Basin of Colorado. (*U. S. Geological Survey*)

Such landslides may be set off by heavy rains or by earthquakes. A dramatic example is the landslide in Yellowstone National Park, caused by the Montana earthquake of August, 1959, in which twenty-eight campers lost their lives. See Fig. 17–8.

Landslides occur in areas where the

FIG. 17–10. The great Slumgullion mudflow at Lake San Cristobal in Colorado. Notice that the glacierlike mudflow is partially covered with vegetation. (*U. S. Geological Survey*)

topography is not smoothly adjusted to the prevailing conditions. Where very steep slopes have been brought about by glaciation, faulting, or other causes, landslides are frequent. As we have seen (Chapter 14), landslides are common in young mountain regions, especially in alpine topography. Rejuvenation also causes landslides in regions with steep slopes.

Rock structure influences the occurrence of landslides. Masses of resistant rock that are underlain by weaker rocks tend to slide down the slopes, especially if the rocks become saturated with water. The activities of man may tend to undermine the rock structure in road and railway cuts, and destructive slides have occurred in such places.

Usually landslides occur in stages, a small amount of land slipping first in one part of the slope and then in another. Such minor landslides are called *slumping* and tend to give many slopes a hilly, bumpy appearance. Sometimes large amounts of rocky material accumulate in valleys of mountainous regions and move slowly down to lower ground in the manner of a glacier. See Fig. 17–9. These are actually called *rock glaciers.*

In mountainous regions that are ordinarily very dry, heavy rains may produce an odd flowing movement of a mixture of fine rock particles and water. In such a *mudflow,* masses of mud move through mountain valleys, frequently spreading out in a sheet at the piedmont plains. See Fig. 17–10.

Soil erosion and conservation. Erosion is a natural process. It is a part of the complex train of events that is constantly changing the shape of the earth's surface. Erosion of the soil covering of the mantle rock is the natural wearing down of the crust and would occur even if man were not present on the planet. However, in areas unaffected by man, soil erosion is a slow process and is kept

FIG. 17–11. Gullying has ruined great areas of valuable farmland. (*U. S. Geological Survey*)

FIG. 17–12. Dust storms cause tremendous damage. Above, the storm cloud; below, a farmyard deserted after repeated storms. (*U. S. Dept. of Agriculture*)

FIG. 17–13. Contour plowing helps to prevent gullying. (*U. S. Dept. of Agriculture*)

in balance by the accumulation of new soil. If human activities did not disturb this balance, new soil would be formed as fast as the existing soil was eroded. But when men use the land to grow crops and to pasture their animals, the natural balance between soil erosion and soil formation may be upset, so that the eroded soil is not replaced.

Soil erosion is encouraged when the natural plant cover of the soil is removed. Land is cleared of trees and vegetation in preparation for farming, or grazing animals are allowed to remove the grasses and low plants. Deprived of its protective shield of living plants and plant litter above the surface, and of the network of roots that binds the soil particles in place below the surface, the topsoil is exposed to the full effect of erosion.

The water washes out small gullies, particularly if crops have been planted in rows running up and down slopes. The plowed furrows form small channels, allowing the water to run swiftly along the bare soil. Once begun, each gully enlarges with every rain until a series of miniature canyons is produced. See Fig. 17–11. This type of erosion is called *gullying*. A more inconspicuous but equally destructive form of soil erosion is *sheet wash*. This occurs when water strips away exposed topsoil slowly and evenly, leaving a smooth but barren surface of subsoil or rock on a once fertile field.

In periods of drought, wind replaces water as the means of erosion and the topsoil in exposed areas is blown away as clouds of dust and drifting sand. See Fig. 17–12.

Continued erosion by water and wind reduces the fertility of the soil by removing the rich topsoil and exposing the subsoil, which is lacking in organic matter and is difficult to cultivate. The inability of the subsoil to support a heavy growth of plants means continuing erosion: a vicious cycle that ends in complete removal of the topsoil. Erosion may be slowed by application of fertilizers which provide the necessary minerals for the rapid growth of cover crops to hold the soil in place. Other methods of soil conservation are intended primarily

FIG. 17–14. Strip cropping helps to hold the topsoil in place on gentle slopes. Runoff is reduced by the strips of cover crops. (*U. S. Dept. of Agriculture*)

to decrease the erosion of cultivated soil on slopes. These include

1. Contour plowing. Plowing in furrows which follow the contours of the land, thus preventing formation of gullies by the direct flow of water down the slopes. See Fig. 17–13.

2. Strip cropping. Arrangement of crops in alternate bands of row crops and cover crops which help to hold the soil. See Fig. 17–14.

3. Terracing. Construction of steplike ridges following the contours of the field. These hold or slow down the runoff water and prevent extensive erosion on the slope.

4. Crop rotation. Alternation of row crops one year with cover crops the next year to arrest the early stages of erosion and allow small gullies to fill with soil.

Large areas of our country have already been seriously damaged by erosion. See the map, Fig. 17–15. Government agencies such as the Soil Conservation Service of the United States Department of Agriculture are providing information and help to farmers and ranchers. But to protect the soil while using it is a continuous struggle that requires increasing knowledge and skill.

FIG. 17–15. Soil erosion in the United States. (*U. S. Dept. of Agriculture*)

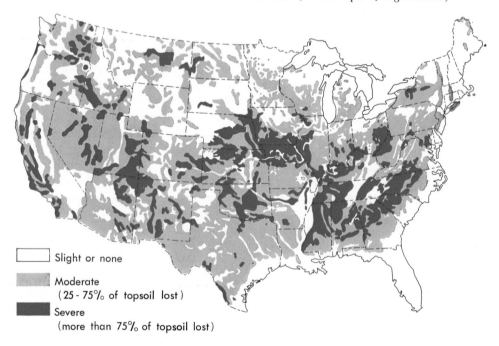

☐ Slight or none

▨ Moderate
(25 - 75% of topsoil lost)

■ Severe
(more than 75% of topsoil lost)

SUMMARY

☯

THE crust of the earth is subject to constant change due to the chemical and mechanical factors of the atmosphere. Alteration of the rocks and minerals by these factors is called weathering.

Mechanical weathering results in the physical disruption of rocks or minerals without formation of new minerals or change in their molecular structure. Frost wedging and exfoliation are examples of mechanical processes due to changes in temperature.

Chemical processes such as oxidation, carbonation, and hydration result in the alteration of the compounds in minerals. Normally both phases of weathering are acting at the same time, so that the physical disintegration speeds up the chemical reactions that are involved in rock decay.

Weathering is the first step in the preparation of materials for erosion. The nature and extent of erosion are related to the prevailing climatic conditions and the type of rock or mineral.

Any agent that will set the weathered material in motion can be considered as an agent of erosion. Gravity, wind, water, and ice all act as agents of erosion. Gravity produces earth movements such as soil creep, landslides, mudflows, and rock glaciers.

The natural process of erosion has undesirable effects when the balance of soil removal and soil formation is disturbed by human activities. Man has learned to arrest the destruction of fertile land by proper application of conservation practices to restrict erosion. Contour plowing, strip cropping, terracing, and crop rotation are helpful.

VOCABULARY REVIEW

Match the phrase in the left column with the correct word in the right column. *Do not write in this book.*

1. Loose weathered rock
2. Combination of carbon dioxide with minerals
3. Movement of soil and rock fragments
4. Accumulated weathered rock at the base of a slope
5. Combination of oxygen with minerals
6. Decomposed plant and animal remains
7. Flaking of rocks
8. Combination of water with minerals
9. Removal of minerals from soil by water
10. Minor landslide
11. Destructive form of soil erosion

a. oxidation
b. leaching
c. talus
d. silt
e. terracing
f. exfoliation
g. carbonation
h. slumping
i. hydration
j. gullying
k. mantle
l. erosion
m. humus

QUESTIONS   ·   GROUP A

Select the best term to complete the following statements. *Do not write in this book.*

1. The construction of steplike ridges according to the contour of the land is (*a*) contour plowing (*b*) slumping (*c*) terracing (*d*) assortment.
2. If a cubic foot of water froze it would expand approximately (*a*) 20 cubic inches (*b*) 5 cubic inches (*c*) 173 cubic inches (*d*) 125 cubic inches.
3. When carbon dioxide dissolves in water it forms (*a*) limestone (*b*) limonite (*c*) carbonates (*d*) carbonic acid.
4. If a sandstone appears reddish-brown, the cementing agent is probably a compound of (*a*) magnesium (*b*) iron (*c*) sodium (*d*) calcium.
5. Feldspar is to kaolinite as (*a*) iron is to iron oxide (*b*) frost is to wedging (*c*) hematite is to limonite (*d*) calcite is to marble.
6. Leaching may result in (*a*) rich top soil (*b*) rich deposits of ores (*c*) rich humus (*d*) rich deposits of coal.
7. Tropical vegetation (*a*) encourages weathering (*b*) increases erosion (*c*) decreases chemical weathering (*d*) has no effect on weathering or erosion.
8. The most abundant rock-forming mineral is (*a*) quartz (*b*) mica (*c*) granite (*d*) feldspar.
9. Four inches of topsoil would represent approximately (*a*) one year of decomposition (*b*) 1,000,000 years of decomposition (*c*) 2000 years of decomposition (*d*) 100 years of decomposition.
10. Ice is considered an agent of erosion because it (*a*) splits rocks (*b*) transports rocks (*c*) occurs only in the winter (*d*) expands.
11. Mantle rock formed from the underlying bedrock is considered to be (*a*) residual (*b*) glacial (*c*) transported (*d*) alluvial.
12. Frost would have the greatest weathering effect on (*a*) shale (*b*) limestone (*c*) quartz (*d*) quartzite.
13. Rejuvenation results most commonly in (*a*) exfoliation (*b*) hydration (*c*) landslides (*d*) glaciers.
14. Strip cropping involves (*a*) rotation of crops (*b*) removal of crops (*c*) formation of gullies (*d*) alternate bands of row crops and cover crops.
15. Talus would predominate in (*a*) a plains region (*b*) a mountainous region (*c*) the arctic (*d*) the tropics.
16. Mechanical and chemical weathering usually (*a*) work together (*b*) work against each other (*c*) never occur simultaneously (*d*) cause the same effect on the mineral's molecular structure.
17. Exfoliation is believed to be caused by (*a*) heat alone (*b*) frost alone (*c*) a combination of heat changes and chemical changes (*d*) water.
18. Limestone would weather the fastest in (*a*) the Sahara Desert (*b*) Antarctica (*c*) Texas (*b*) Brazil.
19. The mineral least susceptible to weathering is (*a*) quartz (*b*) shale (*c*) granite (*d*) kaolinite.
20. The most prominent features of a weathered landscape are usually made of (*a*) shale (*b*) limestone (*c*) igneous rock (*d*) silica conglomerate.

GROUP B

1. Clearly distinguish between chemical and mechanical weathering.
2. Explain fully the difference between residual and transported soil. Make labeled diagrams to illustrate the characteristics of residual and transported soil.
3. Explain the origin of mantle rock.
4. Discuss the relationship of climate to weathering and erosion.
5. Describe four methods to prevent the erosion of farm soil.
6. Distinguish between the terms in the following pairs: soil creep and sheet wash, slumping and landslide.
7. How could the removal of topsoil from one area be beneficial to another area?
8. Describe the step-by-step process from rock to fertile soil.
9. Account for the fact that granite weathers into sand.
10. What is the role of each of the following in relation to weathering: lichens, earthworms, gophers, and shrubs?
11. Explain fully each of the following processes: carbonation, hydration, and oxidation.

TOPOGRAPHIC SHEETS

Bright Angel, Arizona; Vishnu, Arizona. *Differential weathering.*
Yosemite Valley, California. *Exfoliation domes and cliffs.*
Shiprock, New Mexico. *Gully deeply eroded.*
San Cristobal, Colorado. *Mudflow.*
Red Rock, Washington. *Landslide.*
Frank, Alberta (Canadian Geological Survey). *Landslide (Turtle Mountain, 1903).*
Ventura, California. *Alluviated lowland.*

All of the above are in the 15-minute series.

CHAPTER 18

RUNNING WATER

WATER is the greatest of all the agents of erosion. In wearing down the land surface, water is more effective than all the other agents of erosion combined. Each drop of water that falls on the land has its share in a long process of grinding and wearing and transportation of rock. The process does not end until the water finally makes its way to the sea with the products of its work in changing the face of the land.

Each year about 9000 cubic miles of water fall on all the land surfaces of the earth. Some of it seeps into the spaces and pockets within the rocks, thus becoming the earth's supply of *ground water*. Some is returned to the atmosphere by evaporation, and the remainder runs

VOCABULARY

Ground water. Water which penetrates into spaces within the rocks of the earth's crust.

Water table. The upper boundary of the ground water, below which all spaces within the rock are completely filled with water.

Stalactite (stuh-*lak*-tyt). A stony projection from the roof of a cavern, formed from minerals deposited from dripping water.

Stalagmite (stuh-*lag*-myt). A raised deposit on the floor of a cavern, formed from minerals deposited from dripping water.

Sink. A depression in the earth's surface formed by the collapse of the roof of an underground cavern.

Pothole. A rounded depression in the rock of a stream bed.

Levee. The raised bank of a stream.

Delta. A triangular deposit at the mouth of a stream.

Tributary. A stream which flows into a larger stream.

Meanders (mee-*an*-derz). Wide curves typical of well-developed streams.

Rejuvenation. Any action which tends to increase the gradient of a stream.

over the earth's surface in a vast number of streams. It is these streams, ranging from the smallest trickle to the mightiest of rivers, that most effectively sculpture the land. This chapter deals with the ways in which water, both above the surface and below, is able to accomplish its work.

GROUND WATER

Source and distribution of ground water. The most important source of ground water is rain and melted snow that sinks into the ground through pores, faults, joints, and cavities within the rock. Some of this water is returned to the surface through springs and wells and the action of plants; some of it, as we have seen, is combined with the rocks through alteration of minerals by hydration. However, most of the water seeping downward into the earth fills the openings in the rock of the mantle and in the bedrock itself, in some cases. Rocks and soils differ greatly in the degree to which they allow water to penetrate and pass through; this quality is called *permeability* (per-mee-uh-*bil*-i-tee). Loose rock of the mantle layer is usually very permeable because of the spaces between the rock fragments. However, even the apparently solid rock beneath the mantle may be subject to penetration by water. Most permeable of the solid rocks are those composed of cemented grains, such as sandstone, which have many pores between the grains. Very dense rocks, such as granite, may become permeable as a result of fracturing, which forms many cracks through which the water easily penetrates. Ground water ordinarily continues to sink deeper into the earth until it strikes a completely solid or impermeable layer. The rocks and soil

FIG. 18–1. Young mountain streams like this one are actively cutting down their rock beds. (*Ewing Galloway*)

above this layer become completely saturated to an upper level that varies with conditions. This upper level, the top of the saturated zone, is the *water table.* The depth of the water table at a given location generally depends upon the amount of rainfall in the recent past, the permeability of the rock and soil in that locality, and the depth of the impermeable layers which prevent the water from sinking deeper. Underground water may flow about within the permeable rock layers so that water entering the ground

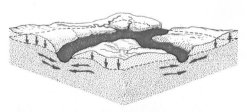

FIG. 18–2. The water table. Ground water circulates as shown by the arrows.

FIG. 18–3. A limestone sink in Weston County, Wyoming. Sinks are a feature of erosion by underground water. (*U. S. Geological Survey*)

FIG. 18–4. Natural Bridge in Rockbridge County, Virginia. (*Virginia Dept. of Conservation and Development*)

at one place may appear elsewhere some distance away. Such movements of ground water will be taken up more fully in Chapter 24.

Work of ground water. We have seen that in the weathering processes, pure water does not readily dissolve rocks and minerals, with the exception of a few, such as halite (rock salt). If ground water were pure, it would not react chemically with underground rocks. Most rocks, however, are affected by ground water since it contains dissolved carbon dioxide, oxygen, and acids acquired during its passage through the air and down into the rock. Thus oxidation, carbonation, hydration, and other chemical processes operate freely as ground water circulates.

Rocks composed mainly of calcite, such as limestone, dolomite, and marble, are especially subject to carbonation. They react slowly with water containing dissolved carbon dioxide, forming cal-

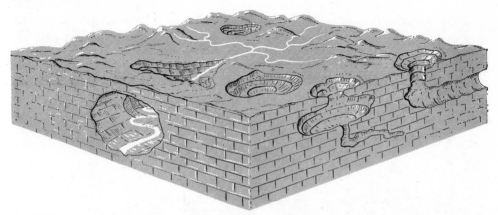

FIG. 18–5. Karst topography in a limestone region, showing some of the features of underground drainage that are commonly found.

cium bicarbonate according to the following equation:

$$CaCO_3 + H_2O + CO_2 \rightarrow Ca(HCO_3)_2$$

Calcium bicarbonate, being slightly soluble, is carried away in solution. Ground water penetrating into cracks in these rocks gradually enlarges the cracks, forming channels through which the water drains away. Continuing dissolving action may eventually produce a *cavern*. The caverns are usually enlarged by the constant dissolving action of ground water until a network of connecting rooms and chambers is formed. In the United States, at least thirty states have extensive limestone regions that contain caverns of considerable size. The Carlsbad Caverns of New Mexico and Mammoth Cave in Kentucky are among the most famous. Both these caverns are set aside as national parks.

Sometimes part of the roof of a cavern collapses, leaving a more or less circular hole at the surface of the ground. Water draining through underground channels may produce a similar depression. Such holes, called *sinks,* are a common feature in the limestone regions. See Fig. 18–3.

It is thought that *natural bridges* may be formed when parts of the roof of a cavern collapse, leaving a section still standing between. Most natural bridges, however, are formed in other ways, as by the action of surface streams which disappear into sinks or similar openings in the ground. A natural bridge such as that in Fig. 18–4 results when a stream flows into an opening in the rock, dissolves a tunnel through the rock and emerges on a slope or cliff. In some cases, streams flow into sinks or openings into caverns and disappear underground. Sinks and other surface depressions frequently become clogged and fill with water, forming ponds or lakes.

Limestone regions often develop a characteristic type of landscape. Sink holes and very large depressions, natural bridges, and fluted limestone ledges are surface features produced by the dissolving action of ground water. Ponds and lakes are common, but there are almost no surface streams, so that few valleys are formed. This type of landscape is often called **karst** topography or a karst plain, after the Karst region of northern Italy and Yugoslavia. Karst topography

FIG. 18–6. Typical formations are shown in this view of the Papoose Room, Carlsbad Caverns. (*Paul F. Spangle from Carlsbad Caverns National Park*)

is found in the United States in the limestone regions of Kentucky, Tennessee, and southern Indiana, as well as in Florida. See Fig. 18–5.

If a cavern lies above the water table and is therefore not filled with water, it very often contains remarkable formations of stone produced by the action of water dripping into the cavity from above. As drops of water containing the dissolved calcium bicarbonate drip from the ceiling of the cavern, some of the bicarbonate decomposes to yield carbon dioxide and water. This leaves behind solid calcium carbonate in the form of calcite, as seen in this equation:

$$Ca(HCO_3)_2 \rightarrow CaCO_3 + H_2O + CO_2$$

Water dripping continuously from the same spot will eventually produce a long iciclelike deposit of calcite called a *stalactite* (stuh-*lak*-tyt), which hangs from the cavern roof. At the point on the floor of the cavern where the drops of water fall, another deposit of calcite, called a *stalagmite* (stuh-*lag*-myt), is formed. Frequently the two grow toward each other until they join, making a continuous column of stone. Stalactites and stalagmites in a cavern are shown in Fig. 18–6. Under special conditions, fantastic and beautifully colored forms develop.

Minerals dissolved in ground water often are deposited in cavities within the rock, due to changing conditions encountered by the water as it flows. Crystals may fill a more or less spherical cavity, producing a *geode*. See Fig. 18–7. In cracks and fissures, valuable minerals are often concentrated, deposited by the action of the water. Even the tiny spaces between the grains of rock in a loose sediment are often filled with mineral matter by ground water. A solidly cemented rock type is thus formed. Occasionally ground water may completely remove the original substance in the remains of a living thing and replace it with mineral matter. The petrified wood found in Arizona and in Yellowstone Park was formed in this way.

SURFACE WATER

How running water erodes the earth's surface. As water flows over the land on its way to the sea, it passes over the large variety of rocky materials that compose the upper parts of the earth's crust. Each variety of rock, no matter how hard and resistant, is subject to some erosive action by running water. Loose rock fragments and soil are simply picked up and carried away by the moving water. Even large boulders can be rolled along by the motion of the swiftly flowing rivers. Once it begins to carry rock fragments, the moving water has the means to attack the unweathered, solid rock. Each rock fragment becomes a tool for *abrasion;* the process by which the bedrock is worn down by grinding against other rocks. Each contact between the loose rock fragments carried by the water and the bedrock of the stream bed wears off a tiny amount from both. Gradually the rock fragments become rounded and smooth, while the bedrock is worn down to a lower level (Fig. 18–1). A peculiar type of abrasion occurs when eddies in a stream swirl small rocks around for some time at the same spot on the stream bed. This causes a bowl-shaped cavity called a *pothole* in the rock of the stream bed. See Fig. 18–8.

Rocks that are relatively resistant to abrasion may be affected by solution. The products of chemical weathering are carried away, dissolved in the water of the streams. The stream water itself also dissolves the more soluble minerals. The amount of material dissolved by running water is surprisingly large. It has been estimated that a total of five billion tons of dissolved minerals are washed into the sea each year.

Transport of material by streams. The dissolved substances, the suspended particles, and the rock fragments rolled along by the water are the *load* of a stream. Much of this material is washed into the stream by rain and melting snow; some simply falls into the water. Most of a stream's load, however, consists of the weathered rock and soil particles picked up from erosion of the bottom and sides of its channel. The most important factor affecting the carrying capacity of a stream is the swiftness with which the water flows. At higher velocities the stream is able to move large fragments as well as the fine material, thus greatly increasing the total possible load. A change in conditions that doubles the velocity of a stream may increase the capacity of the stream to transport rock particles of a given weight as much as 32 times. A twofold increase in velocity may also increase up to 64 times the weight of the objects the water can move along the stream bed. The total effect of abrasion by transported rock fragments

FIG. 18–7. A geode, broken open to show calcite crystals. (*American Museum of Natural History*)

FIG. 18–8. Potholes in the bed of the Susquehanna River near Falmouth, Pennsylvania, revealed during a period of extended drought. (Intelligencer Journal, *Lancaster, Pennsylvania*)

may be increased up to 4 times. When rivers are in flood, their velocities may be 10 to 20 times greater than normal. Thus at times flood rivers are able to increase their load many times over the normal amount and accomplish their greatest work of erosion and transport.

The carrying power of a stream depends also on the nature of the material that makes up its load. Even a slow-moving river, such as the Mississippi, can carry large quantities of very fine silt in suspension. A swift stream that flows over resistant bedrock cannot carry away very much material.

In the United States alone, according to one estimate, the rivers carry at least 800 million tons of material each year. Most of this, approximately two-thirds, is made up of fine rock particles suspended in the water and heavier rock fragments pushed along the stream bed. The remaining one-third is mineral matter dissolved in the water.

Deposits by streams. Some conditions cause a stream to decrease its load. Just as greater velocity is the principal factor in increasing a stream's ability to carry its load, so lesser velocity is most effective in causing a decrease in a stream's carrying capacity. When the water in a stream is slowed down, the part of the load that it can no longer carry is dropped as a deposit. Since stream velocities are constantly changing, the loads of streams are continuously increasing and decreasing, and deposits are formed and then picked up again many

FIG. 18–9. Sand bars often form in winding rivers like the Mississippi, especially on the inside of the curves. (*U. S. Army Air Corps*)

FIG. 18–10. A braided stream flowing down the northern slope of Mount McKinley in Alaska. (*Bradford Washburn*)

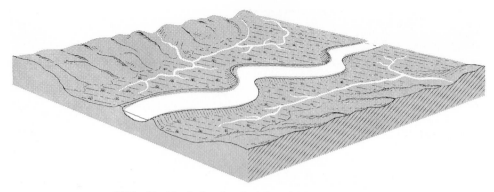

FIG. 18-11. A flat flood plain with natural levees.

times. In some cases, the deposits by streams remain for only a short time. In others, they remain for thousands of years and become a more or less permanent feature of the land.

An example of the deposits formed by a stream that has slowed down is shown in Fig. 18-9. Here a sand bar has been produced from material deposited by the more slowly moving water on the inside of a curve. Such bars are likely to be formed at any point in a stream where the water moves more slowly. In some cases a stream channel becomes so filled with deposits that the stream is split into many small channels. Such a stream is said to be *braided.* See Fig. 18-10.

When a stream overflows its banks in flood stage and spreads out over the nearby land, its velocity is greatly decreased and part of its load is deposited along the borders of the flooded channel. Continuous flooding and the resulting accumulation of deposits along the edges of the stream eventually produce elevated banks or *natural levees.* These long embankments have considerable height along well-developed rivers and are often the most prominent features on the floor of a stream valley. Not all the

FIG. 18-12. The delta of the Mississippi River looking toward the Gulf of Mexico. (*New Orleans District Corps of Engineers*)

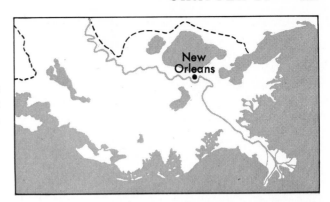

FIG. 18–13. In this map the landward edge of the delta is outlined by the dotted line.

load deposited by a stream in flood stage goes into the formation of levees. Large amounts of sediment are left behind in a fairly even layer over the flooded land after the water has receded. Continuous flooding eventually produces a series of thin layers of fine deposited material. Since this accumulation is generally level, the part of the valley floor covered by flooding becomes a relatively flat *flood plain.* A flood plain with levees is shown in Fig. 18–11. Swampy areas are common on flood plains because drainage is usually poor in the area between the levees and the outer walls of the valley. Tributary streams, called *yazoo streams* after a typical one on the Mississippi flood plain, often flow parallel to the main stream. Large rivers may have extensive flood plains which are very valuable farmlands, since the soil formed by the fine material deposited by the water is quite fertile. The flood plain of the Mississippi River broadens as it approaches the river mouth, and is about 80 miles wide in places. It has a total area of 30,000 square miles.

Not all of the load carried by a stream is deposited before the stream reaches its final destination in a larger body of water. Large deposits forming a low plain are generally built up at the mouths of streams as they empty into the relatively quiet water in a sea or lake. The plain is characteristically in the form of a triangle with one point of the triangle turned directly upstream. From the Greek letter Δ (delta) these deposits at the mouths of streams are called *deltas.* Generally, the stream divides into a number of channels through the delta, particularly when large volumes of water are emptied from the stream during floods. This results in the creation of smaller streams, called *distributaries,* through which the larger main stream empties across the delta.

Along the Gulf Coast of the United States, river deltas account for some of the most prominent features of the coastline. Most conspicuous is the delta of the Mississippi River. Here more than a million tons of sediment per day are emptied into the Gulf of Mexico. Most of this material mingles with the waters of the Gulf, but a large amount settles around the mouth of the Mississippi and constantly extends the river delta into the Gulf. The delta plain slopes gradually, increasing slightly in elevation upriver, at the rate of about 20 feet for each 100 miles. The Mississippi delta is unusual in having only four main distributaries. The channels are deep, with narrow clay banks, giving the delta its characteristic "bird's foot" shape when viewed from above. See Figs. 18–12 and 18–13.

Other rivers of the world have built

FIG. 18–14. A group of alluvial fans at the edge of the Mojave Desert in California. (*U. S. Geological Survey*)

large deltas: the Nile into the Mediterranean, the Rhine into the North Sea, the Danube into the Black Sea, the Tigris Euphrates into the Persian Gulf, and the Niger into the Gulf of Guinea. Like the Mississippi, all of these rivers empty into the sea on relatively sheltered coastlines. Here the ocean currents are not strong enough to carry away the sediment rapidly.

Deposits which resemble deltas in shape are commonly formed when streams flow down a steep slope from high land and out onto a level plain or valley floor. The heavy loads carried down by the swift streams are deposited as velocity abruptly changes when the stream enters the level plain. The fan-shaped deposit formed in this way is called an *alluvial fan.* (The word "alluvial" means deposited by running water.) See Fig. 18–14.

Sometimes several alluvial fans form so close together that their margins blend to produce a continuous region called a *piedmont alluvial plain.* The higher parts of these plains are composed of large boulders and coarse gravel. In drier

areas vegetation is sparse. The lower parts, however, are composed of finer rock materials. Here, with the help of irrigation, good crops may be grown, as in the Sacramento and San Joaquin valleys of California.

A large part of the plains portion of eastern Colorado and Nebraska is a vast piedmont alluvial plain formed at the base of the Rocky Mountains. The mountain ranges of the Great Basin area in Nevada and Utah are flanked with alluvial fans and plains. Similar alluvial plains occur in northern Italy at the base of the Alps, in southern France at the base of the Pyrenees, and in northern India at the base of the Himalayas.

ANATOMY OF A RIVER SYSTEM

The beginnings of a river system. Water falling on land surfaces must run off in established streams or erode its own channels. If a new path must be carved by the runoff water, the process begins as the water runs in broad sheets down

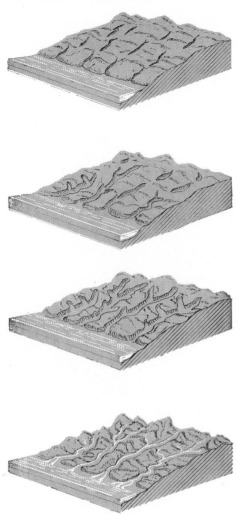

FIG. 18–15. Stages in the development of rivers and streams. Top, gullies appear on the steeper slopes. Middle, gullies expand by downcutting and headward erosion. Bottom, streams establish separate drainage basins.

the slopes and collects at the low places. Thus the natural contour of the land partly determines the places where major streams will eventually develop.

Joining of runoff from several slopes at a depression greatly increases the eroding power of the water and soon a

gully is formed. The gully then serves as a collecting channel for water and the increasing volume of water further enlarges the gully. These are the earliest stages in the development of a river. However, at this point it would be a little premature to apply the term "river" to the beginning stream, since a river is generally understood to be a large stream that flows more or less continuously. The beginning stream is not likely to flow except immediately after rains. Even so, each time the water flows, it enlarges the gully and collects still more water. Eventually this process results in a fully developed valley containing a permanent stream.

Simultaneously with the growth of the beginning river and its valley, branch gullies are produced by streams of water flowing in from the sides. These streams become the *tributaries* of the growing river. See Fig. 18–15. Erosion at the head of the gullies causes them to lengthen, extending up the existing slopes. This is called *headward erosion* and is the main process by which a beginning river system extends its branches and collects the runoff water from a large area of land.

With continuous headward erosion, the main stream and its tributaries eventually form a branching system of channels draining a series of slopes that comprise the *drainage basin* or *watershed* of the developing river system. The ridges or regions of high ground that separate the various drainage basins from each other are called *divides*. See Fig. 18–15. Divides between adjoining stream systems gradually become lower as erosion continues from both sides. The rate of erosion is not often equal on both sides of the divides, due to differences in the resistance of the rocks or the velocity of the streams. Since headward erosion is

FIG. 18–16. The V-shaped valley of the Snake River. (*Oregon State Highway Commission*)

faster in swiftly flowing streams, the divides tend to shift toward the more slowly eroding stream system. Occasionally the greater rate of erosion of one stream may cause it to cut through a divide and divert the water of the stream on the other side. This process is called stream capture or *stream piracy* and is another means by which a stream system is enlarged.

Development of river valleys. The ability of water to cut a channel into the earth over which it flows is basically due to the force of gravity causing the water to run to a lower level. As we have seen, the effectiveness of water as an erosional agent depends largely upon the velocity of the stream. In turn, the velocity depends on the amount of water in the

stream channel and on the stream's slope or *gradient:* the difference in elevation between the head and mouth divided by the total length of the river. Rivers having a steep gradient have a high velocity, causing them to transport more material than they deposit, and thus to erode their beds rapidly. As the river grows older, however, its gradient becomes less steep as the channel is gradually cut down toward the level at the mouth. With the decrease in the gradient, the velocity of the river decreases until its ability to transport is just equal to the rate at which it deposits material in its channel. The river is then said to be *at grade* or *graded.*

In its early stages, when the gradient is still steep, a river will tend to deepen its channel more rapidly than it widens it. This produces a V-shaped valley. The depth to which the valley can be cut is determined by the *base level* of the stream: the level of the body of water into which the river flows. If the river flows directly to the sea, its base level is sea level and it may cut its channel to this level. However, if the river flows into a lake which is above sea level, the valley can be cut only to the level of that lake.

In its later stages, when the river has become graded, the chief work it does is in the erosion of the sides of its valley walls. Thus an older river tends to have a wider valley with a relatively flat floor. Erosion of the stream against the walls widens the valley so the river channel normally occupies only a small part of the valley floor. This allows the river to develop many wide curves called *meanders* (mee-*an*-durz). The way a meander develops is shown in Fig. 18–17.

Frequently the meanders become so curved that the river cuts across the narrow neck of land at both ends of the curve and isolates the meander from the river. If water remains in the isolated meander it is called an *oxbow lake.* The process by which a meander becomes an oxbow lake is shown in Fig. 18–18.

Most river valleys pass through a series of changes caused by the gradual

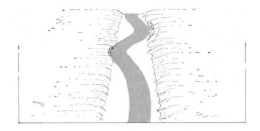

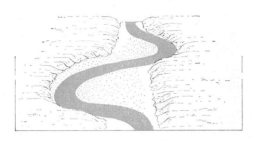

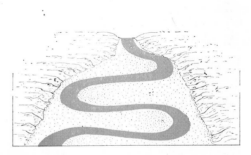

FIG. 18–17. The development of meanders. Compare these diagrams with the photograph of meanders of the Mississippi River, Fig. 18–9.

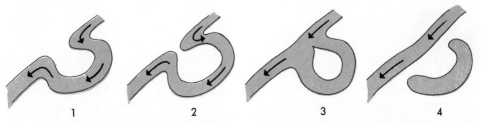

FIG. 18–18. Stages in the formation of an oxbow lake by cutting off of a meander loop. The river cuts deep into the bank along the outside of the meander curves.

shifting from down-cutting to side-cutting as the gradient is slowly lessened. The entire process is usually divided into the three stages of youth, maturity, and old age. It should be kept in mind that these stages in the development of a river valley, as of any other landform, refer to certain characteristics of the river valley rather than the passage of a definite number of years. Many factors, such as rainfall and rock structure, strongly influence the speed with which a river valley passes from one stage to another. Also, all parts of a valley are not usually in the same stage of development. Continued headward erosion at the source may be creating youthful valleys while the older parts of the same river valley near the mouth are in the mature or even old-age stages of development.

THE RIVER CYCLE

Youth. One of the most outstanding characteristics of rivers in the youthful stage is the narrow V-shaped valley. The river is still well above its base level and its chief work is the erosion of the bed of its channel. In some cases the downcutting of the river has occurred much faster than the walls of its valley have weathered or eroded. This results in a narrow, steep-walled valley, called a *canyon* or *gorge* (Fig. 18–16). Another very common feature of youthful rivers is the presence of *waterfalls* and *rapids*. Both occur at points in the river channel where the gradient is very steep and the rock of the stream bed is resistant to erosion. Waterfalls are often very spectacular features along a young river, occur-

FIG. 18–19. Both Horseshoe Falls (left) and American Falls (right) have been worn back as shown here. (*Niagara Frontier State Park Commission*)

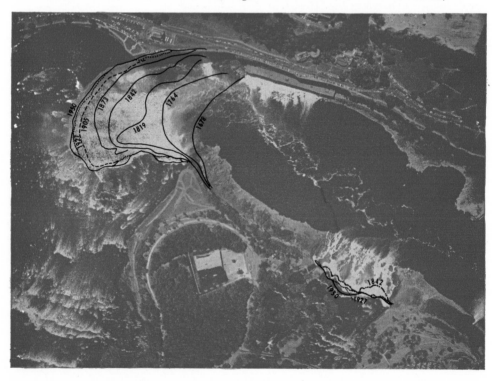

FIG. 18–20. The Lower Falls of the Yellowstone River. The water drops 308 feet over a ledge of lava. (*National Park Service, Yellowstone Park, Wyoming*)

ring where there is a vertical or nearly vertical natural slope in the channel. The slope that produces the waterfall may be due to one of several different conditions. As a river cuts down through rock layers of different hardness, a particularly resistant formation (such as a lava dike) may remain as a barrier across the channel, thus forming a waterfall. Often the river flows over a cliff or scarp in its course. Niagara Falls is an example of such a waterfall. It was originally formed by a cliff over which the Niagara River flows on its way to Lake Ontario. Like most waterfalls, Niagara is being slowly worn back by the erosion of the water passing over it. See Fig. 18–19. In a few cases, waterfalls are relatively permanent features be-

cause they are formed by barriers of very hard igneous rock. An example of this type of waterfall is the Lower Falls of the Yellowstone River. See Fig. 18–20. Most waterfalls, however, are only temporary features of young rivers. The constant erosion of the water passing over them makes them continuously recede upstream, to be eventually worn down to a series of rapids.

Occasionally, a main stream valley may be cut down more rapidly than the valley of a tributary, leaving the tributary valley hanging above the main valley and converting the tributary stream into a waterfall. See Fig. 18–21.

The fall line, described in Chapter 14 as marking the boundary between the Piedmont and the Atlantic Coastal

FIG. 18–21. Upper and Lower Yosemite Falls. The deepening of Yosemite Valley by the glacier which occupied it left the stream to plunge 2,435 feet to the valley floor. (*Dan Adams, Union Pacific Railroad*)

Plain, is characterized by small falls and rapids. These are due to the difference in resistance between the metamorphic rocks of the Piedmont and the weaker sedimentary rocks of the plain.

Young rivers usually have few tributaries since there has not been time for an extensive system of tributary streams to develop. Because of the lack of tributaries and a well-developed system of feeder streams at its headwaters, a young river carries a small volume of water. Much of the water falling in the watershed of a young river does not reach the river at all. It remains in the uplands forming lakes and swampy areas.

Maturity. A river passes out of its youthful stage when it has well-established tributaries and effectively drains off the water falling in its drainage basin. Because of its many tributaries and good drainage, the river carries its largest volume of water at this stage in its development. The lakes and swamps of the youthful phase disappear along with the waterfalls and rapids. The channel becomes almost completely graded, with both the main stream and its tributaries at or near base level. A mature river valley is wide and usually possesses a well-developed flood plain. The river itself normally wanders through its wide valley and flood plain with many meanders in its course.

Old Age. Continued development of the features characteristic of the mature period of the river brings it into old age. Sideward erosion and constant flooding resulting from the large volumes of water carried in the mature stage enlarge the river valley to a very broad and flat flood plain. The combined action of weathering and erosion tends to reduce the entire region in the vicinity of the river to a peneplane (Chapter 13).

The river in old age has a great many meanders and oxbow lakes, and follows a twisted and crooked course wandering over the wide flood plain. Usually there are large swampy areas on the flood plain because the well-developed natural levees of the river, combined with the flatness of the land, prevent good drainage into the river. The number of tributaries is greatly reduced because of the low relief of the surrounding land.

Actually, very few rivers ever reach the old-age period in their development. The lower parts of the Mississippi River are one of the few examples in the world of a river that has closely approached this stage. Usually diastrophic movements of the land interrupt the normal development before the river completes the full cycle.

Interruption of the river cycle. When the surface of the land is lifted or sinks due to diastrophic movements of the crust, the developmental cycles of the streams flowing over the land are interrupted. Any movement that increases the slope of the land changes the gradients of existing streams and increases their rate of erosion. A stream whose gradient has been increased in this way is said to be *rejuvenated.*

In most cases, the steeper gradient in rejuvenation causes the stream to cut deeper into the valley floor. Rejuvenation often results in the formation of steplike *terraces* in stream valleys, caused when the stream cuts to a deeper level in its existing flood plain. See Fig. 18–22.

When a stream that has meanders is rejuvenated, the meanders may become *incised,* meaning "cut in," forming a winding gorge. See Fig. 18–23. (Incised meanders are not necessarily due to rejuvenation, however; a young river may cut deep meanders directly as it follows a winding course.)

When the rising of the land surface is very slow, the existing rivers cut down as fast as they are elevated, so their course is not changed. As indicated in

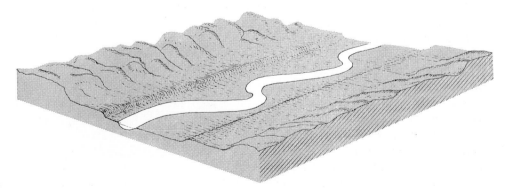

FIG. 18–22. Terraces are often seen in the valleys of streams that have been rejuvenated by diastrophism.

FIG. 18–23. Incised meanders in the San Juan River in southern Utah. The river cut deep in its old-age pattern after the rejuvenation of the Colorado Plateau area. Because of the tightly looped curves, this feature is known as the Goosenecks of the San Juan. (*Spence Air Photos*)

earlier chapters, if a mountain is raised across the channel of an existing river, a water gap will be cut through the mountain as it is raised. Frequently the river that cuts the water gap is captured by streams which run parallel to the mountains, and thus the water gap is abandoned. It then becomes a wind gap since only the wind flows through it. See Fig. 18–24.

Lowering of the land surface also affects the cycle of development of a river. General sinking of the land over a wide area decreases the gradient and tends to hasten the later stages of the cycle. However, if the lowering occurs only in one stretch of the river, the gradient upstream from this region may actually be increased, causing that part of the river to be rejuvenated.

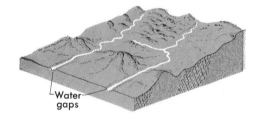

FIG. 18–24. The process by which a water gap may become a wind gap following stream capture.

SUMMARY

☯

RUNNING water is more effective in wearing down the land than all other agents of erosion combined.

Water which accumulates in mantle rock, joints, and other openings in the crust of the earth is known as ground water. The upper surface of a saturated area is called the water table. This level varies according to the porosity of the soil and rock and the amount of precipitation.

The dissolving of limestone by ground water may undermine a region by forming underground channels and caverns. Sinks are depressions resulting from solution of the rock near the surface. Karst topography is the term applied to a region of underground drainage, showing sinks, natural bridges, and other typical features. Dripping water in limestone caverns may form stalagmites and stalactites.

Every stream carries a load of sediment and deposits it in varying quantities. The destructive force of running water is directly related to the velocity of the stream. Loss of velocity will cause a stream to deposit some of its sediment. A delta is one form of underwater deposition. Alluvial fans and plains develop in mountainous and semiarid regions.

Most of the world's river systems develop from the initial headward erosion of gullies. Gradually a drainage pattern develops and the river passes through the cycle of youth, maturity, and old age. Rarely does a river ever attain old age because diastrophism rejuvenates the area and increases the velocity of the stream.

VOCABULARY REVIEW

Match the phrase in the left column with the correct word or phrase in the right column. *Do not write in this book.*

1. Separates river drainage basins	**a.** levees
2. Elevated banks	**b.** load
3. Crystal-filled spherical cavity	**c.** braided stream
4. All materials carried by a stream	**d.** pothole
5. Wide curves in river	**e.** permeable
6. Flows parallel to main river	**f.** meanders
7. Slope of river	**g.** gradient
8. Allows water to seep through	**h.** yazoo stream
9. Small streams flowing across delta	**i.** natural bridge
10. Network of small channels	**j.** geode
11. Bowl-shaped cavity in stream bed	**k.** karst landscape
12. Grinding process	**l.** base level
13. Region dotted with sinks	**m.** abrasion
	n. divide
	o. distributaries

QUESTIONS · GROUP A

Decide whether these statements are true or false. Reword the false statements to make them true. *Do not write in this book.*

1. Wide interstream areas are typical of a young river system.
2. Natural levees are associated with flood plains.
3. Rocks are worn down by the process of abrasion.
4. Streams that flow across a delta are called yazoo streams.
5. Braided streams are common in humid regions.
6. Rocks through which water can pass are said to be permeable.
7. Cutoff meanders result in tributary streams.
8. Stream piracy may convert a wind gap to a water gap.
9. The load of a stream is mainly determined by the volume of water.
10. Swamps are associated with old rivers.
11. Rejuvenation of an area decreases a stream's velocity.
12. An alluvial fan is composed of residual soil.
13. The upper surface of the ground water is called the water table.
14. A terrace is the high land that separates two drainage systems.
15. Deltas are the result of deposition of sediment in a fast-moving body of water.
16. Sinkholes are numerous in an area of igneous rock.
17. Canyons are characteristic of young river valleys.
18. Alluvial fans form when there is a sudden increase in the gradient of a stream.
19. Gullies are extended by a process known as headward erosion.
20. The fall line is cut by many young rivers.
21. Limestone dissolves readily in pure water.
22. An iciclelike deposit of calcite found in caverns is called a stalagmite.

GROUP B

1. Construct a table to show the characteristics of young, mature, and old rivers.
2. Discuss the difference between an alluvial fan and a delta.
3. What factors determine the nature and size of a stream's load? What causes a stream to deposit its load?
4. Discuss the formation of a meander, cutoff, and oxbow lake. Illustrate your explanation with a labeled diagram. Show both a top view and a cross-section across a meander.
5. Discuss how stream piracy may divert the water of one system to another system.
6. What is headward erosion? How does this process contribute to the formation of a river system?
7. How is base level related to the mouth of a river? How is the velocity of a stream affected as base level is approached?
8. Describe the formation of karst topography.
9. What is a yazoo stream? Why is it incorrect to call a yazoo stream a tributary?
10. If you were studying a topographic map, how could you determine whether certain small streams were distributaries or tributaries? Make a labeled diagram to illustrate your explanation.

11. What is the origin of potholes?

12. Would it be possible for a tributary to form a delta in its main stream? Explain.

13. Would it be better to buy land on the inside or outside bank of a meander? Explain the reason for your choice.

14. Would levees increase or decrease in elevation during a flood? Explain the reason for your answer.

15. Are alluvial fans or deltas likely to be composed of coarser material? Explain the reason for your answer. Would you be more likely to discover fossils in a delta or in an alluvial fan? Explain.

16. In which region would the rocks be more permeable, the Columbia Plateau or the Atlantic Coastal Plain? Explain the reason for your answer.

17. Explain the formation of a natural bridge.

18. How is a geode formed?

19. What is meant by rejuvenation of a stream?

TOPOGRAPHIC SHEETS

Furnace Creek, California. *Natural bridge.*
Mammoth Cave, Kentucky. *Karst topography, slipoff slope.*
Arredondo, Florida. *Sinks.*
East Brownsville, Texas. *Natural levee.*
Norris, Tennessee. *River development.*
Philippi, Mississippi. *Alluvial plain, meander patterns.*
Campti, Louisiana. *Natural levee, oxbow lake.*
Yakima East, Washington. *Types of streams.*
Ennis, Montana. *Braided stream, alluvial fan.*
Whitwell, Tennessee. *Divides.*
Bright Angel, Arizona. *Young stream.*
Amsterdam, New York. *Divides.*
Cumberland, Maryland–Pennsylvania–West Virginia. *Water gap, stream piracy.*
Hillsboro, Kentucky. *Imminent stream piracy.*
Ithaca West, New York; Niagara, New York (special). *Waterfall.*

All of the above are in the 15-minute series.

CHAPTER 19

GLACIAL ICE

ABOUT ten thousand years ago the bands of hunters who were the ancestors of modern man witnessed the end of an important chapter in the history of the earth. Great sheets of ice that covered about one third of the earth were melting, exposing land that had lain under thick layers of ice for thousands of years. The earth was emerging from the latest ice invasion during which enormous sheets of ice covered much of Europe, Asia, and North America. In our coun-

VOCABULARY

Névé (nay-*vay*). Granular ice formed from accumulated snow which later becomes glacial ice.

Crevasse (kreh-*vas*). A deep crack in a glacier.

Cirque (surk). A bowl-shaped depression in a mountainside, formed at the head of a valley glacier.

Arête (a-*rayt*). A sharp, narrow ridge separating two cirques or glacial valleys.

Striae. Scratches on the surface of rocks resulting from the movement of glacial ice.

Roche moutonnée (*rawsh*-moo-taw-*nay*). A rounded and smoothed rock projection, shaped by glacial action.

Drift. A general term for the material deposited by a glacier or by glacial meltwater.

Till. Glacial deposits which have not been stratified or sorted by water action.

Moraine. A ridge or mound of boulders, gravel, sand, and clay carried on or deposited by a glacier.

Kame. A mound of stratified drift deposited by streams running off a glacier.

Kettle. A depression remaining after the melting of large blocks of ice buried in glacial drift.

Esker. A winding ridge of stratified drift deposited by streams running under or through glacial ice.

try this ice sheet extended as far south as present-day New Jersey, Ohio, Illinois, Kansas, Montana, and Washington.

Today the landscape throughout much of the world and particularly in the northern United States shows the scars and evidences left by those massive tongues of ice. Evidence contained in older rocks of the earth shows that the world has become cold enough at least four different times to cause the ice to accumulate and move as solid sheets that covered a large part of the land.

Today the earth seems to be in a warming period when the glaciers still scattered over the earth are melting. Whether this marks the end of the most recent ice age or is merely a temporary shrinking of the glaciers is not known.

THE ORIGIN OF GLACIERS

Formation of glaciers. Most of the rain and snow which falls over the world is returned to the oceans by streams. However, in regions where the average yearly temperature is near freezing, large amounts of snow remain from one year to the next, piling up in deep masses. The great weight of the snow presses against the layers underneath, causing the snow crystals there to melt, then refreeze, thus forming small pellets of ice. The granular ice thus produced is called *névé* (nay-*vay*). In the lowest layers the pressure is so great that the névé is recrystallized into a solid mass of ice. Each winter thick blankets of snow are added to the top, contributing more material to the growing mass of snow and ice. Eventually the weight of the accumulated ice becomes great enough to cause the entire mass to move slowly. This moving body of ice is a *glacier.*

Today, relatively few places on earth have low enough average temperatures and sufficient snowfall to permit the formation of glaciers. One location where such conditions are found is in the upper levels of mountains. Near the equator, mountains must be at least 18,000 feet high to allow for glacier formation. In the United States 10,000 feet is usually high enough; in the polar regions ice may survive all year at sea level. The *snow line,* the elevation above which snow remains all year, varies with different locations, being higher near the equator and lower near the poles. At locations where the amount of snow and ice that accumulates during a year is greater than the amount melting during the warm season, a *snow field* is formed. Snow fields are found in low latitudes only at high altitudes but in high latitudes they occur at all levels.

Types of glaciers. Piling up of snow in mountain valleys above the snow line may produce *valley glaciers,* also called *alpine glaciers.* These range in size from only a few hundred square yards to huge rivers of ice many square miles in area. See Fig. 19–1.

A second general type of glacier is found presently only in the polar regions. There, even at sea level, the average temperature is below freezing. Most of the snow that falls remains from year to year, forming a continuous *continental glacier* that covers the entire land surface. Greenland, the largest land body near the north pole, is buried almost completely under a continental glacier that covers 666,300 square miles. Measurements show that this ice sheet reaches a thickness of 8000 feet. Antarctica at the south pole is completely buried under the largest of all glaciers: 5,019,900 square miles. Accurate measurements of the ice thickness in Antarc-

FIG. 19–1. A valley glacier, Worthington Glacier in Alaska. The glacier's advance down the slope is evident. (*C. Puhr from Shostal*)

tica during the International Geophysical Year reveal a maximum depth of over 14,000 feet at some locations. See Fig. 19–2. It has been estimated that if all the ice in the two great glaciers of Greenland and Antarctica were melted, the water released would raise the sea level more than 200 feet.

Movement of glaciers. As snow builds up on top of a glacier, the weight causes tremendous pressures on the ice at the bottom. The ice under this pressure becomes very compact, and at the same time the weight of the glacier causes it to move. Just how a glacier can move over the irregular surface of the land is not completely understood. Many scientists who have studied the problem have concluded that although glacial ice seems to be hard and rigid, it actually becomes somewhat plastic and flows slowly under great pressure. Also, ice

tends to melt when subjected to pressure and to refreeze when the pressure is reduced. The melted ice at the bottom of the glacier flows around projections, then refreezes later when the pressure is diminished. This continual melting, freezing, and remelting of ice allows the glacier to move slowly in a twisting path although the ice itself remains rigid. The complete explanation for glacial movement probably involves the fracturing of ice, the flowing of ice under pressure, and melting and refreezing, as well as other processes not yet understood.

Glaciers formed in mountain valleys follow the path of least resistance and slowly move downward through the valley to lower elevations. The weaving and twisting of the ice as it is forced to follow the general path of the valley causes large cracks or *crevasses* (kreh-*vas*-ez) to appear on the top and sides of the glacier. These crevasses generally run across the glacier; however, near the lower end they may run lengthwise also. See Fig. 19–3. Crevasses are often more than a hundred feet deep, and may be concealed by a thin crust of snow which breaks at the slightest weight. Thus traveling over the top of a glacier can be a very risky undertaking, requiring experience and great caution.

Several valley glaciers may merge where their valleys join, as in Fig. 19–4. A number of valley glaciers may also blend together to form a huge *piedmont glacier* as they move out onto a plain at the base of the mountains.

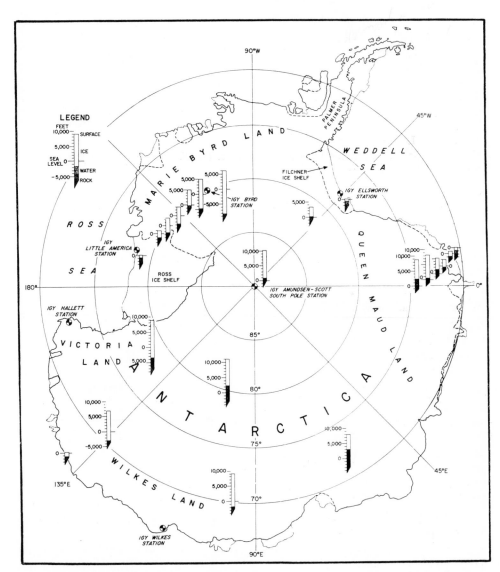

FIG. 19–2. The thickness of ice at various points on the great Antarctic continental glacier. (IGY Bulletin, *National Academy of Sciences*)

FIG. 19–3. Left, crevasses on the top of a glacier. Right, a crevasse as seen from the side. Note the rock debris on the glacier's surface. (*U. S. Geological Survey; Geological Survey of Canada*)

FIG. 19–4. Small valley glaciers may merge to form a much larger valley glacier. (*Bradford Washburn*)

Continental glaciers are pushed outward to the edges of the land mass by the continuous pressure of additional snow accumulating inland. The continental glacier that covered the northern portion of North America during the last ice age had three major centers of accumulation from which the ice masses moved slowly outward in all directions. The ice sheets now covering Antarctica and Greenland move outward toward the coasts. The edges of glaciers that reach the shore are called *tidewater glaciers* because the rise and fall of the tide snaps off large sections of the ice that float away as icebergs.

How fast a glacier moves depends mainly on the rate of snow accumulation, the steepness of the underlying rock surfaces, and the temperature conditions. Some glaciers barely move; others have been known to move 50 feet in one day. A glacier in the Alps carried the bodies of three guides, lost in an accident, a distance of 8000 feet during the 41 years between the time they were lost and the time their bodies were recovered at the lower end of the glacier. Extraordinary speeds have been measured on the ice flows which descend from the continental glacier down the submerged valleys of the coast of Greenland. On these swiftly moving glaciers speeds of nearly 100 feet per day have been observed. However, in the same regions the ice farther inland moves only a fraction of an inch per day.

Stakes driven in the ice across the tops of glaciers in the manner shown in Fig. 19–5 indicate that the ice at the center of the glacier moves faster than that at the sides. Stakes driven into the steep sides of exposed glaciers show in a similar manner that the upper ice also moves faster than that at the bottom. These results are apparently due to the friction of the ice against the ground at the sides and bottom of the glaciers.

A glacier is always in a delicate balance between ice added by snowfall and ice lost by melting and evaporation. Very slight differences in the average yearly temperatures may alter this balance one way or the other and the glacier then advances or retreats accordingly. For this reason glaciers are very sensitive indicators of climate change and can be used as signals of rising or falling trends in the average temperatures over periods of many years. At the present time, most glaciers are shrinking, which seems to indicate that the climate over the world is growing warmer.

GLACIAL EROSION

The work of a valley glacier. The breeding place of a valley glacier is in the high mountain snow fields. At the head of a valley, above the snow line, snow accumulates until the upper end

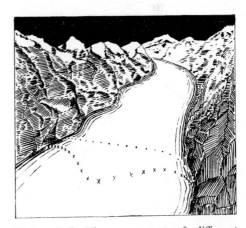

FIG. 19–5. The movement of different parts of a valley glacier can be measured if stakes (dots) are driven into the ice. The crosses show the positions of the stakes at a later time.

of the valley is filled and the slow change of snow into glacial ice begins to take place. Glacial meltwater seeps into the cracks in the rock walls of the valley and freezes, causing chips of rock to break off and fall into the growing mass of ice. Constant breaking away of the upper valley walls by this frost action causes the head of the glacial valley to become very steep-walled and roughly semicircular in shape. Most valley glaciers have their heads in one of these rugged U-shaped depressions, called *cirques* (surks). This French word, meaning "circus," refers to the resemblance of the head of a glacial valley to an amphitheater.

When a number of cirques are formed close together, the dividing ridges between them become very sharp and jagged as the cirques enlarge. These ridges are called *arêtes* (a-*rayts*) which means "spines." See Fig. 19–6. The jagged appearance of many peaks, such as the famous Matterhorn in Switzerland, is due to the development and overlapping of several cirques, leaving rugged pinnacles of rock standing between, as in Fig. 19–7. Much of the ruggedness of the Rocky Mountains and the mountains of Alaska is caused by numerous cirques, arêtes, and other features produced by the erosion which took place at the heads of valley glaciers.

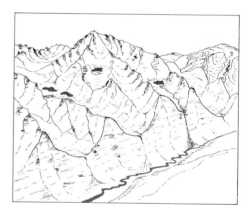

FIG. 19–6. The cycle of glacier formation and the development of glacial features: cirques, arêtes, and matterhorn peaks.

With continued growth of the mass of ice in the head of the valley, the glacier eventually begins to move slowly to lower levels along the general path of the existing valley. The erosion at the head of the valley causes large amounts of rock fragments to become mixed in the ice of the developing glacier; it also picks up more rock from erosion of the sides of the valley as it creeps along. Thus, from its beginnings, the glacier contains a great load of rock ranging from microscopic pieces to large boulders broken off by frost wedging or by the weight of the moving ice. Such rock debris included in the ice helps to explain why a glacier is so effective in eroding even the most resistant rock. The ice itself is not hard enough to scour and scratch rock, but the rocks imbedded in the ice act as the teeth of a gigantic file. These pebbles and boulders, anchored in the ice of the glacier, gouge and mark the rocks rubbed by the glacier as it moves. The marks, called *glacial striae* (*stry*-ee) if they are scratches, or *glacial grooves* if very deep, are plainly visible in all glaciated regions. See Fig. 19–9.

The action of the glacier along a valley floor tends to smooth out the rock, and in some cases, especially where the valley is very uneven, large blocks of rock are pried out and moved along. The remaining bedrock is rounded and marked with striae to become what are called *roches moutonnées* (*rawsh*-moo-taw-*nay*), a French term meaning "sheep rocks." This name is explained by the fact that in one section of the Alps the white dolomite rocks shaped in this way remind observers of a flock of large sheep. Many French terms are used to describe glaciers and glacial action because of the pioneer work of the French-speaking Swiss in the study of

FIG. 19–7. The Matterhorn in Switzerland is a rugged pinnacle of rock characteristic of glaciation. (*Bradford Washburn*)

glaciers in their mountainous country.

As the glacier moves through a valley, the deposits of rock material along its edges grind away the valley walls, changing the original V-shape of the valley to a U-shape. See Fig. 19–11. These U-shaped valleys are considered to be positive evidence of glacial erosion, since glaciers are the only known means by which they can be produced.

Examination of a glacial valley shows that the ice moves ponderously along the general course of the original valley, tending to straighten its sharp bends and changing it into a broad U-shaped depression. Side valleys leading into the main glacial valley often become *hanging valleys* when the glacier scoops out the main floor. These tributary valleys end in mid-air high above the new main valley bed, and rivers flowing through them form steep waterfalls.

Yosemite Valley of California shows many of the features typical of a valley

FIG. 19–8. The region surrounding Eagle Glacier, British Columbia, shows many features of glacial carving. (*Geological Survey of Canada*)

carved by glacial erosion. It is one of many such valleys produced by an extensive system of glaciers which flowed down from the Sierra Nevada Mountains to the base of these mountains in the Central Valley of California. Small remnants of these glaciers still exist along the crest of the Sierra Nevadas, but the main evidence of their past extent is contained in the glacial features of which Yosemite has many outstanding examples.

The work of continental glaciers. Because of their great thickness and tremendous mass, continental glaciers completely override most existing land features. The result of continental glaciation is unlike the sharp jagged topography produced by the plucking action at the upper ends of valley glaciers. As they move out from their centers, continental glaciers tend to produce relatively smooth surfaces by grinding down

the higher parts of the land. In a few cases existing valleys may be gouged out and deepened, especially if the direction of ice movement is parallel to the valley. In most places, however, the landscape is smoothed; the ponderous sheet of ice erodes the tops of the higher features and partially or completely fills the depressions with debris. Many of the mountains in the northeastern part of the United States, particularly in New Hampshire and Vermont, show smoothing effects that have been attributed to the continental ice sheets that moved over the region during the last ice age. However, much of this might be due to preglacial erosion.

When a continental glacier moves over level plateaus or plains, its principal erosional work is likely to consist of pushing and dragging along most of the loose soil and rock, leaving bare, rounded bedrock with a striated surface. Also,

FIG. 19–9. Deep grooves were gouged in solid limestone by the great continental glacier, on Kelley's Island in Lake Erie. (*Ohio Historical Society*)

FIG. 19–10. Lembert Dome is a granite roche moutonnée in Yosemite National Park. (*National Park Service*)

FIG. 19–11. Glacial valleys have a characteristic U shape, shown in this view of Crawford Notch, New Hampshire. The V-shaped stream valley has been widened and rounded by the passage of the ice. (*Lawrence Lowry from Rapho-Guillumette*)

the movement of the ice sheet tends to create many shallow basins where the softer rock is worn down more than the surrounding resistant rock. Many of these basins remain after the ice retreats and fill with meltwater from the glacier to become lakes. Actually many of the lakes now in existence originated as a result of the work of the ice sheets of the last glacial period. The origin of glacial lakes will be taken up in Chapter 24.

GLACIAL DEPOSITS

Types of glacial deposits. When the ice of a glacier encounters higher temperatures, either through movement that carries it to lower altitudes or by changes in climate, it gradually melts. The debris carried by the glacier is dropped, forming various kinds of deposits known under the general name of *glacial drift.* Actually, the term "drift" covers two distinct types of deposits:

1. Till, the material deposited directly from the ice either by being scraped from the bottom of the glacier or by being left behind when melting occurs.

2. Stratified drift, material that has been sorted and deposited in definite layers by the action of the meltwater from the glacier.

Usually, it is easy to spot glacial deposits by the characteristic worn and striated appearance of the rock surface and by the presence of large boulders, called *erratics,* whose composition is entirely different from that of the native bedrock. One must dig into the deposit, however, to distinguish the conglomeration of small rocks, gravel, sand, and clay found in till from the sorted layers of water-smoothed rocks and pebbles found in stratified drift. In glaciated regions, the deposits exposed when highways are cut through hills help to reveal the exact nature of the material so that it can be identified.

Glacial deposits formed of till or stratified drift are fashioned into many characteristic topographic features by the action of the glacier and its meltwater. Some of these features are described in the following sections.

Direct deposits. The material carried along by the glacier often forms ridges or mounds on the glacier itself or on the ground over which the glacier passes. These deposits are called *moraines.* An accumulation of rocky debris along the edges of a valley glacier often forms ridges: these are *lateral moraines.* Joining of two or more valley glaciers brings the lateral moraines together to form *medial moraines.* See Fig. 19–13.

The bottom portion of a glacier may become so loaded with debris that the ice cannot carry it all. Part of this material is deposited below the ice and is overridden as the ice moves along. Especially large deposits fill depressed areas in the underlying bedrock. All the material left beneath the advancing glacier, together with that deposited during melting, makes up the *ground moraine.* It is composed largely of powdered rock, which gives the meltwater a milky appearance, and clay with pebbles and larger rocks scattered throughout. It is usually laid down unevenly so that its surface has a gentle hilly appearance after the glacier has disappeared. Much of the topography of the glaciated region from eastern Ohio west to the Rocky Mountains in Montana and north into Canada is formed by ground moraine.

At the melting edge of the ice, a glacier usually forms a large moraine deposit. It is produced by accumulation of material pushed along ahead of the moving ice and by dumping of debris from the melting ice at the glacier's edge. This end deposit is called a *terminal moraine.* See Fig. 19–14. In glaciated regions the old terminal moraines are often seen as belts of small hills with many hollows that frequently contain lakes. Large terminal moraines occur in Minnesota, the Dakotas, Wisconsin, northern Illinois, Indiana, and Ohio. Some of the islands along the northern part of the Atlantic Coastal Plain, such as Martha's Vineyard, Nantucket, Block Island, and Long Island have hilly belts formed by terminal moraines.

Some glaciers do not leave much of a terminal moraine because they are located on such a steep incline that the meltwater carries the deposits away. In places where a glacier pushes out upon the piedmont plains and halts there for

FIG. 19–12. A soil profile showing the typical unstratified structure of glacial till. (*U. S. Geological Survey*)

FIG. 19–13. The joining of lateral moraines to form medial moraines is clearly seen in this view of an Alaskan glacier. (*Bradford Washburn*)

a number of years, crescent-shaped or horseshoe-shaped heaps of till are built up with their concave sides facing the hills. The height of these deposits depends upon the length of time the glacier front remains in one position. If it shrinks rapidly, the material is scattered over a larger area and little is piled up at any one location. In this case no large terminal moraine is formed.

Some special surface features are formed in continental glacial deposits. A frequent feature of areas covered with ground moraine are mounds of till which are long and low, rounded off on one end and pointed at the other. They are seldom more than a mile long or more than 100 feet high. See Fig. 19–15. These small hills are called *drumlins*. How they were formed is not definitely

known. They may have been produced when a second glacier overran and reshaped the till left by an earlier glacier. Or, they may be the result of a particular kind of erosion as the till was deposited by the glacier. Drumlins are formed only where clay is plentiful in the till, and the clay acts as a kind of plaster in shaping the mound. Whatever their causes, drumlins are a clue to the glacier's motion since their pointed tails always point in the direction in which the glacier moved.

Deposits formed by glacial meltwater. The melting of a glacier is a continuous process. If the glacier is growing by the addition of snow to its upper parts, its lower end is always melting; if snow is added faster than water is lost, the glacier grows and probably advances. If,

FIG. 19–14. The lower margin of a valley glacier in Oregon, showing the terminal moraine. (*U. S. Geological Survey*)

FIG. 19–15. This drumlin in Middlesex County, Massachusetts, shows the characteristic shape. (*U. S. Geological Survey*)

FIG. 19–16. An esker in Wisconsin. Eskers are found only in areas once covered by stagnant continental glaciers. (*U. S. Geological Survey*)

however, water is lost faster than new ice is added, the glacier shrinks. In either case the meltwater flows out from the lower end, usually carrying with it enough of the drift to produce a large fan-shaped *outwash plain* below the end of the glacier. The southern part of Long Island is such an outwash plain. The outwash plain is often crisscrossed by many streams which cut though the terminal and ground moraines.

The outwash plain is also frequently pitted with various sized basins, or *kettles,* which are formed when pieces of ice break off the edges of the glacier and become covered over with drift. As the ice melts, the drift sinks down, producing a depression. Kettles may fill with water and become ponds or lakes.

One characteristic feature of glacial plains is the presence of a number of mounds called *kames,* hills of stratified drift left by streams flowing over the surface of the glacier or off its edge.

Sometimes on a glacial plain there is what appears to be a crooked raised roadway extending for some distance. This is an *esker:* a ridge of stratified drift deposited by a stream of meltwater flowing in a tunnel within or beneath a glacier. When the glacier melts, this narrow ridge is left as an unusual feature of the landscape. See Fig. 19–16.

When glacial ice melts very rapidly, many streams form on the surface of the glacier, under it, and along its margins. Large boulders, pebbles, sand, and fine rock are carried along by these streams and the heavier materials are dropped as the streams divide and lose much of their carrying power. Where the streams empty out onto a plain, the debris is deposited as a long alluvial fan. If the glacial streams empty into a narrow valley, the deposits are confined by its walls, resulting in a long *valley train* composed of the stream-deposited materials. These range from large boulders near the glacier to coarse gravel, fine sand, silt, and powdered rock at a distance of several miles from the glacier's end.

Glacial features such as kames, eskers, and outwash plains are especially characteristic of the *stagnation* of continental glaciers. They were deposited chiefly at times when the glaciers were melting and shrinking at the ends of the great glacial periods.

THE GLACIAL PERIODS

The four great glacial periods. A great mass of evidence indicates that parts of the earth have been covered by great ice sheets at least four times in the past. The first glacial period occurred about 800 million years ago; then there was a period of about 300 million years of freedom from general glacial activity. The second big freeze came about 500 million years ago and was followed by a warm spell of about 300 million years. Then the ice sheets formed again for the third time about 200 million years ago. The latest ice invasion took place only about 1 million years ago—recently enough so that our very distant ancestors were no doubt chilled and forced to migrate by the advancing glaciers. This latest period of glaciation is usually referred to as the Ice Age and has been divided into four separate stages of active growth and advance of the glaciers. These four colder stages were separated by warm interludes when the ice sheets shrank.

At the present time the earth seems to be in a period that is not definitely glacial or nonglacial. Average temperatures all over the world seem to be climbing upward and the level of the oceans appears to be rising about 2½ inches each century from water released by melting of existing glaciers. However, since 1000 B.C. there have been two periods, one about 500 B.C. and another between A.D. 1600 and 1800, when the climate all over the world grew colder and the glaciers tended to grow again. From around 1850 to the present time gradually warmer temperatures have been recorded.

Possible causes of the glacial periods. As yet, no one knows why the earth's climate is so changeable. A number of theories have been proposed to explain the cooling which caused the glacial periods since all evidence indicates that the earth is normally warm and that the periods of glaciation are the result of some kind of disturbance. A brief description of some of these theories may indicate the general trend of thought on the subject and the problems involved:

1. Variation in the amount of heat received from the sun. One theory is based on the assumption that the glacial periods have been caused by changes in the amount of energy the earth receives from the sun, due to several factors.

FIG. 19–17. A melt cave under Paradise-Stevens Glacier on Mount Rainier, Washington. This passage is about three-quarters of a mile long. (*Louie Kirk*)

Small changes in the inclination of the earth's axis, along with irregularities in the earth's orbit around the sun result in variation in the radiant energy received on the earth. A decrease in temperature due to such variation might alter the earth's climate enough to cause glaciation. However, the changes in the inclination of the axis and in the orbit occur at regular, relatively short intervals (21,000- to 90,000-year cycles) whereas the glacial periods have come at irregular times, and are much more widely spaced in time (more than 300,000 years between some stages in the recent Ice Age).

It has also been suggested that the known irregularity in the actual amount of radiation given off by the sun may cause changes in the earth's climate. Although the evidence is not conclusive, there is reason to believe that the amount of solar energy varies around the average figure, and that the variation may have been great enough in the past to cause the earth's surface to become slightly warmer or cooler. However, a great deal more will have to be learned about the relationship between the sun and the earth before this theory could be accepted as an explanation of the periods of glaciation.

2. *Topographical factors.* A completely different theory assumes that the cause of glaciation lies in events that take place on the earth itself. For example, it has been noted that at least two of the periods of glacial activity have occurred during times of mountain building. High mountains produced prior to the glacial periods would act as snow-collecting areas, and would tend to lower the earth's surface temperature generally. Also, volcanic activity associated with mountain building might bring about cooler temperatures due to large amounts of volcanic dust in the air which would shade the earth's surface from the sun's radiation. Broad continental uplift would also affect the world climate, reducing temperatures over the land. Such topographic changes require long periods of time, and so cannot fully account for the retreats and advances of the glaciers. It is also difficult to account for the increased snowfall that would be needed to form the glaciers.

3. *Melting of the Arctic ice.* A recent theory is based on the fact that the Arctic Ocean is presently covered with a thick layer of ice which never melts. Calculations indicate that if warmer water from the North Atlantic were to circulate into the Arctic Ocean, the ice pack might melt. But the North Atlantic water does not flow into the Arctic because there is a ridge along the sea floor that tends to keep the two oceans from mixing. However, if the level of the Atlantic were to rise, water would pass freely over the barrier and cause the ice cover to melt.

Actually the level of the Atlantic (and all other oceans) is rising today because the glaciers are melting and adding their water to the seas. Theoretically, this is exactly what is needed to produce another Ice Age. If the warmer Atlantic water begins to mix with the Arctic water, the ice cover will slowly melt. When the Arctic is finally free of ice, more water vapor will escape into the atmosphere, causing heavier snowfall on the land masses bordering the north polar regions. This increased snowfall could slowly build up the great ice sheets characteristic of the glacial periods. Eventually so much water would be trapped in the glaciers that the ocean levels would drop again, separating the Arctic Ocean from the Atlantic and restoring the ice cover on the Arctic. The glaciers

FIG. 19–18. During the last Ice Age, the continental glacier advanced and retreated around three centers, as shown here. Evidences of glaciation are found in the areas outlined.

would thus be again deprived of the snowfall needed to replenish their ice, and would begin to disappear. So the cycle of advance and retreat of the ice sheets would be complete.

This theory is attractive because it does not require any basic changes in the conditions on the earth's surface to account for the appearance and disappearance of the glaciers. However, there is no definite proof that removal of the ice cover on the Arctic Ocean would cause formation of the ice sheets. Also, the general circulation of the water of the oceans is not yet well enough understood for us to establish whether such mixing of Arctic and Atlantic waters can take place. More questions need to be answered before any explanation of the baffling advances and retreats of continental glaciers can be accepted as adequate.

SUMMARY

A GLACIER is a mass of flowing ice which is formed where more snow accumulates than melts. Alternate freezing and thawing changes the snow to a granular ice called névé. The two general types of glaciers are alpine or valley glaciers and continental glaciers. The principal work of glaciers is erosion, transportation, and deposition.

Alpine glaciers are formed in mountain areas. The ice moves through the valley to a point below the snow line. There are no glaciers in eastern North America; they are confined to the western third of the continent. A glaciated valley has a U-shaped cross-section, bowl-shaped basins called cirques, and many rugged peaks.

Continental glaciers cover vast areas and originate where climatic factors cause the excessive snowfall necessary to form glacial ice. Gradually the ice moves away from the centers of accumulation. Geologic evidence leads us to believe that vast areas of the earth have been subjected to four glacial periods. Drumlins and striae indicate the direction of the ice front of the continental glacier. Roches moutonnées are characteristic of glaciated bedrock.

Transportation and subsequent deposition of drift result in such features as moraines, eskers, kames, erratics, and outwash plains.

VOCABULARY REVIEW

Match the phrase in the left column with the correct word or phrase in the right column. *Do not write in this book.*

1. Glacial crack	**a.** arête
2. Milky appearance	**b.** drumlin
3. Debris along the edge of a valley glacier	**c.** striae
4. Winding ridge	**d.** outwash plain
5. Indicates direction of glacial movement	**e.** kame
6. Granular ice	**f.** hanging valley
7. Depressions	**g.** piedmont glacier
8. Forms icebergs	**h.** lateral moraine
9. A jagged ridge	**i.** névé
10. Glacial deposits	**j.** medial moraine
11. Glacial scratches	**k.** meltwater
12. Formed by a tributary glacier	**l.** tidewater glacier
13. Blending of many valley glaciers	**m.** crevasse
14. Fan-shaped deposit	**n.** kettle
	o. esker
	p. drift

QUESTIONS · GROUP A

Decide whether these statements are true or false. Reword the false statements to make them true. *Do not write in this book.*

1. Glacial valleys are U-shaped.
2. A kame is a type of glacial lake.
3. Cirques result from the accumulation of drift.
4. Glacial scratches are called crevasses.
5. Narrow winding ridges of glacial material are called eskers.
6. Outwash plains are formed along the sides of valley glaciers.
7. The snow line is higher in Alaska than on the equator.
8. Yosemite National Park has some excellent examples of continental glaciers.
9. Glacial soils are residual soils.
10. Striae result from the melting of a glacier.

11. Alpine glaciers are found in the Adirondack Mountains.
12. If a glacier moved in a southerly direction the pointed slope of a drumlin would point south.
13. The center of a glacier moves faster than the sides.
14. Since 1000 B.C. the earth's temperature has steadily grown warmer.
15. Drumlins are very common along the sandy shores of the Atlantic Ocean.

GROUP B

1. Compare glaciers and streams as to erosion, transportation, and deposition.
2. Describe the formation of hanging valleys.
3. Describe the formation of an outwash plain.
4. How is glacial ice formed?
5. Give a possible explanation for the unequal movement of the sides of a glacier as compared with the center.
6. What are some differences between glacial drift and sediments deposited by water?
7. How is a kettle formed?
8. Would a ground moraine make good farmland? Explain.
9. Compare the topography of land that has been subjected to continental glaciation with that of land subjected to alpine glaciation.
10. Differentiate between till and stratified drift.
11. Describe the formation and arrangement of sediments in a valley train.
12. Discuss the three theories advanced to explain the occurrence of the glacial periods. Which theory seems most plausible to you? Explain.
13. Why are there no glaciers in the eastern part of North America? Excluding those in Alaska, name some mountains in the United States that have alpine glaciers.

TOPOGRAPHIC SHEETS

Mt. Tom, California. *Many features of alpine glaciation.*
Mt. Ranier, Washington. *Glacier, medial moraine, hanging valleys.*
Chief Mountain, Montana. *Many glaciers, glacial lakes, glaciated peaks, arêtes, and U-shaped valleys.*
Whitewater, Wisconsin. *Features resulting from continental glaciation, such as a terminal moraine and drumlins.*
Ayer, Massachusetts. *Drumlins and kames.*
Delaware, Michigan. *Esker.*
Monadnock, New Hampshire. *Kettle holes.*
Jackson, Michigan. *Pitted outwash plain.*
Amsterdam, New York. *Dissected glaciated plateau.*

All of the above are in the 15-minute series.

★

Plastic relief map of Iceland. Army Map Service. *Ice sheet, fiords, and other features resulting from glaciation.*

CHAPTER 20

WIND AND WAVES

In previous chapters, we have seen how the rocky materials of the crust can be sculptured by water and ice. The erosional effect of these agents is due to their motion. Motion is also essential in the widespread erosion accomplished by the earth's two great bodies of fluids: the sea and the atmosphere. In the sea there is movement of waves and currents, and in the atmosphere, there is movement of the wind.

The sea does its work along the shore, where waves and currents attack the margins of the land. Without the con-tinuous flinging of water against the shore, the sea would probably have little erosive effect. In the interiors of continental land masses, where the work of water is less evident, wind action is most effective as an erosional agent.

WIND EROSION AND DEPOSITION

Transportation by wind. The chief work of wind is the movement of loose particles of soil and rock. In humid re-

VOCABULARY

Deflation. Blowing away of loose soil and rock particles by wind.

Dune. A hill or ridge of wind-blown sand.

Barchan (*bahr*-kan). A crescent-shaped dune.

Loess (luhs). An extensive deposit of wind-blown silt.

Wave-cut terrace. A level surface of rock under the water along the shore, formed as waves cut back the shoreline.

Stack. An isolated column of rock left standing as waves erode a shoreline.

Offshore bar. A sand bar more or less parallel to the mainland.

Spit. A sand bar extending outward from the shore into open water.

Hook. A curved spit.

Fiord (fyawrd). A drowned glaciated valley.

Lagoon. The body of water between an offshore bar and the mainland.

Ventifact. A stone which has been smoothed by wind abrasion.

gions, where rainfall is abundant, there is usually sufficient vegetation to act as a ground cover. In arid or semiarid lands, the plant cover is spotty and much of the loose dry upper portion of the mantle rock is exposed. Under these conditions wind becomes an important agent of erosion through the process of *deflation* (from the Latin "to blow away").

Deflation is most conspicuous in the very dry deserts of the world. Here even gentle breezes move fine silt particles from the desert floor. Strong winds create great sand storms: dust fills the air for thousands of feet and sheets of heavier sand particles race along close to the ground. Such storms are common in the interior deserts of Asia and Africa, making travel there a dangerous undertaking. Over long periods, wind action may completely strip away all loose material from the desert floor, exposing the bedrock. For this reason, many desert areas are composed of nothing but bare rock. Often, however, the desert floor consists of small stones, too big to be moved by the wind, tightly fitted together to form a relatively smooth surface known as *desert pavement.* See Fig. 20–1.

To be subject to serious deflation, a region must be dry. Semiarid lands that ordinarily are fairly well protected by a plant cover, such as the western parts of the Great Plains of the United States, are subject to disastrous wind erosion in dry periods. During the 1930's (and again in 1954) a combination of poor farming practices, which removed the natural ground cover, and several dry years produced dust bowls in parts of Texas, Oklahoma, Kansas, and Colorado. Large amounts of topsoil were removed by the wind, resulting in widespread destruction of farmland and great hardship on the inhabitants. Recurrence

of the dust bowls can only be prevented by soil conservation practices that do not allow the land to be exposed to the erosional action of the wind.

Deposits made by wind. All the material transported by wind is eventually deposited. The transporting capacity of the wind, as of running water, diminishes as the velocity decreases. Deposits are formed where a decrease in wind speed causes part of the load to be dropped. Such deposits are often only temporary and are carried away by the next strong wind. Sometimes, however, the material undergoes consolidation, and perhaps cementation, to become a relatively permanent part of the crust as sedimentary rock.

The most common of all wind deposits are *dunes,* which are hills of wind-

FIG. 20–1. A desert pavement, the result of severe wind erosion. (*U. S. Geological Survey*)

blown sand. Dunes are formed where there is a supply of dry, unprotected sand and winds strong enough to move it. In the United States, extensive areas of sand dunes are found along the sandy shores of the Atlantic and Pacific Oceans. Along the east coast of Lake Michigan and in some of the larger stream valleys of the West, sand dunes also appear. Large parts of the deserts of Africa and the Near East are covered by dunes, although not to the extent commonly supposed: dunes appear in only one-ninth of the Sahara Desert of North Africa. This desert, like all the great deserts of the world, consists mainly of bare rock or expanses of boulders and pebbles swept clean of finer material by wind.

A dune is started by an obstruction which breaks the speed of the wind, causing a small deposit of material to accumulate on the sheltered or lee side of the obstacle. As the small mound of material grows, it acts as a larger windbreak and increases the amount deposited. This process continues until the dune reaches a height of at least several feet. If there is a plentiful supply of sand and winds are steady and strong, the dunes may reach a height of several hundred feet. A dune typically has a gentler slope on its windward side because the force of the wind tends to move the sand along so as to flatten the side of the dune against which it blows. The lee side has a steeper slope since the wind pushes the sand over the crest where it tumbles

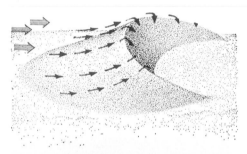

FIG. 20–2. At left, the formation of a barchan. Below, barchans in the desert of Peru. (*Servicio Aerofotográfico Nacional*)

FIG. 20–3. This deposit of loess in Linn County, Iowa, is about 35 feet deep. (*U. S. Geological Survey*)

down. The wind sweeping around the sides of the growing dune often builds two long pointed extensions which give the dune a crescent shape as seen from above. See Fig. 20–2. These crescent-shaped dunes are called **barchans** (*bahr-kans*) and are most common where there is a limited supply of sand to be blown about by the wind.

Long-continued movement of sand grains up the windward slope and over the crest of dunes takes material from one side and deposits it on the other. If the wind is generally from the same direction, this action will cause the dunes to move with the wind. In fairly level areas, this movement continues unless plants sufficiently cover the sand to hold it in place. Sometimes it is necessary to plant grasses, trees, or shrubs or to build protective fences to prevent dunes from drifting over highways, railroads, farm-lands, or buildings.

Dunes are formed of the heavier sand particles carried by the wind for relative-ly short distances. The finer particles are carried much longer distances and much of the finest wind-blown material is probably deposited in such fine layers that it is not identifiable as a wind deposit. However, there are scattered throughout the world a number of thick unstratified deposits of a yellowish, fine-grained sediment which are believed to have been formed by the accumulation of fine wind-blown dust. This material is known by its German name of **loess** (luhs). Although soft and easily eroded, it sometimes forms steep bluffs, because it tends to break in vertical slabs. See Fig. 20–3.

An extensive region of northern China is covered with loess which is apparently an accumulation of wind-blown dust from the interior deserts of Asia. Large deposits of loess are also found in central Europe, and in the United States in the Mississippi Valley and in eastern Oregon and Washington. These deposits probably consist of dust from the beds

FIG. 20–4. These sandstone rocks have been smoothed and rounded by wind abrasion. (*American Museum of Natural History*)

of lakes and streams which dried up after the disappearance of the glaciers of the last Ice Age.

Wind-caused abrasion. Although the principal erosional work of the wind is to transport rock material, wind is also able to break down unweathered rock. The wind abrades solid rock by means of the rock particles it carries. The hardness of sand grains, most of which are quartz, helps to explain their effectiveness as tools of wind erosion. In certain situations, it rapidly cuts away exposed rock. See Fig. 20–4.

Pebbles, cobbles, or boulders exposed to the wind in deserts, along beaches, or on other dry sandy surfaces often develop one or more smooth polished faces as a result of wind abrasion. Such pebbles are called *ventifacts* (from Latin *ventus*, meaning "wind").

Various landforms such as natural bridges, rock pinnacles, rocks perched on pedestals, and even large desert basins have been attributed to abrasion by wind-driven sand. However it is very doubtful that such major features of the landscape are actually produced by the scouring action of wind. Abrasion by wind-blown particles against large masses of rock is ordinarily quite slow and is effective only close to the ground where

the heavier sand grains are concentrated. It is probably a significant factor in the creation of surface features in only a few locations where there are strong and steady winds, quantities of loose sand, and relatively soft rocks.

EROSION BY THE SEA

The attack on the shore. The basic cause of erosion of land along shores is the effect of the waves which pound against the rock. The origin of waves will be treated in more detail in Chapter 26, but it should be mentioned here that they are caused almost entirely by wind blowing over the water surface. When waves reach the shore, much of their energy is spent in eroding the rock of the coast. How rapidly the rocks are worn back depends upon the nature of the rock material. Some of the coast of England has been worn back two miles since the time of the Romans: the shore at Cape Cod retreats at the rate of one to six feet each year. These coasts are composed of comparatively weak material, but the same process takes place more slowly in the hardest rock. It is only because the diastrophic forces within the earth repeatedly uplift the land, that the oceans have been prevented from completely levelling it by wave erosion.

Not only waves attack the shores; currents created by wave action also play a part in shore erosion. There is the **undertow current** which moves toward the sea along the bottom, close to shore. It is caused by the return of the water which is piled against the shore by waves. The undertow tends to move rock debris out to sea along the bottom. However, the force of the waves rushing against the shore is stronger than the undertow. Therefore larger and heavier rock fragments tend to be carried in toward shore while only the light, finer particles are moved seaward. The result is a sorting effect which tends to keep larger rock fragments near the shore until the constant wave action reduces them to small pieces that are carried out by the undertow and dropped on the sea floor.

Waves which strike the shore at an angle cause a *longshore current* which moves parallel to the shoreline. See Fig. 20–5. Longshore currents are common and tend to move loose material along the coast. This material is usually deposited in sheltered parts of the shoreline, such as coves and bays.

Erosion due to wave cutting. The effect of water alone flung against loose and unconsolidated sediments such as sand, volcanic ash, and glacial till is sufficient to wash them away. However, water by itself has little effect, except by solution, on solid rocks. As in the case of streams, ice, and wind, waves acquire cutting tools in the form of rock fragments. Abrasion greatly increases the ability of the waves to erode. Thus a shoreline may at one stage of development be very irregular because there is rapid cutting back of weak rocks, while

FIG. 20–5. Longshore currents (black arrows) are produced when waves strike the shore at an angle.

the more resistant rock remains as seaward projections. Later, even these rocks are worn back through the long-continued grinding action of the accumulated rock debris and the shoreline becomes more regular.

As waves break against a rocky cliff, they first cut a notch into its base. Eventually the undercutting of the cliff becomes sufficient to cause the overhanging rock to fall. Debris accumulates at the base of the cliff and is slowly ground up by wave action. As this process continues and the cliff gradually retreats, a platform called a *wave-cut terrace* is left, extending out beneath the water at the cliff base. See Fig. 20–6. Much of the ground-up rock produced as wave

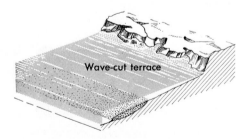

FIG. 20–6. The formation of a wave-cut terrace by wave erosion and deposition at the base of a cliff.

action cuts the terrace is carried seaward where it may be dropped, building an extension to the wave-cut terrace called a *wave-built terrace*. The finest particles, however, are often scattered widely over the sea floor by currents.

After a time, the width of the terrace may become so great that the waves are forced to expend most of their energy in the shallow water some distance out from the base of the cliff. When this occurs, the erosion of the cliff is retarded or halted unless the wave action or currents remove the rock debris of the terrace and again expose the cliff to the force of the waves. A change in sea level may also allow erosion to proceed.

Often, as a rocky cliff is cut back, islands of the bedrock are left offshore as a result of unequal erosion. If the rock has well-developed vertical joints, irregularly spaced, the less fractured portions may remain as narrow projections or headlands. Further erosion of sections

of these narrow projections may leave isolated columns called *stacks*. Unequal erosion of the rocks in sea cliffs may result in the formation of *sea caves*.

Shore deposits. Wave action carries rock materials up on the shore. These deposits are *beaches,* and may consist of sand, pebbles, cobbles, or boulders, or mixtures of these materials. Most beaches are affected by both wave action, which tends to deposit debris on the shore, and undertow and longshore currents, which tend to remove it. Beaches remain only as long as these two opposing processes are in balance. A beach may suddenly disappear if, for example, a storm piles up water against the shore, increasing the strength of the undertow sufficiently to remove the beach deposits. Fairly permanent beaches, however, are the result of a relatively stable adjustment between the rate of deposition and removal of sediment along the shore.

FIG. 20–7. A long offshore bar on St. Lawrence Island in the Bering Sea, Alaska. (*U. S. Geological Survey*)

FIG. 20–8. A spit is formed on a headland or island near the mouth of a bay or inlet by offshore currents moving parallel to the shore. (*Fairchild Aerial Surveys, Inc.*)

If a wide shelf of deposits builds up beneath the water just offshore, the resulting gentle slope of the sea floor away from the shore causes waves to form a low sand bar, called an **offshore bar.** The water between the bar and the mainland is a **lagoon.** See Fig. 20–7.

The shorelines of Texas and Florida have extensive offshore bars. For great distances they are fringed with long sandy islands, sometimes called *barrier islands.* Likewise, the Atlantic coast south of Rhode Island is characterized by many offshore bars. Many of the resort cities of the Atlantic coast, such as Atlantic City and Miami Beach, are located on these narrow sandy islands.

Longshore currents, moving generally parallel to the shore, also form deposits. One of the common shoreline features formed in this way is a **spit.** As the longshore current reaches the mouth of a bay or inlet, the deeper water causes the current to lose speed. Thus some of its load

of sediment is deposited, gradually building up a long bar parallel to the general shoreline and projecting into the open water of the bay or inlet. See Fig. 20–8. Commonly, tidal currents entering the bay or inlet cause the end of a spit to curve inward, producing a **hook** or curved spit. Out-flowing currents due to tides and rivers, on the other hand, tend to deflect the tip of a spit toward the sea, and it is washed away by waves.

Coral reefs. Coral reefs commonly cause characteristic shoreline features in tropical and subtropical waters. Unlike the reefs and bars that result from wave erosion and deposition, these reefs are the work of organisms—coral and other sea animals and plants. The reefs, however, are modified by the work of waves. Corals belong to one of the simpler groups of animals (the coelenterates) and exist in a wide variety of strange and beautiful forms. They live only in the sea and usually in shallow water which is clear and warm. The animals themselves, known as polyps, are soft and small, but they extract calcium carbonate from sea water to build hard skeletons. They reproduce by budding and usually remain attached to each other, forming large colonies. The typical coral reef consists of great numbers of such colonies together with many other kinds of animals and plants. Beneath the living portion, at the top, the reef is composed of skeletons of dead corals together with the shells of other organisms compacted into rock. Wave action on a reef often breaks up the skeletons and coral rock and grinds them into coral sand.

Three forms of coral reefs are typical. A *fringing reef* is one that is closely attached to the shore of an island or continent. A *barrier reef* is a long narrow strip some distance from the shore with a lagoon between. A barrier reef around an island may be approximately circular. An *atoll* is a roughly circular reef which encloses a lagoon; there is no island in the lagoon, however.

Many theories have been offered to account for the development of coral reefs. One that is widely accepted suggests that the reefs represent three stages in the gradual subsidence of an island. The island may be a more or less circular volcanic cone. At first corals and other organisms growing in the shallow water around the island build a fringing reef. As the island subsides slowly, its shoreline shrinks. Upward growth of the reef keeps the coral in shallow water. Finally the island disappears beneath the sea, and if the reef organisms can survive, the atoll is formed. This theory is demonstrated in Fig. 20–9.

Another theory attempts to explain barrier reefs and atolls on the basis of changes in sea level during the last Ice Age. According to this theory, coral reefs established themselves on the outer edges of rock platforms. Such platforms may have been formed when volcanic islands were eroded by waves at a time when sea level was low. Other theories propose that the reefs are due to building up of material on circular banks and platforms. Probably no one theory can account for all coral reef structure.

THE CYCLE OF SHORELINE EROSION

Shorelines of submergence. At the height of the last Ice Age, sea level was probably several hundred feet lower than at present, because a tremendous amount of water was trapped in the extensive glaciers. At the close of the latest period of glaciation melting of the glaciers raised the level of the oceans sufficiently to cause many coastal areas to be submerged. This rise seems to be the basic reason why most ocean shorelines today show evidence of submergence of the land. Shorelines of submergence may also be produced by diastrophic movement which causes land to sink and be covered by the sea. It is extremely difficult to determine whether submergence of a region was caused by a rise in sea level or by sinking of the land. Both processes have played a part in the development of existing shorelines of submergence.

Whatever its cause, a shoreline of submergence has characteristic features. In youth, its outline is produced by drowned stream valleys which were eroded before the land was submerged. These valleys fill with water to become bays, while the divides and highlands between the valleys become headlands and points jutting into the sea. The highest parts of the

FIG. 20–9. In the diagrams below are shown the possible stages in the formation of an atoll, and a cross-section of a coral reef. Note that growth of corals does not proceed below a depth of about 120 feet. The photo at the right shows an atoll which forms a well-known Pacific island group. (*U. S. Air Force photo*)

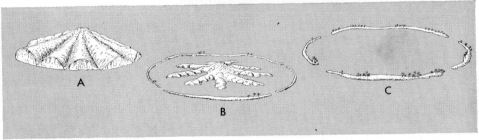

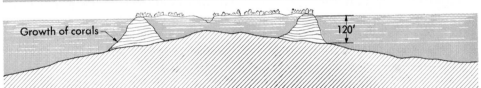

submerged land often remain above water as offshore islands. The irregular shorelines typical of submergence are very common along the continental coasts throughout the world, but the coasts of Alaska, Norway, Greenland, Chile, and British Columbia show an additional development. Extending down into the sea along these coasts are many deep U-shaped glacial valleys which have been drowned as submergence has taken place. The result is a shoreline with many very narrow, deep, steep-walled bays called *fiords.*

Submergence of a stream valley along a coast may produce a shallow bay which

extends far inland if the valley has a gentle gradient. Such a bay, always located at the mouth of a river, is called an *estuary* (*es*-chu-ehr-ee). Many of the world's best harbors are located on estuaries since they provide shelter that is easily accessible from the sea. San Francisco Bay, an unusually fine harbor, is a particularly good example of a drowned system of river valleys or estuaries.

A shoreline of submergence is immediately subject to wave erosion. Its features are slowly altered during the three stages of the life cycle of all landforms—youth, maturity, and old age. See Fig. 20–10.

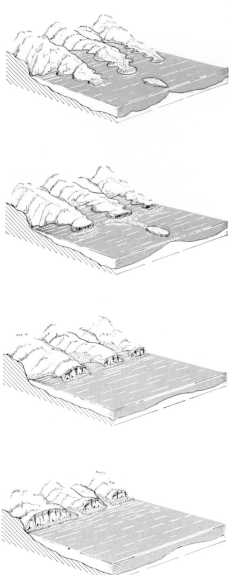

FIG. 20–10. The erosional cycle in a coastline of submergence. From top to bottom: initial stage, youth, maturity, and old age.

1. Youth. Typically the shoreline is very irregular, with many bays and inlets formed by the drowning of stream valleys. Islands are common. Wave action has begun to attack the shore to form cliffs and wave-cut terraces on the most prominent points. By late youth the projecting points of land have been worn back considerably and beaches have formed, along with bars, spits, and hooks. Islands may be connected to the shore by bars.

2. Maturity. By the time this stage is reached, most of the youthful features have been completely destroyed by wave erosion. Spits, hooks, and even the islands have been worn away and the projecting headlands cut back and nearly connected by bars crossing the mouths of the bays. The bays have been partially filled with sediment carried down by streams running off the land. The outline of the shore is much more regular.

3. Old. Age. At this stage erosion has smoothed out most of the irregularities so that the shoreline is nearly straight. By this time, the coast itself may have been worn down nearly to sea level. Shorelines of submergence seldom reach this stage of development because the diastrophic movements or changes in sea level interrupt the full cycle.

Shorelines of emergence. Shoreline features may also result from emergence of land from the sea by uplift of the land or a lowering of sea level. However, since the earth is now in a period of rising sea level, all emerged shorelines indicate diastrophic uplift of the land.

Since the action of waves and currents tends to make the shallow sea bottoms smooth and level, land which has been recently raised from beneath the sea is usually a plain. Farther inland, wave-cut cliffs and terraces may mark the former shoreline. The low relief of the uplifted land causes the emergent shoreline to be at first straight and very regular, but it is immediately attacked by waves and currents and undergoes a characteristic cycle of development. See Fig. 20–11.

1. Youth. The first action of the waves cuts a low cliff along the shore of the emerged plain. At the same time, the shallow water offshore causes waves to build a bar parallel to the shore. This offshore bar tends to protect the mainland from wave action. Openings into the lagoon between the bar and the mainland generally occur at intervals as a result of storms and the action of tides which forces water in and out of the lagoon.

2. Maturity. The offshore bar slowly works its way toward the mainland as a result of wave action in storms by which material is taken from the seaward side of the bar and carried over the bar, to be deposited in the lagoon. This process, along with deposition of sediment by streams running off the land, tends to fill the lagoon. If the lagoon becomes shallow enough, the growth of plants will produce extensive tidal marshes.

3. Old Age. The offshore bar eventually is pushed back against the mainland and then washed away by wave erosion. Disappearance of the bar and the lagoon allows direct wave action against the mainland, which then develops a wave-cut cliff. The development of a shoreline of emergence is generally interrupted, however, before this stage is reached.

Almost the entire Gulf Coast and the east coast of the United States, from Rhode Island south to Florida, show features of emergence, mostly in a mature stage of development.

Compound shorelines. Many shorelines cannot be simply classified as indicative of either submergence or emergence, since they show characteristics of both processes. These are usually called *compound shorelines.* Uneven warping of a coastline may cause part to be emergent and part submergent. Diastrophism may alter a shoreline in the midst of its development. Volcanic activity may pour

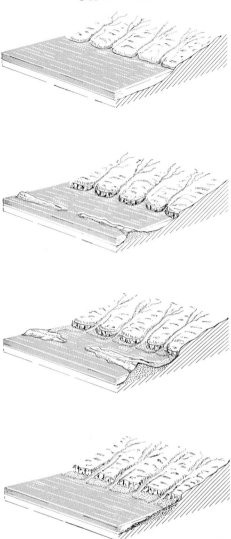

FIG. 20–11. The erosional cycle in a shoreline of emergence. From top to bottom: initial stage, youth, maturity, and old age.

lava onto a shore and create an emergent coastal plain along an otherwise submergent shore. Sediments washed down by streams extend a shoreline seaward and change its original nature. Only intensive study of a given shoreline can reveal its history and account for its present form.

SUMMARY

WIND as an agent of erosion, transportation, and deposition is effective in arid or semiarid areas and in humid regions occasionally subject to drought. Dunes are the most common feature of wind deposits. Loess is a very fine-grained wind deposit. Wind abrasion produces ventifacts.

Waves result from the friction of wind against the surface of the water. The margins of the land are modified by waves, which use rock debris as tools of erosion. Undertow and longshore currents aid erosion by the removal of debris, depositing material in quiet water. Spits and offshore bars are depositional features of waves and currents.

If environmental conditions are favorable, the growth of corals results in such features as fringing reefs, barrier reefs, and atolls.

Shorelines are classified as emergent or submergent, but may show features of both kinds. Shorelines of submergence are typically irregular in youth; erosion smooths the outlines in later stages of development. Fiords result from deepening of valleys by glacial action, followed by partial submergence. Shorelines of emergence are typically regular in youth. Later erosion and deposition produce characteristic features.

VOCABULARY REVIEW

Match the phrase in the left column with the correct word or phrase in the right column. *Do not write in this book.*

1. Crescent-shaped
2. Parallel to shoreline
3. Regular shoreline
4. Rock column
5. Drowned river valley
6. Stone with polished faces
7. Curved spit
8. Circular reef
9. Smooth layer of small stones
10. Yellowish, fine-grained sediment

a. loess
b. stack
c. submergent shoreline
d. desert pavement
e. hook
f. ventifact
g. longshore
h. emergent shoreline
i. barchan
j. atoll
k. estuary

QUESTIONS · GROUP A

Select the best term to complete the following statements. *Do not write in this book.*

1. The principal work of winds is (*a*) building dunes (*b*) transportation of soil (*c*) developing spits (*d*) causing dust bowls.
2. A wave-formed ridgelike deposit some distance from shore is (*a*) a spit (*b*) a hook (*c*) a barrier reef (*d*) an offshore bar.

3. When the prevailing winds are from the west, dunes (*a*) migrates westward (*b*) have steep east sides (*c*) are composed of silt (*d*) remain stationary.
4. A fiord is (*a*) a bay (*b*) a glacier (*c*) an island (*d*) a wave deposit.
5. Sand is composed mostly of (*a*) loess (*b*) granite (*c*) slate (*d*) quartz.
6. Spits are built up by the action of (*a*) undertows (*b*) rivers (*c*) longshore currents (*d*) glaciers.
7. The Sahara Desert is mostly (*a*) bare rock (*b*) sand (*c*) alluvium (*d*) drift.
8. Coral polyps are (*a*) limestone formations (*b*) small plants (*c*) ring-shaped reefs (*d*) tiny marine animals.
9. Sea caves result from the combined action of (*a*) sand and wind (*b*) currents and deposition (*c*) submergence and emergence (*d*) jointing and waves.
10. Large deposits of loess are found in (*a*) Central Alaska (*b*) Antarctica (*c*) Northern China (*d*) east coast of Maine.
11. The combined action of waves and undertow (*a*) move all rock debris seaward (*b*) move heavy debris seaward and light material shoreward (*c*) move all rock debris shoreward (*d*) move light debris seaward and leave heavy material near the shoreline.
12. Most of the world's best harbors are located along (*a*) emergent shorelines (*b*) lagoons (*c*) submergent shorelines (*d*) barrier reefs.

GROUP B

1. Discuss the surface and climatic conditions that favor wind erosion.
2. Discuss, with the aid of labeled diagrams, the formation of dunes, their shape, and their migration.
3. How can conservation prevent the occurrence of dust bowls?
4. Discuss the cause and effect of wind abrasion.
5. How are wave-cut and wave-built terraces developed? Include a fully labeled diagram.
6. Distinguish between each term in the following pairs, giving a similarity and a difference: stacks—seacaves, offshore bar—barrier reef, barchan—dune, fiord—estuary, lagoon—bay, beach—spit, undertow—longshore currents.
7. Discuss the cause, effect, and life cycle of an emergent shoreline. Include a series of fully labeled diagrams.
8. Discuss the cause, effect, and life cycle of a submergent shoreline. Include a series of fully labeled diagrams.
9. Discuss the cause, effect, and characteristics of a compound shoreline.
10. Briefly explain the importance of waves in shoreline development.

TOPOGRAPHIC SHEETS

Fennville, Michigan. *Lakeshore dunes, buried town.*
Ashby, Nevada. *Dune topography.*
Moses Lake, Washington. *Barchans, migrating sand dunes.*
Aransas Pass, Texas. *Coastal sand dunes, truncated headland, lagoon, barrier beach, hooked spit.*

Point Reyes, California. *Barrier beach, sea cliff, wave-cut cliff, sea stacks, sand spit.*
Boothbay, Maine. *Submergent shoreline.*
Mt. Desert, Maine. *Fiord.*

All of the above are in the fifteen-minute series.

UNIT REVIEW QUESTIONS

1. Explain why deposits of clay and sand may be found in an area composed principally of granite.
2. Explain how weathering causes changes in the color of rocks and minerals.
3. What kinds of rocks and minerals are most easily attacked by frost action? Explain.
4. How does the sun cause mechanical weathering?
5. How is weathering aided by the actions of animals?
6. Explain fully the processes of carbonation, hydration, and oxidation. Give a balanced chemical equation for each process.
7. How are expansion and contraction related to granular disintegration?
8. What is the difference between residual soil and transported soil? Include two fully labeled diagrams.
9. How are spheroidal boulders produced?
10. What is meant by headward erosion? How does this process contribute to the development of river systems?
11. Define gradient of a stream. How is stream velocity related to gradient? What factors may alter a stream's gradient?
12. What is alluvium? Account for the fact that it is stratified.
13. Account for the greater velocity and volume of a stream during the spring.
14. Why does a glacier move?
15. How does a glacier change the shape of a river valley?
16. What is the general relationship between latitude and the snow line?
17. Describe four types of moraines.
18. Name the three centers of accumulation during the last glacial period.
19. Which continent has no glaciers? Explain.
20. Explain why the fronts of alpine glaciers extend below the snow line.
21. What is the significance of a drumlin to a glacial geologist?
22. How are icebergs formed?
23. Explain the formation of loess deposits.
24. What would be the shape of dunes if the prevailing winds were from one direction only? In an area of constantly shifting winds what would be the shape of sand dunes?
25. What conservation measures should accompany extensive cultivation and plowing in Oklahoma, Kansas, and other semiarid states?
26. Why does an uplifted coastal plain have a regular shoreline?
27. Explain the following statement: A lagoon is a temporary shore feature.

28. What is the relationship between type of shoreline and development of population centers?

29. Why are estuaries of economic importance?

ACTIVITIES

1. Prepare a display of photographs that show local weathering and erosion. Under each photograph give the location, probable agent of weathering or erosion, and some possible preventive conservation procedure.

2. On a local topographic map, use crayons to show the direction of local drainage.

3. Make a model of a glaciated region. Show moraines, drumlins, outwash plains, etc.

4. Make models or dioramas to show the erosional cycle of shorelines.

5. Make models or dioramas to show the features of karst topography and the erosion of the underlying strata.

6. If the region in which you live was subjected to glaciation, collect samples and pictures that show evidence of past glaciation.

7. Prepare a report on the relationship of soil composition and drainage to the use of septic tanks. Check to see if there are any local laws governing the disposal of sewage in your community.

8. Make a model or diorama to illustrate a region that is subject to wind erosion.

9. Prepare a report on the cause and effect of the dust bowl of the nineteen-thirties.

10. Collect samples that illustrate various types of weathering. Label each specimen and describe how the process probably took place.

11. Determine the speed of a local river or stream every day for a month. This can be done by recording the time that a floating object takes to cover a known distance. Each day collect samples of the water. Record the clearness of the water; then allow the water to settle and measure and record the level of the sediment and the type of sediment. Draw graphs to show the relationship between the speed of flow and the amount of sediment carried by the stream.

FURTHER READING

THE WORLD WE LIVE IN. L. Barnett, 1955. *Time, Inc., New York.*

GEOLOGY. W. H. Emmons, G. A. Thiel, C. R. Stauffer, and I. S. Allison, 1955. *McGraw-Hill Book Co., New York.*

EXPLORING AMERICAN CAVES. Franklin Folsom, 1956. *Crown Publishers, Inc., New York.*

ROCKS, RIVERS, AND THE CHANGING EARTH. Herman and Nina Schneider, 1951. *Scott, Foresman and Co., Chicago.*

THIS SCULPTURED EARTH: THE LANDSCAPE OF AMERICA. John A. Shimer, 1959. *Columbia University Press, New York.*

PRINCIPLES OF GEOMORPHOLOGY. W. D. Thornbury, 1954. *John Wiley and Sons, Inc., New York.*

LIKE the human civilization that flourishes upon it, the physical earth has a complex history. Already, in earlier chapters, the broad outlines of the earth's past have been sketched in—its probable origin from a cloud of cosmic dust, heating to a molten state and then cooling to form the apparently solid sphere we now know; its shaping and sculpturing by constructive and destructive forces. But like human history, which covers only a brief span of our planet's past, earth history is made up of small details. It is filled with countless events, each one of which has left its mark.

Now, a few billion years after it came into existence, the earth still bears a nearly complete record of its history. This story is available to all who can understand the difficult codes in which it is written. This unit is concerned with the details of the earth's long history, and with the methods by which that record can be known.

UNIT 6

THE RECORD
OF EARTH HISTORY

CHAPTER 21

THE ROCK RECORD

THE patient detective work of geologists, so essential in reconstructing the development of landforms, is even more important in another way. In their study of rocks all over the world, geologists turn up clues that allow them to piece together the long and eventful history of the earth. To reconstruct the past, they must examine the rocks carefully for bits of information about the kinds of plants and animals that existed at different periods, the changing climatic conditions, and the geography and topography. Infinite patience is needed to put the various bits together to obtain as much of the story as possible, and the gaps are many. Yet, practically every rock tells a story of some kind and the clue to many a missing chapter has been found in a rock previously unknown.

Paleontology (*pay*-lee-on-*tol*-uh-jee) is an important source of evidence; it is the study of the fossils of ancient plants and animals. A *fossil,* the remains or evidence of ancient plants and animals, may be either the whole organism or a part of it, or sometimes only an imprint. The paleontologist digs into the rocks which are the graves of animals and plants that lived thousands or even millions of years ago and from their fossilized remains learns many important facts about the nature, habits, and development of living things. Another source of evidence used by the geologist is *stratigraphy* (stra-*tig*-ruh-fee) or the study of rock layers. These layers give

VOCABULARY

Paleontology (*pay*-lee-on-*tol*-uh-jee). The science which deals with the study of fossils.

Stratigraphy (stra-*tig*-ruh-fee). The study of rock layers.

Fossils. The remains or evidence of ancient plants and animals.

Environmental fossils. Fossil evidences that reveal environmental conditions in past geologic periods.

Index fossils. Fossils that are found only in rocks of one particular period of geological time.

Half-life. The time interval during which half of a given amount of radioactive material disintegrates.

clues to the location of ancient seas, mountains, plateaus, and plains, and even reveal geologic processes that have occurred in the past and perhaps may be taking place today. A third line of investigation useful in assembling the facts of earth history is *petrology.* This includes the careful examination of the rocks to find out their nature and composition as well as their origins, which in turn, may be significant in piecing together the story of the earth's past. Many scientists in the various specialties of geology, working together as well as independently, have added to our knowledge of earth history. Current investigations continue to broaden and deepen our understanding of the rock record.

THE PATTERN OF THE PAST

Crustal disturbance. Evidences of crustal disturbances or movements, followed by long periods of relative quiet,

are found in the rock record. Deformation of the crust has been discussed in Unit 4; the periods of quiet are usually characterized by erosion and deposition, as described in Unit 5. In Chapter 13, we considered the several theories which have been proposed to explain crustal deformation. Whatever its cause may be, we know that many times in the past the earth has gone through cycles of mountain building and continental uplift. The periods of erosion which followed resulted in the deposition of the transported materials in lakes, inland seas, and oceans.

Geologists have estimated the total thickness of sedimentary rocks deposited since the time when the earth was formed as approximately 100 miles! This does not mean that this much sediment was laid down in any one area. The estimate was obtained by adding the maximum known thickness of each different stratum deposited during successive divisions of time. In many places there was practically no deposition for long periods, because at times erosion

FIG. 21–1. These paleontologists are unearthing bones of prehistoric animals which will be sent to a museum for study. (*New York State Museum*)

went on very slowly. In other places, thick deposits of sediment accumulated in the basins of geosynclines adjacent to mountains, sometimes to a thickness of 20 miles. However, the inland seas in which most of these deposits were laid down were relatively shallow. Evidence of this is furnished by cross bedding, ripple marks, fossils, and other features that characterize shallow water deposition. How can such seemingly contradictory facts be explained? The best explanation is that the accumulation of these thick deposits of sediments in shallow water was made possible by a continuous subsidence of the basin in which the deposition took place. When the sinking kept pace with the rate of uplift of the adjacent highland, tremendous amounts of materials were deposited and great thicknesses of sedimentary rocks were formed. On the other hand, when the crustal movements were slower, the mountains were eroded faster than they were uplifted. As they were worn down, the streams flowed less rapidly, and the sediments, composed of fine particles, accumulated slowly over long periods of time.

Geologic revolutions. In the periods of extensive violent deformation of the earth's crust, there was uplift in some areas and subsidence in others. Major earthquakes were common and volcanic eruptions usually accompanied these crustal movements. These periods of disturbance, called *revolutions,* produced new mountain ranges, changed the shapes of the continents, and altered the circulation of the atmosphere and oceans. Revolutions resulted in rapid changes of climatic conditions, which in turn caused relatively rapid changes in the types of living things on the earth. New forms of life developed which were better adapted to the changed conditions, and older forms died off because they could not adapt to the rapid changes in environment.

During periods of revolution the climates in different parts of the world were extremely varied, with glaciers in some regions, swamps and lakes in some, or extensive deserts in others. Between periods of revolution, on the other hand, during the much longer periods of relative quiet, the entire earth tended to have a much more moderate and uniform climate.

Unconformities. Picture for a moment the North American continent as it was about 500 million years ago. Geological evidence indicates that much of our present continent was submerged and

FIG. 21–2. Fossil ripple marks in solid rock indicate that this area was once under water. (*American Museum of Natural History*)

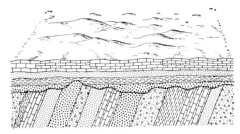

FIG. 21–3. An angular unconformity shows layers of horizontal rock above tilted, folded, or faulted layers.

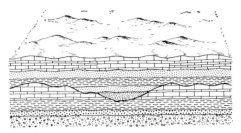

FIG. 21–4. An erosional unconformity or disconformity shows parallel strata separated by an erosional surface.

most of the land was low and flat. An inland sea probably extended from what is now Southern California east to the present Mississippi River area. A branch of this same sea is believed to have extended northward up through present-day Canada to the north polar region. What is now the Atlantic Ocean extended inland to cover a region from the northeastern section of Canada to the present Gulf of Mexico. When seas flood the land in this way, as we know from our study of destructional processes, they leave a record of their invasion. Thick horizontal deposits of sedimentary rocks are formed, composed of fragments carried in by streams and limestone materials deposited by animal life, such as the corals. Then, if diastrophism takes place, these horizontal rock layers may be folded, faulted, or lifted above the sea. When the vertically lifted rock layers are exposed to erosion, much of their topmost portions may be removed and the lower layers may in turn be exposed to weathering. Following this interval of erosion, the layers may be again submerged, and the eroded surface may be covered with new horizontal layers of sediments. Thus the record of repeated uplift and submergence is left in the rocks for man to read. The relationship between the rock layers laid down in one period of deposition, and those laid down in a later period, separated by a period of erosion, is called an **unconformity.**

If the lower rock layers are tilted, folded, or faulted, and the upper layers are horizontal, the relationship is called an *angular unconformity.* See Fig. 21–3. When, on the other hand, rock layers separated by an erosional surface are parallel to each other and relatively horizontal, the relationship is called an *erosional unconformity* or a **disconformity.** See Fig. 21–4. From the evidence of unconformities observed over wide areas, much of the past may be reconstructed.

INTERPRETING THE RECORD

Order of superposition. The sequence in which rocks are found is a highly important clue to the past. We know that sediments are laid down in layers, or strata. These strata are usually formed horizontally, with the youngest rocks on the top and the oldest ones, which are formed first, on the bottom. If sediments horizontally arranged are apparently undisturbed, we can conclude that the relative position of the strata—that is, the *order of superposition*—indicates their age relationship.

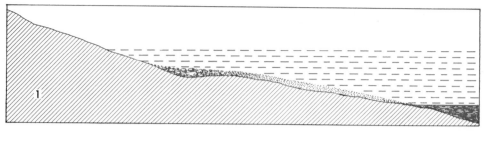

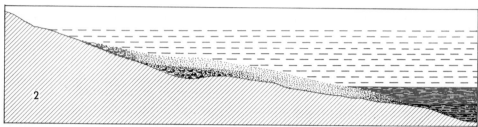

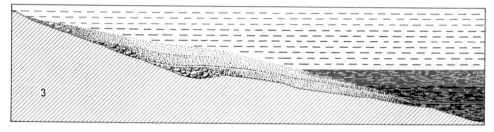

FIG. 21–5. This series of diagrams shows how gradation of sediments in overlapping sedimentary layers may suggest that the sea bottom was sinking or the sea level was rising during their deposition.

Today, as in the past, sediments are being deposited by wind, water, or ice. A look at a cliff along the seashore reveals rock fragments at its base ranging in size from huge blocks of stone to boulders, pebbles, and particles of sand and silt. Wave action has sorted the materials so that the larger particles are inshore, the sand is farther out, and the mud is at low tide level. During the course of time these sediments may eventually become consolidated and cemented into rock. This rock may be pushed up sooner or later by diastrophic forces. If this occurs, these uplifted layers undoubtedly will become exposed

by erosion, possibly millions of years from now in some future canyon wall or sea cliff.

Now let us take a closer look at the sea cliff which, by means of weathering and erosion, is today providing the different-sized fragments that are being deposited at its base. If this cliff is of sedimentary rock, it is the product of deposition which occurred over a period of many years in the far distant past. Examination of its strata might show lower layers of conglomerate formed from pebbles, on which lie sandstones composed of sand particles. Above these we might find shale, which is consolidated mud, and limestone, made from animal remains. From this succession of graded sedimentary rocks we might conclude that during their formation, the sea bottom was gradually sinking, or the sea was rising. See Fig. 21–5.

Internal evidence. There are clues to the past in the rocks themselves as well as in their sequence. It has been said that every rock tells a story. For instance, a piece of sandstone may show ripple marks, wave marks, or crossbedding, and worm burrows, tracks, or animal shells like those in the sand at the seashore today. Thus by their structure, texture, general physical and chemical composition, and fossil content, sedimentary rocks carry telltale signs of environmental conditions of the past. It is plain that the interpretation of ancient sediments is made possible by a knowledge of the conditions under which similar sediments are being deposited today. Thus we see once more that the present is a key to the past.

The existence of ancient shallow seas, extinct lakes, desert regions, former ice sheets and other earth features of the past is recorded in their sediments. These tell us much about the region from which they were derived: the nature of its rocks, its relief, its climate, and other conditions in the past. These rock layers are the pages in the book of geologic history, although reading it is not so simple a task as it may at first appear.

Methods of interpreting the record. The fact that rock layers are usually buried beneath mantle rock, soil, and vegetation makes it difficult to see their relationship except as this is revealed in canyons, cliffs, and other outcrops. Also, the layers are often faulted, folded, and sometimes even turned upside down. Some rock layers have been meta-morphosed until they are hardly recognizable. Moreover, they have been eroded so that often only remnants of the strata are left, and many of them have been lost forever. Even so, geologists have been able to place most of the remnants in their correct chronological order, using their knowledge that normally any layer of sedimentary rock is older than the next layer above. Also, they are able to match strata of the same age in different regions of the earth.

Igneous rocks are also useful in understanding earth history. Those, like dikes and sills, which were intruded into sedimentary rocks are younger than the rocks they invade. Likewise, extrusive formations such as lava flows are obviously younger than the rocks they cover. However, it is not always obvious which rocks are older. It is sometimes difficult to determine whether a formation of igneous rock between layers of sedimentary rock is actually intrusive and therefore younger than the layers above and below it, or whether it may have been an extrusive lava flow which was later covered by the younger sedimentary rocks above it.

Certain time relationships are easily deciphered if the two types of rocks

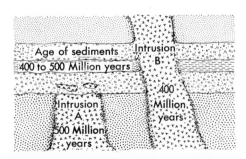

FIG. 21–6. From the evidence here it is easy to see why the rock in intrusion *B* is younger than that in intrusion *A*.

involved are carefully examined. If, for example, a conglomerate contains granite pebbles identical to a granite batholith located nearby, it is almost certain that the granite in the batholith is older than the conglomerate. If a second mass of igneous rock, such as a dike, cuts through the layers of conglomerate, it is obvious that the dike is younger than both the conglomerate and the granite.

The examples given here are simple illustrations of how geologists judge the age relationships of various rock formations. In actual practice, it is sometimes extremely difficult to understand these relationships. In fact, there have been occasions when even trained geologists disagreed on the interpretation of the relative ages of rock formations. However, we now have a fairly clear picture of rock relationships over most of the earth's surface.

Gaps in the record. Although the general sequence of geologic time is clear, the sedimentary rocks that were laid down in the earliest geological periods are difficult to identify and study. Our knowledge of the early geologic history of the earth is therefore incomplete. Almost all of the rocks formed during a period of about 1½ billion years have disappeared through erosion, are deeply buried, or have been greatly metamorphosed. Their loss leaves a great gap in the sedimentary record. Earlier geologists, therefore, usually made no attempt to decipher the history of the most ancient rocks, and merely classified them as the *basement complex.*

Modern geologists, however, are gradually developing a more satisfactory picture. Younger rocks above the basement complex are generally easier to study, and from them geologists have gained a reasonably adequate understanding of early earth history. In recent years, more

information has been gathered so that rocks can be compared with related strata in other regions. Recent techniques in submarine drilling will undoubtedly help to close the gaps, since the deep sea bottom is more likely to preserve a continuous sequence of deposits than any area above sea level.

THE FOSSIL STORY

What fossils tell us. As we have seen, piecing together the record of the rocks is largely a matter of discovering their relation to each other. In doing this, the paleontologist compares the appearance, composition, and fossil content of the rocks in the various layers.

Comparison of the appearance and composition of rock has little value in establishing the relative age of rocks, except in a localized area. For instance, sandstones of similar characteristics have been formed in nearly all periods of earth history. Chalk, once thought to have been formed only in one geological period, is known to form in deep oceans even today. However, within small areas, rocks of similar composition, especially whole series of similar rocks in neighboring areas, are probably of the same age. We assume this because we know that in general the same types of deposits were formed over wide areas in earlier geologic times as are now being formed today. This assumption is by no means always certain, and cannot be used accurately in widely separated regions, as on different continents.

By far the most valuable means of classifying the rocks in all parts of the world is close comparison of their fossils. If we find a general similarity of species of living things in different rock formations, we conclude that the rocks belong to approximately the same age. Yet, we cannot expect all rocks of the same age to contain the same fossils. We must take into account other factors, such as whether the deposits were formed in shallow water or deep seas, or in fresh water or salt water. Likewise, we must allow for differences among related fossils which lived under similar conditions in different parts of the world during any one time period. Thus, we can expect general similarity, but not exact resemblance, between fossils in the rocks laid down on different continents during the same geologic period. We must also keep in mind, however, that the whole earth has been inhabited at different times by entirely different species, and that each geologic time period had its own distinctive fauna and flora.

While he was still a boy, the great paleontologist, William Smith, became interested in the different rock layers of his native England. Exposed rock layers were very common and most of them were rich in fossil remains. He observed that a layer of one kind of rock usually contained the same types of fossils, and that the layers above and below this layer contained different types of fossils. The relationship was evident even in widely separated localities. On the basis of the characteristics of the different strata and their fossils, he constructed geological maps of the varied strata throughout England. Smith also noticed that the distribution of some kinds of fossils was largely independent of variations in the character of a given type of rock. For example, a formation of sandstone traced over a great distance might grade into shale and then into limestone, but many of the same fossil types could be found throughout the three kinds of rock. Later work by many other paleon-

FIG. 21–7. The great British geologist William Smith laid the foundations for the study of historical paleontology. (*Bettmann Archive*)

tologists showed that the distribution of some species of fossils is extensive, sometimes even worldwide.

Smith developed a scheme of classification of the various rock layers based on the characteristic fossils they contained. He often amused and amazed his friends by picking up unlabelled fossils from their collection cabinets and telling them the exact area and rock formation from which each had come. He was able to do this because he knew that the fossils found in a given rock layer were characteristic of that rock layer; that any specific layer of rocks always yielded a definite group of plant and animal remains which was different from those found in any other layer above or below it in a rock series.

Environmental fossils. We can observe today that changes in their environment cause certain forms of life to become extinct. At the same time, others

Brachiopod

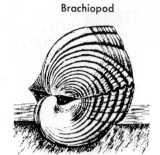

Platystrophia biforata
middle Ordovician only

Trilobite

Phacops rana
middle Devonian only

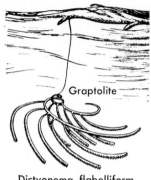

Graptolite

Dictyonema flabelliform
early Ordovician only

FIG. 21–8. These index fossils are used by geologists to judge the geologic ages of various rock strata. (*Adapted from Fenton and Fenton*)

continue, and some new forms arise as a result of the changing conditions. The geologic revolutions of past ages caused changes in the environment over large areas of the earth. Thus, if a species of fossil is not found in layers above a certain rock formation, we may assume that it became extinct because it was unable to live and reproduce under new environmental conditions. For example, paleontologists believe that some dinosaurs may have become extinct when the marshy environment to which they were well adapted gradually disappeared. The presence of dinosaur tracks in hardened mud gives evidence of this type of environment. We may assume that if such tracks are found in bedrock in New Jersey, then that area of New Jersey was swampy during the age of these giant reptiles. Such fossil footprints, and other evidences besides actual remains of plants and animals, may be classed as *environmental fossils.* Frozen fossil elephants indicate the presence of glacial conditions with a bitterly cold climate at about the time that the woolly mammoth lived. The boundaries of extensive prehistoric seas have been quite accurately traced through the re-

mains of marine animals and plants which were different in structure from those living at the same time in fresh or brackish water. Rock layers containing fossil sharks' teeth located a thousand miles from the nearest ocean and thousands of feet high in the mountains are evidence of great environmental changes in the past. Fossils of tropical palms have been found in bedrock close to the Arctic Circle and fossil corals have been found in rocks in almost all regions of the earth.

Index fossils. Certain fossils are found in rock layers of only one geologic age. These fossils are called *guide* or *index fossils* because they serve to identify specific rock layers. Index fossils must meet certain requirements. First, they must be found in rocks over a wide area of the earth's surface. Second, they must exhibit characteristic features which clearly distinguish them from other species. Third, the organisms that formed them must have lived during only a relatively short span of geologic time. Fourth, they must occur in fairly large numbers within the rock layers. If a fossil meets most of these conditions, it gives the geologist important clues in correlating events of ancient times. Index fossils are of great help in establishing the relative ages of the rock layers in different series of strata. They identify the particular rock formation, or part of a formation, in which they are found. Often they also indicate the environmental conditions in their area at the time in which they lived. Each is like a signpost identifying a small part of the total picture of the world during a particular section of geologic time.

One practical use of index fossils is in the location of gas and oil formations. Petroleum and natural gas are apparently derived from fossil plants and animals by complex chemical processes. Trapped under domes of nonporous rock, these fossil fuels await man's discovery and use. It is interesting that index fossils of certain types are commonly found in the layers of sedimentary rock above the elusive gas and oil formations. These often aid in locating the underlying oil-bearing rocks. The location of oil-bearing formations by this means is of utmost importance in one of the world's greatest industries. Success or failure in finding oil and gas, often involving billions of dollars, may depend on correct identification of specific index fossils by highly trained field and laboratory workers.

ESTIMATING GEOLOGIC TIME

Time duration. It is not enough for the paleontologist to know the relative age of the rock strata, if he has no way of determining the duration of the time represented by the rocks. The length of the different geologic periods indicated by fossils and other evidence was estimated in the early days of geology. Such estimates, however, fell far short of the time spans later scientists came to accept as probable. The historical geologist today makes use of various methods in estimating the duration of the divisions of geologic time. Both laboratory and field studies are helpful in this phase of the task of interpreting the rock record.

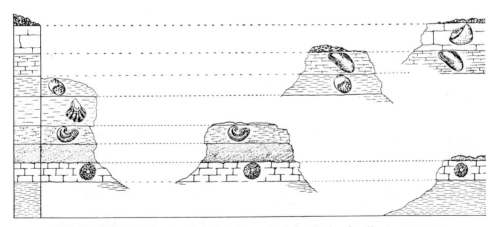

FIG. 21–9. Isolated outcrops of rocks containing index fossils are very useful to geologists. Even though the rock layers are in widely separated areas, as shown here, the relative ages of the rocks can be established. (*Adapted from Fenton and Fenton*)

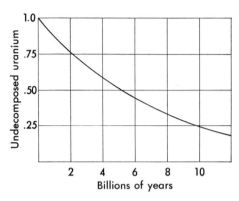

FIG. 21–10. The rate of decay of uranium is shown in this graph.

Radioactivity. One means of determining the age of a rock is an application of fairly recent research in the field of radioactivity. Atoms of certain elements, such as uranium and thorium, naturally break up to form radium, releasing radiant energy and helium gas. Radium in turn disintegrates into a number of other elements, the final product of which is a particular type of lead often called *uranium lead*. This decomposition goes on at a very slow, absolutely constant and measurable rate. Researchers have calculated that it takes five billion years for half of any given amount of uranium to change into uranium lead.

This constant rate of atomic disintegration is not affected by changes in temperature, pressure, or other environmental conditions. At the end of five billion years half of the original uranium remains; the other half of the original uranium has been changed to lead and radiant energy. Now the remaining half of the uranium continues to disintegrate at the same rate as before and at the end of the second period of five billion years just half of that (one fourth of the original uranium) is left. Thus the *half-life* of uranium is said to be five billion

years. A graph showing the rate of radioactive decay of uranium is given in Fig. 21–10.

Since the rate of disintegration is independent of environmental factors, radioactive dating is a very useful method of determining the approximate age of rocks which contain uranium, as igneous rocks often do. The method is less accurate for measuring the age of sedimentary rocks because uranium ores are not commonly found in such rocks.

If the age of a rock is to be determined by the uranium-decay method, the rock must not contain radioactive impurities that have been introduced by disturbances after the rock's original formation. Complicated mathematical calculations, using accurate measurements of the rock's radioactivity, can be used to obtain a reasonably accurate estimate of the age of the rock in which the uranium is found. Approximate determinations can also be made on the basis of the proportions of uranium and helium present in rocks.

A more recent method of radioactive dating, particularly useful for estimating the age of sedimentary rocks, is based on the decay rate of radioactive carbon-14. This form of carbon is found in sedimentary rocks containing the remains of plants and animals, because carbon is one of the fundamental elements in the chemical composition of all living things. Since this radioactive element decomposes at a measurable rate, just as uranium does, rocks containing it can be dated by the proportion of this element present in the fossil remains contained in the rock. Dating by radioactive carbon is used for determining the age of relatively recent rock formations, whereas the uranium method is most widely used in estimating the age of much older rocks.

Rate of erosion. Careful studies indicate that on the average, erosion of rock and soil takes place at the rate of about one foot in 5000 years. While this is by no means an exact figure, it is based on scientific observations and is a fair approximation rather than a mere guess.

The Grand Canyon is, in places, about 6000 feet deep. Using the erosion rate above, multiplying 6000 feet by 5000 years, we arrive at 30,000,000 years as the estimated length of time required for the Colorado River to erode the deepest part of its canyon. This estimate can be checked by comparing it with the rate at which the sediment was deposited to build new rock layers on the continental shelf beyond the mouth of the river.

The method of erosion rates is best employed in determining the age of more recent geologic features such as Niagara Falls (Fig. 18–20). The recession of these falls has been studied for about two hundred years and the rate of recession has averaged about five feet per year. Using this rate as a basis for calculation, the time involved in the erosion of the original brink of the falls back to their present position is from 18,000 to 25,000 years. This gives us a fairly reasonable idea of the time interval since the last great ice sheet retreated from the Niagara area, making possible the plunge of the Great Lakes water over the Niagara escarpment. However, this figure is somewhat in doubt because recent studies indicate that the last ice sheet receded from the Niagara area only about 10,000 years ago.

Rate of deposition. Geologists estimate that, on an average, it takes between 4000 and 10,000 years for a one-foot layer of sedimentary rock to be formed. For millions of years, sediments have been deposited in one place or another. Through the ages, layer on layer has been built up, with the older ones at the bottom and the more recent ones at the top.

Some sedimentary deposits show definite annual layers, or *varves,* as seen in Fig. 21–11. Since each layer represents one year's deposition, a series of varves indicates the number of years during which the deposits were formed, in much the same way that the annual growth rings in the trunks of trees show the age of the tree when it was cut.

Varves are often lake deposits. Some were formed from sediments that were deposited on the bottom of a lake at the edge of a melting ice sheet during the last Ice Age. During the summer the ice probably melted rapidly, resulting in a rush of water that carried large amounts of sediment into the lake. Most of the coarser particles settled quickly to form a thick layer on the bottom. With the coming of winter, the melting stopped and the lake froze over. The finer clay

FIG. 21–11. The age of some rock strata can be estimated by counting the varves, or annual layers, found in some sedimentary rocks. (*U. S. Geological Survey*)

particles, still suspended in the water, settled slowly to form a thin layer above the coarser sediments. A summer layer and the overlying winter layer make up one varve. Thus, each varve represents one year's deposition.

Other types of deposits may also be seasonally banded. For example, the banded Green River shales in Colorado and adjoining states are 2600 feet thick and were probably deposited in a non-glacial lake which once covered this region. If the bands are true varves, as some geologists believe, these deposits represent about 6,500,000 years of deposition. This figure supports the estimates of the age of the earth obtained by other means.

Salinity of the oceans. Another method used in estimating the age of the earth involves finding the age of the oceans. This is done by calculating how much salt is now present in all the oceans. Then by estimating the average amount of salt carried into the oceans by all of the rivers of the earth in a year, it is possible to estimate about how many years the oceans have been receiving salt. However, the rate at which salt was added to the oceans in the past was probably slower than it is today. Therefore, this method of age determination is not very accurate.

Alteration of rock materials. Another type of evidence that indicates the great age of the earth is the chemical and physical alteration of rocks that has taken place over many years. The reduction of large masses of igneous rocks to clay and sand obviously has required long periods of time. The thick deposits of loess (Chapter 20) are further evidence of the many years that passed after the weathering of the original rock occurred. The great deposits of minerals formed by chemical alteration of the original igneous rocks emphasize the long periods of time required for such changes to occur. Deposits of organic materials, in the form of coal and petroleum, also lead to the conclusion that the earth is very old. While these evidences are not easily used to estimate the total age of the earth, they do support the general picture of the great age of our planet.

SUMMARY

GEOLOGISTS determine environmental and physiographic conditions of the past by utilizing the sciences of paleontology, stratigraphy, and petrology.

Evidence of diastrophism, volcanism, erosion, and submergence is found when rock strata are exposed. Interpretation is difficult due to faulting, folding, and igneous intrusions, which complicate the strata, leaving gaps in geologic history.

Fossils establish relationships of rock layers, indicate environmental conditions, and correlate different periods of geologic history.

The age of rock layers may be estimated by radioactivity, deposition rates of sediments, salinity of the oceans, and physical and chemical alteration of rock materials.

VOCABULARY REVIEW

Match the word or phrase in the left column with the correct phrase or word in the right column. *Do not write in this book.*

1. Rock layers
2. Study of fossils
3. Study of rock structure and composition
4. Fossil footprints
5. Found in rocks of only one geologic age
6. Product of the decomposition of radium
7. Pioneer paleontologist
8. Study of the earth's rock layers

a. stratigraphy
b. petrology
c. uranium lead
d. strata
e. Charles Darwin
f. index fossil
g. William Smith
h. environmental fossil
i. paleontology

QUESTIONS · GROUP A

Decide whether these statements are true or false. Reword the false statements to make them true. *Do not write in this book.*

1. As the rate of erosion increases, the rate of decomposition decreases.
2. The basins of most ancient inland seas were geosynclines.
3. Ripple marks are characteristic of rocks formed in deep basins.
4. Diastrophism is accompanied by decrease in volcanism.
5. Unconformities result from peneplanation.
6. Mud is a consolidated sediment.
7. A dike is geologically older than the strata in which it is found.
8. Chalk was formed only during a limited period of geologic time.
9. Granite gravels precede the formation of granitic mountains.
10. A prehistoric type of elephant roamed the earth during a glacial period.
11. Index fossils are of great value in locating sources of petroleum.
12. Lead decomposes to form uranium, which in turn may form radium.

GROUP B

1. Compare and contrast stratigraphy and petrology.
2. What characteristics lead us to believe that inland seas were shallow basins?
3. What processes occurred during geologic revolutions?
4. Compare and contrast the climatic conditions during periods of geologic revolutions with conditions during periods of quiescence.
5. Why is it difficult to interpret the story of very ancient rocks?
6. Compare and contrast an angular unconformity and a disconformity. Include two labeled block diagrams.
7. Discuss the contributions of William Smith to the science of geology.
8. What are the difficulties of using salinity to determine the age of oceans?
9. What is meant by the "half-life" of a radioactive element? How is this information used to determine the age of rocks?

CHAPTER 22

GEOLOGIC TIME

THE story of the earth's past is a drama. The passage of time brings with it a changing cast of characters, changing scenes, and a constantly unfolding plot. To follow the development of the drama, we must divide the long story into acts and scenes. These divisions are the subject of this chapter.

We believe that the history of the earth extends back for at least 3 billion years, perhaps even more. Most of what we know about this history, at least from the time that life first appeared, is revealed by the fossils in the rocks, but the history of the earth before the appearance of life is still largely a mystery.

The Cosmic era. Earlier in this book (Chapters 3 and 6) we have considered some of the theories which attempt to explain the origin of our earth. As you will recall, it seems likely that at one time the earth was a cloud of dust and gases. Later, the materials became a molten mass, the substances separated according to their densities, and the earth eventually cooled to form a sphere with a solid surface.

The period of millions or billions of years during which the earth formed is called the *Cosmic era*. It may have been a relatively short span of time or it may have extended over a length of time

VOCABULARY

Era. A major division of geologic time.

Period. A subdivision of an era.

Epoch. A subdivision of a period.

Flora. Forms of plant life of a particular region or time period.

Fauna. Forms of animal life of a particular region or time period.

Rock sequence. The rocks laid down in one particular era.

Revolution. A time of marked crustal movement separating one geologic era from another.

Root reptiles. The ancestors of modern reptiles.

Vertebrates. Animals with backbones.

Invertebrates. Animals without backbones.

equal to all other parts combined. We know that many changes have occurred since this original formative period came to an end.

The Azoic era. After its development as a separate planet, the earth probably underwent many chemical and physical changes. Scientists call this time in the earth's history the *Azoic era,* meaning "without life." Its duration is uncertain, but it may well have lasted for a few billion years.

At first the earth was probably too small to hold an atmosphere. However, after it accumulated enough matter to equal 40 percent of its present mass, it would have been able to retain the gases that were given off from its crust. These probably included water vapor in large amounts, carbon dioxide and carbon monoxide, nitrogen, and other gases. During this period of change, the atmosphere was formed and the depressions in the crust were filled with water to form primitive seas and oceans. The higher elevations then became the continents of that time. It seems likely that crustal disturbances, widespread volcanic activity, and frequent earthquakes were characteristic of the era. Earth conditions were not then suitable for the support of life as we know it, but gradual changes took place. Some of these were cooler temperatures, changes in earth chemistry to produce the carbon dioxide necessary to green plants in food

FIG. 22–1. An artist's conception of the probable appearance of the earth's surface during the Azoic era.

making, neutralization of strong acids in the waters, and increase in the oxygen content of the air. Even though present-day life would have been impossible during both the Cosmic and Azoic eras, the gradual changes taking place during the latter era may have helped to prepare an environment which would be suitable for living things. In fact, recent studies indicate that these environmental changes may have resulted in the creation of organic compounds which were the forerunners of living things.

The geologic timetable. The kind of history we are now discussing extends over such incredibly long periods of time that it is convenient to use a special calendar called a *geologic timetable* to study it. In reading this section of the textbook you will need to refer constantly to the timetable on pages 388–389. You should be familiar with the various aspects of it and be able to recognize its main divisions.

The longest division of time in the geological timetable is called an *era.* Eras are subdivided into *periods* and these are further broken down into smaller time units called *epochs,* which are shorter and less distinct time units than periods. The end of an epoch is usually marked by *crustal disturbances* which caused changes in the erosion cycle and withdrawal of the shallow seas from the continents. Such a disturbance is indicated by more or less localized unconformities in the rocks. Periods are usually separated from each other by geological disturbances which were more severe and widespread than those which marked the ends of epochs. Thus, evidences of changes in living things, climate, and topography are greater at the close of a period than at the end of an epoch.

The rocks of one era are separated from those of the previous era by evidences of gigantic geologic *revolutions.* Evidence of such revolutions is observed in widespread unconformities, the presence of igneous rocks, the metamorphosis of older rock layers, and changes in topography and climate. During these revolutions, crustal movements formed the great mountain belts of the world and drained extensive, shallow seas from continental interiors. One of the most dramatic long-term effects of a revolution is the fact that these new conditions resulted in the extinction of many species and sometimes large groups of living things. New and often more complex forms of plants and animals then took the place of the extinct forms. This is indicated by fossil evidence in the rocks. Thus, each era is usually characterized by different types of plant life, *flora,* and animal life, *fauna,* from those in the previous era.

The rocks laid down during an entire era are called a *rock sequence;* and, just as the eras are divided into periods, epochs, ages, and stages, so are the corresponding rock sequences of each era broken down into *systems, series, groups,* and *formations.*

The rocks of the Erian (*ee*-ree-an) group, for example, were formed during the Middle Devonian epoch of the Devonian period. They belong to the Devonian rock system, a part of the sequence of rocks deposited during the Paleozoic era.

The specific names of the periods and systems, as well as their subdivisions, usually relate to *type areas,* which are the localities where the particular rocks were first studied by geologists. Thus, we may speak of Devonian (from Devon, England), Pennsylvanian, Permian (from Perm, Russia), Erian (from Lake Erie), and Cazenovian (from

Cazenovia, a village in upstate New York).

The table below gives examples of the units of time and the rock designations.

● ●

Time	Rocks	Examples
Era	Sequence	Paleozoic
Period	System	Devonian
Epoch	Series	Middle Devonian
Age	Group	Erian
Stage	Formation	Hamilton

DIVISIONS OF GEOLOGIC TIME

Pre-Cambrian time. As you will notice by referring to the geologic time-table, a large part of the geologic history of the earth occurred during *Pre-Cambrian time*. The fossil evidence in Pre-Cambrian rocks is scanty, and for the most part unclear. This seems to be due to the simplicity and small size of the living things of those times, and to their lack of skeletons and other hard parts.

1. The Archeozoic era. Geologists estimate that this era began more than two billion years ago. It was characterized by widespread volcanic activity, the formation of mountain ranges, and the deposition of metallic ores. During this era the seas repeatedly advanced over and retreated from the existing land areas.

Nowhere on earth have we found remnants of the earth's original rock crust. The lowest and oldest known layers are the Archeozoic, which have been so twisted, deformed, and compacted that it is hard to determine exactly what they were like originally or to unravel the sequence of events that took place after they were formed. In-

trusions of younger igneous rocks further confuse the picture. Examples of such rocks are the schists and gneisses at the bottom of the Grand Canyon beneath the sedimentary layers, and the surface rocks exposed by erosion in some parts of the Black Hills of South Dakota. There appear to be no fossils in Archeozoic rocks. For this reason, some geologists consider the term *Archeozoic,* meaning "very ancient life," to be misleading. They would prefer to use an alternate name, *Archean,* which means "very ancient" but omits reference to living things.

There is a great deal of graphite, a form of carbon, in some Archeozoic rocks. In fact, geologists estimate that there is more carbon (in the form of graphite) in these rocks than in those of the Pennsylvanian period which contain vast deposits of coal. The presence of such immense quantities of carbon in these Archeozoic sedimentary rocks strongly suggests that there was abundant life at the time the deposits were laid down, since carbon is an essential element in all forms of living things. In addition, some paleontologists have found structures which they think may be fossils of algae and sponges in Archeozoic rocks of the Great Lakes region, although this interpretation has been questioned by others. Nevertheless, it seems reasonable to suppose that early very simple forms of life such as viruses, bacteria, algae, and sponges may have existed during this era.

The Laurentian-Algoman revolution ended the Archeozoic era. At this time great diastrophic changes occurred in what is now Canada, the Great Lakes region, and the Adirondacks. They were followed by a long period of quiet during which the mountains were gradually worn down to peneplanes. Some of the

GEOLOGIC

Era	Period	Epoch	Flora
CENOZOIC (Age of Mammals)	**QUATERNARY OR NEOGENE**	HOLOCENE (RECENT)	FLOWERING PLANTS
		PLEISTOCENE	
	TERTIARY OR PALEOGENE	PLIOCENE	
		MIOCENE	
		OLIGOCENE	
		EOCENE	
		PALEOCENE	
MESOZOIC (Age of Reptiles)	**CRETACEOUS**		CONIFERS
	JURASSIC		
	TRIASSIC		
PALEOZOIC (Age of Invertebrates, Fishes, and Amphibians)	**PERMIAN**		FERNS, HORSETAILS, CLUB MOSSES
	PENNSYLVANIAN	*CARBONIFEROUS*	
	MISSISSIPPIAN		
	DEVONIAN		LIVERWORTS AND MOSSES
	SILURIAN		
	ORDOVICIAN		
	CAMBRIAN		BACTERIA, OTHER FUNGI, ALGAE
PROTEROZOIC (Algonkian)	**KEWEENAWAN**		
	HURONIAN		
ARCHEOZOIC (Archaean)	[Primeval Oceanic]		
AZOIC	[Waterless]		
COSMIC	[Earth's Origin]		

TIMETABLE

Fauna

	Duration in millions of years	Millions of years ago
	1	
	54	55
	65	120
	35	155
	35	190
	25	215
	85	300
	50	350
	70	420
	60	480
	70	550
	650	1200
	900	2100
	400	2500

MAMMALS · BIRDS · REPTILES · BONY FISHES · AMPHIBIANS · INSECTS · FISHES · TRILOBITES · BRACHIOPODS · ANNELID WORMS · GRAPTOLITES · CORALS · SPONGES · PROTOZOANS

Variation in width of bar indicates relative abundance of a group.

After Miller and Haub General Zoology Holt, Rinehart and Winston, Inc.

FIG. 22–2. The Laurentian Mountains of Quebec, Canada, are believed to be the roots of ancient mountains formed during the Laurentian-Algoman Revolution that ended the Archeozoic era. (*Canadian National Railways*)

rock formations in the Adirondacks are thought to be the roots of these ancient mountains.

2. The Proterozoic era. The general, basic shapes of the continents probably first developed during Proterozoic times.

FIG. 22–3. The North American area during the Proterozoic era. Colored areas are regions that were land at that time.

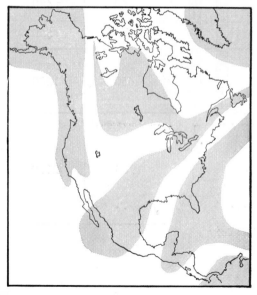

Also, during this era, extensive masses of igneous rocks were formed, some as thick as 15,000 feet. In the Keweenawan (*kee*-wee-*naw*-un) period, rich deposits of copper and silver were formed. Masses of native copper weighing as much as 400 tons have been found in rocks of this period. During the Huronian period of this era, immense deposits of iron ore, probably derived from the weathering of great masses of basalt, were laid down in sedimentary layers in what is now the Great Lakes region. It is interesting to note that *tillite,* a rock formed from glacial till, is found in some Proterozoic rocks. It contains faceted and striated boulders similar to those found in glacial deposits. This indicates that during part of the Proterozoic era, the climate was cold enough to maintain large glaciers.

Extensive deposits of graphite and limestone, and the occurrence of a few types of fossils indicate a probable widespread existence of living things in this era. These probably included simple plants like algae and fungi, and soft-bodied animals without skeletons, like worms and jellyfish. However, no really well-preserved fossils have been found in Proterozoic rocks. Therefore, some scientists call this era the *Algonkian,* rather than Proterozoic, which means "time of earlier life."

The Proterozoic era closed with great crustal upheavals and volcanic disturbances. Sedimentary layers in what is now the Great Lakes region were folded and metamorphosed, forming the Killarney Mountains. This revolution is called the *Killarney–Grand Canyon revolution.*

A long period of erosion followed this revolution. During this time it is probable that marine animals of every group of invertebrates developed. However, there is no certain fossil evidence of these animals in the rocks laid down during this long interval of erosion. Therefore, this gap between the Proterozoic and Paleozoic is called the *Lipalian* (lost) *Interval.*

The Paleozoic era. This comparatively long era lasted approximately 350 million years. Geologists divide it into many well-defined periods, each of which seems to be characterized by the appearance of some new forms of plant and animal life, ranging from tiny invertebrates to giant tree ferns. Paleozoic seas teemed with a wide variety of life. Thousands of species of invertebrates constantly struggled for survival. The earliest known fishlike vertebrates developed during this era, and the first land plants appeared. Evidence of repeated emergence and submergence of portions of the continents have made it possible for geologists to divide this era into the following distinct periods:

1. The Cambrian period. During the Cambrian, large parts of the present North American continent were submerged under shallow seas and much of the land was low and flat. The climate was probably warm and apparently there were no land plants or animals. Sedimentary rocks of this period con-

FIG. 22–4. A reproduction of some forms of undersea life that existed during the Cambrian period. (*University of Michigan*)

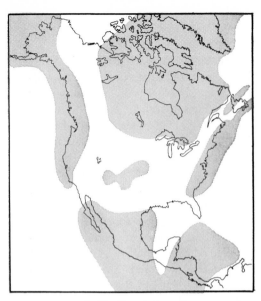

FIG. 22–5. The North American area during the Cambrian period. Colored areas indicate regions that were land at that time.

tain large numbers of invertebrates such as jellyfish, sponges, brachiopods (clam-like animals), snails, and cephalopods (animals like the squid and octopus). The most common animals of this period were a now-extinct group of invertebrates known as the *trilobites* (*try*-loh-byts). They were of many kinds, all with

FIG. 22–6. The North American area during the Ordovician period.

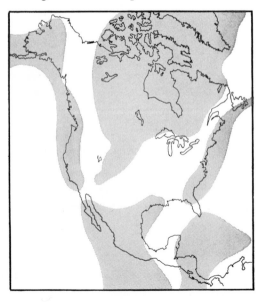

segmented bodies covered with a tough hornlike exoskeleton. Some had immovable eyes to cover small segments of the field of vision, while others seem to have had no eyes at all. The abundance of fossil trilobites makes it possible to trace their development from very simple to highly complex forms. Their wide variety and relatively short existence as a form of life make them excellent index fossils for identifying and correlating the rock formations in which they occur.

The Cambrian period ended with the *Green Mountain disturbance,* at which time some of the folds and faults in the present Vermont mountains were formed.

2. The Ordovician (or-do-*vish*-an) period. About 60 percent of the North American continent was apparently under water during the first part of the Ordovician period. Geologists think that these inland seas were shallow and that the continental areas were mostly lowlands, because extensive limestone deposits were formed in this period. Higher land would have produced swift streams carrying mostly clay and sand, which would have then formed sandstones or shales instead of limestones. In this period the earliest known vertebrates made their appearance in the form of primitive fishes, but invertebrates continued to be the dominant group of animals. Some *nautiloids,* related to the present-day octopus and squid, were protected by shells up to 15 feet long. They and the primitive fishes undoubtedly fed on trilobites, which were still abundant at that time.

The Ordovician period closed with the *Taconic disturbance,* revealed in the folded rocks of the Taconic region along the Massachusetts–New York boundary and extending into southern Vermont.

3. The Silurian period. Following the

FIG. 22–7. A reproduction of some forms of Silurian life. (*New York State Museum*)

Taconic disturbance, widespread flooding of the central part of the North American continent occurred. Thick beds of salt and gypsum were formed in New York, Ohio, Michigan, Pennsylvania, and West Virginia. These deposits are evidence of an arid climate in this region during parts of the Silurian period. The sedimentary rocks at the top of the Niagara gorge were formed during this period.

The Silurian rocks of Scotland contain fossils of the earliest known land animals in the form of air-breathing scorpions and millipedes ("thousand leggers"). Other more abundant types of fossils in these rocks are corals, brachiopods, nautiloids, and trilobites. Although corals first appeared in the Ordovician period, they were much more numerous in Silurian times and formed widespread coral reefs.

4. The Devonian period. In Devonshire, England, for which this period is named, geologists long ago made detailed studies of the fossil-bearing rocks. Many types of sediments have been found in these ancient Devonian rocks, including tillites of glacial origin. There

is evidence of considerable volcanism in some areas. Lake and stream deposits with typical fresh-water fossil forms also occur.

The earliest known large land plants made their first appearance during the Devonian period. Among them were huge fernlike trees, some of which grew to heights of 40 feet. The first simple types of amphibians also appeared, and

FIG. 22–8. The North American area during the Silurian period.

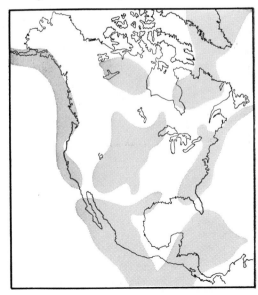

FIG. 22–9. A reproduction of some forms of life that existed during the Devonian period. (*New York State Museum*)

the seas supported a large variety of fishes, including armored types and primitive sharks. Fishes appear to have been the dominant form of water life in these times. The Devonian period ended with the Acadian disturbance, which elevated mountains in what is now northern Maine and eastern Canada.

5. *The Mississippian and the Pennsylvanian periods.* These two periods together are called *the Carboniferous pe-*

FIG. 22–10. The North American area during the Pennsylvanian period.

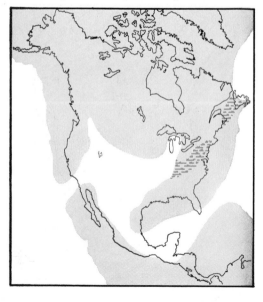

riod. The term *carboniferous* means "carbon-bearing" and refers to the vast coal deposits laid down during these periods. At that time the land in many parts of the world seems to have been low, moist, and generally warm. Great swampy forests supported a profuse array of large land plants, including scale-trees, horsetails, ferns, seed ferns, and primitive cone-bearing plants. The land in some areas where these forests grew sank very gradually and huge deposits of the remains of plant roots, stems, and leaves accumulated. These were slowly covered by water which partially preserved them. Eventually these areas of land sank below the level of the seas and the plant remains were buried under deposits of sediment hundreds of feet thick. The resulting pressure and heat caused chemical changes which converted the plant remains into coal.

Land animals were common in the Carboniferous period. About 800 species of fossil insects have been identified in rocks of this period, including cockroaches up to four inches long and dragonflies with two-foot wingspreads. Land snails appeared for the first time. New types of amphibians also arose.

FIG. 22–11. During the Coal Ages many changes also occurred among the sea-dwelling animals and plants. This is a reproduction of an underwater scene in the Mississippian period. (*University of Michigan*)

FIG. 22–12. An artist's conception of the types of plant and animal life that were found during the Pennsylvanian period. (*Yale Peabody Museum*)

FIG. 22–13. An artist's version of the types of life during the Permian period. Compare this with Fig. 22–12. Note that plant forms did not change much during the long time interval, whereas some of the animal forms changed considerably. (*Yale Peabody Museum*)

During the later part of this period the earliest known reptiles appeared. These were apparently the first vertebrates that could survive entirely free of a water habitat, since reptiles breathe by lungs all through their lives and hatch from eggs laid on land.

6. *The Permian period.* The low swampy lands of the coal ages began to rise in the Permian period, and many of the swamp plants were no longer able

FIG. 22–14. The North American area during the Permian period.

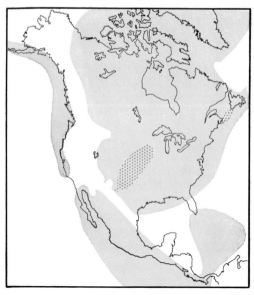

to survive in a drier climate. They were largely replaced by new forms of seed plants that had developed gradually in higher and drier areas. In similar fashion, many other types of land plants and animals became extinct as a result of the changes in environment. They also were replaced by forms of life better adapted to cooler and drier conditions. Outstanding among these new forms of life were the reptiles, which rapidly ascended to dominance over the other land animals. Two important lines of reptiles developed during the Permian period: (1) the *root reptiles,* which were probably the ancestors of our modern reptiles; and (2) the *mammal-like reptiles* whose teeth and skulls resemble those of mammals, and from which the first mammals probably developed.

The Permian was the last period of the Paleozoic era. Geologists believe that it ended with the great *Appalachian revolution.* During this revolution the ancestral Appalachian Mountains were formed, folds and faults of which are still visible today. Although there is no way of telling the height of these ancient mountains, they may well have been as lofty and rugged as the modern Rockies. As a result of the diastrophic changes during the Appalachian revolution, the shallow inland seas of eastern North America were drained and have never returned to cover this part of the continent.

The Mesozoic era. This era occupies the middle zone of time in which life has existed on the earth. The name means "middle life," indicating an era of transition between the time of "ancient life" (Paleozoic) and that of "recent life" (Cenozoic). The environmental changes that took place during the Appalachian revolution wiped out many groups of animals and plants, but those that survived became the ancestors of many thousands of new forms.

1. The Triassic period. During Triassic times the North American continent was very much as it is now except that the Atlantic and Gulf coastal plains had not been formed. The land was generally high and dry. Desert conditions probably prevailed in some areas, as indicated by the red color of the sedimentary formations and the deposits of salt and gypsum. Many animals and plants of the early Triassic closely resembled those of the late Paleozoic, but some new forms appeared. In the Triassic forests grew giant *cycads* (*sy*-kadz) and conifers resembling some of our modern evergreens. From the root reptiles of the Permian period, many descendants arose. These developed further in the Triassic, producing both the dinosaurs and the ancestors of most modern reptiles. The first birds, probably descendants of reptiles, and the primitive mammals also appeared in this period.

The *Palisades disturbance* marked the end of the Triassic period. During this disturbance the sills and lava flows

exposed today in the Palisades along the Hudson, the Watchung Mountains of New Jersey, the ridges near Meriden and New Haven in Connecticut, and the Holyoke Range in central Massachusetts were formed.

2. The Jurassic period. The Jurassic period closely resembled the preceding Triassic. The eastern parts of North America were still generally dry and elevated. Erosion of the ancestral Appalachians was well on the way toward the formation of a peneplane.

The Jurassic is perhaps best known for its unusual reptiles. This was the period when the dinosaurs were dominant and indeed some of them were, as their name signifies, "terrible lizards." Many were enormous creatures whose movements were probably slow and awkward. Others were only a foot or two long and could presumably move about quite rapidly. One of the most familiar forms was *Brontosaurus,* whose body length was about 65 feet but whose brain must have weighed less than a pound! Another was *Diplodocus* (di-*plod*-oh-kus), who was about 80 feet long and whose

FIG. 22–15. The North American area during the Triassic period.

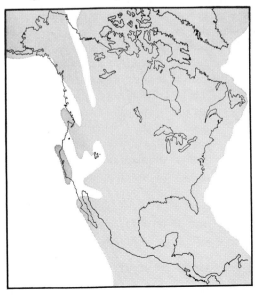

FIG. 22–16. An artist's drawing of Brontosaurus, crocodiles, and pterosaurs that lived during the Jurassic period. (*Buffalo Museum of Science*)

brain was also extremely small for the size of its body. Still another was *Stegosaurus,* with a row of triangular bony plates along its back, apparently as protection against its many enemies. These and many other forms of dinosaurs apparently lived entirely on a diet of plants and therefore could exist only where there was ample vegetation to provide them with extremely large amounts of food.

Another large dinosaur was *Allosaurus,* whose daggerlike teeth indicate that it was a flesheater or *carnivore.*

The first flying vertebrates were the *pterosaurs* (*ter*-oh-sawrz) meaning "winged lizards." Their huge wings, without feathers, were as much as 26 feet long. Although pterosaurs were not birds as we know this group today, the Jurassic did produce true birds. The best known type, called *Archaeopteryx* (*ar*-kee-*op*-ter-iks), was about the size of a pigeon. Although its skeleton and

teeth resembled those of reptiles, its wings and body were covered with feathers, so that it is generally classified as a bird.

In the oceans swam fishlike reptiles called *ichthyosaurs* (*ik*-thee-oh-sawrz), similar in size and appearance to modern porpoises. Another group of swimming reptiles, called *plesiosaurs,* were long, slender animals with necks which resembled snakes. All in all, Jurassic lizards were masters of the sea, land, and air.

Fossil insects representing about 20 modern orders have been found in Jurassic rocks, but no fossil moths or butterflies have ever been found in rocks of this period.

The Jurassic period ended in the *Nevadan disturbance,* during which the Sierra Nevada and Coast Ranges on the West Coast were formed. Associated igneous activity formed gold ores whose erosion led to the placer deposits in the streams of California which stimulated the famous gold rush of about 100 years ago.

3. The Cretaceous period. The Cretaceous is noted for the thick chalk deposits formed during this period, especially those in England and France. (The name of the period is taken from the Latin word *creta,* meaning chalk.) During this period the present Rocky Mountain area became flooded with a shallow sea extending from the Gulf of Mexico to the Arctic Ocean. On the land grew trees such as figs, poplars, willows, magnolias, and maples. Apparently there were deep forests in some areas, much like those of today. Grasses, grains, and fruit and nut-bearing plants appeared, furnishing food for some of the early mammals. Many of the coal deposits in western United States were formed at this time.

FIG. 22–17. A reproduction of many of the forms of life that inhabited the seas during the Cretaceous period. (*University of Michigan*)

The mightiest dinosaur of all, *Tyrannosaurus,* flourished during this period. This lizard had a skull slightly over four feet long and a body standing 20 feet high. A carnivore, it must have been able to kill and eat any other animal living at that time. Although these animals were as large or larger than modern elephants, their brains were about the size of a hen's egg. Although dinosaurs dominated most of the Mesozoic fauna, they apparently became extinct during the last 10 to 15 million years of this long period.

The *Laramide revolution* brought the Mesozoic era to a close. It created the ancestral Rocky Mountains and re-elevated the ancient Appalachians, which by this time had been worn down to a peneplane.

FIG. 22–18. The North American area during the Cretaceous period. The dotted region indicates large swampy areas in some parts of our western states, where coal deposits were formed.

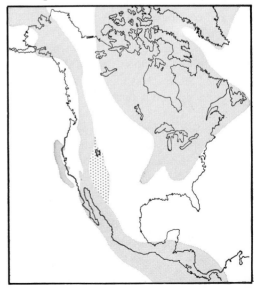

The Cenozoic era. The *Cenozoic* ("recent life") *era* is the latest of the great eras of earth history. It is also called the *Age of Mammals.* Some geologists consider the brief period of human history, including the present, as a part of the Cenozoic. Others prefer to think of this period of human existence as the first epoch of a separate new era they call the *Psychozoic,* because of the superior intellect of man, who dominates the present scene.

The Cenozoic is sometimes subdivided into two periods, the *Tertiary* and the *Quaternary* (kwah-*ter*-na-ree), although some geologists prefer to call these periods the *Paleogene* and *Neogene* instead.

The Tertiary or Paleogene period. Tertiary rocks consist mostly of loose, incompletely consolidated marine sediments. In North America these are largely found along the margin of the continent because the seas of this period did not often invade the continental interior. The salt domes of the Gulf states, containing immense quantities of sulfur, gas, and oil, are located in Cenozoic sediments. Intense diastrophic movements began in western United States toward the close of the *Miocene epoch* and continued with increasing intensity, ending in the *Cascadian revolution* which closed this period. In places the resulting lava flows are 4000 feet thick. The Sierra Nevada Mountains were lifted up about one mile and the California Coast Range was re-elevated. The *San Andreas rift* developed at about this time. As you recall, movement along this fault is responsible for the many recent earthquakes in the California area. There is evidence that this uplifting still goes on in the western and northeastern parts of our continent.

1. The Paleocene epoch. This epoch

FIG. 22–19. An artist's version of several of the primitive mammals that lived on the earth during the Eocene epoch. (*Buffalo Museum of Science*)

might be regarded as the "early morning" of the development of mammals. Gone were the dinosaurs, although ancestors of present-day alligators, turtles, lizards, and snakes were fairly abundant. The mammals were generally small in size, and most of them bore only slight resemblance to modern forms. The first of the primates, the order of mammals which includes man, developed during this epoch. It was a small tree-dwelling animal with bushy hair and a long tail. The vegetation resembled present-day subtropical plants, including figs, breadfruit, and palmettos.

2. The Eocene epoch. In this epoch the climate remained similar to that of the Paleocene. The mammals in general became larger, although most of them still did not look much like the familiar forms of today. Numerous forms of rodents appeared, and hoofed animals began to develop specialized adaptations

FIG. 22–20. Oligocene mammals as they might have appeared in the area that is now South Dakota. (*American Museum of Natural History*)

for survival. *Eohippus,* the first horse, was about the size of a fox terrier, with slender legs suited to running and teeth fitted primarily for eating plant food. Lemurs, animals like monkeys but with foxlike faces, developed at this time and have continued down to the present. Birds were also numerous in this epoch. One unusual species, *Diatryma* (dy-a-try-ma), was a running bird seven feet tall, with a powerful hooked beak.

3. The Oligocene (*ol*-i-go-seen) *epoch.* During this epoch diastrophic forces produced the first folds of the European Alps, and the beginnings of the Himalayas in Asia. Volcanic activity was widespread in North America, whose climate grew cooler, thus favoring the growth of grasses, conifers, and hardwoods, which replaced the older subtropical forests of the Paleocene and Eocene epochs. Also replaced were the more primitive mammals of those epochs, as the animals of this group became more like the modern forms. *Brontops* was a huge hoofed and horned beast, somewhat like a rhinoceros but 14 feet long. *Mesohippus* was a three-toed horse of this epoch, with longer

legs and a larger body than *Eohippus.* The carnivores had begun to separate into the dog and cat families, and primitive camels, similar to the modern llama, had also appeared.

4. The Miocene epoch. Mammals flourished in the Miocene epoch, which is often called the *Golden Age of Mammals.* Great herds of early horses and camels roamed the plains and fed on the

FIG. 22–21. The North American area during the Miocene epoch.

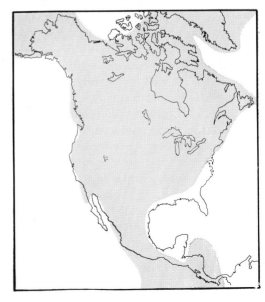

FIG. 22–22. An artist's reproduction of various types of Pliocene mammals. (*American Museum of Natural History*)

abundant grasses which flourished in the cooler, drier climate. Members of the deer family, the rhinoceros family, the pig family, and other groups of familiar mammals left fossils during the Miocene. The fossils of monkeys similar to those we know today have also been located in Miocene deposits.

5. *The Pliocene epoch.* This epoch ushered in many new changes in living things. A large number of new genera had their start at this time. These included other groups of horses, camels and elephants, but these were different from their present-day relatives. Many members of the horse family—*Protohippus, Pliohippus,* and finally *Equus* (*ee-*kwus)—and great numbers of the camel family, as well as several elephants, mastodons, and mammoths, roamed in herds over the American continent. The Pliocene also produced many carnivores, including *Agriotherium* (an enormous bear) and *Amphicyon* (am-*fis*-ee-on), (a huge bearlike dog).

It is interesting to note that not a single Tertiary mammal has survived to the present. All are extinct, but there is a continuous line of descent from these earlier forms to the modern types which cannot be overlooked in tracing the development of Cenozoic life. While many of the Tertiary mammals were somewhat similar to modern forms, there were noticeable differences in size and appearance.

The similarity of Tertiary invertebrates to modern ones is, on the other hand, so marked that we shall draw attention only to two of the most interesting groups. The history of oysters is noteworthy. These mollusks apparently started in the Jurassic, increased in numbers and species in the Cretaceous, continued to flourish in the Tertiary, and then declined. Some Eocene oysters were several times larger than the edible modern ones. *Ostrea titan,* of the Miocene, was still larger, being about 13 inches long and 6 inches thick.

Insects are usually closely associated with land vegetation and the kinds of insects common in prehistoric times were often determined by the nature of the plant life then in existence. In the Tertiary, for the first time, the highest flowering plants were abundant, and so also were such insects as the butterfly and the bee, which are especially adapted to take their food from flowers.

Vertebrate fossils of fishes, amphibians, reptiles, and birds also occur abundantly in Tertiary deposits.

Many familiar types of forest trees first appeared in the Cretaceous and all continued in the Tertiary, although various new species arose during that period. In North America during the Eocene epoch, palm, fig, and tropical evergreens were present. Fossils discovered in South Dakota indicate that the climate in those days was about the same as it is in Florida today.

The Quaternary or Neogene period. This period is subdivided into the *Pleistocene epoch,* also known as the *Ice Age,* and the *Holocene epoch* which includes contemporary life, also called the *Recent epoch.*

The transition from Pliocene to Pleistocene was accompanied by great environmental changes. Continental glaciers overlying northern Europe, Asia, and North America began to spread huge ice sheets southward. As large quantities of the earth's water were locked in these glaciers, the level of the seas and oceans fell and land bridges were established between North and South America in the region of Panama and between Asia and North America in the area of the Bering Sea. Thus

groups of animals that had formerly been separated for many millions of years were allowed to mingle, resulting in the extinction of some forms and the rapid development of many new groups.

1. The Pleistocene epoch. Most of the plants and invertebrate animals of this epoch were almost exactly like those of the present time. However, their range of geographical distribution varied considerably from time to time with the advance and retreat of the great ice sheets. Although climates were probably colder than they are today, there were warmer interglacial periods.

The mammals of this epoch, in contrast to the invertebrates, were quite different from present-day forms. They included huge mastodons, woolly mammoths, and other elephantlike types. Giant beasts similar to present-day rhinoceros, hippopotamus, and bison roamed the plains and forests. Unusual mammals like *Boreostracon* (a large armadillolike animal with a spiked tail) and *Megatherium* (a giant sloth that stood 20 feet above the ground on its hind legs and weighed several tons) probably were preyed upon by the most powerful mammalian carnivores of all time—*Smilodon,* the saber-tooth cat, and *Canis diris,* or dire wolf, a six-foot animal resembling the modern wolf. The remains of early man have also been found

FIG. 22–23. Pleistocene mastodons and bison (*American Museum of Natural History*)

among the fossils of the Pleistocene epoch.

2. *The Holocene Epoch.* Today, we find the world characterized by extremes of climate at different localities during different seasons. The earth still has, as it did in the past, areas of deserts and swamps, forests and grasslands, mountains and glaciers, and salt and fresh-water seas. In addition, there are tropical rain forests and frigid polar regions, as well as barren tundras. Our planet, in this twentieth century, also has many young mountain ranges, plateaus and plains. Plant and animal forms are probably more varied than at any other time in the earth's history and new forms are still appearing, some naturally and others due to man's ability to cross-breed living things.

SUMMARY

THE earth's geologic history has been divided into eras. Each era is separated from the subsequent one by vast crustal movements called revolutions. Minor subdivisions of the eras are periods and epochs.

During the Archeozoic era there was much volcanic activity and many changes in sea level occurred. The fossil record of this era is scanty. Simple plants and animals appeared during the Proterozoic, which was an era of glaciation and volcanism.

Wide diversity of organic life is characteristic of the Paleozoic. Great areas of the United States were inland seas. Oceans were teeming with life, and primitive land plants appeared. Early amphibians and reptiles evolved near the end of this era.

Dinosaurs were the dominant creatures of the Mesozoic. They became extinct, probably because they could not adjust to changing environmental conditions, and were gradually replaced by the warm-blooded mammals and birds of the Cenozoic.

VOCABULARY REVIEW

Match the phrase in the left column with the correct word in the right column. *Do not write in this book.*

1. Rock formed from glacial sediments
2. Animals with backbones
3. Carbon-bearing
4. Forms of plant life
5. Era in which the earth was formed
6. Flesh eater
7. Animals without backbones
8. Plants resembling modern evergreens
9. Ancestor of the horse
10. Forms of animal life

a. carnivore
b. invertebrates
c. cosmic
d. Eohippus
e. vertebrates
f. fauna
g. tillite
h. flora
i. Azoic
j. carboniferous
k. cycads

QUESTIONS · GROUP A

In each of the following groups of terms, three are related in some way and one is not. Select the unrelated term and give a reason why you believe it is not related. *Do not write in this book.*

1. (*a*) saber-tooth cat (*b*) mastodon (*c*) trilobite (*d*) mammoth
2. (*a*) Triassic (*b*) Devonian (*c*) Silurian (*d*) Ordovician
3. (*a*) Cambrian (*b*) corals (*c*) Mesohippus (*d*) sponges
4. (*a*) Oligocene (*b*) Pterosaurs (*c*) flowering plants (*d*) rodents
5. (*a*) salt beds (*b*) Pre-Cambrian (*c*) coral reefs (*d*) Niagara Gorge sediments
6. (*a*) Ostrea titan (*b*) tree ferns (*c*) bony fish (*d*) simple amphibians
7. (*a*) glaciation (*b*) Carboniferous period (*c*) swamp forests (*d*) abundant land plants
8. (*a*) root reptiles (*b*) dry climates (*c*) insects (*d*) nautiloids
9. (*a*) Allosaurus (*b*) Diplodocus (*c*) Brontosaurus (*d*) Stegosaurus
10. (*a*) Tyrannosaurus (*b*) plesiosaurs (*c*) Archaeopteryx (*d*) ichthyosaurs
11. (*a*) primitive primates (*b*) hoofed mammals (*c*) Paleocene (*d*) sea scorpions

GROUP B

1. Briefly discuss the probable history of the early formation of the earth.
2. How is a particular rock formation named?
3. Why is it difficult to find Pre-Cambrian fossils?
4. Why is it difficult to interpret the rocks of the Black Hills and the lower Grand Canyon?
5. Discuss the relationship between Archeozoic graphite deposits and the possibility of life?
6. How do the Killarney-Grand Canyon and Laurentian-Algoman revolutions illustrate how the face of the earth has changed?
7. What were the characteristics of the trilobites?
8. Describe the topography of the Ordovician period. What is the evidence for this description?
9. List the ancestors of the modern horse in the correct chronological order.
10. Account for the fact that although man was one of the last organisms to appear, he now dominates the earth and to some degree controls the earth's environment.
11. List the major revolutions that separated the geologic eras. Tell how each revolution affected the area that is now North America.

CHAPTER 23

THE FOSSIL RECORD

THERE may have been a time when there was no life of any kind on the earth. During the earth's formative period, living things as we know them probably could not have existed. One might then ask: How did all of today's many forms of life get their start? Where and how did they originate? Although there are many theories about the origin of life, as yet no one knows definitely what occurred. However, even though geologists have not completely solved the puzzle, they can reveal many facts about some of the plants and animals of long ago.

Paleontologists are able to assemble a fairly good picture of ancient animals and plants, because living things tend to record their own history. This story of ancient life is written in the fossil remains of living things. The great scientist Louis Agassiz once said, "The earth is a vast cemetery. The rocks are tombstones on which the buried dead have written their own epitaphs." Fossils are interesting not because they are dead, but because they were once alive so many years ago.

Exactly what is a fossil? We have defined it as the remains or evidence of plants or animals of past ages. The word comes from the Latin *fossilis* which was derived from the word *fodere* meaning "to dig." It is an appropriate term because paleontologists find fossils chiefly by digging.

The most interesting and perhaps the rarest fossils are the actual remains of

VOCABULARY

Petrifaction. A process in which the original substance of a fossil is replaced by mineral matter.

Carbonization. A process in which remains of living things are partly decomposed, leaving a residue of carbon.

Molds. Imprints of prehistoric organisms or their parts.

Coprolites. Fossil excrement.

Gastroliths. Fossil gizzard stones of reptiles.

Artifacts. Structures or articles made by prehistoric man.

Pseudofossils. Structures resembling fossils but not made by prehistoric organisms.

organisms. One example is the carcass of a woolly mammoth found frozen in the mud and ice of Siberia around the year 1900. This gigantic elephant, now extinct, had been frozen solid for thousands of years since the time of the Pleistocene glaciers. The low temperature had so retarded decay that the animal remained in an unusually good state of preservation. The hair, hide, flesh, and even the internal organs were very nearly intact. Injuries of the chest and fractures of the leg bones indicated a sudden and violent death. In the animal's mouth were remnants of its last meal of buttercups. Apparently the mammoth slipped while trying to get more buttercups and fell off a cliff to the bottom of a gorge.

The fact that the body cells of this animal had been frozen solid without the formation of ice crystals shows that it had somehow become frozen very rapidly. Frozen-food experts estimate that the animal must have been frozen at temperatures below minus 150° F. This is lower than any known natural temperature on earth today. Since the original carcass was found in Siberia, others have been discovered in Alaska.

FORMATION OF FOSSILS

Fossil variety. Fossils may be formed in many different ways under many different environmental conditions. In rare instances, such as that of the mammoth described above, the complete animal is preserved. More frequently, the more durable parts of the organism are preserved in relatively unaltered condition. Fossils may, however, be altered so that little of the original material remains, although shapes and textures are recognizable. Other fossils are not remains at all, but evidences that life has existed. Such evidence is often remarkably clear and detailed, however.

Unaltered remains of organisms. Usually a dead plant or animal must be buried quickly if it is to form a fossil. Otherwise it will be eaten by other organisms, decay, or become broken up and scattered by wind or water. Fleshy parts are preserved in an unaltered condition only if they are in an environment in which decay cannot take place. The bacteria and other organisms that cause decay need food, water, oxygen, and a suitable temperature, usually a warm one. They cannot function in an extremely hot environment like volcanic ash, nor in an extremely cold one like snow. The frozen mammoth fossil was preserved by natural refrigeration.

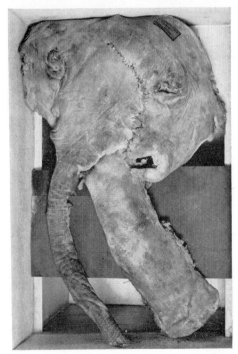

FIG. 23–1. A portion of a well-preserved woolly mammoth, found in Alaska. (*American Museum of Natural History*)

FIG. 23–2. Above, the mummified remains of *Trachodon,* the duck-billed dinosaur. Left, closer detail of the skin. (*American Museum of Natural History*)

Another example of unaltered remains of life of a past geologic time is provided by an interesting discovery in the Antarctic. A party of American explorers came upon a large quantity of ice that was as red as blood. Fragments were chipped off and carried back to base camp where microscopic examination of the melted ice showed the presence of thousands of living *Euglena,* plantlike organisms of a species that bore a red pigment in their chlorophyll-containing bodies. Evidence led to the belief that they had been frozen alive and had remained in a state of suspended animation for thousands of years—a true living fossil. When thawed out, they continued their life cycles exactly as they did before refrigeration had "fossilized" them many years ago.

The remains of other animals have been found preserved in soil saturated with oil, in deposits of volcanic ash, in wax, and in caves covered with bat droppings. Some remains, such as those in dry caves, became mummified (*dessicated*) and their bodies are still available for careful examination.

Hard parts of animals are often preserved in an unaltered condition. The pearly shells of fossil mollusks commonly found in many localities, and the bones of the saber-tooth cat of the Rancho La Brea tar beds of California are famous examples.

Although some of the fossils just mentioned are thousands of years old, they are considered comparatively recent by the geologist, who reckons time in hundreds of millions of years.

Altered remains of organisms. Under certain conditions fossil specimens originating hundreds of millions of years ago may be completely altered. In many cases the original parts have been replaced by mineral substances by a process called *petrifaction.* Such a fossil is said to be "turned to stone." This does not mean that the original organic matter has been changed into stone. Actually, minerals have replaced the original cell materials which have long disappeared. Some of the common petrifying minerals are silicon dioxide, calcium carbonate, and pyrite, which is a combination of iron and sulfur.

When the skeleton of an ancient animal became buried, the cell materials in the bones were gradually lost as mineral water soaked into the cell spaces. Then the water evaporated, leaving the minerals behind as a layer of solid material lining each cell cavity. Repeated soaking, followed by drying periods, resulted in the final complete *replacement* of the original cells with mineral matter in the same pattern as the animal bone. So perfect was the substitution of mineral for cell material that sometimes thin sections of these fossils clearly show the detailed cell characteristics of the original tissues when viewed under a compound microscope. In some circumstances the details of the original organism are lost and only the general outline remains. This is characteristic of some pyrite fossils. Usually the replacement of the cell materials is a very slow process which probably takes place molecule by molecule.

The vast coal deposits of today are fossil remains of plants which have been changed by the process of *carbonization.* Coal beds were formed when the remains of trees and other plants accumulated in swamp water and started to decompose. Some of the plant material changed into marsh gas (CH_4), water (H_2O), and carbon dioxide (CO_2). Much carbon remained behind because these products carried away more oxygen and hydrogen than carbon. The cell materials such as cellulose ($C_6H_{10}O_5)_x$ were gradually changed by the concentration of this carbon, and after many years, the final product became what we know as coal.

FIG. 23–3. Below, an artist's conception of a scene at the Rancho La Brea tar pits in prehistoric times. Right, the remains of Pleistocene animals in a typical excavation of the pits. (*American Museum of Natural History; Los Angeles County Museum*)

FIG. 23–4. A fossil crinoid, perfectly preserved by the process of petrifaction. (*American Museum of Natural History*)

Indirect evidence of ancient organisms. Besides the actual or the altered remains of organisms, there are many other kinds of fossil evidence.

Some fossils may take the form of *imprints*. These are such things as the footprint of an animal or the outline and veinings of a leaf. A giant dinosaur may have wandered along the shore of a lake long ago and left his large, deep footprints in the soft mud. Later, sand or silt may have been blown or washed into the footprints so gently that they were not destroyed. Still later, more sediment may have been deposited above the prints, so the layers of mud containing the imprints of the huge reptile were hardened into solid rock as the ages passed. Thus a record of the footprints was preserved. Imprints of fossil leaves, stems, flowers, and fish were often produced in soft mud or clay in a similar way, as were footprints of amphibians, birds, mammals, and even Stone Age man.

Shells of snails, branches of trees and various other organic remains often became buried in sediments which later solidified to form rock. Eventually these remains decayed or were dissolved, leaving in the rock empty cavities which are called **natural molds.** Particularly fascinating natural molds are those of insects that are found in amber. Millions of years ago, the amber was resin flowing from wounds in trees. It acted like sticky flypaper, trapping insects which then became embedded in it. In time, the resin hardened, and when the trees became buried in sediment and

FIG. 23–5. A fossil imprint of a huge dinosaur's foot in solid rock. (*American Museum of Natural History*)

converted to *lignite,* the resin changed to the substance we now know as amber. The insects dried out to almost nothing, leaving their forms preserved as cavities in the transparent amber. Such details as bristles, wing scales, and other structures can be easily examined with a microscope.

Natural molds may be studied as they are, or they may be filled with plaster of Paris or some other substance to make duplicates of the original fossils in shape and surface detail. These replicas are called **artificial casts.** Sometimes **natural casts** are formed when sand or mud fills natural molds and then hardens.

Trails and burrows may also be preserved as fossils. Some examples of these natural molds include the trails of trilobites, snails, and the burrows of sea worms and crabs. Sometimes small animals bored into the shells of larger organisms and ate their soft bodies. Many snails, sponges, and crabs are known by their borings or burrows, as much as by their hard remains. Of particular interest are the "devil's corkscrews" found in Nebraska. They are thought to be the homes dug by ancient beavers, each be-

FIG. 23–7. Types of fossil formation. The dots represent the sedimentary rock in which the shell fossil is formed. The vertical lines represent later filling with fine sediment. In *A* the shell was buried in mud, and has dissolved away to leave a hollow *mold.* In *B* the hollow mold has been filled by deposition of silicates or carbonates from solution, forming a *cast.* If the rock were broken, the cast would drop out of the mold. In *C* the empty shell was filled with mud. The shell has dissolved to leave a space the size and thickness of the shell. In *D* this hollow space has been filled by deposition of minerals from the water.

FIG. 23–6. An ant, perfectly preserved in amber. Amber is a fossil gum derived from the sap of prehistoric plants. (*American Museum of Natural History*)

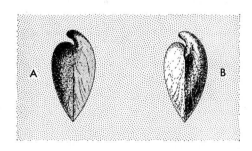

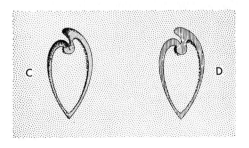

FIG. 23–8. A devil's corkscrew, believed to be the fossil burrow of a beaver. (*American Museum of Natural History*)

ing a spiral mold eight feet deep which ends in a tunnel that slopes upward. Some of these molds have become filled with sand which has hardened to form casts of the original burrows.

Ancient sea worms swallowed sand or mud in order to eat the small organisms contained in it. After the food was extracted, the sand or mud was expelled (regurgitated) in the form of *castings* of various shapes. These are found as fossils in some marine rocks. *Coprolites* are masses of waste materials (excrement) that have been preserved as fossils. They can be cut into thin sections and carefully analyzed, to learn about the feeding habits and food of animals long since extinct.

Anyone who has watched a chicken being cleaned has noticed that the muscular stomach or gizzard contains numerous small stones. These help grind the food as it is churned by the gizzard muscles. Some dinosaurs had such *gizzard stones,* often larger than those of

chickens, to grind their food. They can be recognized by their smooth, rounded, and polished surfaces and by the fact that they occur in strata that contain dinosaur remains. Identification is more certain if these *gastroliths* are found within the skeleton of a dinosaur, in the region of the body in which the gizzard was once located.

Artifacts. Artificial structures produced by primitive man are called *artifacts.* These are fossils in a sense. They include paintings made on the cave walls, figures carved from bone, baked clay pots, knives and spear points, and stone ax heads. In caves which were occupied for thousands of years, these are normally found in the lowest layers of debris on the floor. More advanced and skilled workmanship appears in or near the surface layers.

Pseudofossils. Some rock structures superficially resemble fossils in appearance but were not made by animals or plants. These are called *pseudofossils* (false fossils). Some pseudofossils are crystalline aggregates or other accumulations of mineral matter of inorganic origin known as *concretions*. Some of these look like petrified eggs or potatoes. Others have cracks filled with minerals and may be mistaken for fossil turtle shells. Although concretions are not fossils, some of them contain fossils such as shells, fish, or insects.

INTERPRETATION OF FOSSILS

What fossils tell us. Some fossils, such as imprints, tell us what the organism did but reveal little or nothing about the creature itself. Some dinosaurs are known only by their fossil footprints, which show that they walked on muddy

FIG. 23–9. An artist's conception of prehistoric men making paintings on the wall of a cave. (*American Museum of Natural History*)

banks. Some evidences of fossil snails are merely furrows formed as the animals moved along on top of the mud. Thus, imprints are rather discouraging to a scientist who wants to know the traits of these early animals so he can place them in a group to which they belong.

Only a very small proportion of the animals and plants that have lived on earth have left traces that geologists can study. To piece together pictures of life in the various geological ages is somewhat like trying to reconstruct a whole city by examining only its parks or cemeteries. However, when all the bits of evidence are assembled and carefully examined, the scientist finds that some of them provide an amazing amount of detail. One such example is a fossil in amber of a spider in its web showing the silken strands so clearly that individual threads can be traced to separate spinning tubes.

When the many facts are assembled, an over-all view brings one main picture of life into clear focus. This picture shows a continuous parade of living things on earth starting with the oldest and simplest forms. These are often found in the lowest layers of rocks, although not necessarily always. The forms of life then continually change, becoming more and more complex in structure until the diverse forms of the recent past, some of which are still in existence today, appear. Many of the simple life forms are still with us, of course, and many new forms occur among the flora and fauna we know today.

Fossils tell us that certain plants and animals flourished during past ages and then became extinct. As these forms disappeared, probably because of an inability to adjust to a changing environment, new forms took their places.

Where fossils are found. Those who contemplate making a collection of fossils commonly ask, "Where can I find them?" Maps of good collecting areas are available in technical books, pamphlets, and magazines. Information about the best collecting areas can be

FIG. 23–10. An unusual photograph of a fossil trilobite in a typical coiled position. (*Ward's Natural Science Establishment*)

obtained from other collectors or from museum labels. Many students go out into the field and search the rock layers exposed in gorges, in quarries, and rock cuts along railroads or highways.

Fossils may be found in almost any kind of sedimentary rock. Shales and limestones are especially likely sources. Dolomite and sandstone are often good. Unusual sedimentary rocks that are frequently sources of unique or well-preserved fossils include chalk, diatomaceous earth, and coal. Fossils are not found in igneous rocks, and those present in rocks which underwent metamorphism were usually destroyed or greatly distorted. Searching conglomerates and cherts brings poor results because any fossils that exist in these rocks are usually difficult to remove.

The collector should note the exact locality and bed from which his fossils come. Essential data should be written on the label for each specimen as soon as possible in order to avoid confusion at a later date. The necessary collecting tools include a geologist's hammer with a chisel end, or an ordinary hammer with a cold chisel one inch wide. A butcher knife to separate the layers of soft shale, and a 24-inch wrecking bar to move large slabs of rock are useful tools. (Be very careful with them.) Other equipment which is valuable includes a notebook, knapsack, a pocket magnifier, and containers such as cigar boxes and paper bags.

Specimens should be cleaned at home in order to avoid wasting time and breaking them in the field. Fossils can be cleaned by washing with water. The rock enclosing them can be trimmed down by using a hacksaw, a knife, or a chisel. Needles are used to clean small specimens. Silicified fossils in limestone often nearly perfect, may be obtained by dissolving the rock in weak hydrochloric or sulfuric acid.

If you decide to make a collection of fossils, you will want to classify them into groups with, let us say, the brachiopods together in one section, the trilobites in another section, and so on. Each group should be composed of those members that have characteristics in common. An excellent system of classification has been set up by experts, and scientists all over the world use it.

CLASSIFICATION OF FOSSILS

The Linnaean system. Fossils are classified by geologists in the same way in which plants and animals are classified by biologists. The system used today was employed by Carolus Linnaeus (li-*nee*-us), a Swedish scientist. About the middle of the eighteenth century, he set out to classify and name all the then known plants, animals, and minerals of the earth, including the fossils. The Linnaean system of classification is based on structures which indicate relationships among groups of living things.

The millions of known organisms are classified in this system in one of two kingdoms; the *plant kingdom* and the *animal kingdom.* Within each kingdom are set up a number of smaller divisions called *phyla.* Each of these phyla is subdivided into *classes* which are further broken down into subdivisions called *orders.* Orders are divided into *families,* which in turn are composed of *genera.* Each genus comprises one or more closely related kinds of animals or plants and each different kind is known as a *species.* Some species are even further divided into minor categories called *varieties.* The relationship of these terms is clearly seen in the following arrangement:

FIG. 23–11. Carolus Linnaeus, who developed the scientific system of classifying living things. (*Bettmann Archive*)

Kingdom
Phylum
Class
Order
Family
Genus
Species
Variety

Under the Linnaean system each animal and plant has a *scientific name.* This name is used by scientists in all countries and consists of two Latinized words. The first word is the name of the genus (always capitalized); the second is that of the species (never capitalized). Thus, the name of the white oak is *Quercus alba L.* (The "L" stands for Linnaeus, and indicates that he was the scientist who named the plant first.) *Quercus* is the name of the genus to

which *all* oak trees belong. The name *alba* refers only to the species white oak, but remember there are many different species of oaks. The red oaks belong to the species *rubra* (*Quercus rubra*), the live oaks to the species *virginiana,* and so on.

The Linnaean system is used both for living and fossil forms of organisms. Because each organism has a name consisting of two parts (genus and species), the system is referred to as the *binomial system of nomenclature.*

In the pages that follow, you will see photographs and labeled diagrams of fossils representing the types of organisms in each phylum of plants and animals. You will find the diagrams helpful in understanding the more technical descriptions of fossils found in certain reference books. The descriptions given here will serve as an introduction to the fascinating study of fossil classification.

PROTOZOA

Protozoa are a phylum of animals whose entire body is composed of a single cell containing living protoplasm enclosed by a cell membrane. Present-day protozoans are very much like the fossil forms. Although most are so small that they cannot be seen without a microscope, they carry on the same basic life activities as larger and more complex forms in the animal kingdom. For instance, like many-celled animals, protozoans obtain energy from food. With the exception of some forms which contain chlorophyll and produce food by photosynthesis as green plants do, protozoans must obtain their food from the environment. The food must enter the living cell through the cell membrane and waste products leave through this membrane. Only two groups of present-day protozoans left important fossil records: the *foraminifers* (for-uh-*min*-i-ferz) and the *radiolarians*. Foraminifers are small, most being microscopic in size, and most of them secrete a shell of calcium carbonate. Most live on the bottom of shallow seas, but a few float. Their remains have been found in both shallow and deep water deposits. The extensive chalk cliffs of England and France are

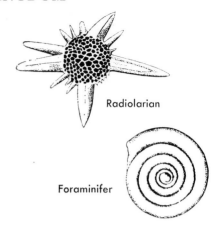

Radiolarian

Foraminifer

composed wholly of the remains of simple organisms, mostly foraminifers.

Radiolarians usually have silicious shells of remarkably intricate design. Some shells are needlelike, some round, but almost all have open network structures of delicate beauty.

The reason relatively few protozoans have left fossils is chiefly that most of them consist only of protoplasm. Those with skeletons or other hard parts have left us evidence of their past existence. Most of these are so small that they are usually overlooked.

Since some of the earliest known rocks do contain protozoan fossils, most geologists think that protozoans have existed longer than any other animals.

Fossil Radiolarian

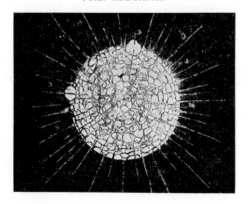

Fossil Foraminifer

PORIFERA

The bodies of the phylum Porifera, or *sponges,* contain not one, but many cells. They are usually classed in the next position above the protozoans on the scale of complexity. They always live in the water, often attached to other objects. Their bodies are composed of an outer and inner layer of cells, separated by another layer of jellylike protoplasm. These bodies are supported by a framework of calcium carbonate, silica, or a substance called *spongin.* The supporting structure varies greatly. In some species, called the "glass sponges," it consists of glasslike fibers of silica intricately arranged to form a beautiful network. These hard skeletal structures are the part of sponges usually preserved as fossils. Their remains are found in rocks from the Cambrian to the Tertiary.

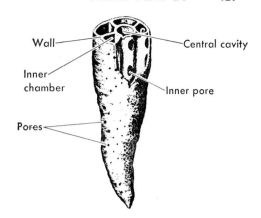

Fossil Sponge

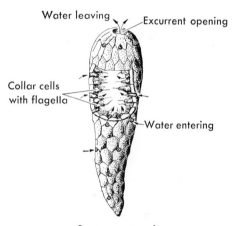

Sponge restored

Fossil Silicious Sponge

Fossil Calcareous Sponge

The body walls of sponges are perforated by pores. Through these pores, water is carried into a central cavity and flows out through one or more larger openings. Special *collar cells,* which possess flagella (whiplike projections of protoplasm), push a current of water into the central cavity. With the water, food particles enter the collar cells and are digested in the central cavity.

The outer, flat, protective cells receive their nourishment by absorption from the interior cells. This division of labor among the sponge cells represents an advancement over the protozoans.

COELENTERATA

This phylum includes such familiar animals as the *jellyfishes,* whose soft bodies rarely produced fossils; the *hydroids* (including *Hydra*), which are colonial forms that resemble plants in one stage of their development and free-swimming, saucerlike individuals in another stage; the *corals,* a group noted for their limy skeletons; and the *sea anemones.*

The mouth opening of the coelenterates (suh-*len*-ter-ayts) is usually surrounded by tentacles and serves both as an entrance to or exit from the digestive cavity. Most members of this group

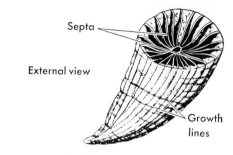

Septa

External view

Growth lines

Fossil cup coral

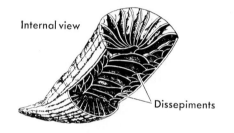

Internal view

Dissepiments

Fossil Cup Coral

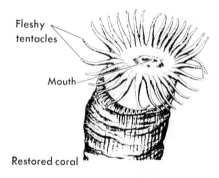

Fleshy tentacles

Mouth

Restored coral

Fossil Chain Coral

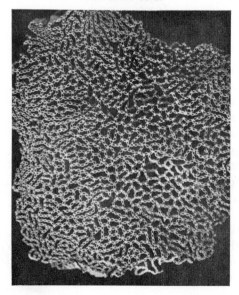

have stinging cells which serve as a means of protection. Almost all live in salt water.

Fossil corals are found in every geologic period from the Ordovician to the present. In the past, just as today, they formed many extensive reefs. Three forms were common during the Paleozoic era: (1) *cup corals,* (2) *chain corals,* and (3) *honeycomb corals.* Chain corals were abundant during the Silurian period. The specimen shown here stands out clearly because the limestone enclosing it has been dissolved away by natural acids.

Another group of fossils characteristic of the Silurian period are the *graptolites.* The term *graptolites,* meaning "written stones," comes from the fact that the fossils resemble pen or pencil marks on the rocks. Although graptolites are abundant in some formations, they have been a puzzle for many years.

The earliest known graptolites formed small colonies and were anchored to shells or to firm mud. It is probably for this reason that they seem not to have become widely distributed. Some colonies were fanlike and consisted of branches that divided again and again with connecting cross-bars called *dissepiments.* They had short stalks and were attached at the base to the sea bottom. Other graptolites grew suspended downward from the bottoms of floating seaweed. These drifted great distances and so had a wide distribution.

Although graptolites were probably widespread in ancient seas, their fossils are seldom found in rocks other than black shales. One possible reason for this is that their skeletons were so delicate they were ground to bits by sand and coarse sediments. In addition, it is likely that trilobites may have destroyed many skeletons. However, black shales seem generally to have been deposited

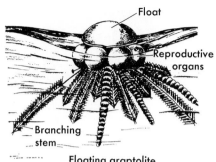

Floating graptolite

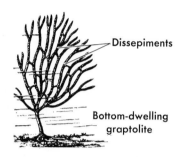

Bottom-dwelling graptolite

in stagnant waters which contained little, if any, oxygen, but a considerable amount of poisonous hydrogen sulfide. Under these conditions scavengers and organisms of decay probably were scarce or absent, and so the dead graptolites which settled to the bottom were undisturbed until they became buried in the fine black mud. Most fossil graptolites are found today carbonized, in black shales formed from such mud.

Fossil Graptolites

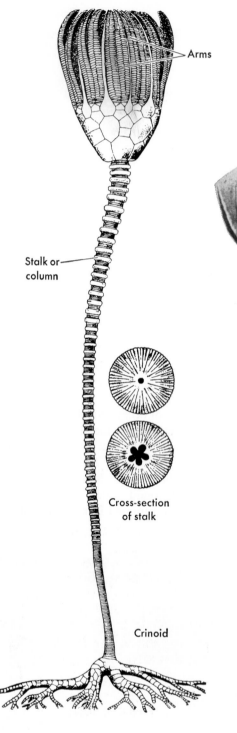

Arms

Stalk or column

Cross-section of stalk

Crinoid

Blastoid

Cystoid

ECHINODERMATA

The echinoderms (e-*kyn*-o-derms) show *radial symmetry,* which is a body plan like a star or wheel. The skeletons of this phylum are calcareous plates with many spines, some movable. All are marine animals, of six main classes:

1. Cystoids, many of which were shaped like sausages attached to the bottom by a stalk, lived from Cambrian to Permian times. They all are now extinct.

2. Crinoids (*krin*-oydz), or sea lilies, are somewhat like starfish. They were abundant in the Paleozoic and exist today.

3. Blastoids, or sea buds, looked like little nuts anchored to the ends of short stalks. They are now extinct.

4. Asteroids, or free-swimming starfish, are common today as they have been from the Devonian on.

5. Echinoids, or sea-urchins, were probably abundant during early geologic times, but fossils are not very common.

6. Holothurians (hoh-loh-*thoo*-ree-unz), called sea cucumbers, have soft bodies and therefore only rarely formed fossils, but they are well known today.

VERMES

Any classification of animals must take into account the fossil worms which paleontologists consider in a category called *Vermes*. Biologists, however, divide the modern worms into three distinct phyla.

1. Platyhelminthes (*plat*-ih-hel-*min*-theez) is the group which includes the *flatworms*. These are the simplest of worms and the earliest animals that have bodies composed of three distinct layers of cells instead of only two, as the coelenterates do. No free-living flatworms have been found as fossils, but a few parasitic forms have been observed in carbonized insects.

2. Nemathelminthes (*nem*-a-thel-*min*-theez) includes the *roundworms* or *threadworms*. Parasitic types have been found in fossil insects.

3. Annelida (a-*nel*-ih-da) includes the *segmented worms,* such as *earthworms, leeches, sand* and other *sea worms,* with bodies composed of ring-like sections. The large majority of worms belong to this phylum. The only

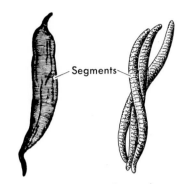

Fossil annelid worm and worm burrows

Scolecodonts of fossil worms

hard parts preserved are toothlike structures called *scolecodonts* (sko-*lee*-ko-donts). Indirect evidence in the form of cylindrical borings, worm trails, and casts are found in many rocks.

Fossil Starfish

Fossil Worm Casts

BRACHIOPODA

Brachiopods are a phylum of marine, shelled animals, many of which resemble some types of clams and scallops. They were very abundant during the Paleozoic era but few species are living today. Brachiopods have digestive systems, reproductive systems, nervous systems, and muscle systems; they show greater complexity than coelenterates. Brachiopods have shells consisting of two valves. In clams the valves are located along the sides of the body, but in the brachiopods one valve lies on the ventral (stomach) side and the other on the dorsal (back) side. The deeper and more projecting valve is the ventral one. Projecting from the point of this valve is a muscular stalk (*pedicle*) by which the animal is attached to solid objects. The various genera and species of brachiopods are identified in part by the structure of the valves. The names of these structures are in the diagrams.

Many modern brachiopods inhabit ocean bottoms 150 to 1500 feet deep although some thrive at depths of 2500 to about 18,000 feet. Most, however, live in shallow waters or in the tidal zone. Rocks from the Cambrian, as well as Devonian, containing both brachiopods and wave marks, indicate that some of these ancient forms inhabited the old shore areas.

Many brachiopods are excellent index fossils and therefore are a great help in correlating the rock layers of the earth. Growth lines on the shells of brachiopods indicate changes in size and shape from early stages to maturity and into old age. These growth lines and other structures that show attachment or changes in form and habitat are helpful clues to the history of ancient brachiopods.

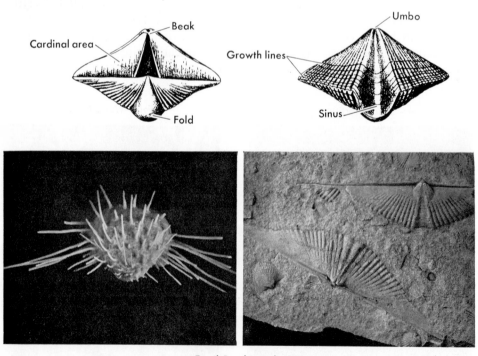

Fossil Brachiopods

BRYOZOA

Bryozoans are a little-known phylum whose general structure resembles most closely the brachiopods. These very small animals have simple calcareous skeletons which are in the form of small tubes or boxes. They form colonies which have built up extensive limestone deposits, and are thus of geologic importance. Bryozoan colonies show considerable variety of form. Some are branching and leaflike, while others look like mosses. This is why the members of the group are called "moss animals." Sometimes they are confused with corals, but careful observation shows that the individual animals which make up the colony are much smaller than those of the coral colony. Early stages of the bryozoan colony differ from those of the corals in that the coral larva develops directly into a fleshy animal called the *polyp,* which produces others like itself. A larval bryozoan becomes a round

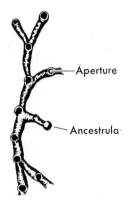

Aperture

Ancestrula

Fossil bryozoan

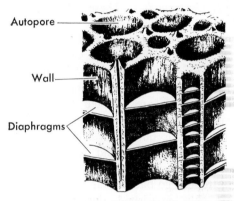

Autopore

Wall

Diaphragms

Enlarged section

Fossil Bryozoans

ancestrula from which a tubelike structure develops. The living part of the bryozoan has a saclike body composed of three layers of cells. The lowermost end of the body is closed, but the other end bears a ring of tentacles around the mouth. *Cilia* (hairlike structures) on these tentacles beat back and forth, producing currents that aid in capturing food. Digestion takes place in a U-shaped tract that ends in an anus lying outside the tentacles and a short distance below the mouth. The boxlike compartments, or tubes, of the colonies are easy to observe; these complex structures as seen in cut sections are the basis of identification of the various species.

MOLLUSCA

The word *Mollusca* means "soft bodied." The members of this large phylum have no true appendages and their bodies are not divided into segments. Most of them are protected by calcareous shells produced by a structure called the *mantle* that covers the body of the animal underneath the shell. The lower part of the body is a muscular structure that is generally used for locomotion and is called the *foot*.

There are three classes of Mollusca.

1. Gastropods. These *"stomach-footed"* animals include the snails, conches, and abalones. Most of the members of this class have single shells, which are coiled, but some are straight or irregular tubes. Some of the members of the group are adapted for life in marine waters, others live in fresh water, and still others on land. All the land-dwelling snails and some of the fresh-water snails have simple lungs. Gastropods go back as far as the Paleozoic, but flourished during Triassic times. They are fairly common today.

2. Pelecypods (peh-*les*-ih-podz). These *"ax-footed"* animals include the *clams, mussels, scallops* and *oysters.* Their shells usually are composed of three layers of protective material—an outer horny layer, a middle layer of limy material similar to china, and an inner pearly coating. The oysters have no definite symmetry, but most of the others of the group are *bilaterally symmetrical,* having definite right and left sides. The pelecypods lack eyes, separate heads, and tentacles. The foot is the under part of the body, although in most species it is narrow and hatchet-shaped rather than broad and flat. These animals absorb oxygen from the water with platelike gills. Many kinds of fossil shells belonging to these fresh-water and marine mollusks occur in rocks of the Ordovician period and those of the Triassic contain great quantities of them. They are also abundant today in shallow waters of lakes and oceans.

3. Cephalopods (*sef*-uh-loh-podz). The *"head-footed"* animals include the nautilus, the squid, and the octopus. Most members of the group have bilateral symmetry. The shells are external in some species and in others are internal or absent. Cephalopod shells differ from those of gastropods in that the interior of the cephalopod shell is divided into compartments by walls called *septa.* The animal lives only in the outer compartment. The nature and position of the septa can be seen on the surface of the polished shell as cracks called *sutures,* which aid in their identification. *Nautiloid* shells have smooth sutures. Their

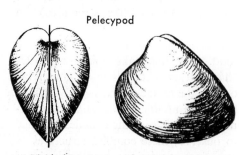

Pelecypod

Divided into two equal parts by a line between the valves

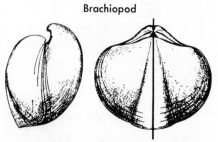

Brachiopod

Divided into two equal parts by a line across the valves

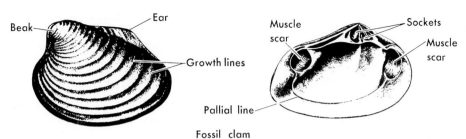

Beak — Ear — Growth lines

Muscle scar — Sockets — Muscle scar

Pallial line

Fossil clam

coiled shells range in size from a fraction of an inch to a diameter of three feet in one species. *Nautiloids* are related to the giant Paleozoic *Orthoceras* (or-*thos*-er-as) a straight-shelled type which reached a length of 15 feet. *Ammonites* are similar to nautiloids.

One extinct group of mollusks, *belemnites* (*bel*-em-*ny*-teez), had bodies with a vestigial shell, similar to that of *Orthoceras,* buried inside its flesh.

In the modern *squid* and *octopus* the shell is reduced to nothing. Some squids reach a length of 50 feet. These animals are propelled by jets of water. They have eyes that are able to see images, and some deep-sea species are luminescent. Ancestral forms of these soft-bodied creatures are rarely found as fossils.

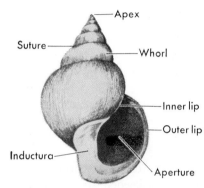

Apex — Suture — Whorl — Inner lip — Outer lip — Inductura — Aperture

Fossil Snail

Fossil Ammonite

Fossil Cephalopod

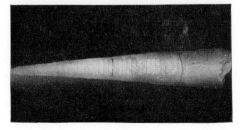

ARTHROPODS

Members of the arthropod phylum are characterized by jointed appendages (*arthros,* joint; *poda,* feet), segmented bodies, and a protective outer skeleton (exoskeleton). The phylum includes land dwellers and forms that live in both fresh and salt water.

One class of arthropods, the *crustaceans,* which includes crabs, lobsters, and shrimps, is represented by many fossil and modern forms. The modern horseshoe crab, or king crab, is famous as a living "fossil," because it has survived with only slight change since the beginning of Permian times. Related to this crab are the fossil *eurypterids* (yoo-*rip*-ter-idz), or sea scorpions, which sometimes exceeded six feet in length, and are the largest known arthropods.

Trilobites are an extinct group of marine arthropods that varied in length from a fraction of an inch to 24 inches, but most species were under 3 inches long. Some species were blind, but most had eyes which had a complex structure well adapted to receive an image.

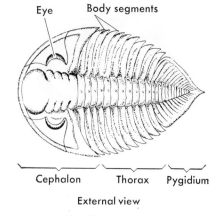

External view

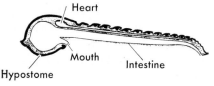

Lengthwise section

The upper shell of these animals was convex and the lower shell concave or flat. The outer skeleton was divided into many movable joints which allowed the animal to roll into a ball for protection. Several segments were consolidated to form a *cephalon* or head shield, and several hind segments were joined to form a *pygidium* (py-*jid*-ee-um) or tail shield. The upper surface of the shell from the back of the cephalon to the tail end was divided by two depressions into three lobes—the characteristic from which the name *trilobite* comes. The trilobites had leaflike swimmers, similar to those of the king crab, which absorbed oxygen from the sea water by means of gills. The trilobites molted frequently, so their fossil remains present a bewildering array of different types.

Ostracods are relatively small crustaceans that are exceptional in that they have two valves and unsegmented bodies. At one time many types of ostracods ranged widely over the earth, but none

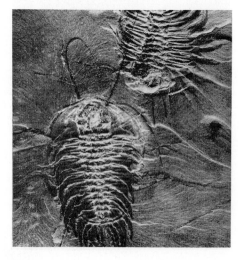

Fossil Trilobites

of these species survived very long. They made their first appearance in the Ordovician period of the Paleozoic era, but apparently became extinct after the Pennsylvanian.

The modern *arachnids*—spiders, mites, ticks, and scorpions—are another class of arthropods that are closely related to the king crab and the eurypterids. They have four pairs of legs and two body parts called the *cephalothorax* and the *abdomen*. This group appeared first during the Devonian period and still exists today.

Of the modern arthropods, *insects* are the largest and most successful group. They have three pairs of legs and three main body parts: the head, the thorax, and the abdomen. They breathe through tiny abdominal openings called spiracles. Their 900,000 species outnumber all other living things four to one. We first meet the insects in the early Devonian, where their fossils occur in some strata of that period.

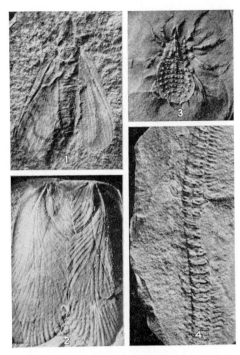

Fossil Arthropods; 1 and 2 Cockroaches; 3 Spider; 4 Myriapod

Fossil Ant

Fossil Sea Scorpion

CHORDATA

The *vertebrates,* animals with backbones, have more highly organized bodies than the invertebrate animals which we have been discussing. Vertebrates have a hollow, central *nerve cord* running the length of their backbone. They have heads with highly specialized sense organs, and well-developed brains. Their supporting skeletons are internal (endoskeletons) consisting of bone or cartilage, with skulls, backbones, ribs, pelvic and pectoral girdle bones, and pelvic and pectoral limb bones, as shown in the diagram.

There are five main classes of vertebrates: fishes, amphibians, reptiles, birds, and mammals.

Pisces (*pis*-eez). Fishes are a class of cold-blooded marine or fresh-water animals with single or paired fins. Most of them are covered with protective *scales* and have *gills* or accessory organs similar to lungs. Most types develop from eggs which are laid in the water.

The *ostracoderms* (*os*-tra-koh-dermz) are extinct fishlike animals, probably not closely related to true fishes. They had neither backbones nor ordinary jaws, but were protected on the outside by bony plates in the head region and flexible plates over the rest of the body.

The *elasmobranchs* (ee-*las*-moh-brangks) are the sharks and rays. They have skeletons of *cartilage.* The only hard parts are the teeth and the fin spines. These parts are found as fossils in rock layers as old as the Silurian, and the group is represented today in marine faunas.

The *teleosts* (*tel*-ee-osts) are the fishes with bony skeletons. They include common fishes such as trout, bass, cod, tuna, and mackerel, and occur in both salt and fresh water.

The *dipnoans* (lungfishes) are an interesting group because they have lungs capable of absorbing oxygen from the air, in addition to gills. They are rare today, but were common during the Devonian.

The *ganoids* (garfishes) are heavily

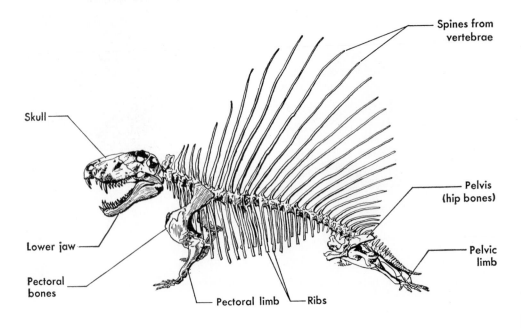

Spines from vertebrae

Skull

Lower jaw

Pectoral bones

Pectoral limb

Ribs

Pelvis (hip bones)

Pelvic limb

Fossil Bony Fish

land vertebrates. In these surroundings amphibians flourished and advanced from primitive *stegocephalians* of the late Devonian to the more highly developed amphibians that were likely to become the ancestors of reptiles. Evidence indicates that during the Permian, dry climates prevailed and vast forests were largely replaced by deserts. Living things were probably greatly influenced by these changes. It may be that some amphibians that underwent changes in their body structures were able to survive the dry conditions and that these changed forms of amphibians gave rise to the first reptiles.

Fossil Amphibian Skeleton

armored and are represented today by the sturgeon and garpikes.

The *crossopterygians* (kro-*sop*-ter-*ij*-ee-anz), or fringe-finned ganoids, are fossil forms with lobed front fins which are thought to have developed into the limbs of terrestrial vertebrates, such as the amphibia.

Amphibia. Amphibians (frogs, toads, salamanders) are a class of *cold-blooded* animals with a smooth, slimy skin. The eggs of most of them hatch in water and develop into tadpoles which swim by means of fins and have gills to absorb oxygen from the water. The tadpoles go through a series of changes (metamorphosis) to become adults, usually with legs and lungs.

In the warm, moist climate of the Carboniferous period, living conditions appear to have been excellent for the development of land snails, insects, and other animals that provided food for the

Reptilia. The reptile class includes the fossil dinosaurs and fossil and present-day lizards, alligators, turtles, and snakes. They breathe with *lungs* throughout their lives. Their eggs are laid on land or hatch inside the mother, and the young emerge fully developed. All reptiles are *cold-blooded* and have scales or armor plates.

Reptiles were dominant from the Triassic to the Cretaceous but they declined during the Tertiary period. The *ichthyosaurs* (fish lizards) and the *plesiosaurs* (long-necked lizards) began to develop during the Cambrian and reached their greatest distribution during the Permian.

By far the most spectacular of the prehistoric reptiles were the dinosaurs, many of which reached gigantic size. The two main groups are based on the structure of their pelvic bones, as shown in the diagram. Those of the first group, called the *Saurischia* (saw-*ris*-kee-uh), were arranged in a radial fashion, as in the lizards. This group includes all of the flesh-eating dinosaurs, such as *Tyrannosaurus,* and some plant-eaters such as *Brontosaurus.* The second group of dinosaurs, called the *Ornithischia* (awr-nih-*this*-kee-uh), had pelvic bone structure similar to that of birds. These were plant-eaters which walked on all four legs, such as *Trachodon* and *Stegosau-*

Fossil Crocodile Skull and Jaws

rus. They either developed a bony armor for protection, or escaped from their enemies by running or by retreating to river and swamp environments. *Stegosaurus* had hind legs which were longer than its front legs, so that its hips stood higher than the other parts of its body. Its head was carried close to the ground and its back was protected by a series of plates with sharp edges pointed upright at alternating angles. Its tail carried two pairs of massive spikes. One of the animals in this group, the duck-billed dinosaur, *Trachodon,* was a favorite food of the flesh-eating *Tyrannosaurus.* Scientists know this because they have found marks of the teeth of *Tyrannosaurus* in the bones of this harmless, plant-eating dinosaur.

Ornithischian pelvis

Saurischian pelvis

The *pterosaurs* (*tehr*-oh-sawrz) were winged reptiles closely related to the dinosaurs. Their wings were made of sheets of skin similar to those of bats, which are flying mammals. Some flying reptiles were extremely large, while others were as small as present-day crows. Their bones were hollow and therefore light, enabling the animals to fly. The hind limbs of the largest species, Pteranodon, were so small that they could not have borne its weight. In spite of their efficient adaptations for flying, the pterosaurs became extinct at about the same time as the dinosaurs, that is, at the end of the Cretaceous period.

The *Chelonia* (ke-*loh*-nee-uh), the turtles, and the *Crocodilia,* the crocodiles and alligators, made their appearance during the Triassic and continued to the present.

The *Lacertilia* (*las*-er-*til*-ee-uh), the true lizards, are still abundant today in many regions of the world. Fossils of the earliest known lizards are found in Jurassic rocks.

Skeleton of Tyrannosaurus

The *Ophidia* (oh-*fid*-ee-uh), the snakes, first appeared in the Cretaceous and have continued in the present day. Snakes are closely related to lizards, although they lack legs and have a peculiar type of hinged jaw not found in any other reptiles.

Skeletons of Homo (man) and Brontosaurus

Aves. The birds are a class of *warm-blooded* animals that lack teeth and have wings as forelimbs. The young hatch from eggs protected by a hard shell. Birds seem to have first appeared in the Mesozoic era at the time when the reptiles were most predominant on earth. This is not surprising because birds apparently came from reptilian ancestors. The scales on the legs of birds resemble those of reptiles, and feathers are really modified scales.

Archaeopteryx (*ar*-kee-*op*-ter-iks) is a fossil animal which shared both reptilian and bird traits. It had feathers like those of birds but teeth and a bony skeleton similar to those of reptiles. The fossil pictured here was found in Jurassic rocks in Germany. Its jaw, neck, and head were covered with a scaly skin and it had a long, bony tail like that of lizards. The skeletal framework shows that *Archaeopteryx* was probably a glider and not a true flyer. Claws on the

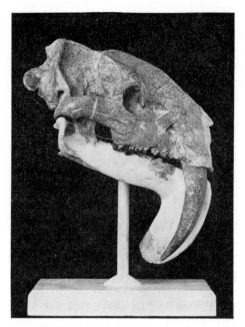

Skull of Fossil Sabertooth Marsupial

Archaeopteryx

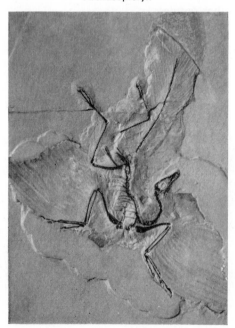

wings undoubtedly served as fingers, which may have been used for climbing trees.

A group of animals known as the *toothed birds* became extinct at the close of the Cretaceous, but their fossils are rare. The ancestors of modern birds were thus in existence before the age of mammals.

Mammalia. Mammals, like birds, are a *warm-blooded* class, but their bodies are covered with *hair* instead of feathers. They breathe by means of lungs, as do the reptiles and birds, but most of the mechanical work of breathing is done by a muscular diaphragm that separates the chest and abdominal cavities.

Mammals usually have two sets of teeth: the milk teeth, which are temporary, and the permanent teeth. The class takes its name from the *mammary glands* which provide milk for the young.

Scientists believe that the first mammals may have descended from reptiles called *theromorphs,* which had unusually large brains for reptiles. Theromorphs also had incisor, canine, and molar teeth, which no other reptile group possessed.

The earliest known mammals lived in the Permian and possibly as early as the Carboniferous, but the large majority of them developed during the Tertiary period of the Cenozoic era.

To simplify the study of mammals it is common practice to group them into three major subclasses, each of which is then divided into several orders. We can here examine very briefly only the three subclasses.

1. Monotremes are the egg-laying mammals. The duck-billed *platypus* and the spiny anteater are examples of this primitive branch that has retained the reptilian trait of laying eggs with tough shells. This is the most primitive mammalian group.

2. Marsupials are pouched mammals. The development of an outer pouch is considered to be the next step in the advancement of mammals. Marsupials like the opossum and kangaroo do not lay eggs like those of reptiles. Instead, the eggs are retained inside the uterus of the mother where the young begin to develop. They are born in this immature stage, and continue their development in the pouch which contains mammary glands. These glands furnish food for the growing young animals.

3. Placentals are mammals that have a *placenta,* a spongy pad that lines the inside of the uterus of the mother. Food and oxygen are brought to the placenta by the mother's blood stream and there pass through the walls of blood vessels into the blood stream of the embryo (developing organism). Meanwhile the body wastes of the embryo pass out of the placenta into the mother's blood. Most present-day mammals belong to this group. Some important members of this subclass include: gnawing mammals, or *rodents* (mice, rats, squirrels); hooved mammals, or *ungulates* (cows and horses); meat eaters with sharp canine teeth and claws, or *carnivores* (dogs and cats); those with trunks, the *proboscids* (elephants); and *primates* (monkeys, apes, and man).

Restoration of Mastodon, left, and Mammoth, right.

THALLOPHYTA

There are two systems of classification of plants but for convenience we will use the older, traditional system here, dividing plants into four phyla.

The thallophytes comprise a large group of many different kinds of relatively simple plants. They possess a soft, nonwoody structure and lack circulatory (vascular) tissue. Many of them grow in or near water, or in a moist environment. The phylum is divided into two main groups, the *algae* (pond scums, seaweeds) and the *fungi* (mushrooms, molds, smuts). Only the algae have chlorophyll, which enables them to manufacture food from water and carbon dioxide with the aid of the sun's energy.

The earliest known fossil thallophytes are one-celled bacteria and blue-green algae which occur in the Huronian rocks of northern Michigan.

1. Algae. In California there are deposits of soft, light earth many feet thick and many square miles in area. This material, seen under the microscope, is composed of the remains of the group of algae called *diatoms* (*dy*-uh-tomz). The cell wall of each diatom consists of two valves fitting over each other at top and bottom like a pillbox. The walls are made of silica. Today we find diatoms in both fresh or salt water and even in damp soils.

Some algae in the blue-green group secrete lime and thus are important rock builders. Many of the red and brown algae (sea weeds) also secrete lime. Some seaweed fossils from Silurian deposits have been reported as being more than 100 feet long and 2 feet wide.

The algae have contributed greatly to the high carbon content of some of the Pre-Cambrian rocks. In some cases whole series of parallel or concentric layers of fossil algae may have formed reefs as early as the Proterozoic era.

2. Fungi. Bacteria are the smallest of the fungus plants but they rank first in importance economically. They take part in the process of fermentation, cause disease, and decompose organic matter just as they have for hundreds of millions of years. Fossil plant tissues from the Pennsylvanian coal beds show, in some cases, destruction of cell walls which is thought to have been caused by bacterial action.

Bacteria may have originated early in the Archeozoic era but there is no evidence of their presence at that time. Nevertheless, the deposition of Pre-Cambrian iron ores is generally ascribed, at least in part, to bacterial action. Paleozoic oil deposits contained bacteria which probably aided in the formation of petroleum and gas by feeding on organic matter in the rocks.

Fossil fungi are scarce because these plants lack hard parts.

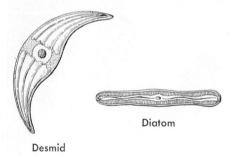

Diatom

Desmid

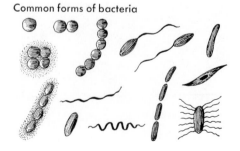

Common forms of bacteria

BRYOPHYTA

The bryophytes (mosses and liverworts) were the first plant phylum to become well established on land. Mosses have stems and simple leaves but no true roots nor vascular tissue. They take in water through short rootlike structures called *rhizoids* (*ry*-zoydz). Because water is necessary for one phase of the reproductive process, bryophytes succeed best in moist environments. In another phase of reproduction, these plants produce microscopic one-celled reproductive structures known as *spores*. These spores are carried by the wind, enabling the bryophytes to spread from one area to another.

Liverworts have green, sheetlike plant bodies and may have been the earliest land plants. Some scientists think that Pre-Cambrian fresh-water lakes were the site of the migration of primitive aquatic plants onto the land. Early lakes became smaller in size during dry weather; as a result the lake margin became first a swamp and finally a marsh or merely damp ground. In this type of environment modern liverworts grow in

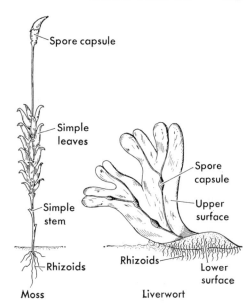

great abundance. They are also found growing on rocks along shady streams.

There are doubtful specimens of fossil mosses in Silurian and Mississippian rocks but no positively identifiable examples appear until the Jurassic. Bryophytes are unimportant as fossils. Scientists believe that these primitive, specialized, land plants have not evolved into other types of plants.

Fossil Diatoms

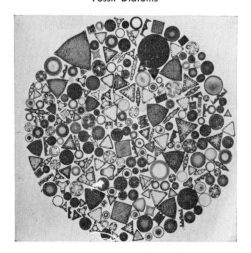

Fossil Algae

PTERIDOPHYTA

The pteridophytes (*ter*-ih-doh-*fyts*) were the first plant phylum to develop true roots, stems, and leaves. Here we find the ferns and fern allies, distributed today in both temperate and tropical climates. Some of the tropical ferns grow to tree size as they did in past geological eras.

The fossils *Rhynia* (*rin*-ee-uh) and *Psilophyton* (sy-*lof*-ih-ton) belong to an order of fern allies called the *psilopsids,* which appeared at the close of the Silurian period and probably became extinct before the end of the Devonian period. During this time some of them may have given rise to the first club mosses, horsetails, and true ferns. *Rhynia* seems to be a relatively simple plant but careful examination shows that it is more complex than any of the bryophytes or thallophytes. The fossil remains show it has an *epidermis* of protective cells as well as special *pores* for the exchange of carbon dioxide and oxygen and for the elimination of sur-

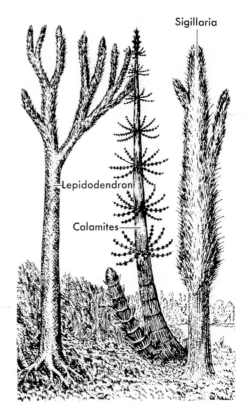

Sigillaria

Lepidodendron

Calamites

Fossil Fern Leaf

plus water. Its cells contained *lignin* (*lig*-nin) a chemical substance that makes the cell walls woody. These features, together with the fact that they show a great advancement in their method of reproduction (which resembles that of modern ferns), indicate clearly the great progress in development made by the ancient psilopsids.

Another group of fern allies, the lycopods (club mosses) include about 900 living species, all of which are small, as well as fossil species, many of which were gigantic. During the Carboniferous, large tree-forms, like *Lepidodendron* and *Sigillaria* (*sij*-il-*lay*-ree-uh) pictured here, were common. Their plant bodies helped to form extensive coal beds.

The group known as the equisetums (horsetails) are represented by only 25 living species but many extinct fossil species, including some as large as trees, have been discovered in the rocks. The small leaves of living species are in whorls and the woody stems are jointed, hollow, and green. *Calamites* (*kal*-a-*my*-teez) is a fossil horsetail which seems to have formed great jungles beside rivers and lakes and in prehistoric swamps. Frequently fossil specimens of Calamites are found as sandstone casts, the sediment replacing the pith that once occupied the center of the stems. These usually show characteristic ridges, nodes, and pits to which the branches were attached. Horsetails of the Carboniferous period helped greatly in the formation of coal.

The *Filicales* (*fil*-i-*kay*-leez), or true ferns, are the largest group of pteridophytes today. These plants also dominated the Carboniferous period and their bodies formed organic matter, a large amount of which eventually became coal. There are known many species of fossil ferns, including giant tree ferns, which shaded numerous smaller types that covered the jungle floors. Most modern ferns are small, but some tree ferns found in Hawaii and other tropical

Restored Fossil Seed Fern

environments often reach a height of 30 or 40 feet.

Deposits of coal include great numbers of fossil leaves that were once thought to be those of true ferns. However, ferns always reproduce by means of spores and these plants bore seeds. Thus they belong in a special extinct group called the *seed ferns,* or *pteridosperms.* They are distantly related to our present-day cone-bearing trees (conifers), but seem to be more closely related to modern *cycads.*

Fossil Calamites

SPERMATOPHYTA

The spermatophytes are a phylum which includes those plants which reproduce by seeds. They normally bear either *true flowers,* or *cones.*

1. Gymnosperms or conifers (pine, spruce, fir, cedar) which bear their seeds on the exposed scales of cones, and

2. Angiosperms or true flowering plants, whose seeds develop inside a dry or fleshy fruit.

The gymnosperms are probably the older of the two groups of seed plants. They are pollinated by wind and their leaves are usually needle-like. The *Cordaitales* (*kor*-dah-ey-*tay*-leez) are a group of primitive gymnosperms of the late Paleozoic and may have been the ancestors of the modern conifers. The *Ginkgoales* (*gink*-go-*ay*-leez) are another primitive group of gymnosperms whose fossils have been found in rocks.

Walchia seems to be the earliest simple conifer. It thrived during the Permian with various tree ferns, club mosses and plants like our modern

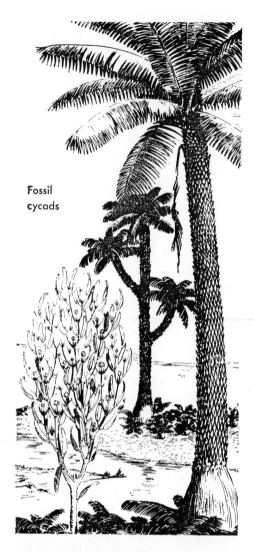

Fossil cycads

Foliage of a fossil conifer

cycads. In the Mesozoic, *cycads* (sago palms) dominated the flora and seed plants continued their remarkable development.

Development in size, while spectacular, was not as important as the increase in complexity which is found in the angiosperms. They are divided into two main groups, the *monocots* and the *dicots.* The monocots have leaves with parallel veins, stems without growth rings, and seeds containing a single seed leaf or *cotyledon* (*kot*-ih-*lee*-dun).

Cordaites, fossil gymnosperm

They include such familiar plants as the orchids and lilies, as well as the grasses, like corn, wheat, oats and rye, which serve as food for many forms of life. Dicots have net-veined leaves, stems with annual growth rings, and seeds containing two cotyledons. Willows, maples, poplars, tulip trees, oaks, roses, beans and thistles are dicots.

Angiosperms probably evolved from some extinct group of gymnosperms. The first members of this most complex and most recently evolved group of plants appeared in the upper Cretaceous. Since then the group has increased in numbers and variety.

Early in the history of the angiosperms, methods of distributing pollen came to be important. The gymnosperms were pollinated by wind, as were the primitive angiosperms, but with the appearance of bright-colored petals, the flowers attracted new pollinators—the insects. Not only did the insects find pollen, but also a sweet drink of nectar for food. As they gathered the food they carried pollen grains on their bodies from flower to flower and thus helped the seeds to form. Without insects, the angiosperms would probably not have been as successful as they now are. In the same way, it may be said that insects might not have been so successful without the flowering plants on which many of them depend.

Fossil Figs

Fossil Ginkgo Leaf

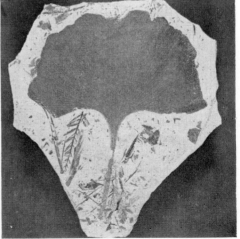

SUMMARY

☯

FOSSILS of prehistoric plants and animals range from patterns or impressions to entire unaltered remains of mammoths.

Fossils are the means of correlating rock layers. If the same group of fossils are found in a New York sandstone and a Georgia sandstone, we assume that the sediments were deposited at the same time. Animals and plants changed through the ages, therefore the succession of rock layers from the past to the present can be worked out.

There are several ways that fossils may form. Animals may be preserved in such a way as to prevent decay. Ground water that contains such mineral matter as silica or pyrite may replace the parts of a shell or other organism. Footprints or trails may be retained when mud hardens into shale.

Fossils are classified by comparing their structure with that of modern plants and animals. The binomial system of Carolus Linnaeus is used in naming fossils as well as modern forms.

VOCABULARY REVIEW

Match the phrase or word in the left column with the correct word or phrase in the right column. *Do not write in this book.*

1. Gizzard stone	**a.** coprolites
2. Product of prehistoric man	**b.** spiders
3. Concretion	**c.** Protozoa
4. Wheel or ringlike structure	**d.** pseudofossil
5. Replacement of parts by mineral matter	**e.** teleosts
6. Jointed legs and exoskeletons	**f.** artifact
7. Fossil resin	**g.** gastroliths
8. Arachnids	**h.** radial symmetry
9. Cartilaginous skelton	**i.** elasmobranchs
10. Fossil waste material	**j.** arthropods
11. Imprints of prehistoric organisms	**k.** molds
12. Single-celled animals	**l.** petrifaction
	m. amber

QUESTIONS . GROUP A

Decide whether these statements are true or false. Reword the false statements to make them true. *Do not write in this book.*

1. The Latin *fodere* means "ancient life."
2. Fossilized regurgitated sand is known as castings.
3. Internal molds are examples of concretions.
4. Index fossils have a wide geological distribution and a narrow geographical range.
5. Fossils bear out the belief that simple organisms developed from complex organisms.
6. The scientific name of man, Homo sapiens, includes the phylum and order.
7. Chalk is composed mainly of fossil foraminifers.
8. Collar cells are used by sponges to force water out of the central cavity.
9. The structure of valves identifies the class and genus of brachiopods.
10. A characteristic of gastropods is bilateral symmetry.
11. An example of a "living fossil" is the horseshoe crab.
12. The Chelonia are virtually unchanged since the Triassic.
13. Marsupials at birth are better developed than other mammals.
14. Amphibians have a well-developed placenta.
15. Diatoms are microscopic fungus plants.
16. The bryophytes gave rise to specialized land plants.
17. The ginkgo is an example of a modern flowering plant.
18. Angiosperms are the highest form of plant life.
19. Invertebrates all have backbones.
20. All animals with two shells are classed as mollusks.
21. All seed plants are classed as gymnosperms.
22. Trilobites are now all extinct.

GROUP B

1. Why are most fossils altered rather than unaltered?
2. Describe the process of petrifaction.
3. Compare and contrast external, internal and artificial molds.
4. Explain why there are few protozoan fossils.
5. Describe the six main classes of echinoderms.
6. How does metamorphosis of the amphibians illustrate the process by which water animals developed into land animals?
7. Name an animal that probably linked the reptiles and the birds. What similar characteristics are possessed by both birds and reptiles? In what characteristics do they differ?
8. Compare and contrast algae and fungi.
9. How is it possible for paleontologists to give a fossil a scientific name when they may only have portions of the plant or animal for identification?

UNIT REVIEW QUESTIONS

1. Discuss the three lines of evidence used by geologists to reconstruct past geologic events.
2. Prehistoric inland seas were usually shallow. Account for the thickness of the sediments deposited in these basins.
3. Explain how mountain building may have affected the climate in past ages.
4. Describe the North American continent during the late Cambrian.
5. What is meant by the consolidation of sediments? Give some examples.
6. Is coal being formed today? Explain the reasoning behind your answer.
7. How do fossils indicate radical changes in climate and sea level? Supply examples.
8. What is the importance of index fossils?
9. Discuss the changes that took place during the Azoic era that made the earth a more suitable place to support life.
10. Discuss the differences between a rock sequence, system, series, group, and formation.
11. Why is the term Archean preferred by some geologists to Archeozoic?
12. What is the relationship of the Proterozoic to present industrial achievement?
13. Why was the sea a more suitable environment than the land for the development of early forms of life?
14. Why do mammals have a wider geographical distribution than reptiles or amphibians?
15. How does the San Andreas rift illustrate that geologic history is not complete?
16. What are some of the mysteries that surround the discovery of the frozen woolly mammoth?
17. Discuss fully the process of carbonization.
18. How can a paleontologist distinguish smooth pebbles that were gastroliths from water-worn rocks?
19. What is meant by the binomial system of classification?
20. What are the general characteristics of amphibians, reptiles, fishes, birds, and mammals?
21. Compare and contrast monotremes, marsupials, and placentals.

ACTIVITIES

1. Make a collection of local fossils. A geologic map should be consulted for the names and periods of local formations. Old quarries, talus slopes, and road cuts are good sources of fossils.
2. Construct models or dioramas to illustrate the climate and the plant and animal life of different periods and eras. The Museums of Natural History in New York and in Chicago are good sources of sketches and photographs of museum exhibits of various eras.

3. Set up a display of models of dinosaurs. Models may be constructed or purchased from dime stores, scientific supply houses, or the Museums of Natural History in New York and Chicago.
4. Obtain a geologic map of your area and draw a rock column to show the chronological order of local bedrock formations.
5. Construct models to illustrate different types of unconformities.
6. On an outline map of North America indicate the land and water areas and draw pictures of the plants and animals during some geologic period.
7. Construct charts to show the "family trees" of plant and animal kingdoms. Illustrate them with drawings or pictures of the organisms listed on the charts.
8. Prepare a report on the theories of how life originated on the earth.
9. Make an exhibit showing actual fossils accompanied by drawings or pictures of what the living plants or animals were like.

FURTHER READING

ALL ABOUT DINOSAURS. R. C. Andrews, 1953. *Random House, New York.*

THE FOSSIL BOOK. C. L. Fenton and M. A. Fenton, 1958. *Doubleday and Co., Inc., New York.*

PREHISTORIC WORLDS: ANIMAL LIFE IN PAST AGES. C. L. Fenton, 1954. *John Day Co., New York.*

INTRODUCTION TO HISTORICAL GEOLOGY. W. J. Miller, 1952. *D. Van Nostrand, Princeton, New Jersey.*

INVERTEBRATE FOSSILS. R. C. Moore, C. G. Lalicker, and A. C. Fisher, 1952. *McGraw-Hill Book Co., New York.*

MAN, TIME AND FOSSILS. R. C. Moore, 1953. *Alfred A. Knopf, New York.*

LIFE OF THE PAST. G. Simpson, 1953. *Yale University Press, New Haven, Conn.*

STRANGE PREHISTORIC ANIMALS. A. H. Verrill, 1947. *L. C. Page and Co., Boston.*

STORIES IN ROCKS. H. Williams, 1947. *Holt, Rinehart and Winston, Inc., New York.*

DINOSAURS. H. Zim, 1954. *Simon and Schuster, Inc., New York.*

WATER, a relatively simple compound of oxygen and hydrogen, is present generally in the solar system. Yet, the earth is apparently unique among the planets in its possession of water in great abundance. The hydrosphere, or water-sphere, is essential to most of the earth processes described in the earlier units of this book. Water is also necessary to the existence of all the forms of life that are found on this planet.

The earth's envelope of water consists not only of the vast sea that surrounds the island continents, but also the water that flows above and below the surface, and fills lakes and ponds. This unit is concerned with the earth's water supply, its composition and its motions. The means we have found to explore and study the hydrosphere are also considered.

UNIT 7

THE EARTH'S ENVELOPE OF WATER

CHAPTER 24

THE EARTH'S WATER SUPPLY

THE earth has not always possessed its present supply of water. There certainly were no oceans or other bodies of liquid water until the earth had passed through its earliest stages and had cooled sufficiently to prevent immediate boiling away of water falling upon its surface. Most of the earth's water must have appeared first in the form of water vapor in the atmosphere. It is believed that as the earth mass grew hot, then slowly cooled, water formed in the molten material. It was then expelled as a gas in the violent volcanic eruptions that were common in the earth's early stages. Heavy layers of clouds must have enveloped the young planet as it gradually cooled. Eventually, when the temperature of the surface reached a critical level, the cloud cover began to drop its

VOCABULARY

Hydrologic cycle. The continuous process by which water is evaporated from the sea, precipitated over the land and eventually returned to the sea.

Meteoric water. That part of the ground water resulting from rain and snow.

Connate water. Water bound within tiny cavities in sedimentary rock.

Magmatic water. Water released from rock by the heat of volcanic activity.

Artesian well. A well penetrating through impervious rock to a water-bearing layer.

Aquifer. A water-bearing layer of porous rock.

Geyser. A hot spring which periodically erupts steam and hot water.

Travertine. A type of calcite deposited from the water around hot springs.

Geyserite. A silica mineral deposited around the openings of geysers and hot springs.

Tarn. A lake formed in a glacial cirque.

Peat. Partially decayed vegetable matter filling a former lake basin.

446

accumulated moisture. Rain began to fall and continued without pause for centuries, thus releasing the earth's water supply to run into the ocean basins and begin the endless cycle of evaporation, rainfall, and drainage across the land surfaces.

THE WATER CYCLE

The hydrologic cycle. With the exception of the moisture that is bound up in certain sedimentary rocks, the entire supply of water on the earth follows an unending sequence of evaporation, precipitation, runoff, and storage, known as the *hydrologic cycle.* The cycle may be illustrated in terms of a limited area.

The average rainfall for the United States is about 30 inches per year, although annual rainfall ranges from the 100-inch totals in the Pacific Northwest to the 5 inches or less that fall in the deserts. Of the 30 inches of annual precipitation, 5½ inches finds its way into streams to become direct surface run-off or travels through the uppermost soil layers and enters the nearest stream channel. Another 3 inches seeps down through the soil to the ground water table. After flowing through roundabout subterranean paths, it eventually reaches stream channels or flows directly to the sea. The remaining 21½ inches is evaporated into the atmosphere from the soil, from plants, or from the surfaces of lakes and streams.

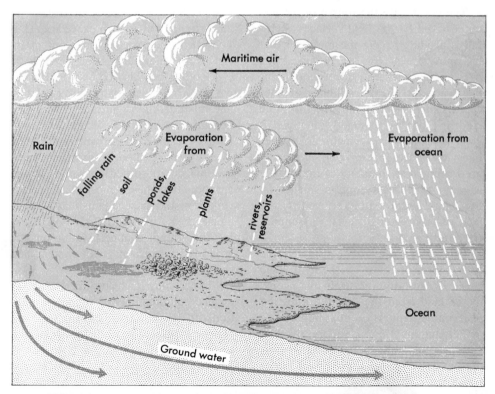

FIG. 24–1. A summary of the hydrologic cycle, showing how water is distributed over the earth by evaporation and condensation.

Since the amount of water returned to the atmosphere by evaporation is about 70 per cent of the total precipitation on the land, it might seem logical to assume that most of the precipitation is simply the return of the recently evaporated moisture. Until a few years ago, this was generally accepted as correct. It was supposed that the evaporation from lakes and large rivers or forests, releasing large amounts of water vapor into the air, made the climate of the immediate vicinity appreciably rainier. Measurements which have been made over a long period do show that large amounts of water are lost by evaporation. However, they also show that this moisture is quickly carried away by air movements and does not return to the land. Most of it falls into the sea as rain.

The oceans are the source of the water received by the land surfaces. Rainfall is produced from the moist air that has moved over the sea surface, then over the land, where it meets conditions that cause it to precipitate its water vapor. Air currents moving from the land to the sea actually function as great invisible rivers which carry water back to the sea. These rivers in the sky are far mightier than any of the surface streams, which carry only a small fraction of the total water received by the land. The hydrologic cycle is summarized in Fig. 24–1.

The oceans may be considered the basic source of water for the hydrologic cycle. Because the moist air must come to the land from the sea, the direction of air movements is of great importance in determining the rainfall received at any location. Without the constant flow of sea air, precipitation cannot occur and a dry climate results. This relationship between air movements and rainfall is discussed further in Chapter 32.

Floods. An adequate supply of fresh water is of such vital importance to our welfare that we often regard the return of water to the land in the form of rain as the crucial part of the hydrologic cycle. Unfortunately for mankind, this is one of the least predictable parts of the process. In most places, rainfall is likely to occur irregularly and in widely different amounts from one time to another. As a result, the streams which carry the surface runoff fluctuate greatly in the amount of water they carry. If the rainfall of a region were governed by the moisture evaporated only from that area, the streams would develop until they were able to accommodate the amount of precipitation characteristic of that particular region. However, rainfall is likely to come in large amounts during storms, and the capacity of streams to carry the runoff is then exceeded. Thus floods can be expected to occur at intervals as a normal part of the cycle.

Flooding can also be expected to occur from relatively light rains if certain natural conditions interfere with the normal runoff. Spring floods are common in regions where winters are cold. The water released by melting snow cannot be absorbed by the frozen ground. It appears mostly as surface runoff in streams. Ice jams may also increase the spring flood hazard by blocking the stream channels. Later on, the ground is saturated with water, and spring rains swell the rivers.

Floods may also be the result of chance combinations of weather conditions. In 1955, hurricanes "Connie" and "Diane" traveled north from the tropics to cause disastrous floods in Connecticut and Massachusetts. In Connecticut, the ground, already saturated with 6 inches of rain from Connie, received 14 inches only one week later from Diane. The

FIG. 24–2. Floods cause tremendous damage in low-lying areas along many of our great rivers. (*Corps of Engineers, U. S. Army*)

normally quiet rivers flooded the heavily populated area with crippling effect. As we have seen (Chapter 18), a small increase in velocity results in a very large increase in the eroding and carrying power of the stream.

In many areas man has increased the size and frequency of floods by removing the natural ground cover which helps to prevent excessive runoff during periods of heavy rain. Plants of all kinds tend to hold the water in the upper soil layers. Forest fires and destructive logging operations or clearing of land to put it under cultivation increase the runoff load on streams. The tendency for each successive flood on big rivers such as the Mississippi to be more destructive than previous ones is probably a result of the destruction of forests, improper agricultural practices, and changing of the natural drainage in the regions that contribute water to the rivers.

Even without interference by man, some degree of flooding is a natural part of the hydrologic cycle and will always occur. It becomes a problem largely because cities and farms are located on the flood plains of streams. The level and fertile land of the flood plains is valuable and often heavily populated. Thus some control over floods in order to protect lives and property becomes necessary. The methods of controlling floods are both direct and indirect. Indirect controls include reforestation and soil conservation measures to prevent the quick runoff of water from the lands drained by rivers subject to flooding. Such measures, to be effective, must be taken by government agencies with power to act over large areas, including parts of several states.

Direct methods of flood control include artificial levees, permanent overflow channels, and dams with artificial

FIG. 24–3. This artificial levee prevents flooding of towns and farms along the lower Mississippi. Note that the homes in the foreground are below the water level of the river. (*Corps of Engineers, U. S. Army*)

lakes to absorb part of the floodwaters. The most common method of flood control is the building of artificial levees which help to confine the streams to their normal channels. This has been done extensively along the Mississippi and other rivers in the United States. See Fig. 24–3. However, it is often a temporary protection against floods because the deposit of sediment in the river beds requires constant increases in the height of the levees. Also, the rivers in flood stage often break through the levees and produce a sudden and much more destructive flood than would have occurred otherwise.

A permanent overflow channel or *floodway,* into which water can be diverted when necessary, is a more effective method of control. Such channels have been constructed along the Atchafalaya River, which parallels the lower part of the Mississippi. The Bonnet Carré spillway, built just north of New Or-

leans in 1932, drains floodwaters into Lake Pontchartrain. In floods in 1936, the floodwater crest at New Orleans was 19.3 feet. According to estimates, the crest would have been 3 feet higher if the spillway had not been available to divert part of the water.

Dams, especially along tributaries of large rivers subject to flooding, help to control floods by creating storage reservoirs to absorb some of the excess runoff. Boulder Dam and Parker Dam, along the upper course of the Colorado River, prevent floods in the Salton Basin of California, which is below sea level. The dams store the water during the heavy spring flow and release it gradually during the low-water period, as it is needed.

The water stored in the reservoirs behind the dams can be used for irrigation as well as flood control, and it generates hydroelectric power as it is released to continue its course down the river. The

WATER USED IN INDUSTRIAL PROCESSES

5 gallons	To process 1 gallon of milk
10 gallons	To produce 1 gallon of gasoline
80 gallons	To generate 1 kilowatt-hour of electricity
300 gallons	To manufacture 1 pound of synthetic rubber
65,000 gallons	To produce 1 ton of steel

··

series of dams in the Tennessee Valley project illustrate how flood control can be achieved on an entire river system. In other cases, a single strategically placed dam, such as Hoover Dam on the Colorado River, may serve the same purposes.

Water conservation. Each person in the United States drinks an average of about 200 gallons of water per year. He consumes another 15,000 gallons each year for washing, laundry, cooking, and the operation of heating and air-conditioning equipment. This personal use of water is insignificant, however, compared with the 160,000 gallons for each person which are used each year by industry. The table above gives some idea of the amounts of water consumed in this way.

To these figures must be added the billions of gallons of water needed by

FIG. 24–4. In many places, water must be purified for human use. This view of a water purification plant shows filtration tanks in the foreground and aeration pipes in the background. (*Puerto Rico News Service*)

agriculture for irrigation. All of this water must be drawn from the approximately 30 percent of the total rainfall in the hydrologic cycle which runs off in streams or enters the ground water supplies. This amounts to about 1300 billion gallons daily in the United States and represents the entire supply of water available for all purposes. As the population of the country grows, the demand for water is exceeding the supply and the conservation of this limited resource becomes a necessity.

On the average, 90 percent of the water used by cities and industries is returned to rivers or the sea as waste. The untreated sewage of more than 30 million people is discharged into rivers in the United States. Also, much of the waste water discharged into rivers by industries contains materials that contaminate the water of the rivers. Such practices mean that cities and industries downstream must purify the water before it can be used. In some cases the contaminating materials render the water unusable even after all practical purification methods have been employed. Thus uncontrolled dumping of wastes into rivers seriously reduces the amount of available water and will become an increasingly serious problem as the population of the country increases. To insure an adequate supply of water for the future it will be necessary to provide better control of water pollution through separation of waste materials so that water may be reused.

It is possible that the supply of fresh water can be increased by treatment of sea water (this subject will be discussed in Chapter 25). However, the best hope in the immediate future for an adequate supply of water at reasonable cost lies in the conservation of the supply which is naturally available.

WATER IN THE EARTH'S CRUST

The water table. In Chapter 18 the water table was described as the surface below which the rocks of the crust for some distance downward are saturated with water. There are three sources of this ground water. Most is *meteoric water:* it is precipitated from the atmosphere as rain or snow. This seeps down into the spaces within the rocks. Some of the ground water is *connate water.* This is the water trapped in microscopic spaces when sedimentary rocks are formed in the beds of seas or lakes. It is usually salty, and unlike meteoric water, it does not move from one location to another within the rocks. A third source of ground water is *magmatic water.* This is water which was formerly chemically bound up in minerals and has been released by heating in volcanic processes.

The depth of the water table at any particular location depends on many factors, the most important being the amount of rainfall in the recent past and the permeability of the rock. Generally speaking, the water table follows the contours of the land surface, sloping down where the surface slopes and rising in higher ground. However, the general slope of the water table is usually not as sharp as that of the land surface because of the resistance encountered by the ground water as it works its way through the cavities in the rock. Thus the water table rises and falls in a gently curving replica of the surface of the ground.

In many places depressions on the land surface dip below the water table. When this occurs, ground water flows out to the surface, forming springs or joining with surface streams, or contrib-

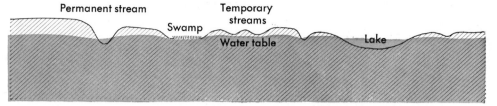

FIG. 24–5. The water table follows the general contour of the land. The permanence of water bodies depends on the depth of the water table below the surface.

uting to the water in lakes or swamps. See Fig. 24–5. Many streams continue to flow in periods of little rainfall because they are fed by a source of ground water.

Just as streams have gradients that are determined by the slope of their beds, the water table has a gradient formed by the slopes corresponding to the slope of the surface. The speed with which ground water moves through the rock depends mainly upon the gradient and the permeability of the rock structure. In very permeable formations with a relatively steep gradient the rate of movement may be several feet per day; however, in most cases it is much less. In times of heavy rainfall the water table rises and conforms more closely to the irregularities in the land surface. Then the gradients are steeper, causing more rapid movement of underground water. During dry periods the water table sinks and becomes more nearly level, so that movement is much slower. In the lowest parts of the zone in which the rocks are saturated with ground water, movement is probably very slight. Here there are gentle gradients and reduced permeability of the rock due to the pressure created by the great weight of overlying rock.

Wells. Any hole dug or drilled into the ground to a depth which reaches the water table will fill with water, forming a well. The rate at which water flows into a well depends upon how rapidly the ground water flows in that particular place. Wells located in sedimentary rocks that are generally permeable in a place where the gradient of the water table is good will usually provide abundant supplies of water. The water withdrawn is quickly replenished by the rapidly moving ground water. However, if the well is too shallow, the water table may drop below the well's bottom in dry periods, and the well goes dry. To insure a permanent supply of water, wells must be sunk deep enough to reach the water table as it drops during dry periods.

In rocks of low permeability, which includes nearly all the igneous and metamorphic types, ground water is restricted to fractures, where there are openings for penetration of the water. Wells sunk in such rock formations only yield water if they happen to intersect a fracture zone; otherwise they are dry. Generally it is not helpful to drill deeper into impervious rocks seeking water because open fractures and cracks diminish with greater depth.

There is one outstanding exception to the rule that sinking a well deeper through impervious rock will not yield water. This is the *artesian well.* In this type of well the water is obtained from a porous rock layer, usually consisting

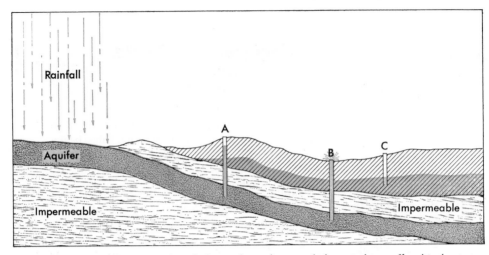

FIG. 24–6. The type of rock formations that result in artesian wells. At *A*, the artesian well does not flow. At *B*, the well flows because it is below the origin of the water, where the aquifer is exposed at the surface. Well *C* collects only ground water from the local area.

of sandstone or loose sand and gravel, which is sandwiched between an upper and a lower layer of impervious rock. The porous layer, called an *aquifer* (*ak-wi-fer*), slants down from the surface. Water entering the porous rock where it is exposed on the surface is confined to this layer, and travels through it, being unable to move either upward or downward through the impermeable layers. See Fig. 24–6. Wells which tap these aquifers are called *artesian* from the region of Artois, France, the location of some of the first such wells. Artesian wells are often drilled several thousand feet deep in order to reach the aquifer. However, ordinary wells are frequently sunk as deep in order to maintain constant contact with the water table; thus it should not be assumed that all deep wells are artesian. Because of its long journey through the aquifer and the shielding against contamination provided by the upper solid layers, the water from artesian wells is generally very pure. However, some artesian wa-

ter does contain objectionable amounts of dissolved minerals. Since they are not dependent on local rains, artesian wells tend to be more reliable than others.

In the United States, artesian wells are common along the Atlantic Coastal Plain where the aquifers are mainly layers of loose sand. In the Middle West, thousands of artesian wells have been

FIG. 24–7. A flowing artesian well. (*Ewing Galloway*)

drilled into an extensive aquifer known as the Dakota sandstone. This highly porous layer of sandstone crops out in the slopes of the Rocky Mountains, the Big Horn Mountains, and the Black Hills. Water absorbed in these mountains is available under large parts of North and South Dakota, Nebraska, Kansas, Wyoming, and Montana. Many other parts of the country have underground rock formations suitable for artesian wells and derive a large part of their water supply from these wells.

Springs. A spring is created wherever the ground water naturally comes to the surface. There are many types of springs, since any opening between the water table and the surface may result in a spring. An example would be a fracture which connects an aquifer with the surface. A spring in such a fracture would be a kind of natural artesian well and would have all the characteristics of most artesian wells, such as purity and continuous flow.

Springs may also occur on hillsides where the water table intersects the land surface. Such springs often do not flow continuously, since the water table may drop too low during dry periods. However, one type of hillside spring which is likely to flow continuously is formed at the zone of contact between permeable and solid rocks. In this case, water filters down through the permeable rock and emerges on a hillside as a spring when it encounters the more dense rock layer. See Fig. 24–8.

Often the water from deep springs contains such a large quantity of dissolved minerals that it is not usable for ordinary purposes. In a few instances, such as the alkali springs of the desert, the water may naturally be poisonous. Sulfur springs contain dissolved hydrogen sulfide gas, which gives the water

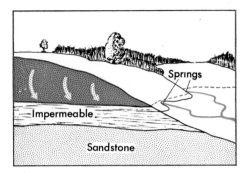

FIG. 24–8. Springs often appear where the water table intersects the surface, above a layer of impermeable rock.

an offensive odor. The water from many springs that contain large amounts of dissolved minerals is supposed to have beneficial health-giving powers. As a result, health resorts have grown up around many mineral springs. There is little scientific evidence, however, to support the belief that water from mineral springs has curative value.

Hot springs and geysers. If ground water is heated as a result of subsurface volcanic activity and then finds its way to the surface before cooling off, a hot spring is produced. The water of a hot spring may be heated by contact with cooling magma or by mixing with steam and hot gases escaping to the surface from bodies of magma deep in the crust. Hot springs are much more common in regions of volcanic activity, since heated rocks lie comparatively close to the surface in these areas.

Temperatures of the various hot springs range from merely warm to boiling; the boiling point varies, of course, depending on the altitude of the spring's location. If a hot spring has a sufficient supply of water to cause a continuous flow, its water normally remains clear and is a deep blue or green color. If evaporation by boiling exceeds the inflow of water, however, particles of mineral matter become concentrated in the water and the spring becomes a mass of boiling mud. Such springs are also called *mud volcanoes.* The mud volcanoes in Yellowstone National Park are known as *paint pots,* because mineral impurities in the mud color the springs purple, red, and yellow.

Hot water is better able to dissolve minerals than cold water. Consequently the water of hot springs is likely to contain unusually large amounts of mineral matter. Much of this dissolved mineral matter is deposited when the water reaches the surface. It accumulates around the mouth of hot springs and tends to build up layers or terraces. See Fig. 24–9. The chief mineral in these terraces is usually *travertine,* a form of calcite. Travertine is white when freshly deposited but turns gray on weathering and may be colored red, brown, or yellow by algae that live in the hot water.

Geysers are a type of hot spring that are distinctive in their ability at intervals to throw steam and water high in the air. Some geysers erupt from open pools and throw up sheets of water and steam. Others erupt through a small opening and eject a column of water and steam. Both types build deposits of silica minerals called *geyserite,* which is usually highly colored by the algae which thrive in the hot water. The frequency of eruption varies a great deal among different geysers. Many are very irregular, with periods of a few hours to several days before eruptions. Some are in almost continuous activity with weak eruptions. A very few, of which Old Faithful in Yellowstone National Park is best known, go into action on a regular schedule. The reasons for this variability become clear when the process which results in of geyser eruption is fully understood.

FIG. 24–9. Terraces formed by hot springs in Yellowstone National Park. (*National Park Service*)

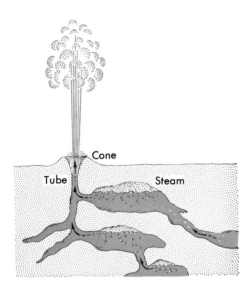

FIG. 24–10. The underground structure of a geyser, with the tubes and caverns in which water is trapped and heated, is diagrammed above, left. On the right, White Dome geyser in Yellowstone National Park is shown in eruption. Right, below, is Liberty Cap, the cone of an extinct geyser, also in Yellowstone Park. (*National Park Service photos*)

The underground structure of a geyser consists of a crooked tube which leads to the surface. Usually several caverns are connected with it, as shown in Fig. 24–10. Ground water fills both the tube and the caverns and is heated by nearby magma or hot gases. If the tube leading to the surface were relatively straight, the heated water would simply rise to the surface and form a hot spring. In the geyser the heated water is trapped in the underground cavities and chambers, where it continues to be heated far above its normal boiling point of 212° F. This *superheating* is possible because of the high pressure on the trapped water, due to the weight of the standing water above. However, the trapped superheated water does eventually boil, and the steam trapped in the cavities creates pressure that forces some of the water out of the tube onto the surface. This causes the small surge of water which precedes all geyser eruptions. Expulsion of the water in the preliminary surge reduces the weight of the water pressing on the superheated

water below. The reduction of pressure causes this water to boil almost explosively, thus driving a roaring column of steam and very hot water out of the tube. The eruption continues until most of the water and steam are driven out of the tube and storage chambers. Afterwards, the ground water begins to collect again to repeat the entire process.

How often a geyser erupts apparently depends upon the balance between the inflow of ground water, the supply of heat, and the exact formation of the geyser tube and its connecting caverns. The difference between these factors is what gives each geyser its own characteristics.

Both geysers and hot springs occur along fault lines because the cracks in the rock form openings which allow the ground water to reach sufficient depth to be heated, and then to rise again to the surface. Geysers typically are found in *geyser basins,* which are grabens or trenches formed by parallel faults. See Fig. 24–11. Almost all of the geysers of the world occur in three regions: Yellowstone National Park, New Zealand, and Iceland.

LAKES

Origin of lakes. The beauty of the many lakes which are features of most regions of the world is celebrated in art; their usefulness is almost as great as their beauty. Lakes provide cheap transportation; they also serve as reservoirs, providing water for generating electric power and for use in industry and agriculture. For millions they are a natural playground. Perhaps a part of the great value attached to lakes arises from their abundance. Lakes are a common element of the landscape and are particu-

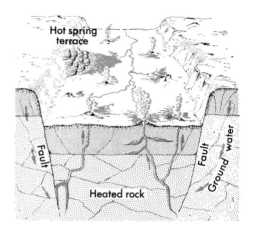

FIG. 24–11. Geysers and hot springs are generally found only in trenches (grabens) formed by parallel faults. Typical features and their origins are shown in this diagram.

larly numerous in the higher latitudes, including the United States. The great number of lakes can be explained mainly by the fact that almost every geologic process results in the basins or depressions which may become lakes if the water supply is plentiful. It would be impossible to discuss here all the ways in which lake basins come into existence, since almost any slight depression may become a small lake or pond during wet periods. However, the larger and relatively permanent lakes can be classified according to the several kinds of processes which form their basins. In the following paragraphs, we will describe these processes and some of the more important lakes which have been formed by them.

1. Diastrophism. Almost any disturbance of the earth's crust by diastrophic activity creates depressions which may become lake basins. Faulting frequently forms lake basins of several general types. A tilted fault block such as that shown in Fig. 24–12 often forms a lake basin in the depression between the tilted blocks. The famous San Andreas fault line in California has created several such lakes a few miles south of San Francisco. Lakes may also be formed in grabens, or rift valleys (Chapter 14). The deepest lake in the world, Lake Baikal in Central Asia, is contained in this type of basin. It has a depth of 5712 feet. Rift valleys of great size and depth are common in East Africa and two of them form the large lakes Tanganyika and Nyasa. Lake Tahoe, between California and Nevada, is also in a rift valley, and although it is only 10 miles wide and 21 miles long, it has a depth of more than 1600 feet.

Folding of the earth's crust also creates lake basins by raising mountains with depressed areas between them. In some of the ranges of the western United States, there were once many such lakes which disappeared as the climate became drier. Folded mountains may also occasionally create lake basins by gradually rising across the course of a river and forming a dam.

2. Glacial action. Glaciers create lakes in a variety of ways. Much of the erosional activity of glaciers described in Chapter 19 forms lake basins. There are hundreds of lakes in New England and New York which were gouged from solid rock by the ice sheet which formerly lay over the region. The Finger Lakes of central New York State were formed from existing stream valleys that were deepened by the ice, then dammed by glacial debris. Almost every glacial cirque in the mountains is occupied by a small lake, called a *tarn*, which remains after the glacier has disappeared. However, most glacial lakes have been caused by deposits from glaciers rather than by glacial erosion. Many lake basins were formed by the uneven nature of the ground moraine that covers much

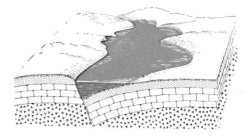

FIG. 24–12. Lakes often occur in depressions formed by tilted fault blocks.

of northern Europe and northern North America. Many of the depressions were filled with water from the melting ice. If they were depressed below the water table, rainfall and ground water helped to fill them. The terminal and lateral moraines of glaciers are very effective in creating lakes by damming existing stream valleys. The belts of terminal moraines across Minnesota and the Dakotas have given rise to many lakes formed by streams which were blocked by the glacial deposits. Similar belts of moraines and associated lakes are found in Wisconsin, Indiana, Ohio, and northern Illinois.

The Great Lakes are the direct result of glacial action. They were formed from existing broad stream valleys which were covered by the ice sheet and were expanded and deepened by glacial erosion. As the glacier receded and the meltwater flowed into these basins, it was trapped by the moraines to the south. In the early stages of their development, the lakes drained to the south through the Wabash and Illinois Rivers, then to the Mississippi. With further retreat of the ice, the lakes grew in size and also established drainage to the Atlantic through the Susquehanna River of western New York and later through the Mohawk and Hudson valleys. When the ice withdrew sufficiently, the Great Lakes reached their greatest size, slightly larger than at present. The lifting of the land as the weight of ice was removed gave the lakes their modern size and established their drainage to the north through the St. Lawrence River. This brief survey of the complicated history of the Great Lakes is summarized in Fig. 24–13.

Another large lake which has since mostly disappeared was Lake Agassiz, formed to the west of the Great Lakes by the retreating ice sheet. It once covered an area greater than all the Great Lakes combined. See Fig. 24–14. Lake

FIG. 24–13. Steps in the formation of the Great Lakes.

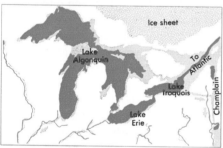

Winnipeg in Canada is the chief remnant of the former Lake Agassiz. (The fertile plains of the lake bed are shown in Fig. 15–6.)

3. River action. The formation of oxbow lakes in meanders abandoned by rivers has been discussed in Chapter 18. Many small lakes are also formed by rivers in depressions on flood plains during flood conditions. Lakes may also be formed in the course of a river if its banks are sufficiently undercut by swiftly moving water to allow trees and brush along the bank to fall in the channel. More debris will accumulate on this barrier until an effective dam is created; a lake then develops as water backs up behind the obstruction. A few lakes occupy depressions formed in river courses where falls have gouged out the rock at the foot of the falls. These are actually very large potholes, and are called plunge pools.

The delta-building action of a river may create lakes. Occasionally the delta deposited by a heavily loaded tributary where it joins the main stream may actually block the larger river and water will be backed up. Delta building may also produce lakes by isolating a part of the sea as the delta deposits gather at the river's mouth. Lake Pontchartrain on the Mississippi delta is an illustration of this type of lake. A particularly interesting example of a salt lake resulting from delta building is the Salton Sea in California. This lake was cut off from the sea by the delta of the Colorado River as shown in Fig. 24–15.

4. Volcanic action. Lake basins are frequently produced when lava flows build a dam across an existing valley. Extinct volcanoes may also give rise to lake basins. A crater or caldera may fill with water. Crater Lake in Oregon (Fig. 16–10) is a well-known example of this

FIG. 24–14. The former glacial Lake Agassiz, shown in light blue, once covered a very large area in Canada, North Dakota, and Minnesota.

type of lake; it is located in a caldera of unusually large size.

In addition to the major processes just described, lake basins are created by a number of minor processes. Mudflows, landslides, and slumps, described in Chapter 17, may block streams and form lakes. In arid regions small lakes may fill the depressions scoured out by wind erosion, particularly depressions between sand dunes. Such lakes are usually highly temporary because of the dry climate. Finally, man himself is an industrious creator of lakes through the construction of dams to store water and generate hydroelectric power. Many of these are highly valuable for recreational purposes.

The life history of a lake. Most lakes are relatively temporary features of the landscape. Even the largest is likely to exist for a much shorter time than other landforms. There are two reasons for the rapid disappearance of lakes: either the lake basin is destroyed or the lake loses its water. The time needed for either of these events to lead to the extinction of a lake varies greatly, depending upon the characteristics of the lake and its surroundings.

One of the principal reasons for the short life span of most lakes is the rapid filling of their basins with sediment. This sediment is carried in mostly by the streams feeding the lake. The inflowing streams build deltas which grow toward the center of the lake and eventually fill the entire basin. See Fig. 24–16. It is estimated that the Colorado River is bringing sediment into Lake Mead (the artificial lake behind Hoover

FIG. 24–15. The Salton Sea was formed as the delta of the Colorado River filled the upper part of the Gulf of California.

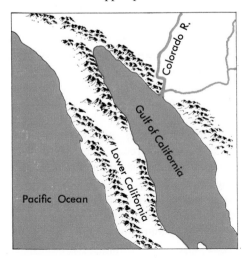

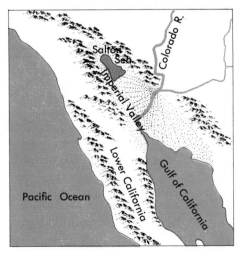

Dam) at a rate sufficient to completely destroy this lake in 225 years.

Filling of lake basins is aided by debris washed down from adjacent slopes, and by wave action of the lake water, which cuts into the banks and washes material into the basin. Volcanic or wind-blown dust, and material carried down by landslides are also factors in the filling process. Often the growth of

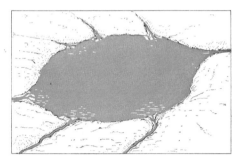

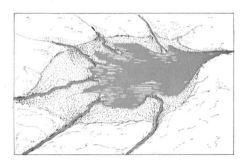

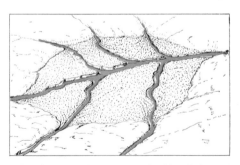

FIG. 24–16. Three stages in the filling of a lake by deposition of sediments from streams flowing into it.

vegetation around the borders of lakes contribute to the eventual destruction of the lake. The plants advance farther and farther into the lake, accumulating more material around the margins until the entire lake becomes a bog or marsh before it fills completely and finally disappears. See Fig. 24–17.

An advancing glacier may destroy a lake by removing the moraine deposits which produced the lake originally. Warping of the land surface by diastrophism may destroy lakes by removing the depression of the basin through an uplifting of the land surface.

Lakes often disappear because their water is drained away or otherwise lost. The most frequent cause is the downcutting of the outlet stream. If the outlet stream of any lake cuts its valley below the level of the lake floor, the water in the lake will be drained out. A lake may also lose its water as a consequence of a change in the climate which brings arid conditions to the region. Evaporation of the water will then cause the lake to disappear eventually. Lakes in this condition often become salt lakes in their later stages.

Swamps. Basins that become partly or completely filled with fresh and decayed vegetation, sediment, and water are called swamps. They usually are a stage in the progress of a lake or pond toward filling completely and becoming dry land. Many basins alternate in character, containing a lake in wet periods and a swamp in times of reduced rainfall. In Africa, four large areas of swampland become shallow lakes in the rainy season. Three of these regions are in northern Africa along the southern edge of the Sahara Desert. The fourth is in southern Africa along the northern edge of the Kalahari Desert. These areas are swamps during the dry season

FIG. 24–17. A small lake or pond may slowly be filled, or converted into a bog, by the accumulation of vegetation around its edges.

of the year, but during the wet season, they receive drainage from the highlands of central Africa and become filled with shallow lakes, some of which are very large.

Lake Chad, between the Sudan grasslands and the Sahara Desert, is at some seasons one of the largest lakes of the continent. However, during the dry seasons, it loses much of its water by evaporation and percolation through the porous rocks of its basin. As the climate of this area becomes progressively drier, it is likely that Lake Chad will eventually disappear.

Generally speaking, there are three types of regions which commonly contain swamps:

1. Glaciated regions in which the streams have been blocked by deposits, producing many lakes and swamps as well. Many swamps occur in the Great Lakes region of the United States, in northeastern Canada, Ireland, and much of northern Europe.

2. Coastal plains that have been lifted slightly above the level of the sea and have very poor drainage due to the gentle gradients. The Atlantic and Gulf Coasts of the United States contain many swamps. Some of these swamps, such as the Everglades in Florida (Fig. 15–3) and the Dismal Swamp of North Carolina and Virginia cover many square miles.

3. Flood plains and deltas of rivers, where the old abandoned river channels have been filled in with vegetation. Such swamps are common along the meandering course of the Mississippi River. Often called *bayous,* they are usually formed from oxbow lakes.

A great deal of the vegetable matter which accumulates in swamps is prevented from completely decaying by the preserving action of the swamp water. This partly decomposed vegetable matter forms a brownish or blackish spongy substance known as *peat.* In many European countries peat is dug from the drier swamps or bogs, and dried for use as a household fuel; however, in the United States the large amount of peat contained in the extensive swamps has not been utilized. Peat is of interest geologically because it represents the first stage in the formation of coal (Chapter 12).

Swamps which can be drained become exceptionally fertile farm lands. However, drainage of many swamps is not easy to carry out, since it involves expensive construction of channels and often creates flooding problems in surrounding streams.

SUMMARY

THE oceans are the primary source of precipitation. Water vapor that is evaporated from these bodies is carried up into the atmosphere where it condenses and later falls as precipitation. This continuous process is known as the hydrologic cycle.

Heavy rains and spring thaws are the major causes of floods. Streams which drain an area are unable to accommodate the increased runoff, with a resulting overflow. Flow control methods like dams and levees confine water to normal channels. Floodways divert water to alternate basins or channels.

The upper level of the ground water is the water table. Slope, elevation, ground cover, and amount of precipitation will increase or decrease the height of this table. Although ground water is mainly meteoric, it also includes connate and magmatic water. Lakes, springs, and swamps result when the surface of the earth intersects the water table. Some lakes become swamps in dry periods.

Artesian wells are drilled through impervious layers of rock to an aquifer. They do not depend on local precipitation for water. The aquifer is a permeable layer such as the Dakota sandstone that outcrops at a higher elevation and at a considerable distance from the location of the well.

Subsurface volcanic action or chemical processes produce hot springs and geysers. Hot water usually has a higher mineral content because it is a better solvent than cold water.

Lakes are temporary features of the landscape. Geologic processes that may form lake basins are diastrophism, glacial action, volcanic activity, and deposition and erosion by rivers.

VOCABULARY REVIEW

Match the word or phrase in the left column with the correct word or phrase in the right column. *Do not write in this book.*

1. Superheating
2. Cirque lake
3. Calcite deposit
4. Water-bearing layer
5. Overflow channel
6. Partially decayed vegetable matter
7. Water-filled caldera
8. Coastal plain swamp
9. Raised bank of a stream
10. Ancient lake

a. travertine
b. Crater Lake
c. geyser
d. floodway
e. tarn
f. Lake Tahoe
g. aquifer
h. peat
i. Lake Agassiz
j. Everglades
k. levee

QUESTIONS   ·   GROUP A

Decide whether these statements are true or false. Reword the false statements to make them true. *Do not write in this book.*

1. An intersection of the water table and the surface of the land may result in a geyser.
2. The present drainage of the Great Lakes is through the Mohawk and Hudson valleys.
3. In the United States the average annual rainfall is 100 inches.
4. Most of the water that falls as precipitation becomes ground water.
5. Geysers are found along fault lines.
6. Lake Baikal resulted from diastrophism.
7. Local evaporation is usually responsible for local precipitation.
8. The average person drinks approximately 500 gallons of water per year.
9. Many lakes eventually become swamps.
10. The earth has always had the same amount of water.
11. The Dakota sandstone aquifer outcrops in the vicinity of the Appalachian Mountains.
12. The Finger Lakes indicate that central New York was subjected to a great deal of faulting.
13. Generally the water table follows the curvature of the land surface.
14. Any deep well is an artesian well.

GROUP B

1. Discuss the processes by which the earth obtained its present water supply.
2. How has man increased the possibilities of floods? How has he decreased the possibilities of floods?
3. Why are flood plains, although dangerous, usually heavily populated?
4. Compare and contrast the long-term effectiveness of direct and indirect flood control.
5. What is the danger of discharging untreated sewage and industrial wastes into a river system?
6. What factors control the level of the water table?
7. Discuss the factors that control the speed and movement of ground water.
8. During which season of the year would you dig a well if you wanted to assure a year-round supply of water? Explain.
9. What factors are necessary for an artesian formation?
10. Account for the numerous health resorts around the areas of mineral springs.
11. Compare and contrast the cause and observable effects of hot springs and geysers.
12. Discuss the four processes that may result in the formation of lakes. Give at least one example for each.
13. How may an outlet stream and an inlet stream destroy a lake? Include a labeled cross section of a lake and a stream to explain the processes involved.
14. Describe the three types of regions where swamps are found, and tell how swamps are formed in these regions.

CHAPTER 25

THE OCEANS

IF MAN ever succeeds in traveling deep enough into space to see the earth from afar, he will be impressed as never before by the realization that this is a water planet. The glittering reflection of the oceans will make the earth a brilliant gem of the sky, probably the most spectacular sight among all the planets. Viewing the earth from afar would drive home a fact we often forget: about three-quarters of the surface of this planet is occupied by the sea.

Man has used the oceans as a source of food, as a highway for commerce and military operations, and for recreation since prehistoric times. However, the systematic study of the oceans is relatively new. The round-the-world cruise of the British vessel H.M.S. *Challenger,* 1873–76, is generally considered to mark the beginning of the science of **oceanography,** a complex science composed of several interrelated parts. For example, the study of the earth's crust beneath the oceans is called *submarine geology*. Studies of ocean currents and especially the sources of energy that produce and retard the cur-

VOCABULARY

Ocean basins. Depressed portions of the earth's crust forming the floor of the oceans.

Continental slope. A zone of rapidly increasing depth in the sea between the edge of the continental shelf and the deeper sea floor.

Deep-sea zone. The area beyond the continental slope, including the major part of the ocean floor.

Mid-ocean ridges. A series of underwater mountain ranges.

Island arc. A chain of islands lying close to the edge of a continent and apparently related to faults in the earth's crust.

Trench. A deep fissure in the ocean floor caused by faulting.

Seamount. An underwater volcanic peak.

Ooze. Fine sediment found on the deep ocean floor.

Thermocline. A zone of rapid temperature change about 150 to 1200 feet below the surface of the sea.

466

rents are included in *physical oceanography.* Similarly, other studies are classified as *chemical oceanography* and *biological oceanography.*

In trying to understand the behavior of oceans, oceanographers are concerned not with the subdivisions themselves, but with the relationships between them. A practical example of these relationships is the attempt of biological oceanographers to learn what parts of the oceans are inhabited by many of the species of fish that are sources of food for man. In the study of tuna fish this led first to a charting of the ocean regions where tuna are found, much as we chart land areas where beef cattle can be grown or where pine forests exist. Knowing this distribution, the obvious question is why tuna prefer certain areas and stay out of others. The answers to this question indicate that tuna are plentiful in areas of the ocean where ocean currents (physical oceanography) bring water from the depths to the surface, a process called *upwelling.* Deep water is rich in dissolved nutrients, the same chemical substances (chemical oceanography) used to fertilize gardens on land. The nutrients permit microscopic marine plants, called *phytoplankton,* to grow profusely in the upper sunlit layers of the oceans (biological oceanography). These organisms in turn become the food for small marine animals, *zooplankton,* just as small land animals feed on land plants. These small animals then become food for larger animals and finally food for tuna. Thus, learning about the tuna involves the putting together of information in the areas of physical oceanography, chemical oceanography, and biological oceanography. The practical result of these studies is that in a search for new tuna fishing grounds we must go to ocean areas in which upwelling is known to occur or can be predicted to occur from our knowledge of ocean circulation. Thus, a large amount of time and effort that might otherwise be spent in searching many thousands of square miles of unproductive water is saved.

This is only one of many examples in which physical, chemical, and biological aspects of a problem must be brought together before we can have a real understanding of how the parts of the oceans behave and interact with one another.

EXPLORING THE SEA

Probing "inner space." One of the most interesting problems of space exploration is the possibility that we may not be able to land on a planet, but may have to find out what we can by hovering above it. To penetrate the dense cloud layer that covers Venus would be

FIG. 25–1. A water sampling bottle about to be lowered into the ocean. (*Woods Hole Oceanographic Institute*)

a special challenge. We would need devices that could be lowered through the clouds or operated from above to obtain data on the conditions of the atmosphere and the surface of the planet.

Exploring outer space is still in the future, but we are not unprepared for its challenges, because we are already exploring "inner space"—an undersea world that presents many similar problems. Oceanographers must investigate a world that can be surveyed systematically only by means of instruments that dangle on long cables in a shifting environment which seldom remains constant long enough to guarantee that measurements are really typical. Descent into the depths in specially designed vehicles gives exciting but brief glimpses only. Yet there is beginning to emerge a picture of the shape of the sea floor and some understanding of the complex processes that take place within the hidden world of the oceans. The information just now being uncovered by the preliminary exploration of the "inner space" within the sea holds more promise for the future of mankind than the more dramatic probes into space beyond the earth. Perhaps the sea holds the key to the problem of finding food for a world population that shows signs of tripling in the next century. Or, it might be that knowledge of the ocean currents and their effect on air movements will prove to be the answer to the control of climate.

Instruments to explore the depths. Oceanography draws on all of the basic sciences, and observations and measurements made during studies of the oceans use many of the techniques and instruments commonly used in physics, chemistry, biology, and geology. Frequently, however, measurements that can be made quickly and simply in shore-based

FIG. 25–2. The bathythermograph is an instrument that records water temperature continuously as it is lowered into the ocean. (*U. S. Navy*)

laboratories are difficult or impossible to make on a seagoing research vessel. For example, it is impossible to use a precise analytical balance to make accurate weighings on a research vessel at sea because the roll and pitch of the ship, caused by waves, produce erratic motions of parts of the balance. Other instruments may be affected by high humidity, rapid changes in temperature, and vibrations of the ship's machinery. For these reasons, specialized instruments have been produced for oceanographic research. Some of these are described briefly below.

1. Water sampling bottles. These are various types of containers which are attached to a cable and lowered into the water. Once the desired depth is reached, a weight is dropped down the cable to close the bottle and trap a water sample at that depth. The trapped water is then brought to the surface for chemical and biological analysis. See Fig. 25–1.

2. *Deep sea thermometers.* Temperature is one of the most important factors measured by oceanographers. Thermometers used to measure temperatures in ocean depths must be specially constructed to withstand extreme pressure. For example, the pressure at depths of 5 miles is about 12,000 pounds per square inch. Ordinary thermometers would probably be crushed by such pressure.

The thermometers used to measure water temperature are often attached to the water sampling bottles and automatically record the temperature at the depth where the water sample was taken. Electronic thermometers provide a continuous record of the temperature at a particular depth over a period of time.

One type of temperature measuring device, the bathythermograph shown in Fig. 25–2, produces a record of the temperature as it is lowered through the water.

3. *Bottom samplers.* Many devices are used to obtain samples of the material on the sea floor. Some types of equipment only collect the sediment on the bottom while others are driven down into the floor and bring up a core that shows the composition of the material for several feet down. See Fig. 25–3. The depth of bottom sediment may also be determined by the reflection of waves from explosive charges, detected at the surface by sensitive seismic instruments.

4. *Current meters.* Different types of meters are used to determine the speed and direction of ocean currents. Most

FIG. 25–3. Two types of bottom samplers: left, an "orange peel" sampler which grasps a sample from the surface of the sea bottom; right, a core sampler whose heavy weight drives the metal tube below it into the sea bottom. The core thus obtained reveals characteristics of sediments below the surface of the sea bottom. (*Woods Hole Oceanographic Institute*)

such meters are suspended from vessels while measurements are being made, but one newer type operates independently of any connection with a ship. It consists of a float tube carefully weighted to sink to a selected depth. An electronic device contained in the float transmits a sound impulse through the water; this is picked up by receiving equipment on the research ship. Thus the submerged float may be followed as it moves with the currents at the selected depth. This instrument makes it possible to determine accurately speed and direction of currents at any depth.

5. *Sonic* (sound) *depth recorders.* Sound waves easily pass through water. This makes it possible to measure depth continuously and accurately from a moving ship. A powerful sound impulse is sent out by equipment on the ship and is reflected from the bottom to receiving equipment on the vessel. The time taken for the sound impulse to re-

turn is automatically translated by the receiving equipment into a depth reading such as that shown in Fig. 25–4.

6. *Deep sea cameras.* Specially constructed photographic and television cameras may be lowered to the bottom to observe the form of the sea bottom and evidences of life. See Fig. 25–5.

THE SEA FLOOR

Ocean basins. The depressed portions of the earth's crust containing the waters of the world's oceans are called *ocean basins.* Since we are land dwellers, we may fall into the error of thinking of the ocean basins as water-filled hollows in the normally dry surface of the planet. Just the reverse is true: the ocean floor is the true surface of the earth. The continents are really great islands raised above the sea floor by the internal forces of the earth.

FIG. 25–4. Tracing of the depth of the sea bottom in the Caribbean, produced by a sonic depth recorder. (*Woods Hole Oceanographic Institute*)

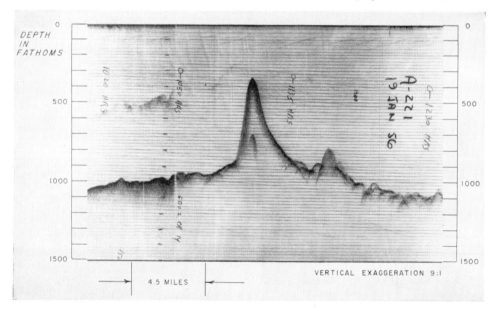

FIG. 25–5. Ripple marks in sediment on the ocean bottom photographed by a deep sea camera. Light for the photograph was produced by the lamp at the right. The round object is a compass. (*U. S. Navy*)

Geologists have long tried to find an explanation for the existence of the continents and ocean basins. Some of their theories have been discussed in Chapter 13—convection and continental drift. A more recent theory of the origin of the continents connects them with zones of fracturing in the crust. Over hundreds of millions of years, the theory goes, lava poured from volcanoes along the fracture zones until the great masses of rock that are now the continents were accumulated.

At the present time there is not sufficient evidence on which to accept or reject any particular theory of the origin of the continents and ocean basins. It is definitely known that the continents are composed mostly of granite resting on a layer of basalt which is continuous with the sea floor.

Zones of ocean depth. The oceans fill their basins and spill over the edges of the continents. Over the continental shelf, the submerged edge of the continent, the sea is very shallow, seldom more than 500 or 600 feet deep. The shelves tend to become continuously wider because rivers flowing into the sea deposit silt on the shelf. Along old coastlines where the widening process has been operating a long time, the continental shelf may be about 100 miles wide. Along new shorelines, the width may be less than 10 miles.

At the edge of the continental shelf the depth of the sea increases very rapidly as the edge of the continent drops off to the depths of the sea floor. This zone is called the *continental slope.* It is a region where great landslides occur. Some of the material washed out onto the continental shelf by rivers is carried out far enough to be deposited on the continental slopes. When a large amount of this material accumulates, its own weight causes it to break loose suddenly and slide into the depths of the sea. If the amount of sliding material is large, a very strong current is created. Such currents are called *turbidity currents* because the water becomes very turbid or muddy. Turbidity currents are believed to be responsible for cutting deep canyons into the edge of the continental shelf off the mouths of many large rivers, which carry large amounts of sediment into the sea.

Beyond the continental slope is the *deep-sea zone* which includes the major part of the sea floor. The average depth of the sea beyond the edges of the continents is 2½ miles.

The oceans of the world. Although it is customary to speak of the oceans as if they were separate bodies of water, it should be kept in mind that they are really just sections of one great sea covering nearly 75 percent of the earth. There are no natural divisions of the sea floor to separate one ocean from another.

Largest of all the oceans is the Pacific, which includes three-eighths of the total area of the sea. It is the deepest of the oceans, with an average depth of about 14,000 feet. Next in size is the Atlantic, which takes in one-quarter of the area of the sea. The Atlantic also ranks second in depth, with an average of about 13,000 feet. The Indian Ocean is third in size, with about one-eighth of the total area of the sea. Around the region of the north pole is the Arctic Ocean, a small ocean with only one-thirtieth of the sea's area. The Arctic Ocean is unusual in being almost completely covered with ice to a depth of about 10 feet. The remaining area of the sea is included in the Antarctic Ocean in the region surrounding the Antarctic continent.

The shape of the sea floor. Until a few years ago it was thought that the sea bottom was a vast plain broken only by gentle rises and depressions, with islands here and there. But the development of the sonic depth recorder has completely changed this picture of the sea floor by giving a continuous picture of the shape of the sea bottom. Maps of the sea floor made in this way have revealed mountains and valleys beneath the sea which rival anything on the continents.

One of the most unusual features of the sea floor is a series of underwater mountain ridges called the *mid-ocean ridges.* Such a mountain chain, the Mid-Atlantic Ridge, averaging 200 miles in width and about 10,000 feet in height, stretches along the entire basin of the Atlantic to the southern tip of Africa. There it turns to join with a similar ridge running through the Indian Ocean. The Indian Ocean ridge in turn joins with several ridges which reach across the Pacific. The peaks of these ridges are higher than those of most continental mountain systems, yet their tops, in most cases, are a mile or more below the surface. The Azores, Ascension Island, and other scattered islands of the Atlantic are the highest peaks. Mount Pico, in the Azores, ascends 7613 feet above the waves and its base is 20,000 feet below the surface. The complete extent and origin of these underwater mountain systems is not fully known, but they are thought to be the result of volcanic activity along a great system of fractures in the crust.

Not all volcanic activity on the sea floor is connected with the mid-ocean ridges. The most active volcanic regions on the earth are in the vicinity of *island arcs,* which are chains of islands lying close to the edges of continents. The

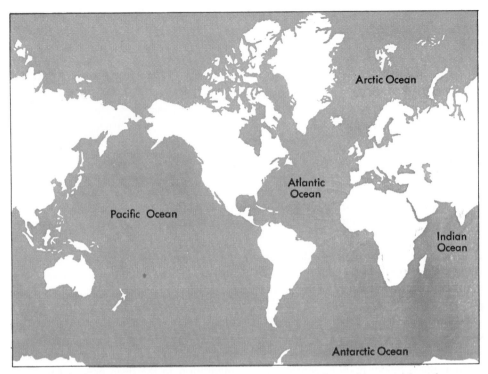

FIG. 25–6. The oceans of the world. It is evident from this map that the various oceans are parts of one continuous sea.

Aleutian Islands off Alaska, and the West Indies are examples. Intense earthquake and volcanic activity is common in these island arcs, which apparently are located on major faults in the crust. Associated with the island arcs are deep gashes in the sea floor called *trenches.* These are formed by the faults in the sea floor, along which occur the volcanic eruptions that have produced the islands themselves. All the deepest spots in the oceans are located in these trenches. The deepest so far measured is a trench near the Mariana Islands in the Pacific. It plunges to nearly seven miles below the sea surface. Other particularly deep trenches are located near the Aleutians, off the coast of Japan, near the Philippines and Java, and off the west coasts of Mexico, Peru, and

Chile. These trenches are all about six miles deep and up to 2000 miles in length.

Faults have also occurred in many other places on the sea floor, leaving as evidence high scarps. Since there is no erosion on the sea bottom to wear away these scarps, they rise up from the sea floor as sharp and as steep as blocks, often as much as two miles in height. Along with the scarps, scattered in great numbers over the entire sea bottom, are thousands of *seamounts.* These are volcanic peaks rising up to 10,000 feet above the sea floor but still not high enough to reach above the sea surface. A number of the seamounts have flat tops, showing that they once were islands whose tops were eroded flat by wave action. The shifting of the earth's

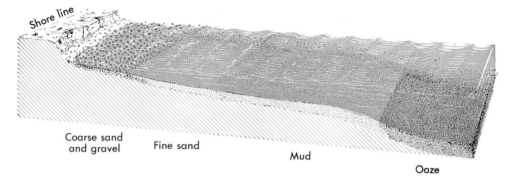

FIG. 25-7. Wave action tends to sort out rock fragments. The larger, heavier particles are deposited near the shore. The finer sand and mud layers blend off into the ooze of the deeper waters.

crust caused these ancient islands to sink beneath the sea, leaving only their flattened tops as evidence of their old prominence.

Bottom sediments. Almost the entire sea floor is covered with a blanket of sediment. This material lies over the bottom like a heavy mantle, completely covering some of its features. The kinds of bottom sediments differ a great deal from one part of the sea to another. Near the shore, over the continental shelves and continental slopes, the bottom is covered mainly with fragments of rock carried out by wave action and by rivers. Since it takes more force to carry the larger rock fragments, coarse gravel and sand are found nearer the shore with fine particles (mud) covering the bottom farther out in the deeper water.

In the deep sea zone the bottom is free of any material washed out from the land. All the sediments in the deep sea are formed from materials that settle from above. Wind-blown dust falls upon the sea surface and eventually settles to the bottom; dust from meteorites also falls continuously on the sea surface and settles to the bottom. The microscopic plant and animal life (plankton) that fills the upper layers of the sea causes a constant rain of debris to fall on the bottom. Altogether these materials falling on the deep sea floor build up a heavy layer of an extremely fine slimy sediment that is called *ooze*. See Fig. 25-7.

Because of the very slow rate of sedimentation in the deep oceans (approximately 0.4 inches per 1000 years), studies of deep sea bottom cores give information about events that occurred in past ages, thousands of years ago. For example, analysis of samples taken from successively deeper layers of a core indicate that the general climate over the oceans has changed in past times, thereby connecting events in the seas with corresponding time periods on land. The oceans have literally written their own historical records of many kinds of physical, chemical, and geological processes. Only in recent times have we begun to learn how to interpret these records with reasonable accuracy.

SEA WATER

Composition of sea water. As stated in Chapter 24, the earth in its early stages was without oceans. All of the water that was eventually to cover three-quarters of the planet's surface was chemically bound within the rocks until volcanism released it. Since some of the volcanic actions that originally produced the oceans are still going on, it is reasonable to suppose that the oceans are growing today. This is probably true, but it is very doubtful that the sea is growing very rapidly at present. Volcanic activity is much less now than in the past and water is not being released from the rocks at nearly the rate that prevailed when the earth was younger. Also, some water is being trapped again by the formation of sedimentary rocks. Water is included as part of these rocks as they are formed. Any changes in the amount of water in the sea now are accounted for by the release of water from glaciers as they melt or the trapping of water in ice during periods when the glaciers increase in extent.

The composition of sea water today is not the same as that of the water that filled the original oceans. When the water that was to fill the sea was first released from the rocks, it was not salty. It only became salty after it had fallen as rain and washed over the land on its way to the ocean basins. As the land was continuously flooded by the downpour of rain, many minerals were dissolved and carried into the sea. Since the oceans were formed, the same process has been repeated again and again with the endless cycle of evaporation from the sea, rainfall, and flow back to the sea. Each year the oceans have become more salty, and now, if all the minerals dissolved in the sea could be recovered and returned to the land, a layer about 450 feet thick would cover every square foot of dry land.

On the average, each 100 pounds of sea water yields about 3½ pounds of dissolved minerals. The most abundant are the ones most easy to dissolve in water, with common salt (sodium chloride) leading the list. Sea water contains lesser amounts of many other substances, as may be seen from the table below.

Minerals are still being carried into the sea by every river of the world. However, because of the extremely great volume of the oceans, the saltiness of sea water is increasing at a rate much too slow to be measured. In addition, some of the dissolved materials in sea water are being continually removed. For example, the building of coral atolls removes dissolved calcium carbonate from the water at about the same rate that it is being added. Other organisms also remove measurable amounts of compounds of sodium, chlorine, silicon, and other chemical elements.

Minerals from the sea. The sea is a treasure-house of minerals. It contains substances of great value dissolved in its water, but it is richest in the most precious mineral of all—the water itself. In many parts of the world the sea washes on barren deserts where millions of people dream of the day when they can use it to drink and to irrigate their

· ·

COMPOSITION OF SEA WATER

Dissolved Substance	Parts per Million Parts Sea Water
Sodium chloride (NaCl)	27,213
Magnesium chloride (MgCl$_2$)	3,807
Magnesium sulfate (MgSO$_4$)	1,658
Calcium sulfate (CaSO$_4$)	1,260
Potassium sulfate (K$_2$SO$_4$)	863
Calcium carbonate (CaCO$_3$)	123
Magnesium bromide (MgBr$_2$)	76
Total	35,000

FIG. 25–8. In huge pipes, sea water is taken into an industrial plant for the extraction of bromine. (*Dow Chemical Company*)

land. In other parts of the world water was once plentiful but is now becoming a precious substance. In the United States, water shortages in some areas threaten to halt normal growth and development. Since 1900 this country has increased its use of water by seven times, and by 1975 the water need will have doubled over the present. There are only two major ways of insuring an adequate water supply for the future: by reducing waste and by increasing the supply of usable water. Wise management will help to preserve the available water resources, but the water supply itself can be increased sufficiently only by obtaining water from the sea. The sea contains plenty of water; the problem is to remove the dissolved minerals to make it fit to use, at a reasonable cost.

The most commonly used method for converting salt water to fresh is *distilla-tion:* heating the salt water and drawing off the steam, which is pure water when cooled. Ships at sea have used this method for years, and some cities in the oil-rich region around the Persian Gulf and in Venezuela now obtain their entire water supply by distillation of sea water. It is very expensive, however, because of the large amounts of fuel needed to heat water to produce the steam. At present, distillation of sea water is only practical when water must be provided without much regard for the cost. Some experimentation has been done on the use of solar heat to vaporize the salt water in order to avoid the high fuel costs. The solar method is promising, but huge areas of equipment are required to capture enough of the sun's heat to convert a large amount of sea water. This increases the cost in spite of the cheap source of heat. Many other methods of converting salt water have been tried but none have been able to supply water at a low enough cost. It is a difficult problem and one which must be solved in the near future.

Some of the dissolved minerals in sea water are useful and valuable. Each cubic mile of sea water contains about 4 million tons of magnesium, the light metal that is used in aircraft and many other applications. Almost all of the world's supply of magnesium is extracted from sea water. The element bromine, used in the manufacture of high-test gasoline, photographic film, and many chemicals, is obtained from sea water. Naturally, the sea is an important source of ordinary salt, which is an essential raw material for several chemical industries. A cubic mile of sea water contains about 90 million dollars' worth of gold. However, no one has yet been able to find a way to treat such a large volume of water cheaply enough to make the recovery of gold a practical undertaking.

The temperature of sea water. The sea is a great storage place for the radiant energy from the sun. Water has a much greater capacity to absorb heat than any of the rocks of the land surfaces or the gases of the atmosphere. The top 30 feet of sea water in all the oceans has as much heat capacity as the entire atmosphere. As a result, the water of the sea is a tremendously important factor in smoothing out the heating and cooling cycles over the entire earth. When the sun's radiations flood down during daylight hours in the warm seasons, the sea accumulates heat. In colder periods this heat is released to the air, thus tending to balance the extremes of temperature caused by the earth's rotation and revolution around the sun. Without the sea, the earth would be a far more uncomfortable planet.

Like the land surfaces, the sea receives most heat near the equator. This results in warmer surface temperatures in the oceans near the equator. The highest of all ocean surface temperatures is found in the Persian Gulf, where readings of 96° F are common; however, most tropical seas have surface temperatures of about 70° F. The other temperature extreme occurs in the polar regions, where the average water temperature in the oceans is about 28° F. In the Arctic Sea, temperatures are low enough to cause the upper layers of sea water to freeze. The exact freezing temperature of sea water varies with the amount of saltiness, but it is always below the freezing point of fresh water (32° F). The Arctic Sea is always covered with an ice pack that averages 10 to 15 feet in thickness. Some melting of the ice pack occurs in the arctic summer, and large sections of the ice float into the North Atlantic past Greenland. These drifting sections of arctic ice are called *floes*. They can be distinguished from icebergs, which are broken-off sections of glaciers, by their flat shape and the fact that they are composed of salt water ice, whereas icebergs are fresh water ice.

Most parts of the sea have surface temperatures somewhere between the extremes of the tropical seas and the polar seas. In any particular location, the surface temperatures are likely to vary considerably from time to time as a result of the movement of water by currents. The entire sea is a maze of currents that transport warm and cool water in great streams. In some places the streams are separate and easily identifiable. In other places the streams merge in gigantic swirls and eddies that mix the water of different temperatures. Thus the surface temperatures of the sea follow a shifting pattern that is set by the currents that bring together and mix the warm equatorial and cold polar waters.

Because the sun's radiations penetrate only a short distance into water, only the upper layers of the sea become much heated. The water of the upper layers becomes slightly lighter as a result of the heating and tends to float on the cooler and denser lower layers. The slight difference in density is surprisingly effective in preventing mixing of the two zones. In most places in the sea, 150 to 1200 feet below the surface, there is a sharp drop in temperature where the upper warm water adjoins the cooler water below. This zone of rapid temperature change, called the *thermocline*, varies in depth from season to season. Measurable thermoclines are also observed in many lakes. One effect of thermoclines in the oceans is to separate the currents in the warm water above the thermocline and deeper currents in the cold water beneath.

SUMMARY

OCEANOGRAPHY is a relatively new branch of earth science. The knowledge obtained through the study of oceanography may help to solve the potential food shortage of a rapidly expanding world population, and perhaps will contribute information leading to the eventual control of climate.

In the exploration of the ocean depths, special instruments are used. Water sampling bottles and deep sea thermometers reveal the condition of the water at various depths; bottom samplers allow examination of the sediments; current meters, sonic depth recorders, and deep sea cameras help to determine other features of the ocean and its basin.

Approximately 75 percent of the earth is covered by water. The largest and deepest of the five oceans is the Pacific. Deposition of riverborne sediments has extended the continental masses to form the continental shelves. At their outer edges, 10 to 100 miles from shore, there is a rapid descent along continental slopes to the average ocean depth of 2½ miles.

The ocean floor is not a smooth basin but is composed of submarine plains, plateaus, and mountain ranges. Since there is no erosion, the relief and ruggedness far exceeds anything above the water. The sea bottom is subjected to a continual rain of microscopic plants, animals, and dust. This accumulation forms a slimy sediment called ooze.

Approximately 3½ percent of the weight of sea water is mineral matter. Processes have been developed to reclaim minerals such as bromine and magnesium from sea water.

Shifting patterns of equatorial and polar currents cause a fluctuation of the surface temperature of oceans.

VOCABULARY REVIEW

Match the word or phrase in the left column with the correct word or phrase in the right column. *Do not write in this book.*

1. Underwater mountain range
2. Drifting sections of arctic ice
3. Canyons in the continental shelf
4. Steep gradient
5. Ocean floor sediment
6. Underwater volcanic peak
7. Island arc
8. Underwater extension of continental mass
9. Gashes in the deep sea floor
10. Zone of rapid temperature change

a. continental slope
b. turbidity currents
c. thermocline
d. floes
e. Aleutians
f. continental shelf
g. seamount
h. trench
i. icebergs
j. mid-ocean ridge
k. ooze

QUESTIONS · GROUP A

Decide whether these statements are true or false. Reword the false statements to make them true. *Do not write in this book.*

1. The true surface of the earth is the ocean floor.
2. Continental shelves are very wide along young shorelines.
3. The average depth of the oceans is 5 miles.
4. Natural divisions of the sea floor separate the five oceans.
5. The greatest ocean depths have been recorded in the Pacific.
6. Arctic ice averages a thickness of 20 to 23 feet.
7. Continental mountains have a greater relief than oceanic mountains.
8. The total relief of Mt. Pico is about 5.2 miles.
9. Deep sea sediments are largely river-deposited gravels.
10. Approximately 740,000 pounds of sea water would have to be processed to extract one ton of sodium chloride.

GROUP B

1. Discuss the proportion, types, uses, and origin of mineral matter in sea water.
2. How are the continental shelves developed?
3. What factors lower the freezing point of sea water?
4. How do oceans affect the climate of continents?
5. Compare and contrast ice floes and icebergs.
6. Describe six types of research instruments used in oceanography.
7. What is the relation of trenches and island arcs to faulting and volcanism?
8. How is ooze formed?
9. Are the oceans still growing in volume? Explain.
10. What is the process of distillation?
11. Discuss the cause and effects of the thermocline.

CHAPTER 26

WAVES, TIDES, AND CURRENTS

ALL of the forces of the earth stir the sea into ceaseless motion. The wind shapes the sea surface into an ever-changing pattern of waves and helps to move the water in currents that run like rivers through the oceans. The heat from the sun produces slow movements in the water and both the moon and sun add their contribution to the swirl of the waters through the rhythm of the tides.

With his ships and cities at the edge of the sea, man is at the mercy of the ocean's more violent moods. Scientists are working hard to discover the causes of the movements of the sea and hope eventually to be able to forecast its behavior. But the motions of the sea are complex and confusing; it is very difficult to find in them patterns that might lead to discovery of their cause. Measurements must be made of temperature, amounts of dissolved materials, the concentration of living things and many other characteristics of the particular oceans. Only then will enough evidence be available to indicate the roles of the various forces in moving the waters. As oceanographers probe farther into the

VOCABULARY

Crest. The ridge of a wave, elevated above the surrounding water.

Trough. The depression on either side of a wave crest.

Fetch. The extent of open water across which a wind blows.

Refraction. The bending of a wave when it approaches the shore at an angle, caused by the slowing down of the part that reaches shallow water first.

Undertow. A constant current running beneath a line of breakers as water from the breaking waves escapes back to deeper water.

Density current. A current caused by the sinking of water as it becomes heavier or increases in density.

Tidal oscillations. Very slow rocking motions in parts of the oceans, occurring in response to the tidal bulges.

Tidal bore. A wave which passes up a river from the sea as the tide rises.

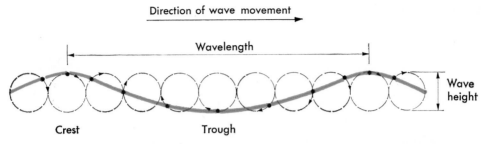

FIG. 26-1. The mechanics of motion in a water wave. As a wave moves forward, the water particles (represented by black dots) move in circles.

many secrets of the sea, more pieces begin to fit into the puzzle. Although the picture is far from complete, the general motions of the sea and their causes can be outlined with accuracy.

OCEAN WAVES

Characteristics of a wave. Waves are created on the surface of any liquid when the liquid is disturbed. A rock thrown into a quiet pool of water will make a series of ripples that race over the surface until they die out or wash up on the edge. Waves on the sea surface are basically no different from these ripples on a small pool. All waves, regardless of their cause or the size of the body of water in which they occur, have certain characteristics in common.

A wave on the surface of water has two basic parts. The ridge which is elevated above the surrounding water surface is called a crest; on either side of the crest is a depression or trough. Any particular wave can be described by its *height,* the distance from the bottom of the trough to the top of the next crest; its *wavelength,* the distance between crests, and its *period,* the time taken for two consecutive crests to pass a given point. See Fig. 26-1. Waves which arise from a single cause, such as

the dropping of a rock into a pool, generally have similar heights, wavelengths, and periods. If only a single influence were at work on the sea producing surface waves, the entire surface would be covered with a neat series of nearly identical waves like the ripples on a pool. However, various forces cause waves on the sea, and they operate at the same time. The wave patterns arising from each separate disturbance merge and destroy the individual characteristics of the separate waves. The surface of the sea thus becomes a jumbled pattern of tossing water.

It has been known for hundreds of years that the waves do not actually move water forward as they seem to. Floating objects are not carried along as the waves pass by, but only rock gently back and forth. A cork floating in the sea moves forward slightly as the crest of a wave approaches, then falls back a short distance as it passes into the trough, ending in almost its original position. Analysis of this behavior of floating objects has led to the conclusion that waves are produced when the individual particles of water move in circles.

As a wave passes a given point, the water particles at the surface trace a circle whose diameter is equal to the height of the wave. Each water particle makes a complete circuit as the wave

FIG. 26–2. Waves are produced chiefly by winds blowing over the surface of the water. (*H. Armstrong Roberts*)

passes by, ending up almost exactly where it started, as shown in Fig. 26–1. Only the wave moves over the surface of the water; the water itself remains in place, transmitting the wave motion by the circular movements of the individual water particles.

Waves and wind. The most important cause of waves on the sea surface is the wind. As the wind blows over the water, small waves are produced by the friction of moving air against the water. At first, only very small waves, called *wavelets,* are created by the wind rubbing against the water. Soon the wavelets make the water surface rougher and the wind is then able to pile up the water into bigger waves. As the waves become larger, it becomes easier for the wind to push on the water so the waves continue to grow larger as long as the wind continues to blow. The

height a wave will eventually reach depends mainly upon the force of the wind and how long a distance the wind moves across the sea. The extent of the open water across which a wind blows is called the *fetch.* Very large waves are produced by strong and steady winds with a long fetch. Such conditions are most likely to occur with storms, and waves 50 feet high are not rare in severe storms. Waves more than 100 feet high have been recorded, and it is thought that even larger wind-produced waves are found in very bad storms.

Most of the time winds are not steady and the fetch is not large, so waves do not grow to very great size. If the wind blows very hard, the wind force may push water off the wave tops, making *whitecaps,* with their foamy white tops. Because the wind usually comes in gusts and changes its direction frequently, waves of all sizes are created. The smaller waves tend to die out, however. Waves with the longest wavelength tend to last because they receive the greatest push from the wind. For this reason, the most common waves on the open sea are long rolling ones called *swells*. They travel great distances from the area in which they were formed. Swells washing up on the Atlantic seashore may have been produced in the windy regions of the ocean far to the south, near the equator. Waves which wash up upon the shore are a combination of swells from some distance away and young, sharp waves produced by winds near the shore. From careful analysis of the waves washing up on the shore oceanographers can determine where the swells originated and often predict the height of waves likely to occur at that point on the shore.

Waves near the shore. When a wave approaches the shore it undergoes a basic change. The reason lies in the circular motion of the water particles as the wave travels along. The diameter of the circle followed by the water particles is the same as the height of the wave.

Therefore when the wave reaches shallow water that is no deeper than its own height, the movement of the water particles is affected by the bottom. The first effect noticed is a slowing down in the speed of the wave due to the rubbing of water particles on the bottom as they make their circular movements. If the wave approaches the shore at an angle, the slowing down causes *refraction*, that is, the wave is bent. As the wave approaches the shallow water at an angle, one end strikes the shallow water first and is slowed down more than the rest of the advancing wave, thus causing it to be bent or refracted. See Fig. 26–3. Refraction tends to line up incoming waves parallel with the shore so that they approach head-on, no matter what direction they originally had. This is the reason waves tend to wear shorelines in such a way that they are straightened. Projecting points of land bear the brunt of the wave action, so they are quite rapidly eliminated and the shoreline is made straight and regular. If wave erosion operated from various directions, a very uneven shoreline would result.

In addition to refraction, which

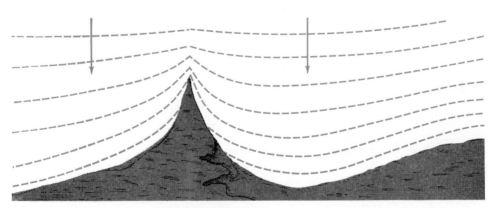

FIG. 26–3. Waves approaching the shore at an angle are refracted so that they tend to break parallel to the shore. The dotted lines represent successive wave crests and the arrows show direction of movement of the waves.

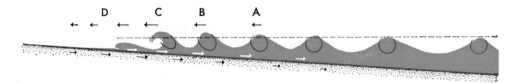

FIG. 26–4. Wave stages A to D show the development of a breaker. The wave advances on the shore in the direction indicated by the black arrows above. The white arrows indicate the undertow, and the lower black arrows show the movement of bottom sediments below the surf.

changes their direction, waves are subject to change in height as they wash up on the shore. Figure 26–4 shows the sequence of events in an incoming wave. In shallow water the circular paths of the water particles are squeezed upward by the bottom. The circular motion is changed to an ellipse which raises the crest of the wave to a greater height, as shown at A in the diagram. As it moves into shallower water, the wave rises

higher and higher until the crest finally tumbles forward into the trough and the wave becomes a *breaker*. These stages are shown at B and C. After the wave breaks, water is thrown up on the shore as a foamy sheet which quickly exhausts its forward movement and runs back into the breakers, as at D. The size and violence of the breakers is determined mainly by the steepness of the shore. If the wave runs into shallow water very

FIG. 26–5. Rip currents (darker areas in the surf) are clearly visible in this aerial view of the beach near Monterey, California. (*Hydraulic Research Laboratory, U. of California*)

quickly, its height increases rapidly and it breaks abruptly, flinging its crest violently into the trough ahead. On the other hand, if the shore slopes gently, the wave rises slowly and spills forward with a rolling motion that continues for some distance as the wave advances.

Water carried up on the shore by the breaking waves escapes back to deeper water in the form of the **undertow**. This is a constant current running underneath the line of breakers. It may become quite strong if there is a heavy wave action carrying large amounts of water up on the shore. An undertow is the natural flow of water that drains off a beach. It is never dangerous to a swimmer because the next wave would carry him back to shore. Some people confuse the relatively weak undertow with *rip currents*. These are swift currents, sometimes attaining a speed of five miles per hour. They are caused by water returning to the ocean through breaks in underwater sandbars close to the beach, as shown in Fig. 26–5. Rip currents may be a serious hazard to swimmers by carrying them out to deeper water in the midst of the breakers. Generally, rip currents occur in spurts lasting only a few minutes at any particular place along the shore. Their presence can be recognized by a gap in the line of breakers, a yellowish color in the water due to sand stirred up by the current, and often a line of foam along their edges in the quieter water inside the breakers.

Giant waves. Waves produced by the wind often become very large and can be extremely destructive. Wind-generated waves, however, cannot compare in size or destructiveness with tsunamis, the giant waves produced by earthquakes or volcanic disturbances on the sea floor. Tsunamis may easily exceed 100 feet in height near the shore and

FIG. 26–6. Damage in Ofunado, Japan, resulting from the tsunami caused by the Chilean earthquake of 1960. (*United Press International*)

frequently occur in series that sweep in without warning, causing great loss of life and damage in inhabited regions of the coast. Such waves have been commonly called "tidal" waves, but this name is very unsatisfactory because it incorrectly suggests that they are caused by the tides.

Tsunamis are caused by violent earthquakes on the sea bottom, volcanic explosions at sea, or great underwater landslides triggered by earthquakes. They are unlike ordinary waves since they travel at speeds up to 500 miles per hour, have periods of several hours and wavelengths of 100 miles or more. In open water, these monster waves are only a few feet high, but close to shore their nature changes, and they rise to great heights and smash down upon the coast. About 225 tsunamis are known to have occurred within the span of recorded history, mostly along the coasts of Japan, southeast Asia, the Caribbean Sea, Mexico, South America, and Alaska. The most destructive tsunami in modern times occurred in 1883 when the volcanic island of Krakatao in the Dutch East Indies blew up. This explosion caused tsunamis more than 100 feet high to sweep over adjacent islands, taking the lives of 36,380 inhabitants of towns and villages near the coast. More recently, a tsunami caused by an earthquake on the sea floor near Alaska struck Hawaii in April, 1946, killing 159. It started south of Unimak Island in the Aleutians, and destroyed a lighthouse there which stood 100 feet above sea level. It continued across the open sea 2300 miles to the Hawaiian Islands at a speed of 490 miles an hour. As the waves approached shallow water, they rose 10 to 20 feet in some places, and as high as 50 feet above sea level in others. The water rushed upon the land for about half a mile, destroying buildings, railroads, bridges, piers, and ships. Since the Hawaiian tsunami of 1946, a network has been set up to measure waves and give advance warning of the coming of the giant waves. As a result of the warning given by this system, a tsunami which hit Hawaii again in November, 1952, caused no loss of life and much less damage to property than the disaster of 1946.

OCEAN CURRENTS

Causes of currents in the sea. The water of the sea is in constant motion. Vast currents twist their way across the oceans in complex paths, responding to forces in ways that are just beginning to be understood. For many years it was believed that the currents in the sea were caused entirely by the winds, because ocean currents generally follow a pattern set by the prevailing winds. As more is learned about water movements, it is clear that although the wind is a powerful force in determining the currents, other influences are equally strong.

Some currents, especially those which flow close to the surface of the sea, are caused almost entirely by the wind. Water is simply pushed along by the wind by an action separate from that which causes waves. Heating of the oceans in the warmer climate near the equator and cooling near the poles also produces currents. Since water becomes slightly heavier when it is cooled, the cold water from the regions near the poles tends to sink and the warmer water near the equator tends to remain near the surface of the sea. There is a slow but steady movement of very cold water along the sea bottom toward the equator, as a result of this sinking of the icy water around the polar regions. Therefore water near the bottom of the sea is always near freezing temperature even in warm tropical seas.

The rotation of the earth also has its effect on the system of ocean currents. Because the earth's surface itself is moving, the path of a moving object, in relation to the earth, tends to veer off to the right in the northern hemisphere and to the left in the southern hemisphere. This tendency is called the *Coriolis effect,* after the nineteenth-century French mathematician who first described it. Ocean currents are subject to this effect and move in a direction partly determined by it. Movements of the atmosphere are more strongly influenced by the Coriolis effect, since the atmosphere is lighter and freer of motion. See Chapter 28.

Surface currents. Water within the upper 1000 feet of the sea moves mainly in response to the force of the winds. If the earth were entirely covered with water and the winds always blew with the same force and from the same direction, the surface currents of the sea would move in a great circle around the earth. But the earth is not entirely covered with water; there are the land masses of the continents which act as barriers to the currents that might circle the globe. Neither do the winds always blow in the same direction with the same force; they come from many different directions with varying strengths. The result is that the surface currents of the oceans move in complicated patterns determined mainly by the general force and direction of the wind and the effects of the continental land barriers which

displace the currents thus set into motion.

Many measurements have been made of the directions of the surface currents. It has been found that the principal motions are in the direction of the average winds. In all the oceans there is a powerful current near the equator moving toward the west, driven by the steady winds characteristic of the warm equatorial regions. If there were no continents to deflect this current, it would continuously circle the earth like a great river flowing in the sea. The continents, however, form barriers which not only deflect this current to the north and south but turn it back upon itself as well. The equatorial currents flow in each ocean that lies along the equator. In each case there are two westward-flowing parts, the **North Equatorial**

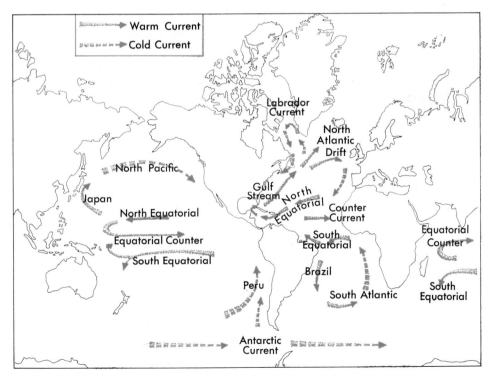

FIG. 26–7. Ocean currents of the world.

Current and the *South Equatorial Current.* Separating these is the east-flowing *Equatorial Counter Current.* See Fig. 26–7.

In the Atlantic and Pacific Oceans, the North and South Equatorial Currents are turned to the north and south along the shores of the continents. These currents form the basis for great circular movements within these oceans. In the Atlantic, the North Equatorial Current piles water against the east coast of North America in the region of the Gulf of Mexico. This water then moves north along the east coast of the United States as a warm swift current called the *Gulf Stream.* This is one of the strongest currents of the entire world, moving along at 3 to 4 miles per hour in a path about 100 miles wide. The effect of the earth's rotation causes the Gulf Stream to move to the right, toward the northeast, which takes it into the North Atlantic. Here it branches into three weaker currents. One branch, the *Labrador Current,* doubles back to the south and carries colder water back along the northeast coast of the United States. Another branch turns southward in the direction of the mid-Atlantic, where it eventually disappears. A third branch is the *North Atlantic Drift,* which crosses the North Atlantic and then turns south along the west coast of Europe, finally rejoining the North Equatorial Current to complete the circle. These currents completely surround the Atlantic, leaving in the center a vast still area, the *Sargasso Sea,* only slightly disturbed by the movements of the water. Great quantities of seaweed float in this quiet area; it is named for the sargassum seaweed typical of these waters.

In the Pacific, the pattern of currents is similar to that in the Atlantic. The North Equatorial Current of the Pacific sweeps across the ocean without interruption for 9000 miles from Panama to the Philippines. When it meets the barrier of the islands, the greater part of the current turns to the north as the *Japan Current.* The warm waters of the Japan Current, the Pacific equivalent of the Gulf Stream, pass along the Asian coast, then swing to the northeast as the *North Pacific Current.* This current carries the cool water from the north Pacific down the west coast of North America to rejoin the North Equatorial Current off the coast of Mexico.

In the southern parts of the Atlantic and Pacific, the current patterns are mirror images of those in the northern halves of the oceans. In the south Atlantic the South Equatorial Current is turned to the south and passes along the coast of South America as the *Brazil Current,* then circles east as the *South Atlantic Current.* It finally moves northward along the African coast to merge with the South Equatorial Current. In the south Pacific, the presence of numerous islands makes it difficult to trace the South Equatorial Current as it approaches Asia and is turned to the south. The islands weaken the current by dividing it into a number of smaller ones. The only strong current of the south Pacific is the cold and powerful *Peru Current,* which carries cold water from the south polar regions along the coast of South America and unites eventually with the South Equatorial Current of the Pacific.

In the most southerly regions of the Atlantic and Pacific, constant west winds produce the *Antarctic Current.* This intense current completely circles the antarctic continent, since there are no land masses to interfere with its movement.

Surface currents within the Indian Ocean follow a two-part pattern. In the southern part of the ocean, the South Equatorial Current is deflected to the south along the coast of Africa, then east toward Australia, where it mingles with the many smaller currents among the islands of the south Pacific. Currents in the northern portion of the Indian Ocean are governed by winds that change with the seasons.

Deep currents. In addition to the wind-driven currents in the upper parts of the sea, there are also mighty currents that flow deep beneath the surface. The most powerful deep currents are caused by the sinking of water as it grows heavier (more dense) from cooling or from an increase in its salt content. Such currents caused by the increase in density or relative heaviness are called *density currents.* The slow movement of cold water along the sea bottom from the poles toward the equator mentioned earlier in this chapter is an example of a density current. A current may be produced by differences in density caused by changes in the amount of salt in sea water. The very strong deep current that occurs at the entrance to the Mediterranean Sea is an example. Being a relatively shallow sea, so that a good part of its water is exposed at the surface, the Mediterranean has a high rate of evaporation. This causes its water to be more salty than the water in the Atlantic. At Gibraltar, where the Mediterranean and Atlantic join, the heavier water from the Mediterranean runs out into the Atlantic in a very strong deep current along the sea bottom past Gibraltar.

Wind may cause deep currents, since water that is moved away on the surface by the wind may be replaced by water from below. Such upwelling is of great importance for the living things of the sea. The organisms which inhabit the upper parts of the sea in huge numbers use up the supplies of dissolved substances necessary to carry on life. Upwelling brings to the surface a fresh supply of these materials from the deep water. Many of the regions of the sea rich in plant and animal life are areas where upwelling brings up the rich water in which life thrives.

Because they circulate very slowly within the recesses of the sea, deep currents are difficult to follow and study. The pattern of these currents is still largely unknown, although there is little doubt that they are an important link in the complicated motions of the sea. Better understanding must await a better knowledge of the unexplored ocean depths.

TIDES IN THE OCEANS

The tidal pulse. By far the strongest of the forces that work to move the ocean waters are those which cause the tides. In Chapter 4 the influence of the moon and sun was described; their gravitational pulls cause the tidal bulges, the twice daily movement of billions of tons of water. Although the basic cause of the tides is the gravity of the distant moon and sun, the tides that occur at any particular place are determined mainly by conditions here on earth.

Many discrepancies exist in the basic rhythm of two high and two low tides per day that may be expected as the two tidal bulges move around the earth. Tides along the shores of the Atlantic generally follow this basic rhythm, each succeeding high and low tide reaching about the same height as the previous one. On the shores of the Pacific, however, each high tide and each low tide rises to a different height than the one

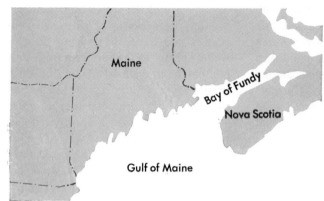

FIG. 26–8. An unusual combination of geographical circumstances results in great tidal variations in the eastern sections of the Bay of Fundy.

before. At some locations along the shore of the Gulf of Mexico, there is only one high and one low tide each day. In some small and shallow parts of the sea, such as the Baltic, there are no tides at all or only very slight ones.

Such great differences in the timing and range of the tides at different places make it obvious that different parts or sections of the sea respond in their own way to the rhythmic gravitational pull of the moon and sun. Although the sea is all one body of water, the irregularities of the sea floor and the position of the land masses divide it into smaller parts. Each part seems to have its own particular tidal pattern. One of the critical factors in determining the way the tides occur in any particular ocean is the size and depth of the basin that contains that part of the sea. Both the size and depth have great influence on the peculiar motions of the water known as *tidal oscillations* (*os*-uh-*lay*-shuns).

FIG. 26–9. These two photographs, taken at different hours on the same day, show the great difference between high and low tides in the Bay of Fundy. (*Nova Scotia Film Bureau*)

FIG. 26–10. The tidal bore of the River Severn near Gloucester, England. The force of the high tide is strong enough to push the wave of water far upstream. (*British Information Services*)

These are very slow rocking motions which occur in various sections of the sea in response to the movement of the tidal bulges. Similar oscillations can be seen in any container filled with water if the water is stirred with just the right rhythm. The water in a bathtub, for example, can be kept rocking back and forth easily if it is agitated with a rhythmic motion suited to its particular size. In parts of the sea, the rhythm of the passing of the tidal bulges creates oscillations which may either reinforce or partly cancel the effect of the tidal bulges.

A particularly good example of tidal oscillations which reinforce the ebb and flow caused by the tidal bulges occurs in the Bay of Fundy on the shore of New Brunswick, Canada. The bay is located at the end of the Gulf of Maine, which happens to have just the right shape to be set into pronounced oscilla-tions by the twice daily passage of the tidal bulges. See Fig. 26–8. As the water rocks back and forth in the Gulf, it first floods the Bay of Fundy, producing 50-foot tides. Then, as the water slowly rocks back to the other end of the Gulf, the resulting low tide almost completely drains the bay. See Fig. 26–9. Nantucket, not far from the Bay of Fundy, does not receive the effect of the tidal oscillations in the Gulf of Maine and has tides of only 1½ feet.

Along straight coastlines and in the open sea, tidal oscillations are much less pronounced than in smaller bodies of water such as the Bay of Fundy. However, the great differences in both the heights and times of the tides at different points along the same shore can often be explained in terms of tidal oscillations.

Tidal currents. Movement of the water in the sea caused by the rise and fall of the tides often produces some of the most violent currents known to exist. In some harbors ships cannot enter or leave except in the slack period between tides, because of the dangerous rush of water through the harbor entrance. When a river empties into the sea at a point where there are unusually high tides, a particularly strong tidal current known as a *tidal bore* may occur. This is a wave of water which passes up the river from the sea as the tide rises. A tidal bore often occurs in a river that has a bar at its mouth. The bar blocks the incoming tide until the mounting water finally gains enough force to rush over the barrier and up the river as a rapidly moving wall of water. See Fig. 26–10. This happens, of course, at each high tide. The tidal bore generally exhausts itself after traveling a few miles up the river; however, in the Amazon River of South America, the tidal bore reaches almost 200 miles upstream.

Power from the tides. The energy contained in the rush of billions of tons of water moved by the tides can be harnessed in some cases and put to man's use. To utilize power from the tides, dams must be constructed to trap the water at high tide, then direct its flow to turn electrical generators as it escapes at low tide. To be practical, a location must be chosen where a dam can be constructed without difficulty and where the tides are large enough to cause great quantities of water to flow in and out through the generators.

An experimental tidal power plant has been constructed in France at the entrance to the Rance River, which experiences tides of 37 feet. This is the first step in the building of a series of tidal power stations by which the French hope to supply their future need for electricity. A similar project has been considered as a joint Canadian-American undertaking in the region of the Bay of Fundy. Once constructed, tidal power stations provide power indefinitely and at little cost. Perhaps the tides will be called upon to supply a portion of the increasingly great power needs of the world.

SUMMARY

☯

WAVES result from the friction produced when wind acts upon water. The wave form results from water particles moving in a circle whose diameter is equal to the height of the wave. Refraction of waves keeps them parallel to the shore, increasing their erosional effect. Breakers, undertow, and rip currents are features of wave action near the shore.

Differences in temperature, salinity, winds, and the rotation of the earth result in currents. In the northern hemisphere they move clockwise, while in the southern hemisphere they move counterclockwise. Usually they enclose areas of quiet water such as the Sargasso Sea.

Tides are the periodic rise and fall of the ocean's water, produced by the attraction of the moon and the sun. In some bays and rivers leading to the oceans strong tidal bores are developed. Attempts are being made to harness tidal energy.

VOCABULARY REVIEW

Match the word or phrase in the left column with the correct word or phrase in the right column. *Do not write in this book.*

1. Caused by differences in salinity and temperature
2. Extent of open water across which wind blows
3. Occurs during rising tides in rivers
4. Long rolling wave
5. Water forced off wave top
6. Wave bending
7. Current beneath breakers
8. Response to tidal bulge
9. Current through break in offshore bar
10. Giant waves caused by submarine earthquakes
11. Depression in wave
12. Ridge of wave

   a. fetch
   b. crest
   c. refraction
   d. undertow
   e. Coriolis effect
   f. trough
   g. whitecap
   h. density current
   i. swell
   j. tidal oscillation
   k. tidal bore
   l. tsunami
   m. rip current

QUESTIONS · GROUP A

Decide whether these statements are true or false. Reword the false statements to make them true. *Do not write in this book.*

1. Large waves result from strong winds with a short fetch.
2. Strong winds produce waves of short wavelength.
3. If the height of the wave is 6 feet, the diameter of the circle followed by the water particles is about 3 feet.
4. Surface currents are caused entirely by wind.
5. In a period of seven days, driftwood in the Gulf Stream would move between 500 and 600 miles.
6. A tidal bore occurs in a river during the ebb tide.
7. Tidal oscillations are very pronounced in narrow bodies of water.
8. The Sargasso Sea is noted for its tremendous waves.
9. The undertow moves in the same direction as the wave form.
10. The Peru Current carries cold water from the South Polar region as far north as the California Coast.
11. Wave refraction tends to produce an irregular shoreline.
12. In the development of a breaker, the circular movement of particles in a wave becomes elliptical.

GROUP B

1. How does a wave change as it approaches the shore?
2. Why should a swimmer caught in rip currents swim parallel to the beach rather than straight toward the shore?
3. Discuss the effect of the earth's rotation on the movements of currents.
4. What causes density currents? Discuss two types.

5. Compare and contrast the tides of the Atlantic Coast, the Pacific Coast, the Gulf of Mexico, and the Baltic Sea.
6. How might a dam be constructed to utilize the power from changing tides?
7. What are the basic characteristics of a wave? Include a completely labeled diagram of a wave.
8. How do currents influence the movements of waves?
9. Compare and contrast the currents of the Atlantic and Pacific in both the northern and southern hemispheres.

UNIT REVIEW QUESTIONS

1. Describe the hydrologic cycle, using a diagram to illustrate the processes involved in the cycle.
2. Why is the direction of sea breezes important in determining the climate of an area?
3. What natural and man-made conditions may cause floods?
4. Why is a flood caused by a break in a levee more destructive than one resulting from natural causes?
5. Describe the sources of ground water.
6. What features may result when the land surface intersects the water table?
7. Why do wells drilled into beds of metamorphic and igneous rocks have a low yield of water?
8. How is a knowledge of geology helpful in the location of sites for artesian wells?
9. Account for the formation of mud volcanoes and paint pots.
10. Compare and contrast travertine and geyserite.
11. Discuss the relationship of the terms *superheating, geyser,* and *hot spring.*
12. Discuss how inlet streams, outlet streams, glaciers, growth of vegetation, and climatic changes may destroy lakes.
13. List the various ways that oceans are useful to man.
14. What methods are used to measure ocean depths?
15. Do you believe that oceans were ever composed of fresh water? Explain.
16. Explain with aid of a diagram how the water particles move in a wave.
17. What are the critical factors that determine how tides occur?
18. How do tsunamis differ from ordinary waves?

ACTIVITIES

1. Prepare a bulletin-board diagram to illustrate the hydrologic cycle.
2. Prepare a report on the amount of water used in the principal industrial processes in your area.
3. Make a model or drawing similar to that in Fig. 24–5, showing the relationship of the water table to streams, springs, lakes, swamps, and surface wells in your area.
4. Prepare a report on Lake Bonneville and Lake Agassiz.

5. Construct a model to show the relationship of river channel, levee, and flood plain.
6. Make a model to show the effects of a dam across a river channel.
7. Using topographic maps of the lower Mississippi, construct a model of a floodway such as that used at Lake Ponchartrain.
8. Prepare a report on the future of Lake Mead.
9. Make a report on the work of the Tennessee Valley Authority.
10. Take a trip to the local sewage disposal plant or water purification plant.
11. Prepare a report on Yellowstone National Park.
12. Make a model to show a cross-section of an ocean basin. See the *Life Magazine* series "The World We Live In" for sketches and diagrams.
13. Obtain some sea water and distill it. Attempt to determine the composition of the material left behind.
14. Make charts of the tides and currents associated with some coastal region of the United States.

FURTHER READING

THE WATER YEARBOOK. Department of Agriculture, 1955. *Superintendent of Documents, Washington 25, D. C.*

THE WORLD'S GREATEST LAKES. F. C. Lane, 1948. *Doubleday & Co., Inc., Garden City, New York.*
                          ★

THE SEA AROUND US. R. L. Carson, 1951. *Oxford University Press, New York.*

THE SEA AND ITS MYSTERIES. J. S. Coleman, 1950. *W. W. Norton & Co., Inc., New York.*

THE SILENT WORLD. J. Y. Cousteau, 1953. *Harper & Brothers, New York.*

SCIENCE OF THE SEVEN SEAS. H. M. Stommel, 1945. *Cornell Maritime Press, Cambridge, Maryland.*
                          ★

THE WORLD WE LIVE IN. L. Barnett, 1955. *Time Incorporated, New York.*

BREAKERS AND SURF. H. B. Bigelow and W. T. Edmonson, 1947. *Superintendent of Documents, Washington 25, D. C.*

WIND WAVES AT SEA. H. B. Bigelow and W. T. Edmonson, 1947. *Superintendent of Documents, Washington 25, D. C.*

THE surface of the earth and its inhabitants are sheltered from the harshness of space by an envelope of gas. The dense lower part of the atmosphere in which we live is the only environment that suits our physical needs and we cannot survive long if removed from it. To travel into space or descend into the sea with comfort and safety we must surround ourselves with a bubble of gas that essentially duplicates the atmosphere of the earth.

Our dependence on the atmosphere is sufficient reason for us to study its composition and ever-changing features. The past few years have added more to our knowledge of the atmosphere than the entire span of history. This unit is an introduction to the nature of the atmosphere and some of the discoveries and problems that are related to its study.

UNIT 8

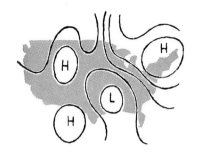

THE EARTH'S ATMOSPHERE

CHAPTER 27

THE AIR

WE ARE accustomed to thinking of ourselves as dwelling on the surface of our planet. Never do we see ourselves as creatures compelled to live within the limits of a vast sea of gases, as a fish is compelled to live in water. Nevertheless, man is designed to live at the bottom of the earth's atmosphere. An envelope of gases at least a thousand miles thick surrounds the entire planet; what we are used to thinking of as the surface of the earth is only the surface of the lithosphere or hydrosphere. There is no true "surface" because the edge of the atmosphere blends into outer space hundreds of miles over our heads. In the relatively narrow region where the atmosphere joins the lithosphere and hydrosphere, most of the life upon the earth, including man, must exist.

The atmosphere has always been a subject of interest and investigation. In ancient Greece, a few writers began the scientific study of the atmosphere when they questioned the accepted belief that wind, rain, and thunder were the acts of gods, and attempted to analyze their observations of the weather. However, this

VOCABULARY

Air pollutants. Foreign substances in air that are harmful to living things.

Temperature inversion. An unusual condition in which the layer of air at the surface is colder than the layer above it.

Troposphere. The layer of the atmosphere closest to the earth's surface, in which most weather activities occur.

Stratosphere. The layer of the atmosphere above the troposphere, in which the temperature remains fairly constant.

Ionosphere. The layer of the atmosphere above the stratosphere, containing molecules of ionized gases.

Exosphere. The layer of atmosphere, above the ionosphere, that blends off into outer space.

Barometer. An instrument to measure air pressure.

Mirage. An optical illusion caused by refraction of light as it passes through air layers of varying densities.

GASES PRESENT IN PURE DRY AIR

Gas	Symbol or Formula	Percent (by volume)
Nitrogen	N_2	78.084
Oxygen	O_2	20.946
Argon	Ar	.934
Carbon dioxide	CO_2	.033
Neon	Ne	.001818
Helium	He	.000524
Methane	CH_4	.0002
Krypton	Kr	.000114
Hydrogen	H_2	.00005
Nitrous oxide	N_2O	.00005
Xenon	Xe	.0000087

scientific approach was buried under a flood of superstition and ignorance that lasted until late in the seventeenth century, when instruments to measure air pressure were invented. It will be many more years before the gaps in our knowledge of the atmosphere are filled in. Someday, however, we will know enough about the sea of gases in which we live to predict its behavior and to some extent control it.

GASES OF THE ATMOSPHERE

Composition of the atmosphere. The bulk of the atmosphere is a mixture of two gases, oxygen and nitrogen. Of these, nitrogen is the more abundant, accounting for 78 percent of the total volume of the air; oxygen makes up 21 percent. The remaining 1 percent is mostly argon and carbon dioxide. The table above shows the normal composition of the atmosphere near sea level.

In addition to the gases always present in approximately the same amounts, there are other substances which may be found in widely varying amounts. The most important is water vapor, which at times may make up 5 percent or more of the total volume of the air. The substances that are usually present in much smaller proportions in the atmosphere are listed in the table on page 500.

Although the composition of the atmosphere is almost constant, the principal gases, nitrogen and oxygen, are being continuously lost into space or combined with other elements or compounds on the earth. If there were no means of replacement, the supply of oxygen in the atmosphere would be exhausted in 3000 years, and that of nitrogen in 100 million years. Replacement is accomplished, however, through the dependence of living things upon the gases of the atmosphere.

An example of the delicate balance that exists between living things and the gases of the air is the *carbon dioxide cycle.* Basic to the carbon dioxide cycle is the process of *photosynthesis,* by which green plants manufacture their food, using energy from sunlight, water, and carbon dioxide from the air. In the presence of sunlight, green plants continuously remove carbon dioxide from the atmosphere and discharge oxygen, which is a by-product of photosynthesis. If only plant life existed on earth, the

VARIABLE SUBSTANCES IN THE ATMOSPHERE

Substance	Symbol or Formula
Water vapor	H_2O
Ozone	O_3
Ammonia	NH_3
Hydrogen sulfide	H_2S
Sulfur dioxide	SO_2
Sulfur trioxide	SO_3
Carbon monoxide	CO
Radon	Ra
Dust (soot, rock, sea salt)	

atmosphere would soon be devoid of carbon dioxide and would contain larger amounts of oxygen than it does. However, the animal population of the earth takes oxygen from the air and releases carbon dioxide, thus balancing the action of plants and helping to maintain the normal composition of the air. The carbon dioxide cycle also includes the weathering of rocks, which removes carbon dioxide from the atmosphere in the formation of carbonates. The loss in this way seems to be balanced by bacterial action in the decay of plant and animal tissues which releases carbon dioxide. Carbon dioxide enters the sea dissolved in water from streams, and is there absorbed by plants, or broken down by sea animals which use carbonates to build skeletal structures. Carbon

Combustion, breathing, decay of vegetable and animal matter, consume oxygen and release carbon dioxide to the atmosphere.

Land and water plants use carbon dioxide in photosynthesis and release oxygen to the atmosphere.

FIG. 27–1. The carbon dioxide cycle. The arrows indicate how the gases are exchanged between the air and water, and between living things and chemical compounds. These exchanges keep the carbon dioxide content of the atmosphere almost constant.

dioxide also passes from the sea back into the atmosphere. Figure 27–1 illustrates the carbon dioxide cycle.

Even more intricate is the *nitrogen cycle,* by which the balance of nitrogen is maintained. Nitrogen is removed from the atmosphere mainly by the action of nitrogen-fixing bacteria living in the soil and in the roots of plants of the legume family (beans, peas, clover, alfalfa, and others). These microscopic organisms take nitrogen from the air and convert it into nitrogen compounds which are vital to the growth of all plants. Thus the nitrogen of the soil is incorporated in the tissues of growing plants. Through plants, some of the nitrogen compounds enter the bodies of animals and return to the soil through their excretions or by decay of their bodies after death. In the soil, decay processes eventually release the nitrogen and return it to the atmosphere as a gas. A similar process takes place in the water. Decaying plants also return nitrogen to the air. Figure 27–2 outlines the parts of the nitrogen cycle.

Origin of the atmosphere. The composition of the earth's atmosphere is very different from what might be expected, considering our knowledge of the materials most common in the universe. The gases of the atmosphere most important to man—nitrogen, oxygen, carbon dioxide, and water vapor—are rare in the universe generally. The elements most common in the universe, hydrogen and helium, are present in the air only in traces. Since the solar system was probably created from materials ordinarily found in the universe, it might be expected that the elements hydrogen and helium would be plentiful in the gaseous portion of the earth. The scarcity of these two light gases indicates that the present atmosphere of the earth is probably not its original one.

Nitrogen is removed from the air by nitrogen-fixing bacteria. From the soil, nitrogen is taken up by plants, which are eaten by animals. Decomposing animal and plant remains return the nitrogen and its compounds to the atmosphere.

FIG. 27–2. The nitrogen cycle.

It is very likely that the earth's first atmosphere *was* composed mostly of hydrogen and helium, but that these gases were driven off into space by the intense heat of the young planet. As the rocks cooled, a new atmosphere began to form. Probably the gases of the new atmosphere were the result of chemical reactions within the cooling rocks and were discharged by volcanoes during the early periods of great volcanic activity. At first there was only nitrogen, carbon dioxide, and water vapor. With further cooling, the water vapor condensed into liquid water, leaving carbon dioxide and nitrogen. Oxygen, which was lacking in the early atmosphere, probably did not appear until the earliest primitive plants began to produce oxygen by photosynthesis. Perhaps as much as 2 billion years were required to reach the present ratios of about ⅕ oxygen to ⅘ nitrogen in the atmosphere, as the plants slowly reduced the carbon dioxide and in-

FIG. 27–3. This view of Los Angeles shows the definite layer of polluted air, or smog, which is caused by a pronounced temperature inversion. (*Los Angeles Air Pollution Control District*)

creased the oxygen. In addition, a large amount of carbon dioxide must also have been removed from the atmosphere by dissolving in the oceans and by formation of carbonate minerals.

Air conservation. It has taken billions of years for the earth to produce the blanket of gases that now make up its atmosphere. Sensitive natural cycles operate with great precision to maintain the relatively constant composition of the air. This balance, however, like many of the earth's delicate natural balances, is upset by the activities of man. Every day thousands of tons of gases and solids not naturally present in the atmosphere are discharged from smokestacks and exhausts. These troublesome and sometimes dangerous substances are referred to as *air pollutants.*

The problem of air pollution is not new. More than 200 years ago laws were passed in some English cities to regulate the discharge of smoke from chimneys. With the growth of populations and industries, the problem has become more widespread and more serious, particularly in large cities. An entirely new problem of air pollution

has arisen with the increase in the number of automobiles moving about in heavily populated areas. Automobile exhaust contains hydrocarbons, compounds which are by-products of the burning of gasoline. When these hydrocarbons are discharged into the air, they are converted into highly irritating substances. This type of air pollution has come to be called *smog* because it is usually associated with hazy or foggy weather. The testing of atomic and hydrogen bombs has still further polluted the atmosphere with dangerous radioactive particles whose harmfulness is not yet clearly defined.

Air pollution becomes a serious problem when weather conditions are such that the polluted air cannot be blown away. Sometimes a layer of warm air exists over a layer of cool air next to the ground. This condition, called a **temperature inversion,** traps the polluted air because the upper warm air acts as a lid to prevent it from being carried away. Some cities, such as Los Angeles, have a particularly difficult air pollution problem because of the combination of frequent inversions and a ring of surrounding mountains, both acting to prevent the movement of polluted air away from the city. In Donora, Pennsylvania, in 1948, twenty deaths were attributed to an unusually severe case of air pollution. In London, England, in 1952, between 4000 and 5000 deaths were reported to be caused by prolonged exposure to a deadly polluted fog. Most of these deaths occurred among the aged and ill. A number of healthy individuals were made temporarily ill. Less dramatic but perhaps more serious are the long-range effects on the health of city-dwellers who breathe polluted air for their entire lives. There is mounting evidence that continuous exposure to polluted air can produce or aggravate disease.

Governing bodies in many areas of this country are attempting to control air pollution by various methods. Factories in some communities are required to install equipment to remove poisonous fumes and smoke particles from their exhaust gases before allowing them to escape into the atmosphere. In California, legislation requires the installation on all motor vehicles of anti-smog devices, which trap or oxidize certain combustion products of gasoline engines that are especially irritating to the eyes, nose, and throat.

More research must be done to discover which of the substances polluting the air are most harmful. When the dangerous materials are identified, we will need to find out how they enter the atmosphere and then try to prevent their doing so. In this way the earth's atmosphere can be preserved as another of the natural resources available for man's use.

THE ROOF OF AIR

Layers of the atmosphere. In solids and liquids molecules cling together, due to the attraction of these molecules for each other. In gases, however, the molecules have little attraction for each other and tend to move apart. As a result, gases spread out or diffuse, to take up as much space as possible. The molecules that make up the gases of the atmosphere diffuse in this way and would continue their diffusion until they were lost in space if each molecule were not held back by the earth's gravity. The gravitational force is sufficient to hold more than half the total weight of the gases of the atmosphere to within 3½

miles of the earth's surface. The remaining half of the atmosphere extends upward for hundreds of miles but gets increasingly thinner. At an altitude of 100 miles, the atmosphere is actually a vacuum better than any ever created by scientists.

The atmosphere is usually considered to be divided roughly into four layers, based on the way temperature changes with altitude. See Fig. 27–4. The zone closest to the earth's surface is a region in which the temperature drops at the rate of about 3.5 degrees Fahrenheit for every 1000 feet increase in altitude. This is usually referred to as the *normal lapse rate.* This zone is called the *troposphere;* almost all weather activity takes place here. It has an average height of about seven miles. The top boundary of the troposphere, called the *tropopause,* blends into the next atmospheric zone, which is the *stratosphere.* Here the temperature is fairly constant, although it begins to rise again at the upper limit of the stratosphere, at an altitude of about 50 miles. At the *stratopause,* the top of the stratosphere, the air undergoes a marked change. This signals the beginning of the *ionosphere,* so named because the powerful ultraviolet rays from the sun tear apart the atoms of the gas molecules, producing electrically charged atoms known as *ions.* In the lowest layer of the ionosphere, there is a high concentration of ozone, a very active form of oxygen, which absorbs more solar radiation than do other gases of the atmosphere. This region is often called the *ozone layer.* The same processes that are responsible for the formation of the ions also raise the temperature of the air. In parts of the ionosphere the temperature may reach several thousand degrees Fahrenheit. However, this statement is misleading because in this region of very thin air the molecules are so far apart that temperature merely indicates the speed of the molecules; the air is far too thin to warm any object that might pass through it. At such high altitude all objects are warmed almost entirely by the amount of solar heat that they absorb. A thermometer shaded from the sun would register a temperature far below zero in spite of the high temperature of the few surrounding gas molecules.

At an altitude of 400 to 500 miles is the fourth zone of the atmosphere, the *exosphere*. This has been called the *fountain layer* of the atmosphere because it is here that the individual molecules and ions spray out toward the void of space. Most fall back again but a few lighter ones escape the earth's gravity and drift away.

Air pressure. The weight of the blanket of air that presses down upon the surface of the earth is tremendous. The total weight of the atmosphere is about 5,000,000,000,000,000 tons: equal to the weight of a block of granite 1000 miles long, 1000 miles wide and half a

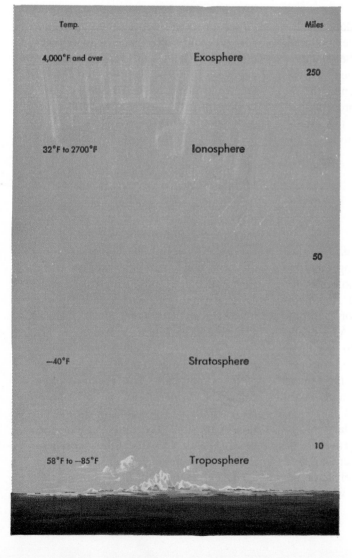

Temp.		Miles
4,000°F and over	Exosphere	
		250
32°F to 2700°F	Ionosphere	
		50
−40°F	Stratosphere	
		10
58°F to −85°F	Troposphere	

FIG. 27–4. The layers of the atmosphere. Note how the temperature varies at different altitudes.

mile thick. Each square inch of the earth's surface supports 14.7 pounds of air. Because this great pressure is the same on both the inside and outside of your body, ordinarily you do not feel it. However, in the thinner air of higher altitudes the pressure on the outer surface of your body is reduced. Then you may become conscious of the change because of its effect on your ears, which are very sensitive to pressure differences. To detect ordinary changes in air pressure, precise measuring instruments must be used.

An instrument which measures atmospheric pressure is called a **barometer.** The type of barometer most commonly used was invented in 1643 by an Italian, a student of Galileo, named Torricelli (tohr-ree-*chel*-ee). His barometer consisted of a long glass tube sealed at one end, filled with mercury, and then inverted so that the open end of the tube dipped into a dish of mercury. The mercury ran out of the tube until the weight of the remaining mercury in the tube was exactly equal to the weight of the air acting on the surface of the mercury in the dish. Mercury was used as the liquid because it is very heavy (about 14 times heavier than water). Thus a relatively small amount of it in the tube was sufficient to balance the pressure of the air. Torricelli found that air pressure at sea level was sufficient to balance a column of mercury about 30 inches high.

The principle of the Torricellian barometer is illustrated in Fig. 27–5. Air pressure is indicated by arrows, *C,* pressing down on the surface of the mercury in the dish. The height of the mercury column, *A* to *B,* is equivalent to the atmospheric pressure, and the space in the tube above the level of the mercury is a nearly perfect vacuum.

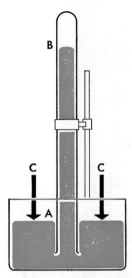

FIG. 27–5. The principle of the Torricellian barometer. The tube containing the mercury has been shortened in this diagram for convenience.

The modern version of Torricelli's barometer is shown in Fig. 27–6. It differs from the original model mainly in having a scale beside the tube to show accurately the height of the mercury column, and a thermometer to indicate correction for temperature changes which affect the height of the column. This type of barometer is called a *mercurial barometer.* Air pressure measured by a mercurial barometer is expressed in inches or millimeters of mercury, referring to the height of the column of mercury supported by that particular pressure. Weather maps often show air pressure expressed in *millibars,* which are international air pressure units used by physicists. The average atmospheric pressure at sea level is 29.92 inches (760 millimeters) of mercury or 1013.25 millibars.

Another type of barometer, widely used because it is more portable and rugged than the mercurial barometer,

FIG. 27–6. Types of barometers. Left, a modern mercurial barometer. Top, an aneroid barometer, showing the sealed metal box whose compression and expansion allow measurement of air pressure. Below, a barograph. The readings of the aneroid barometer are recorded on the drum. (*Bendix Aviation Corporation; top, U. S. Weather Bureau*)

is the *aneroid* (*an*-uh-royd) *barometer,* also shown in Fig. 27–6. Unlike the mercurial type, an aneroid barometer contains no liquid. The heart of this instrument is a sealed metal container from which most of the air has been removed. When the air pressure increases, the sides of the container bend inward, and when the pressure decreases, the sides spring out again. These changes move a pointer on a dial by means of a system of gears and levers. The dial can be marked off to show the pressure in inches of mercury or any other units desired. Aneroid barometers can be constructed so that they make a continuous recording of the air pressure on a revolving drum. Such an instrument, shown in Fig. 27–6, is called a *barograph*.

Aneroid barometers can be used to measure approximate altitude above the earth's surface. A barometer used in this way is called an *altimeter*. At higher altitudes the atmosphere becomes thinner and exerts less pressure, so the lowered pressure reading can be interpreted as an altitude reading. For accurate measurement of altitude, an altimeter of this type must be corrected to compensate for continual changes in pressure due to atmospheric conditions. Information for such corrections is received from ground observatory stations.

THE SUN AND THE ATMOSPHERE

Trapping the sun's energy. More than half of the total energy from the sun falling on the earth reaches the surface of the lithosphere or hydrosphere. Energy is radiated from the sun in the form of waves of many kinds. Most of these waves behave like the light waves which are a part of the total energy band coming from the sun. That is, they are subject to reflection, refraction, and diffusion (scattering). Clouds in the atmosphere form an excellent reflector for most of these energy waves and are largely responsible for reflecting 35 percent of the sun's energy out into space. The remaining 65 percent of the energy is absorbed by the earth.

About 10 percent of the sun's energy is absorbed by the upper parts of the atmosphere, including the ozone layer of the ionosphere. It is this energy that changes the atoms and molecules of the atmospheric gases into the ions characteristic of these upper regions. Fortunately for the inhabitants of the earth, the portion of the sun's energy absorbed in the upper atmosphere is chiefly the very short wavelength (ultraviolet) type. These short waves are very dangerous to living things and would quickly cook to death anyone exposed to their full effect. The few rays of this type that do reach the surface of the earth are responsible for sunburn.

About 55 percent of the sun's energy penetrates the atmosphere and falls on the surface. It is absorbed by the rocks, soil, water, and all the materials of the earth; these are heated by the absorbed energy. The heat is then reradiated into the atmosphere, though not in the same form as it was first received. The substances that make up the solid part of the earth give off heat rays that are much longer in wavelength than the radiations which come from the sun. The gases in the atmosphere easily pass the radiations coming from the sun but tend to block the longer waves going out from the warmed rocks, water, and other materials of the earth's surface. Water vapor and carbon dioxide in the atmosphere are chiefly responsible for blocking the longer radiations. Their effect is to trap the energy from the sun by preventing it from escaping back through the atmosphere into space. This process is very much like the principle by which a greenhouse for plants retains its warmth. In a greenhouse the glass panes pass the short wavelengths of radiations from the sun but block the longer waves as they try to escape. The process by which the atmosphere traps the sun's heat is called the *greenhouse effect*, illustrated in Fig. 27–7.

Since, by the greenhouse effect, the energy from the sun warms the air after having been first absorbed at the earth's

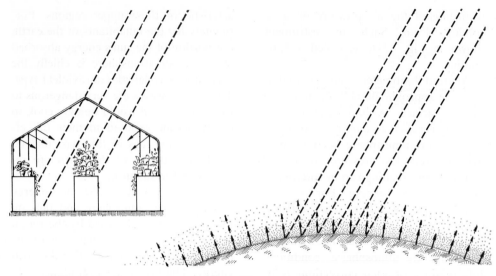

FIG. 27–7. The greenhouse effect. The atmosphere, like the glass in the greenhouse, allows radiations of shorter wavelength to enter, but prevents the escape of radiation of longer wavelength.

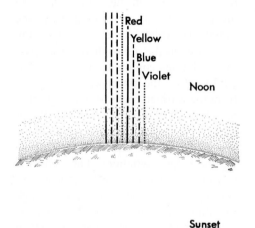

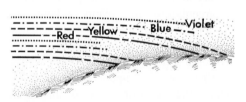

FIG. 27–8. These diagrams show how sunlight can appear as white light, a mixture of all colors, when the sun is overhead, but also give a red or yellow glow at sunrise or sunset.

surface, the atmosphere is warmed mostly in its lower portions.

Sunlight effects in the atmosphere. Visible light from the sun passing through the atmosphere is affected by the gases in the air itself and by the droplets of water, ice crystals, and other particles suspended in the atmosphere. Light from the sun contains rays of all colors, as determined by their wavelength, in a blend that is seen by the eye as the normal white rays of sunlight. Many of the effects of the atmosphere upon sunlight are due to the separation of these light rays of differing wavelengths so that they are visible as individual colors, ranging from the shortest, violet, to the longest, red. The molecules of the gases in the air happen to be the right size to reflect and diffuse the blue rays of sunlight, which are among the shorter wavelengths. When we look into the sky, it is these diffused blue rays that we see; the remainder of the sunlight passes through the atmosphere and we notice it when it is reflected from some object on the surface. Above about 12 miles the air is too thin to cause much diffusion of blue light and the sky darkens to a violet color. At still higher altitudes, the sky becomes completely black and the stars are visible at all times.

Sunlight, being a mixture of wavelengths, appears white unless some of the rays are blocked, as by the dust and water vapor of the atmosphere. When the sun is overhead at midday, sunlight penetrates a minimum amount of air, and the light appears white. In the morning and evening, when the sun is close to the horizon, sunlight passes through more of the atmosphere. At such times, dust particles in the air may block off the shorter wavelengths of light, giving a red or orange glow to the first light of dawn and the last beams of the setting sun.

Rainbows also are caused by the separation of sunlight into its various colors. In this case, raindrops, rather than air or dust, are the means of separation. Refraction and reflection of sunlight in the falling raindrops creates a broad spectrum, or band of colors, which is the rainbow. Because the band of colors is visible only from certain narrow angles, and is produced only in raindrops of certain sizes, rainbows occur infrequently. We are able to see a rainbow only when we are facing the falling raindrops with the sun behind us. The path of light in the production of a rainbow is shown in Fig. 27–9.

Of all the effects that the atmosphere has upon the light which passes through it, none is more impressive than a *mirage* (mi-*rahzh*). Water seems to appear on the dry pavement of a highway, distant buildings appear suspended in the sky or the distant landscape seems

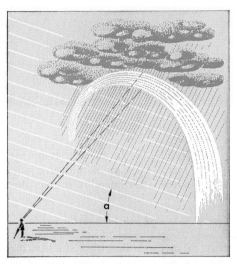

FIG. 27–9. To produce a rainbow, the angle *a* of the sun's rays must be less than 45°. Each raindrop, acting as a prism, produces a spectrum, shown below as a fan of rays. However, only one color from each fan is reflected at just the proper angle to reach the observer, producing a continuous band of color.

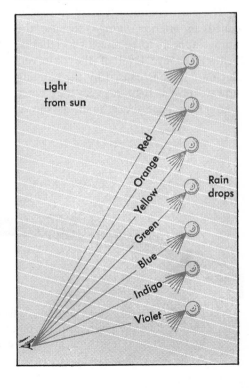

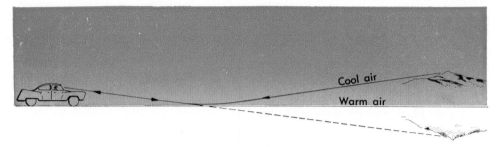

FIG. 27–10. In an inferior mirage, the image seems to be below the observer. This type of mirage is often seen when the air close to the earth's surface is considerably warmer than the air at higher altitudes.

reflected in the water of a shimmering lake. All these are mirages: optical illusions created by the refraction or bending of light rays passing through layers of air that differ in temperature. Cool air is denser than warm air, and light is therefore refracted when passing from a body of warm air into cool air, or vice versa.

The most common type of mirage is called an *inferior mirage* because the mirage appears to be inferior to (that is, below) the eye level of the observer. Such a mirage is caused by the bending upward of the light rays as they enter warmer air near the ground, as shown in Fig. 27–10. The upward bending of the rays has the same effect as if the surface of the earth were a mirror. Distant objects may appear upside down below the horizon as if they were reflected in the surface of a lake. When this type of mirage reflects the sky, the familiar illusion of shimmering water in the distance is seen.

Another type of mirage is the *superior mirage,* also known as *looming,* in which the image seems to be above the observer. This kind of mirage appears most commonly over the sea. Ships, icebergs, shorelines, cities, and other objects which would normally be out of

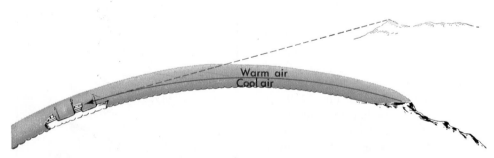

FIG. 27–11. In a superior mirage the image seems to be at a much higher altitude than the position of the object itself. This phenomenon is produced by temperature inversion, in which a layer of warm air overlies a layer of cooler air.

sight over the horizon appear suspended in the sky, sometimes as double mirages, one upright and the other reversed. Superior mirages occur when cool air near the surface causes light rays to be bent downward, as shown in Fig. 27–11. The effect is the same as if a mirror were suspended in the sky, reflecting the image of objects that are out of sight over the horizon.

SUMMARY

THE atmosphere, composed mainly of nitrogen and oxygen, extends to an altitude of at least 1000 miles above sea level. It may be divided into four parts: troposphere, stratosphere, ionosphere, and exosphere.

Natural processes such as the carbon dioxide and nitrogen cycles help to maintain the proper balance of the life-supporting gases. Intense heat of the young planet probably drove off the earth's original atmosphere of hydrogen and helium. Subsequent chemical activity and volcanic discharge of gases apparently led to the present atmosphere. According to locality, the air may contain pollutants resulting from industry, automobile exhausts, and nuclear testing. Periods of temperature inversion make air pollution a potential health hazard.

The bulk of the weight of the atmosphere is within 3.5 miles of the earth's surface. Barometers of several kinds are used to measure the pressure exerted by the atmosphere.

The portion of the sun's energy that reaches the earth's surface is absorbed and in turn heats the lower part of the atmosphere. This phenomenon is known as the "greenhouse effect." Rainbows and mirages are visible phenomena due to the effects of the atmosphere on light from the sun.

VOCABULARY REVIEW

Match the phrase in the left column with the correct word or phrase in the right column. *Do not write in this book.*

1. Atmospheric layer closest to the earth
2. Measures air pressure
3. Electrically charged particles
4. A blanket of warm air above cold air
5. Makes up 78 percent of the atmosphere
6. Optical illusion
7. Hosts for nitrogen-fixing bacteria
8. Measures altitude
9. Manufacture of food by green plants
10. Blends off into outer space

a. temperature inversion
b. legumes
c. stratosphere
d. photosynthesis
e. troposphere
f. mirage
g. exosphere
h. ions
i. altimeter
j. nitrogen
k. barometer

QUESTIONS . GROUP A

Decide whether these statements are true or false. Reword the false statements to make them true. *Do not write in this book.*

1. The gas which makes up about 20 percent of the atmosphere is oxygen.
2. Carbon dioxide is returned to the atmosphere by decay of plant and animal matter.
3. We live in the layer of the atmosphere known as the stratosphere.
4. The stratosphere is located at an altitude of about 50 miles.
5. At sea level the total force of the air pressing on 1 square foot would be about 332.5 pounds.
6. Ultraviolet radiations have short wavelength.
7. The most abundant gases in the universe are helium and hydrogen.
8. Air pollutants have been added to the air by nuclear testing.
9. The "greenhouse effect" refers to the fact that plants grow faster in green-houses.
10. The tropopause separates the troposphere from the atmosphere.
11. As altitude increases, air pressure increases.
12. At an elevation of 100 feet the temperature is 78° F. The temperature 2000 feet above this point should be 56° F.
13. The ozone concentration is greatest in the stratosphere.
14. In the exosphere there is a loss to outer space of a few molecules and ions.
15. If a cubic foot of water weighs 62.4 pounds, a cubic foot of mercury weighs about 221.3 pounds.
16. An atmospheric pressure of 29.92 inches may also be expressed as 760 millimeters.
17. Blue rays are the most easily scattered by the atmosphere.
18. The greater the altitude, the darker the sky.
19. Mirages are caused by the absorption of light.
20. It is difficult to determine the boundary between the upper atmosphere and the beginning of outer space.

GROUP B

1. If the nitrogen and oxygen were not replaced in the atmosphere, how long would our present supply of these gases last?
2. Describe and diagram the carbon dioxide cycle.
3. Describe and diagram the nitrogen cycle.
4. Which do you believe appeared first upon the earth, animals or plants? Explain.
5. How does temperature inversion increase the problem of air pollution? Give some recent examples.
6. What is meant by diffusion?
7. List the characteristics and boundaries of the four layers that make up the atmosphere.

CHAPTER 28

THE WINDS

ONE of the most characteristic features of the atmosphere is its motion. Day in and day out, year after year, the air moves over the earth distributing the sun's heat, transporting water from the oceans to the dry continents and sweeping always along with it the endless patterns of weather. Tremendous energy is used up in this constant motion. At any moment the winds of the earth are using more energy than could be generated by all the power plants of the United States in a century. To keep the great air engine running, energy must be constantly poured into the atmosphere. It is estimated that if the air should suddenly be deprived of its continuous supply of energy, all winds would die out within a week or two.

The source of the energy that drives the movements of the atmosphere is, of course, the sun. The atmosphere is like a great heat engine doing its work by slowly moving air from the boiler around the equator to the cooling chamber at the poles, then back again. It is a complicated engine of many moving parts that fit smoothly together and

VOCABULARY

Trade winds. Planetary winds blowing generally toward the equator in tropical areas.

Doldrums. A belt of calm air under lower pressure near the equator.

Horse latitudes. A belt of calm air under greater pressure at about 30° of latitude, north and south of the equator.

Westerly winds. Planetary winds blowing generally from the west in the middle latitudes.

Subpolar low. A belt of lower air pressure at about 60° north and south latitudes.

Polar easterlies. Weak easterly planetary winds near the poles.

Circumpolar whirl. High-altitude winds moving around the earth from west to east.

Jet streams. Swift high-altitude winds at the edges of the circumpolar whirls.

work with precision. Intensive study is slowly revealing the pattern by which the sun produces the winds of the earth. Understanding the engine that drives the winds is a difficult task for modern science but it is a challenge that is being met.

ATMOSPHERIC CIRCULATION

Heating of the atmosphere by the sun. In Chapter 27 the greenhouse effect was described, by which the atmosphere is warmed by the heat radiated from the earth. This *radiation* is the most important means by which the atmosphere is heated by the sun's energy. Some heating of the air takes place as a result of *conduction:* the flow of heat directly from the warm earth to the cooler layer of air immediately above the earth's surface. Air is not a very good conductor, however, and the atmosphere is heated almost entirely by radiation from the surface.

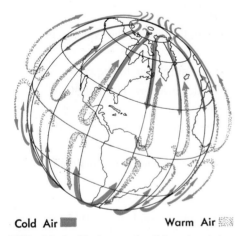

Cold Air ▪▪▪   Warm Air ▒▒▒

FIG. 28–1. If the earth did not rotate, the circulation of the atmosphere would be as shown here.

Each day the atmosphere goes through a cycle of heating and cooling. The air temperature begins to rise shortly after the sun rises, as the earth starts to radiate heat energy. Ordinarily, the temperature of the air continues to rise throughout the day, the highest temperatures occurring in the afternoon. After the sun sets, the amount of heat radiated by the earth slowly diminishes and the air begins to grow cooler, reaching its lowest temperature generally in the early morning hours just before the sun rises again. Cloudy nights tend to be warmer than nights when the skies are clear, because the clouds radiate back to the earth the heat lost in cooling after the sun sets. Moist air also tends to prevent the loss of heat by the earth even if clouds are absent. On the other hand, nighttime temperatures in deserts are likely to be very low, and since air is generally drier at higher altitudes, mountainous regions often have very low temperatures. Different kinds of surfaces influence the heating of the air above them by their differing capacity to absorb the sun's energy. Snow reflects about 75 percent of the light energy reaching it; this reflected energy has no heating effect on the atmosphere because it has not been absorbed by the earth and radiated back to the air. As a result, a snow cover causes very low temperatures in the air above. The amount of the sun's energy absorbed by some other surfaces is shown below.

Surface	Percent of Sun's Energy Absorbed
Snow	25
Water	60 to 95
Sand	75
Plowed field	75 to 95
Grassy field	85
Forest	95

Movements of the air caused by heating. The process of *convection,* the circulatory movement that is set up in gases and liquids by uneven heating, is probably the most important way in which heat is carried to the upper parts of the atmosphere. On a sunny day the air close to the earth is continuously being heated and rises, while colder air flows in to replace it. The colder air is then warmed, rises and is replaced by more cool air.

Air which has been heated, being less dense and lighter, presses down on the earth with less force. Thus the atmospheric pressure is generally less beneath a body of warm air than under cooler air. Many local winds are caused by the movement of cool air from high pressure areas into low pressure areas to replace the rising warm air. The movement of air within the atmosphere over the entire earth, that is, the *planetary circulation,* also is caused mainly by flow from regions of high pressure to those of low pressure.

At the equator the earth receives more of the sun's direct rays and is heated much more than at the poles. Consequently, atmospheric pressure at the equator tends to be low and the heated air is constantly rising. At the poles the colder heavier air creates regions of high atmospheric pressure. So there is a flow of air from the north and south toward the equator, and at higher levels a return flow of warm air from the equator to the poles. If the earth did not rotate, the air would circulate over the entire earth as shown in Fig. 28–1. But the earth's rotation strongly influences the general circulation of the atmosphere. It creates a complicated pattern of air movements within the over-all flow from the equator to the poles and back again.

FIG. 28–2. A rocket fired from the north pole and aimed directly at New York would land near Chicago because of deflection due to the Coriolis effect.

Effects of the earth's rotation on air movements. As pointed out in Chapter 26, in the Coriolis effect, the path of things that move over the earth tends to curve sidewise, due to the earth's rotation. This is sometimes stated as *Ferrel's law:* moving objects are deflected to the right in the northern hemisphere and to the left in the southern hemisphere. In traveling down a perfectly straight highway at a speed of 60 miles per hour, an automobile would drift to the right (in the northern hemisphere) by about 15 feet per mile, if the tires did not prevent sidewise motion. The earth's surface is always, in a sense, spinning out from under a moving object. Figure 28–2 shows how the Coriolis effect might operate on a rocket fired from the north pole and aimed toward New York.

The Coriolis effect has a strong influence on the winds that result from the movements of air between the warm and cool parts of the earth. As we have seen, near the surface there is a flow of air between the equator and poles. The

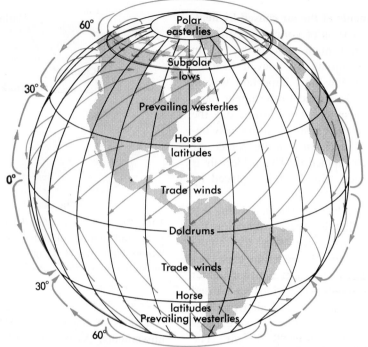

FIG. 28–3. The wind belts of the earth. Note how the direction of the winds is deflected from straight north and south directions according to Ferrel's law.

winds, instead of blowing straight north or south, are deflected according to Ferrel's law so as to produce a series of bands around the earth. Within each band the surface winds move generally in a definite direction.

As pointed out earlier, the origin and the primary driving force of the planetary circulation lie in the lifting action of the heated air at the equator. This movement creates a belt of low pressure around the equator. This is a region of calms and weak, undependable winds, due to the upward motion of the air. It is known as the *doldrums,* a name which originated in the days of sailing ships, which were often becalmed in this area of low pressure for many days.

As the air above the equator rises and moves toward the poles, the Coriolis force deflects it (to the east in the northern hemisphere). At around 30° latitude, the air has cooled sufficiently to begin to sink toward the earth's surface. A part of it descends at these latitudes, forming a belt of high pressure. At the surface the settling air flows both to the north and to the south. The portion moving back toward the equator is the belt of surface winds called the *trades.* In the northern hemisphere, the trades are deflected to the right and become the *northeast trades.* In the southern hemisphere they are turned to the left and become the *southeast trades.*

The belt of high pressure created by the descending air in the vicinity of 30° latitude is the *horse latitudes.* As in the doldrums, the winds here are weak and changeable. The name "horse latitudes" supposedly refers to the fact that when sailing ships carried horses from Spain to the New World, the horses were often thrown overboard to save food and water when the ships were becalmed in this still region of the Atlantic.

The part of the descending equatorial air that moves toward the poles is also deflected, forming the belt of surface winds known as the *westerlies.* In the northern hemisphere the westerlies are southwest winds and in the southern hemisphere they are northwest winds. The westerlies lie in a belt between 40° and 60° latitude and are much less steady winds than the trades.

North of the belt of westerlies, at around latitude 65°, is a second belt of low pressure, the *subpolar lows.* Here warmer air, still moving out from the equator, is being lifted by cold polar air moving toward the equator. Over the polar regions there is an area of high pressure due to the piling up as the warm air at high altitudes cools and sinks. In the regions around the poles, masses of warm and cold air are exchanged. Within the cold air masses at the poles the general movement is toward the equator. The winds thus created are turned to the right in the northern hemisphere and to the left in the southern hemisphere to become the *polar easterlies.* These are extremely weak winds because of the uniformly low temperature of the air at the poles.

The wind and pressure belts over the entire earth are shown in Fig. 28–3.

As the sun's vertical rays shift north and south of the equator during the course of a year, the positions of the pressure belts and wind belts also shift. Their change in latitude is much less than the 23½° movement of the sun's vertical rays; the average change during the year is only about 6°. However, even this small change is sufficient to cause some places to be in different wind belts during the year, thus greatly affecting their climates. An example is southern California, where westerly winds prevail in the winter, while the trade winds prevail in the summer.

High-altitude winds. At high altitudes, the warm air rising at the equator and moving toward the poles is turned toward the right in the northern hemisphere; that is, it moves to the east. About halfway between the equator and the north pole, the eastward-moving warm air meets the cold polar air flowing southward to the equator. The zone where the warm and cool air meet at about 40° N. latitude is a region of high altitude winds and violent motions as the two types of air meet and mix. The eastward motion of the warm air from the equator carries this churning boundary around the earth from west to east as a great band of high-altitude winds known as the *circumpolar whirl,* shown in Fig. 28–4. The winds are strongest in the region of latitude 30° and diminish in strength toward the equator and the poles. There is increasing evidence that

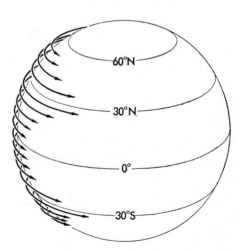

FIG. 28–4. The circumpolar whirl. The length of the arrows indicates the relative speed of the winds.

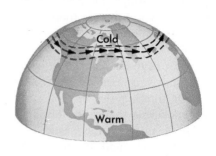

FIG. 28–5. Jet streams, shown on a polar projection. Arrows indicate the general positions and directions of the three segments in the northern hemisphere.

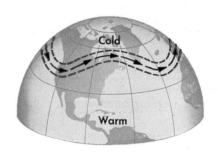

the mixing of polar air and warm equatorial air is accomplished through sporadic waves that develop in the circumpolar whirl.

Near the southern boundary of the northern circumpolar whirl, at an altitude of six to nine miles above the surface, lies a band of variable winds that are the swiftest known to exist on earth. These are the *jet streams*, whose velocities sometimes reach 400 miles per hour. The winds do not blow steadily, but vary in speed, direction, and extent. They do not form a continuous band, but are divided roughly into three segments in the northern hemisphere. See Fig. 28–5. In summer the circumpolar whirl contracts and the jet streams are found closer to the north pole at 35 to 45° N. latitude. In winter they shift to the south and are found at 20 to 25° N. latitude. The altitude of the jet stream also varies with the seasons. In summer

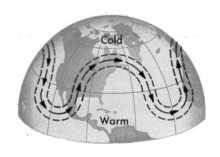

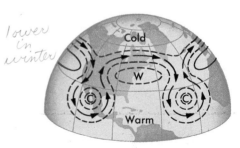

FIG. 28–6. A wave cycle of jet streams. The waves tend to isolate pockets of warm and cold air far north and south of their average locations.

it is at least 7 miles high; in winter only about 4 to 6 miles high. Aircraft can take advantage of the jet stream in winter as a strong tailwind to cut down flying time, but in summer it is beyond all but experimental flights. From time to time the jet streams undergo a cycle during which they form increasingly larger waves. These waves carry cold polar air to the south and warm equatorial air to the north. Eventually the waves break loose, forming pockets of cold air in the south and warm air in the north. A wave cycle of the jet streams is shown in Fig. 28–6. This behavior of the jet streams is known to have a great effect on weather patterns throughout the world, but the exact relationship is not clear. Jet streams are believed to circle the south polar region, as well as the north, but their existence has not been proved.

LOCAL WINDS

Land and sea breezes. When both land and water receive the same total amount of energy from the sun, the land surface is soon heated to a higher temperature than the water. During daylight hours a sharp temperature difference develops between the water and the land along the shore. This temperature difference also appears in the air above the land and water. The warmer air above the land rises and the cool air from above the water moves in to replace it, thus causing a cool *sea breeze* to blow toward the shore. At night the situation is reversed. The land cools faster than the water and a *land breeze* blows from the land toward the water. The daily cycle of land and sea breezes is shown in Fig. 28–7.

The sea breeze generally begins in the late morning hours and dies away in the late afternoon or early evening. Land breezes which blow throughout the night are much weaker than the sea breezes during the day. The land and sea breeze effect may also occur around large lakes.

Mountain and valley breezes. In the daytime, mountains heat faster than surrounding valleys. This is mainly because the exposed slopes of the mountains absorb the sun's energy faster than the valleys, which are generally covered with forests and vegetation. In the daytime, a gentle *valley breeze* blows up the slopes as cooler air from the valleys moves up to replace the rising mountain air. At night the mountains cool faster than the valleys, and the cooler air descends the mountain slopes to the valleys, causing a *mountain breeze*.

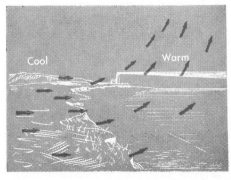

FIG. 28–7. Unequal heating of land and water results in land and sea breezes.

SUMMARY

UNEQUAL heating of the earth's surface produces temperature differences which cause pressure differences. The pressure differences create winds and air currents. Warm air above the equator rises and flows toward the poles while polar air descends and moves toward the equator. This movement of air in combination with the rotation of the earth establishes a system of wind belts and calms.

Winds do not move directly north or south but are deflected by the Coriolis effect. According to Ferrel's law, winds in the northern hemisphere drift to the right; in the southern hemisphere they are deflected to the left.

Seasonal shifting of the vertical rays of the sun causes a migration of the wind and pressure belts, amounting to about 6°. As a result of this shifting, some areas may be in two different wind belts during the course of a year.

At high altitudes the mixing of warm equatorial air with cold polar air creates systems of high-speed winds that appear to have a great effect on the weather pattern. Further understanding of these systems will have a great influence on the accuracy of long-range weather forecasting.

Variations in temperature and pressure over small areas of the earth result in local winds.

VOCABULARY REVIEW

Match the phrase in the left column with the correct word or phase in the right column. *Do not write in this book.*

1. Equatorial low-pressure belt
2. Pressure belts 30° north or south of the equator
3. Deflection of winds
4. Gentle local wind
5. Tropical winds blowing toward equator
6. Band of high altitude winds
7. Low-pressure belts 65° north or south of the equator

a. trades
b. circumpolar whirl
c. polar easterlies
d. horse latitudes
e. doldrums
f. subpolar low
g. breeze
h. Coriolis effect

QUESTIONS · GROUP A

Decide whether these statements are true or false. Reword the false statements to make them true. *Do not write in this book.*

1. Winds always blow from regions of low pressure to regions of high pressure.
2. New York City is located in the northwesterly wind belt.
3. Rotation of the earth causes the winds on the northern hemisphere to be deflected to the right.

4. Sea breezes are strongest when the land and water have approximately the same temperature.
5. The southeast trades occur in the northern hemisphere.
6. The center of the doldrum belt is located at about 23½° N.
7. Winds derive their energy from the sun.
8. Water reflects more of the sun's energy than snow.
9. In the vicinity of the horse latitudes the air is always rising.
10. The swiftest winds are called the westerlies.
11. At high altitudes the atmosphere is heated mainly by conduction.
12. The air above a warm area is likely to have a lower pressure than air above a cold region.

GROUP B

1. Why are cloudy nights likely to be warmer than clear nights?
2. What is the general effect of atmospheric moisture on air temperature?
3. Explain why warm air does not exert as much pressure as cold air.
4. Explain why rotation of the earth causes deflection of the planetary winds.
5. Make a diagram to show the relationship of all the planetary winds and pressure belts. Indicate the correct latitude and direction of the winds.
6. Explain how the migration of the sun's vertical rays influences the planetary winds and pressure belts.
7. Discuss the significance of the circumpolar whirl and the jet streams.
8. Describe the barometer developed by Torricelli. How can it be used to measure atmospheric pressure?
9. Describe the distribution of the sun's energy after it enters the atmosphere.
10. Why does the sky appear blue?
11. Explain why a dry highway may sometimes appear to be wet on a hot day.

CHAPTER 29

WATER IN THE ATMOSPHERE

IF ALL the water vapor contained in the entire atmosphere were to fall suddenly as a world-wide rainstorm, it would cover the earth's surface with a layer of water only one inch deep. Water vapor is not one of the abundant materials in the atmosphere; it is found in varying amounts ranging from nearly zero to a maximum of four to five percent by volume. Yet this relatively rare ingredient of air is one of the most vital.

The absence of water vapor would render the air almost incapable of trapping the heat radiated from the earth. It is this process that produces the regu-

lated temperatures found on the earth alone among all the planets. Weather changes that carry life-giving moisture over the continents are the result of water vapor in the air. With a dry atmosphere, this planet would be a barren desert swept by clouds of dust and subject each night to extreme cold.

Driven by the energy of the sun, billions of tons of water each year pass into the atmosphere, then fall out again to run back into the sea. The key to understanding the mechanism of the winds and weather is the behavior of water vapor in the air.

VOCABULARY

Humidity. Water vapor in the air.

Relative humidity. Ratio between water vapor actually in the air and the maximum possible amount at a given temperature.

Hygrometer. An instrument to measure humidity.

Adiabatic change. A temperature change that takes place without the addition or loss of heat to or from the surroundings.

Cirrus clouds. A family of high-altitude clouds.

Stratus clouds. A family of clouds that form in layers.

Cumulus clouds. A family of clouds that resemble balls of wool, usually having flat bases.

Nimbus clouds. A family of dark clouds, usually producing precipitation.

Precipitation. Moisture that condenses and falls from the air.

522

FIG. 29–1. Clouds form by the condensation of water vapor into droplets of water. (*U. S. Navy*)

ATMOSPHERIC MOISTURE

How moisture enters the air. Any water surface exposed to the air will lose water through the process of evaporation. Water passes into the air invisibly, molecule by molecule, so that we notice only that the water gradually disappears. Millions of tons of water evaporate daily from the surface of the sea. Most of this evaporation takes place in the regions around the equator because higher temperatures greatly increase the rate at which water evaporates. Winds affect the rate of evaporation, since moving air evaporates more water than still air. Still air reaches a point at which it can take up no more water; in moving air the moist layer of air directly against the water is constantly replaced by drier air. Although the sea is the principal source of atmospheric moisture, evaporation from lakes, ponds, and streams also supplies some of the water vapor.

Another important source of moisture in the atmosphere is the action of plants. All plants give off water vapor as they carry on their life processes. Large plants give off a surprising amount of water vapor: a single tree during a year's time will commonly release several thousand gallons. The combined effect of the plants all over the earth accounts for a sizeable share of the total moisture in the air.

A small amount of moisture also enters the air by evaporation from exposed moist land surfaces, from volcanic activities such as geysers, and from burning of fuels.

Measurement of atmospheric moisture. The amount of water vapor in the atmosphere is referred to as the *humidity* of the air. Humidity is not constant, however; the air's capacity to hold water vapor changes with the temperature. Warm air can hold a great deal more water vapor than cold air. We sometimes speak of the humidity of the air in terms of *absolute humidity*. This is a statement of the weight of water vapor actually contained in a certain quantity

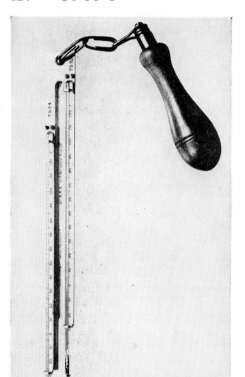

FIG. 29–2. A psychrometer is used to measure humidity. The wick of the thermometer at the left is wet. Evaporation from the wick cools the thermometer bulb. (*U. S. Weather Bureau*)

of air. For example, the absolute humidity of the air at a certain time might be 6 grains per cubic foot. (The grain, 0.002 ounce, is a unit commonly used in measuring humidity.)

A more common way of expressing humidity relates the amount of moisture in a quantity of air to its actual *capacity* at a particular temperature. This method of stating the moisture content of the air is called the **relative humidity.** It is given as a percent which represents a ratio between the amount of

moisture in the air (absolute humidity) and the maximum amount that could be contained at the given temperature (capacity). Air at 70° F, for example, can hold about 8 grains of water vapor per cubic foot. If the absolute humidity of air at 70° is 6 grains per cubic foot, then the air has $\frac{6}{8}$ or $\frac{3}{4}$ of its capacity at that temperature and its relative humidity is 75 percent. The relationship of relative and absolute humidity to capacity can be expressed by the equation

$$\text{Relative humidity} = \frac{\text{Absolute humidity}}{\text{Capacity}} \times 100$$

Substituting the figures in the example above, we have

$$\text{Relative humidity} = \frac{6}{8} \times 100 = 75 \text{ percent}$$

If either the temperature or amount of water vapor changes, the relative humidity also changes. The table opposite shows the relationship of temperature to absolute and relative humidity.

Any instrument used to measure humidity is called a *hygrometer* (hy-*grom*-uh-ter). A common type of hygrometer is the wet-and-dry-bulb thermometer or *psychrometer* shown in Fig. 29–2. It consists of two thermometers; the bulb of one of these is kept wet by a wick which is dipped into water. Cooling of the wet-bulb thermometer is proportional to the rate of evaporation of water from its wick. The rate of evaporation is in turn dependent upon the relative humidity of the surrounding air. When the air is very dry, rapid evaporation of water from the wick cools the wet-bulb thermometer and its temperature reading is lower than that of the dry-bulb thermometer. When the air is very moist, there is little evaporation and the thermometers read about the same.

COMPARISON OF RELATIVE AND ABSOLUTE HUMIDITY

Temperature of Air (F°)				Relative Humidity				
100°	10%	15%	21%	29%	41%	55%	75%	100%
90°	12%	20%	28%	32%	54%	74%	100%	
80°	17%	27%	38%	52%	73%	100%		
70°	24%	36%	51%	71%	100%			
60°	33%	51%	72%	100%				
50°	46%	71%	100%					
40°	66%	100%						
30°	100%							
	1.9	2.9	4.1	5.7	8.0	10.9	14.7	19.7

Grains of Water Vapor per Cubic Foot of Air—Absolute Humidity

It is easy to find the relative humidity if you know the difference between the temperature readings on the wet- and dry-bulb thermometers. In the table below, find the degrees of difference between the two thermometers, as shown at the top of the table. Locate the reading of the dry-bulb thermometer on the left side of the table. The number directly in line with both of these readings is the percent of relative humidity. For example, if the temperature difference between the two thermometers is 9°, and the dry-bulb thermometer reads 65°, the relative humidity is 56 percent. The table here shows relative humidities

RELATIVE HUMIDITY TABLE

Difference Between Dry- and Wet-bulb Thermometers

Degrees	1	2	3	4	5	6	7	8	9	10	11	12	13	14	15
Reading of Dry-bulb Thermometer							*Percent Humidity*								
63	95	89	84	79	74	69	64	60	55	51	46	42	38	33	29
64	95	89	84	79	74	70	65	60	56	51	47	43	38	34	30
65	95	90	85	80	75	70	65	61	56	52	48	44	39	35	31
66	95	90	85	80	75	71	66	61	57	53	49	45	40	36	32
67	95	90	85	80	76	71	66	62	58	53	49	45	41	37	33
68	95	90	85	81	76	71	67	63	58	54	50	46	42	38	34
69	95	90	86	81	76	72	67	63	59	55	51	47	43	39	35
70	95	90	86	81	77	72	68	64	60	55	52	48	44	40	36
71	95	91	86	81	77	72	68	64	60	56	52	48	45	41	37
72	95	91	86	82	77	73	69	65	61	57	53	49	45	42	38
73	95	91	86	82	78	73	69	65	61	57	53	50	46	42	39
74	95	91	86	82	78	74	70	66	62	58	54	50	47	43	40
75	95	91	87	82	78	74	70	66	62	58	55	51	47	44	40

for a narrow range of temperature differences and dry-bulb readings, such as might be found in the classroom. More complete tables, covering greater ranges, are available in some reference books on meteorology.

Another type of hygrometer is the *hair hygrometer,* based on the fact that human hair stretches when wet. In the hair hygrometer specially-treated human hair is arranged so that it stretches when the air becomes moist, and causes a pointer to move on a dial indicating humidity. Such an instrument is convenient to use but is subject to large errors and is slow to respond to changes in humidity. A type of hair hygrometer which gives a continuous record is called a hydrograph. A stylus records the relative humidity on a drum which is rotated by a clock mechanism.

CLOUDS AND FOG

How water leaves the air. For moisture to be removed from the air, it must first be changed from a vapor to a liquid or solid. The water vapor in the air is changed into liquid water or ice largely by cooling. When the temperature is lowered, the capacity of the air for holding water is reduced. If the air continues to grow colder, a point is reached at which the amount of water vapor the air holds is equal to its capacity. At this point the air is said to be *saturated;* the relative humidity is 100 percent. Further cooling results in condensation, the excess water forming droplets or possibly ice crystals if the temperature is below 32° F.

The temperature at which a given quantity of moist air reaches 100 percent relative humidity and begins to condense as water is called the *dew point* for that air. *Dew* which forms on surfaces at night is atmospheric moisture. It condenses on objects that are cool enough to lower the temperature of the air in contact with them below its dew point, as shown in Fig. 29–3. In the same way, droplets of water which form on the sides of glasses containing iced drinks are also dew. If the dew point is below 32° F, the condensed vapor forms solid ice or *frost.* In the formation of frost the water vapor from the air forms ice crystals directly without first becoming a liquid. Sometimes the air temperature may go below freezing and still not reach the dew point. This is spoken of as a "killing frost" because plants are frozen, although no actual frost is formed.

FIG. 29–3. Dew forms on objects that are cold enough to lower the temperature of the surrounding air below the dew point. (*U. S. Dept. of Agriculture*)

FIG. 29–4. Clouds often form as air is cooled in passing over mountains. Such clouds are sometimes called banner clouds. (*Ray Atkeson*)

The formation of clouds. Clouds are almost always produced by the cooling of a body of air. The cloud is the result of a drop in the temperature of the air to the dew point or below with condensation of its water vapor in the form of tiny droplets or ice crystals. Clouds are formed in a particular region of the atmosphere mainly by the upward motion of masses of air. When air rises, it expands because the pressure is decreased. As a result of its expansion the rising air becomes cooler. Downward motion of air has the opposite effect; increased pressure at lower altitude compresses the air, causing it to be heated. The effect of compression and expansion on the temperature of the air may be observed when a compression pump is used. The barrel of the pump may become quite hot in the process of compressing air to inflate a bicycle tire or a basketball. Compressed air escaping from an inflated object feels cool, however; it is expanding rapidly as it is released.

The heating and cooling of air by compression and expansion is due to the behavior of the widely separated gas molecules that compose it. When a gas expands, its molecules absorb energy in the form of heat as they move farther apart. When compressed, a gas releases heat energy as its molecules move closer together. Such temperature changes that take place without the addition or withdrawal of heat by outside influences are called *adiabatic changes.*

Perfectly dry air undergoes a temperature change of 5.5° F for each 1000 feet of change in altitude. This should not be confused with the normal decrease in temperature in the upper air levels. It means that the temperature of a body of *rising* air will decrease by 5.5° and that the temperature of *sinking* air will increase by the same amount for every 1000 feet of change in altitude. The

5.5° figure applies only to dry air and is known as the *dry adiabatic rate.* Normally, air contains moisture, which has a decided effect on the adiabatic rate. When water vapor condenses in the air it releases heat, slowing the rate of cooling in rising air. The *moist adiabatic rate* depends upon the amount of moisture in the air, but an average figure for moist rising air would be a decrease in temperature of 3° F for each 1000 feet of increase in altitude.

The adiabatic changes in air temperature are an important factor in cloud formation because air is constantly being lifted and thus cooled. On a warm sunny day some masses of air may be heated a little more than the surrounding air. The heated air, being less dense, rises and undergoes adiabatic cooling until the dew point is reached and moisture condenses to form a cloud. Clouds like those in Fig. 29–1 were formed above columns of warm rising air. Air may also be cooled as it is lifted over mountains. The tops of mountains are frequently covered with clouds formed in this way, as illustrated in Fig. 29–4. Large areas of clouds are formed when a mass of warm air slides up over a denser mass of cold air. This type of action will be taken up in Chapter 30 in the study of weather.

Cooling is not the only requirement for the formation of a cloud. Even if air is saturated with water vapor, cloud droplets usually will not form unless some kind of microscopic particles are present upon which the water may collect as it condenses. Each cloud droplet is believed to contain a center or nucleus called a *condensation nucleus,* around which the droplet is formed. Condensation nuclei for clouds have been the subject of much study by scientists, but their origin and exact role in cloud formation is still not clearly understood. Many particles present in the atmosphere seem to be suitable condensation nuclei. These include dust, smoke, salt particles from sea spray, and perhaps even particles showered on the earth by disturbances on the sun.

Types of clouds. The most convenient method of classification of clouds is based on their altitude. The major cloud types and their principal subdivisions are as follows:

1. High clouds. The base of these clouds is at an altitude of 20,000 feet or more. They are composed of ice crystals and are generally thin: the outline of the sun or moon may be seen through them. The principal forms are

a. **Cirrus.** Thin, featherlike clouds with a delicate appearance, frequently arranged in bands across the sky.

b. **Cirrocumulus.** Clouds like patches of cotton or a mass of small white flakes, frequently in groups or lines; sometimes called *mackerel sky.*

c. **Cirrostratus.** Whitish layers, like a sheet or veil, giving the sky a milky appearance. They often produce a halo around the sun or moon.

2. Middle clouds. These clouds range from 6500 to 20,000 feet. The principal forms are

a. **Altocumulus.** White or gray patches or layers of clouds having a rounded appearance.

b. **Altostratus.** Gray to bluish layers of clouds, often with a streaked appearance.

3. Low clouds. The bases of these clouds range from near the surface to about 6500 feet.

a. **Stratus.** Low, uniform, sheetlike clouds similar to fog but not resting on the ground.

b. **Stratocumulus.** Large rounded clouds with a soft appearance, usually arranged in some pattern with spaces between.

c. **Nimbostratus.** Low, shapeless, thick layers, dark gray in color. They are usually accompanied by rain or snow.

4. Clouds with vertical development. These are clouds which extend from a lower level of 1600 feet to a maximum of more than 35,000 feet.

a. **Cumulus.** Thick, dome-shaped clouds, usually with flat bases and many rounded projections from the upper areas. Cumulus clouds are often widely separated from one another.

b. **Cumulonimbus.** Towering clouds of large dimensions with cauliflower-like tops, often crowned with veils of thick cirrus, giving the entire cloud a flat top. These are the thunderhead clouds which frequently are associated with thunderstorms.

The various cloud types and forms are summarized in the chart on pages 530–531.

Fog. Like clouds, fogs are the result of condensation of water vapor in the air. The chief difference is that fogs are formed when air is cooled by some means other than lifting, generally by contact with a cool surface. For example, one type of fog results from the nightly cooling of the earth. The layer of air in contact with the earth becomes chilled below its dew point and condensation of water droplets occurs. This type of fog is called a *radiation fog* or *ground fog* because it is caused by the radiation heat loss by the earth. Radiation fogs form most often on calm, clear nights. The fog is often thickest in valleys and low places because the dense, cold air in which the fog forms tends to drain to the lower elevations. Fogs are often unusually thick around cities be-

cause of the greater amount of smoke and dust particles which act as condensation nuclei.

Another common condition which produces fog is the movement of warm, moist air over cold surfaces. A fog produced in this way is called an *advection fog,* referring to the horizontal air movements. Advection fog is very common along seacoasts as the warm moist air from the water moves in over the cooler land surface. Dense fogs may form on the sea when warm, moist air is carried over cold ocean currents. On the Grand Banks, heavy fogs result from chilling of warm air by the Labrador current.

A third type of fog, called an *upslope fog,* is formed by the adiabatic cooling of air as it sweeps up rising land slopes. This is really a kind of cloud formation at ground level.

PRECIPITATION OF MOISTURE

Formation of rain. When water vapor in the air condenses to form clouds, the droplets produced are of various sizes, averaging about 1/2500 inch in diameter. Droplets of this size easily remain suspended in the atmosphere, since even slight air movements prevent them from settling downward. In order to fall as a raindrop, a cloud droplet must grow until it reaches at least 1/125 inch in diameter. Drops of this size are usually heavy enough to fall against rising air currents fast enough so that they will not completely evaporate before reaching the ground. Cloud droplets and a typical raindrop are compared in size in Fig. 29–5.

There seem to be two ways in which cloud droplets are enabled to grow sufficiently large to become *precipitation,*

Cumulus

Cumulonimbus

	35,000	
High clouds	30,000	
Cirrus (Ci)		
Cirrocumulus (Cc)		
Cirrostratus (Cs)	25,000	
	20,000	Clouds with vertical development
		Cumulus (Cu)
		Cumulonimbus (Cb)
Middle clouds	15,000	
Altocumulus (Ac)		
Altostratus (As)		
	10,000	
Low clouds	5,000	
Stratocumulus (Sc)		
Stratus (St)	Altitude in feet	
Nimbostratus (Ns)		

Altocumulus

Altostratus

Cirrus

Stratocumulus

Cirrocumulus

Stratus

Cirrostratus

Nimbostratus

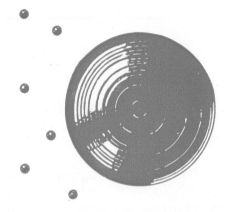

FIG. 29–5. Cloud droplets (left) compared with a typical raindrop (right).

a general term used to refer to rain, snow, and all forms of moisture falling from the atmosphere. Differences in size between cloud droplets lead to their growth. Apparently, the original size of any particular droplet in a cloud depends largely upon the size and nature of its condensation nucleus. Larger nuclei tend to form larger cloud droplets and since the condensation nuclei are of various sizes, the cloud droplets are of different sizes. The larger droplets do not remain suspended in the cloud as well as the smaller ones do, and tend to drift downward. This causes the larger

droplets to collide and combine with the smaller droplets. Figure 29–6 illustrates this process, called *coalescence* (koh-uh-*les*-ens). The larger droplets continue to grow by coalescence until they contain several million times as much water as a single average cloud droplet. By this time, their weight is great enough to cause them to fall to earth.

The presence of ice crystals in a cloud also leads to precipitation in the form of rain. Each microscopic ice crystal cools the water droplets around it and causes them to crystallize. Thus the ice crystal grows steadily as the water vapor crystallizes on its surface. The ice crystals, feeding on the cloud droplets, may grow large enough to fall. The falling ice crystal usually melts in passage, however, and reaches the earth as a raindrop.

Methods of artificially producing rain, by *cloud seeding,* are based on our knowledge of the growth of ice crystals in clouds. One technique consists of scattering pulverized dry ice "seeds" into a cloud from an airplane. The extreme cold of the dry ice causes some of the cloud droplets to become ice crystals, which then grow and eventually fall as rain. Another technique involves

FIG. 29–6. By the process of coalescence, larger raindrops are formed from droplets as they drift downward.

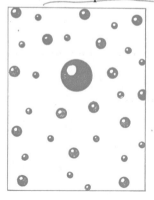
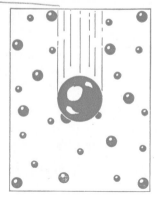
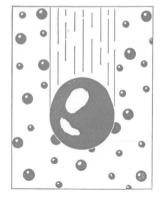

FIG. 29–7. The breaks in these clouds were produced by seeding with pulverized dry ice. (*U. S. Army*)

the release from a generator of a smoke containing millions of tiny crystals of the compound silver iodide. Each crystal of silver iodide resembles an ice crystal, and when it reaches cloud height, it promotes the growth of a larger ice crystal in the same way that a natural seed ice crystal does. The silver iodide generator may be airborne or on the ground. Artificial methods of producing precipitation from clouds do not seem to be successful unless the cloud has nearly the right conditions for natural precipitation. Any rain produced usually falls only over a very limited region. Cloud seeding does seem to be able to cause more rain to fall during a given storm than would fall under natural conditions.

Other types of precipitation. Other than rain, the only type of precipitation of water in the liquid form is *drizzle*. This occurs when cloud or fog droplets that would normally remain suspended fall to the earth because the air is very still. All other forms of precipitation are in the solid form.

The most common form of solid precipitation is *snow*. When the ice crystals which have grown heavy enough to fall from the clouds fail to melt before reaching the ground, the result is snow. Temperatures above freezing near the ground may cause some melting of the falling ice crystals and the resulting film of water causes clumps of them to stick together, forming large snowflakes. Colder temperatures near the ground produce a hard, fine snow, since the individual ice crystals remain separate. The ice crystals that compose snow are always basically six-sided; if the crystal grows very slowly it may develop intricate spokes growing out from the basic six-sided crystal. Some of the basic types of snow crystal patterns are shown in Fig. 29–8.

Very low temperatures near the ground may produce solid precipitation from raindrops. Ice pellets formed when raindrops fall through a layer of freezing air are called *sleet*. Occasionally rain does not freeze until it actually strikes the ground. Then it forms a thick and very destructive layer of *glaze* over everything. Conditions that produce glaze ice are generally called ice storms. *Hail* results from the freezing of raindrops into ice pellets, which then fall through warm air and accumulate a

FIG. 29–8. Snow crystal patterns. (*U. S. Weather Bureau*)

coating of water. As the pellet is carried back up into freezing air or falls through another lower layer of cold air, the coating freezes. This process, repeated a number of times, forms many concentric layers of ice on the hailstone and may produce large chunks of ice which cause great damage when they fall. Hail generally occurs during thunderstorms, when strong vertical currents are created. In the United States, hailstorms are most frequent in the Great Plains.

FIG. 29–12. Glaze ice resulting from ice storms may do tremendous damage in woods and forests. (*U. S. Forest Service*)

SUMMARY

ATMOSPHERIC capacity for absorbing and retaining moisture is regulated by temperature: the higher the temperature, the greater the capacity. Humidity is a general term for atmospheric moisture. Absolute humidity is the weight of water vapor per unit volume of air; relative humidity is the ratio of weight of water vapor to capacity at a certain temperature.

Humidity is measured by an instrument called a hygrometer. It consists of two thermometers, one of which is kept moist by means of a damp wick. Relative or absolute humidity can be calculated by determining the difference between the readings of wet- and dry-bulb thermometers.

If air is cooled below its saturation point, condensation will occur. Depending on elevation and temperature, dew, fog, frost, or clouds may result.

Clouds are formed mainly by the upward motion of masses of air, which are cooled by expansion. Cloud droplets collect around a condensation nucleus, which may be a particle of dust, smoke, salt, or some other substance.

Within clouds, coalescence or crystallization of water droplets around ice crystals may produce rain. If the enlarged, six-sided crystals do not melt while falling, the result is called snow. Sleet and hail are forms of rain that is frozen near the ground.

VOCABULARY REVIEW

Match the phrase in the left column with the correct word or phrase in the right column. *Do not write in this book.*

1. Particle around which water droplets collect
2. General term for water vapor in the air
3. Rise or fall of temperature without gain or loss of heat from surroundings
4. Limit of absorption of water vapor
5. Feathery high-altitude clouds
6. Measures humidity
7. Sheetlike clouds
8. Weight of water vapor in the air
9. Ratio between capacity and actual amount of water vapor
10. Rain clouds
11. Temperature at which water vapor condenses
12. Fair-weather flat-based clouds

a. fog
b. condensation nucleus
c. cumulus
d. hygrometer
e. nimbus
f. humidity
g. cirrus
h. relative humidity
i. dew point
j. absolute humidity
k. stratus
l. saturation
m. adiabatic change

QUESTIONS · GROUP A

Decide whether these statements are true or false. Reword the false statements to make them true. *Do not write in this book.*

1. The air temperature at an elevation of 500 feet is 61° F. According to the moist adiabatic lapse rate, the temperature of the same air at 5000 feet should be 53° F.
2. When a wet-bulb thermometer reads the same as a dry-bulb thermometer, the relative humidity is 100 percent.
3. The greater the temperature, the lower is the air's capacity for holding water vapor.
4. If water condenses on the outside of a glass of water, the temperature of the water within the glass must be above the dew point of the air.
5. The absolute humidity of the air is expressed as a percent.
6. Cirrocumulus clouds give warning of approaching thunderstorms.
7. Fogs occur most frequently when the nights are cloudy.
8. If all of the water vapor in the atmosphere were suddenly to condense, all the major mountain ranges would be under water.
9. The rate of evaporation is increased by the movement of air.
10. If the relative humidity at 70° F is 38 percent, the total weight of water vapor contained in 8 cubic feet of air is 28.6 grains.
11. If the reading given by a dry-bulb thermometer is 68° F and the wet-bulb reads 60° F, the relative humidity is 63 percent.

GROUP B

1. If the relative humidity of the air is 73 percent and its capacity is 10.9 grains of water vapor per cubic foot, determine the absolute humidity. Show all calculations.
2. Discuss the formation of frost, dew, and rain.
3. What is an adiabatic change? Why do adiabatic changes occur in the atmosphere but not in the oceans?
4. Compare and contrast the characteristics of the three major types of clouds.
5. What are the chief differences between radiation fogs, advection fogs, and upslope fogs?
6. With the aid of diagrams, explain the formation of hail, glaze, and sleet.
7. If the absolute humidity is 5 grains of water per cubic foot, calculate the weight of the water vapor in pounds and ounces in a room 25 feet long, 15 feet wide, and 10 feet high.

CHAPTER 30

WEATHER CHANGES

WEATHER involves all the properties of the atmosphere—temperature, pressure, moisture, and winds—but the source of all weather is the heat that is contained in the air. Many of the earth's changes in weather are created around the circumpolar whirl: the zone where cold air moving down from the poles collides with warm air from the equatorial regions. Cold air, clinging close to the earth, pushes in under the warm air, thrusting cold fingers toward the warm tropics. At the same time, warm air slides up over the cold and is pushed toward the poles. From the struggles between these bodies of warm and cold air come the storm centers that are responsible for most of the weather experienced in the middle latitudes.

The modern scientific theories which account for weather in this way are only a beginning in the study of weather origins. Much is still unexplained; often the shifting patterns of the weather defy analysis, seeming to be merely a hopeless tangle of air currents that move in

VOCABULARY

Air mass. A large body of air that has about the same temperature and humidity throughout.

Front. The boundary between two air masses.

Cold front. A front at which a colder air mass thrusts under a warmer air mass.

Warm front. A front at which a warmer air mass overrides a colder air mass.

Cyclone. A large mass of low-pressure air, with winds moving into it in a counterclockwise whirl.

Anticyclone. A large mass of high-pressure air, with winds moving out from it in a clockwise whirl.

Hurricane. A destructive tropical storm over the Atlantic Ocean; such storms over the Pacific Ocean are called **typhoons.**

Tornado. A relatively small, destructive middle-latitude storm, usually originating over the land.

537

response to unknown conditions. However, there is usually a suggestion at least in the changing weather of the influence of the masses of air that continually sweep across the earth.

AIR MASSES

Air masses and their origins. An *air mass* is a large body of air extending across millions of square miles of the earth's surface. The chief characteristic of a given air mass is that its temperature and humidity are fairly uniform throughout at any particular altitude, as shown in Fig. 30–1. Air masses differ

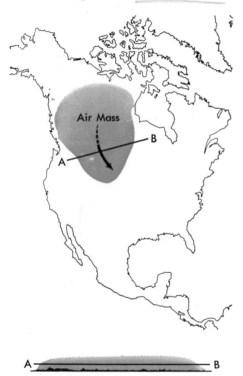

FIG. 30–1. A polar air mass is shown moving from Canada into the United States. A section along the line *AB* is shown vertically below to indicate the uniform conditions that prevail within the air mass.

greatly from each other, and the weather associated with a given air mass is determined mainly by its particular temperature and moisture. Air masses tend to keep their identity; that is, their temperature and humidity do not change easily, because air masses of different densities, like oil and water, do not readily mix.

An air mass is created when the atmosphere remains relatively quiet over a particular part of the earth's surface for a long enough period of time to take on the temperature and humidity characteristics of that region. For example, air remaining over the arctic plains of North America becomes cold and dry. Over a tropical ocean a body of air becomes warm and moist. To serve as a source region for air masses, an area must be fairly uniform (mixed land and water areas are not suitable) and must be free of strong winds.

Air masses are classified mainly according to the source region from which they come. A system of letters is used to designate the source and characteristics of the various air masses that exist at any particular time. The principal source regions are the cold polar (*P*) areas and the warm tropical (*T*) areas. The polar and tropical air masses are further classified as maritime (*m*) if the origin is over the sea and continental (*c*) if the source is over land. Naturally, maritime air masses tend to be moist, and continental air masses are generally dry. It follows that there are four principal types of air masses, which can be described by the following letter combinations: *mP, mT, cP,* and *cT.*

Once formed, an air mass seldom remains over its source region but is carried elsewhere by the general movements of the atmosphere. Air masses often change as they move from their

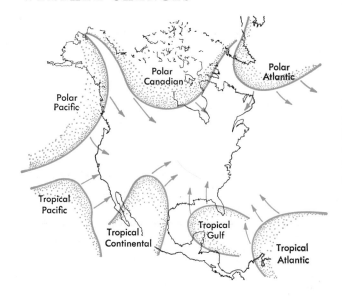

FIG. 30–2. The types of air masses that influence weather in North America. Arrows indicate the general direction of movement of these air masses.

sources. For example, a dry continental air mass may move over the sea and become a moist maritime air mass. Temperatures of the lower layers of air masses also may be modified by contact with the earth's surface. A cold polar air mass may move over warmer land or sea surfaces, so that its lower air becomes warmer than its upper air. When this occurs, the warmed air below rises and tends to produce clouds and precipitation. An air mass whose lower layers are being warmed is *unstable* and generally produces cloudy, unsettled weather. An air mass moving over a surface with a lower temperature is affected in the opposite way; it is said to be *stable* and is characterized by clearer weather. The letters *w* (warm) and *k* (cold—from German *kalt*) are used to indicate whether an air mass has a temperature higher or lower than the surface over which it is located. Here the terms *warm* and *cold* are entirely relative. A warm air mass may become a cold one, without change in its own temperature, if it moves over a region that is warmer than itself. Similarly, a

cold air mass becomes a warm air mass when it moves over a colder region.

North American air masses. Air masses that greatly influence the weather in North America come from seven main source regions. The origin of these air masses and their general direction of movement are shown in Fig. 30–2.

Polar Canadian (*cP*) air masses are formed in northern Canada and generally move in a southeasterly direction across Canada and the northern United States. In the winter they are the cause of the intense cold waves that sweep across the northern part of the country, occasionally penetrating as far south as the Gulf Coast. During the summer, they bring cool, dry weather.

Polar Pacific (*mP*) air masses come from the northern Pacific Ocean and the southwest part of Alaska. They are cool but not extremely cold, and very moist. They affect mainly the Pacific Coast, where they produce rain and snow in winter as the air is lifted over the coastal mountains. In summer, the polar Pacific air produces cool, often foggy weather along the west coast.

Polar Atlantic (*mP*) air masses are formed over the northern Atlantic Ocean. Their general direction of movement is eastward toward Europe, but they may affect the weather of the northeastern United States. In the winter they bring cold, overcast weather with light precipitation, but in the summer they cause cool weather with low clouds and fog.

Tropical Continental (*cT*) air masses affect North America only in the summer. They form over Mexico and the southwest portion of the United States and generally move northeast. They bring clear, dry, and very hot weather.

Tropical Gulf and Tropical Atlantic (*mT*) air masses form over the warm seas of the Gulf of Mexico and the South Atlantic and move north to the United States across the eastern part of the country. In the winter they bring mild and often cloudy weather, while in the summer they produce hot, very humid weather with thunderstorms.

Tropical Pacific (*mT*) air masses form over the warm parts of the Pacific Ocean and reach the Pacific Coast only during the winter. They bring cool, foggy weather.

WEATHER FRONTS

Formation of a front. When two air masses meet, there is generally little mixing of the air contained within the two bodies. The boundary between them, though usually wavy, is definite; this is called a *front*. The colder of the two air masses is denser, and thus tends to push under the warmer air and lift it. Therefore the front always slopes up over the cooler air. See Fig. 30–3.

Air masses are usually in motion, and the nature of a front depends on the motion of the air masses. When a moving cold air mass wedges its way under a warm air mass, a *cold front* is formed. The bottom of the advancing cold air is held back by friction with the ground so that the cold air tends to pile up in a

FIG. 30–3. Vertical view of air masses at cold and warm fronts. Note that fronts, represented by the black lines, do not exist only on the ground, but extend upward along the boundary of the air masses.

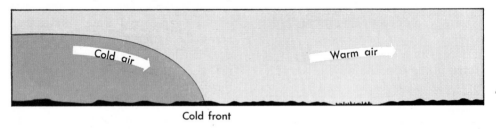

Cold front

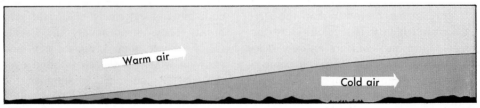

Warm front

About 60 miles

FIG. 30–4. Weather conditions along a cold front as seen from above. The light line at the left, indicating the vertical structure of the front, corresponds to the black line in the upper drawing of Fig. 30–3.

steep slope, as illustrated in Fig. 30–4. Cold air masses tend to move more rapidly than warm air masses because the cold air is heavy and sinks, creating higher pressures which push the air outward from the center of the mass. The average speed of a cold air mass is about 20 miles per hour. Its movement is generally faster in winter than in summer because the air is colder and heavier in winter. At a cold front the rapidly moving cold air lifts the warmer air quickly and causes heavy cloud formation if the warm air is moist. Figure 30–4 shows the towering cumulus and cumulonibus clouds typical of a rapidly moving cold front. Storms created along such a front are usually brief and violent. A long line of heavy thunderstorms, called a *squall line,* may advance just ahead of a fast-moving cold front. A slowly moving cold front lifts the warm air less rapidly, producing a somewhat less concentrated area of cloudiness and precipitation.

When warm air advances over the edge of a retreating mass of cold air, a *warm front* is produced. The slope of a warm front is very gradual, as shown in Fig. 30–5. Because of this gentle slope, the clouds may extend as much as 1000 miles ahead of the base of the front. A warm front generally produces stratus clouds which cover a large area, and heavy but not violent precipitation. Occasionally a warm front will produce violent storms if the warm air advancing over the cold air is very moist.

Sometimes both warm and cold fronts come to a halt and cease to move for several days. In this case, they are referred to as *stationary fronts.* The weather connected with stationary fronts is generally the same as that associated with warm fronts.

Storm centers formed by fronts. Slowly moving cold fronts or stationary fronts frequently tend to develop bulges of cold air which advance slightly ahead of the front itself. These waves can be the beginning of a storm center called a *cyclone* or *low.* (A cyclone in this sense, also called a cyclonic depression, is not the same as a tropical cyclone, or hurricane, nor should it be confused with the small but very violent local storm called a tornado.) It consists of a large body of air moving in a circular fashion with low pressure at the center. Cyclones are very large disturbances ranging from 500 to 1000 miles in diameter and covering as much as 1 million square miles.

In Fig. 30–6 the stages in the development of a typical cyclone are illustrated. At the beginning (*A*), there is only the boundary between the two air masses. At this stage there are winds tending to move parallel with the frontal boundary, since air from one body does not readily penetrate into the other. Slight waves or bulges develop along the front, and faster moving cold air tends to push into the warmer air mass (*B*). At the same time, warm air is pushed forward into the colder air. The result is creation of a warm front moving slowly ahead of a rapidly moving cold front, with a low-pressure area developing at the point where the two fronts merge (*C*). The lighter warm air is lifted as it presses into the cold air along the warm front and is pushed up also by the advancing cold air along the cold front. As a result of this lifting, clouds and precipitation soon appear along both the fronts formed (*D*). Soon the swiftly advancing cold front overtakes the warm front and the warm air trapped between is lifted completely off the ground (*E*). The front at that point is now *occluded* or closed off from the earth's surface. The strong lifting action on the warm air causes the storm to reach its maximum intensity. By this time, the winds are moving in a circle around the low pressure region at the center of the disturbance (*F*). A fully developed cyclone (stage *E*) is shown in greater detail in Fig. 30–7.

During the 12 to 24 hours that it takes a cyclone to develop, the air

FIG. 30–5. Weather conditions along a warm front, as seen from above. The dark blue area is a cold air mass, as in Figs. 30–3 and 30–4.

About 500 miles

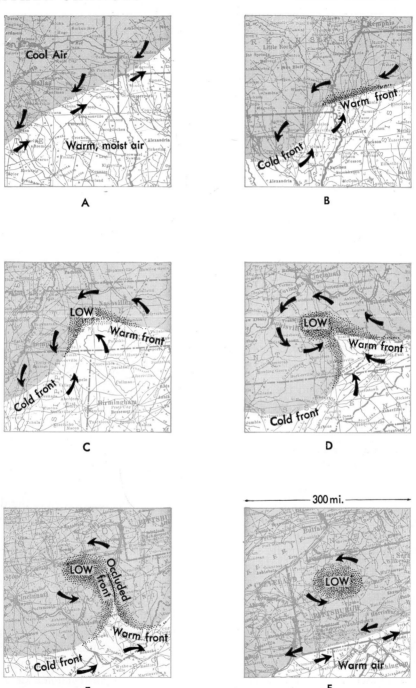

FIG. 30–6. The development of a typical cyclone or low pressure area as seen from above. The underlying maps indicate that this storm area moved northeastward as it developed.

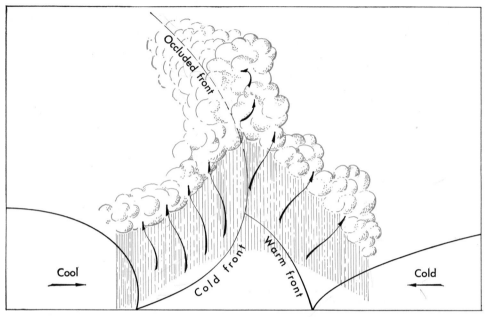

FIG. 30–7. View showing the vertical development of a cyclone or low, corresponding to Stage *E* in Fig. 30–6.

masses are in motion, and the disturbance moves with them. In the United States, prevailing winds tend to make the cyclonic storms move from west to east. The principal routes of cyclones across the country are given in Fig. 30–8. Most cyclones follow the northern tracks and move at the rate of 500 to 1000 miles per day.

The full extent of the lifetime of a cyclonic storm depends upon its supply of moist air. As the winds circling into the low pressure center continue to bring a supply of moist air, the condensation of the water vapor releases the heat energy which converted it into vapor. This supply of energy is capable of sustaining the cyclone. Eventually the supply of water vapor that fuels the storm ceases, and the cyclone gradually dies out and is lost among the winds.

Anticyclones. Since cyclones are regions of low pressure, the general wind direction within these storms is inward toward the low pressure center. This being so, the Coriolis force, plus the friction of the winds against the earth's surface, make the air move in a whirl that is *counterclockwise* in the northern hemisphere.

In regions of high pressure the direction of wind flow is outward from the high pressure center since the air is constantly spreading away from the center. In this case, the Coriolis force and surface friction cause the winds to be deflected so that they move in a *clockwise* whirl in the northern hemisphere. Because the wind circulation in high pressure centers is opposite to that in low pressure centers or cyclones, these centers are called *anticyclones* or *highs.* See Fig. 30–9. Since there is no lifting action associated with anticyclones, the weather within them is usually fair. Cyclones with their stormy weather and

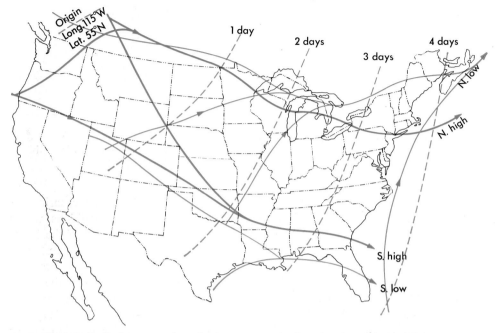

FIG. 30–8. Principal routes of cyclonic storms. The heavier lines represent movements of highs, the lighter lines, movements of lows.

FIG. 30–9. The clockwise movement of winds from a high contrasted with the counter-clockwise flow of winds into a low.

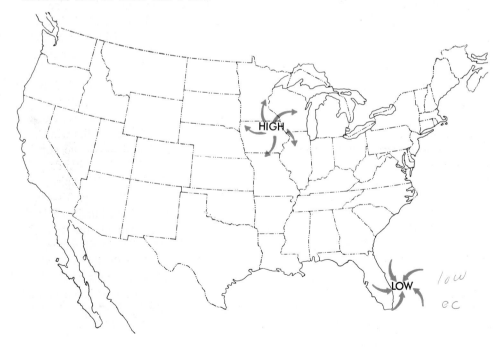

low pressures are generally followed by anticyclones bringing clearing weather and rising pressures.

SEVERE STORMS

Local storms. The cyclonic storms that are associated with the development of fronts are relatively mild and cover very broad areas. The intense storms that develop locally are much smaller in extent. Local storms are of several kinds. Some occur in tropical regions and are characterized by heavy rains and violent winds rotating around a low pressure area. These are called by various names in different parts of the world. Over the Atlantic Ocean, and in Australia, they are called *hurricanes;* in the Western Pacific they are called *typhoons. Tornadoes* are brief, very violent, whirling storms. In *thunderstorms,* the lightning, thunder, and rain are more spectacular features than the winds, although strong gusts are usual. Frontal, or general, thunderstorms occur along the passing fronts of a cyclonic disturbance, as we have seen. Local thunderstorms are the result of strong convection currents in a limited area.

Hurricanes. For reasons not yet clearly understood, relatively small but violent rotating storms frequently develop over the warm tropical seas in the low latitudes close to the equator. These storms bear some resemblance to the cyclones of the middle latitudes. However, hurricanes are seldom more than a few hundred miles in diameter. Thus they are considerably smaller than cyclonic storms, though much more damaging.

Much has been learned about hurricanes in recent years by flying aircraft

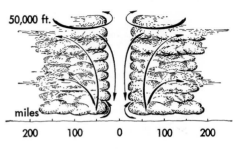

FIG. 30–10. Movement of air within a hurricane, shown vertically.

through the storms and measuring the varying atmospheric conditions within them. Pieced together, all of the information gained by the study of hurricanes indicates that the storm probably begins as a disturbance in the trade winds which blow over the sea near the equator. Very moist warm air is caused to rise at a particular location and is rapidly carried away at upper levels by high altitude winds. The moisture in the rising warm air condenses, releasing large amounts of heat, which by further warming the air causes it to rise even faster. More moist tropical air is drawn into the column of rising air at lower levels, thus introducing a continuous supply of water vapor to keep the process going. The rotating motion of the air as it rushes toward the center of the storm is believed to be the result of the Coriolis force acting upon the winds.

A fully developed hurricane consists of a series of thick cloud bands, with heavy precipitation, which spiral into the storm's center. See Fig. 30–10. In the exact center of the hurricane is the relatively calm *eye;* a quiet region about 12 to 15 miles in diameter. The winds increase in velocity toward the eye, with maximum speeds usually over 100 miles per hour. Hurricane damage is caused partly by the high winds but also by the flooding which accompanies the extremely heavy rains. Flooding along coastal areas is caused by the water piled up against the shore by the high winds.

The principal paths of hurricanes over the entire earth are shown in Fig. 30–11. Those storms reaching the United States are formed in the West Indies region and strike the Gulf Coast, Florida, or the Atlantic Coast. To reduce damage and loss of life from these destructive storms, the U. S. Weather Bureau operates a hurricane warning system. Specially equipped aircraft are used to investigate developing storms and to track them until their probable path is evident. Warnings are then issued to areas likely to be affected.

Tornadoes. The smallest, most violent and short-lived of all storms is the tornado. A tornado is most likely to occur on a hot, humid day when the sky is filled with heavy thunderclouds. Suddenly, one of the cloud bases develops a funnel-shaped twisting extension that reaches down toward the earth. The tip of the funnel touches the earth and moves in a wandering path at a speed of 25 to 40 miles per hour. Frequently, the funnel rises, then touches down again in a short distance. The tornado generally does not sweep a path any more than 500 yards in width, but within that path destruction is very great. Winds whirling within the funnel are estimated to reach a velocity of 500 miles per hour. Because the pressure within the funnel is extremely low, buildings may literally explode from the sudden pressure drop as the tornado passes. Fortunately, the average life span of a tornado is only about eight minutes.

How tornadoes are able to develop their tremendous power is a complete mystery. To form, they seem to require moist warm air at low levels and cool dry air at upper levels, along with some

FIG. 30–11. The principal hurricane and typhoon areas of the world are shown in color. Arrows indicate the normal paths of the storms. Note that these storms all originate over water in tropical regions.

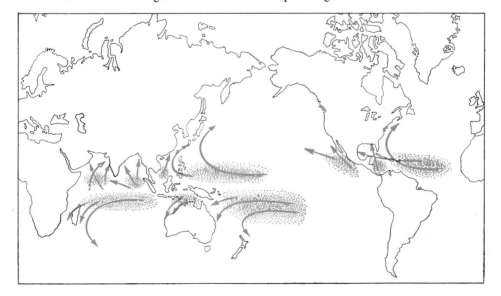

sudden lifting action such as that caused by an advancing cold front. Tornadoes in the United States occur most often in the Midwest during the late spring or early summer.

Thunderstorms. Severe local storms accompanied by lightning and thunder are associated with rapidly rising columns of warm moist air with corresponding downdrafts of cooler air. Thunderstorms are most common during warm weather but may occur whenever warm air is thrust rapidly upward.

Thunderstorm development takes place in three distinct stages, shown in Fig. 30–14.

A. In the *cumulus stage* a swiftly moving current of warm air rises to altitudes above 25,000 feet. The moisture within the rising air condenses as the air is cooled and a towering cumulus cloud is developed. This stage is generally completed in less than one hour.

B. The *mature stage* begins as precipitation occurs from the upper levels of the cloud and heavy showers fall beneath the cloud. The precipitation causes violent up-and-down movements of air within the cloud. Strong downdrafts strike the ground below the cloud and spread out, making the characteristic gusty winds blowing out from the center of rainfall. The vertical air movements frequently cause the precipitation to take the form of hail.

C. The *final stage* begins when the upward air currents cease. As the upward movement of moist air diminishes, the precipitation gradually slows down, then stops completely. The violent up-and-down movements disappear and the ice crystals at the top of the cloud spread out into the anvil-shaped top typical of a cumulonimbus or thunderhead cloud.

Lightning is produced by the accumulation of electrical charges within the cloud as it develops. The top of the cloud becomes positively charged and the lower portions become mostly negatively charged. The positive charge in the upper levels of a thundercloud is believed to be the result of friction of water droplets and ice crystals against the air as they are carried up by the rising air currents. The friction supposedly has a tendency to remove electrons which accumulate in the lower parts of the cloud, thus giving it a negative charge. The rising moisture particles, having

FIG. 30–12. This weather observation plane is flying above a hurricane. The cloud pattern indicates the plane is near the eye of the storm. (*U. S. Navy*)

FIG. 30–13. Tornadoes, unlike hurricanes, cover a small area and always develop over land. (*U. S. Weather Bureau*)

lost electrons, are positively charged and so cause the upper parts of the cloud to become positively charged. When the electrical difference between the top and bottom parts of the thundercloud becomes large enough, a lightning dis-

charge passes between the two parts of the cloud. Such a discharge may also occur when some region of the lower part of the cloud becomes positively charged as a result of the up and down motions within the cloud. The sound of thunder is caused by the rapid heating and expansion of the air through which the lightning passes.

Lightning may also pass between the cloud and the ground if the conditions are right. Ordinarily the ground is negatively charged with respect to the air above it; however, with respect to the negative charge at the base of a thundercloud, the ground may be temporarily positively charged immediately below the cloud. If the electrical difference between the cloud and ground becomes great enough, a lightning discharge will occur. Study of lightning with a high speed camera shows that the stroke starts with a thin leader usually passing from the cloud to the ground but occasionally moving in the opposite direction. Immediately after the leader, a return stroke occurs and is followed by a number of discharges and return strokes all taking place in less than a tenth of a

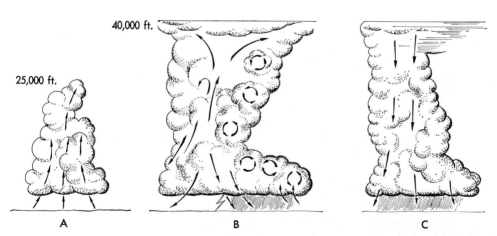

FIG. 30–14. Three stages in the development of a thunderstorm. The arrows indicate direction of air currents.

second. An average lightning discharge is estimated to deliver from 20 to 30 million volts. The distance of a lightning discharge from the observer can be approximated by counting the number of seconds between the flash and the sound of thunder. The number of seconds divided by five gives the approximate distance in miles.

Each year lightning kills about 200 people in the United States, but even a few simple precautions make the risk extremely slight. The first rule for lightning safety is to avoid any prominent feature or high location in open country. Lightning follows the path of least resistance and is most likely to strike the highest part of any particular location. A person standing in an open field may become the target; likewise, trees, tall metal objects and bodies of water are all likely targets and should be avoided during a thunderstorm. Buildings, particularly those with a metal framework,

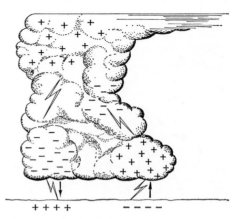

FIG. 30–15. Lightning results from the accumulation of electric charges due to friction between the air and water droplets in the clouds.

are relatively safe, as are automobiles. Airplanes may be struck by lightning and no harm result to the passengers, although some damage may be done to projecting parts of the aircraft and to its radio equipment.

SUMMARY

RELEASE or absorption of heat in the atmosphere is the primary cause of weather changes because it affects temperature, humidity, and winds.

Air masses are formed when the atmosphere is stagnant over an area for a limited time. As air masses move across the earth, temperature and humidity are slowly modified, producing weather changes.

The boundary between two air masses is a front. It is named after the advancing air mass. Interaction of air masses and the subsequent development of fronts form cyclones and anticyclones.

Tropical oceanic storms accompanied by strong winds and heavy rain are called hurricanes. Tornadoes form during hot humid days in continental areas. Although they cover a small area and are shortlived, they are the most violent storms. Rising columns of warm air occurring simultaneously with downdrafts of cooler air produce thunderstorms characterized by gusty winds, short periods of heavy rain, lightning, and possibly hail.

VOCABULARY REVIEW

Match the phrase in the left column with the correct word or phras column. *Do not write in this book.*

1. Destructive tropical storms
2. Large mass of high pressure air
3. Group of heavy thunderstorms
4. Violent middle latitude land storm
5. Gentle slope accompanied by stratus clouds
6. Large mass of low pressure air
7. Caused by a difference in electrical charges
8. Boundary between air masses
9. Preceded by cumulus and cumulonimbus clouds
10. Continental air mass

a. tornado
b. occluded front
c. cyclone
d. cold front
e. anticyclone
f. warm front
g. Polar Canadian
h. hurricane
i. squall line
j. lightning
k. front

QUESTIONS • GROUP A

Decide whether these statements are true or false. Reword the false statements to make them true. *Do not write in this book.*

1. Hurricanes generally move through the midwestern section of the United States.
2. Anticyclones are characterized by low pressures.
3. Thunderstorms often accompany the passage of a cold front.
4. The Great Lakes region meets the criteria for the formation of air masses.
5. Generally a cold front moves faster than a warm front.
6. The life span of a tornado is about 24 hours.
7. Most cyclonic storms move from west to east.
8. The center of a thunderstorm is known as the eye.
9. The earth's surface usually has a negative electrical charge.
10. If the time interval between the sound of thunder and the flash is 15 seconds, the lightning struck about 3 miles away.

GROUP B

1. Why do air masses form more often in some areas than in others?
2. Name the possible source region, meaning, and characteristics of the following types of air masses: (*a*) mP (*b*) cP (*c*) mT (*d*) cT (*e*) cPk (*f*) cTw.
3. Using diagrams, explain the formation of a cold front and a warm front.
4. With the aid of diagrams show the development of a cyclonic storm.
5. Using diagrams, explain the movement of air in a cyclone and an anticyclone.
6. In what direction would the wind blow at each of the following points: (*a*) directly east of the center of an approaching low (*b*) southeast of the center of an approaching high (*c*) southwest of the center of a passing low (*d*) directly north of the center of a high? Using diagrams, explain each answer.
7. How are hurricanes and tornadoes similar? How do they differ?

CHAPTER 31

WEATHER PREDICTION

WEATHER prediction is one of the most practical applications of *meteorology,* the science of the atmosphere. Those who study this science, called *meteorologists,* are able to make fairly accurate weather forecasts. To do this, they rely on various weather instruments, and on techniques that have been developed largely within the last hundred years. Because meteorology is a relatively young science, predictions of the changes in meteorological conditions (weather) are often not as accurate as we might wish. However, the use of new instruments and improved techniques will continue to improve the reliability of weather forecasts.

In the middle latitudes, where the United States lies and most of the world's population lives, weather forecasting is primarily a problem of anticipating the growth and paths of the mobile lows and highs, that is, the cyclones and anticyclones, of conflicting air masses. The foundation of scientific weather forecasting is the high probability of unsettled weather within the furrows of low pressure where air rises and generates clouds and precipitation. Regions of high pressure are expected to produce fair weather since the air currents are mostly descending. The problem of forecasting, then, is one of accurately predicting the path, speed,

VOCABULARY

Meteorology. The science of the atmosphere.

Thermometer. An instrument to measure temperature.

Millibar. A unit of air pressure used in weather observations.

Rain gauge. An instrument to measure the amount of precipitation.

Anemometer. An instrument to measure wind velocity.

Radiosonde. A set of electronic instruments that record and broadcast temperature, pressure, and humidity conditions at high altitudes.

Radar. A short-wave radio device that can be used to locate and track storms.

Isobar. A line on a weather map joining all places that report the same air pressure.

and intensity of the crests of high pressure and troughs of low pressure as they constantly follow each other around the globe.

The behavior of the giant waves that surge through the atmosphere is revealed to the weather observer by his array of instruments. Man's own senses are of little use in the direct detection of the subtle changes in pressure, temperature, moisture, and winds that accompany the changes in weather.

WEATHER INSTRUMENTS

Measurement of temperature. Thermometers used at weather stations to measure air temperature are very similar to ordinary household thermometers. They contain a liquid which expands or contracts with changes in temperature. Mercury is most often used because it is a liquid metal which readily expands and contracts with changes in temperature. The temperature scale used on weather thermometers may be either the *Fahrenheit* (F) or *Centigrade* (C) scale. In the United States the Fahrenheit scale is commonly used; however

the rest of the world uses the Centigrade scale, also called the *Celsius* scale. The difference between the two can be illustrated by a comparison of the boiling point and freezing point of water on both scales. On the Centigrade scale, water boils at $100°$ and freezes at $0°$. On the Fahrenheit scale, water boils at $212°$ and freezes at $32°$. Temperatures given in one scale can be easily converted to the other by the following formulas:

To change Fahrenheit to Centigrade
$$C = 5/9(F - 32)$$
and to change Centigrade to Fahrenheit
$$F = 9/5C + 32$$

For recording the highest and lowest temperatures during a day, *maximum and minimum thermometers* such as those shown in Fig. 31–1 are used. A maximum thermometer is similar in construction to the common clinical thermometer, with a small constriction in the thermometer tube just above the mercury bulb. When in use, the maximum thermometer is held in a horizontal position. As the temperature rises the mercury passes through the constriction but cannot run back again. Thus

FIG. 31–1. Maximum and minimum thermometers. The maximum thermometer is filled with mercury, whereas the minimum thermometer uses alcohol. Note the glass marker in the tube of the minimum thermometer. (*Bendix Aviation Corporation*)

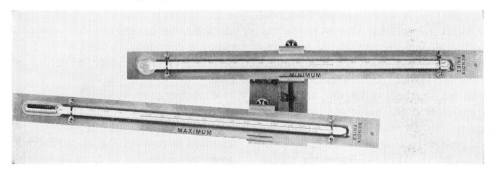

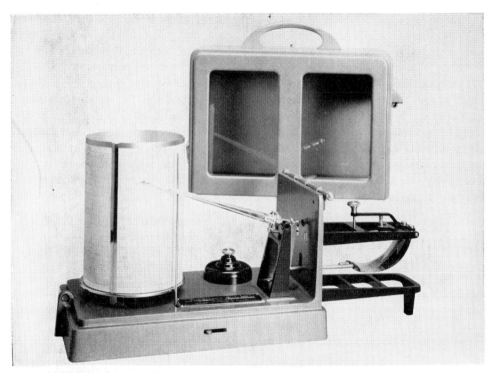

FIG. 31–2. A thermograph with the cover removed to expose the working parts. The bimetallic strip is at the right. As the drum at the left rotates, the pointer makes a continuous record of the temperature changes. (*Bendix Aviation Corporation*)

the mercury column remains at the maximum temperature reached. Whirling the thermometer rapidly forces the mercury to return to the bulb and the instrument is thus prepared to register a new maximum. The minimum thermometer is filled with alcohol rather than mercury because alcohol adheres to glass readily while mercury does not. A small glass marker adheres to the top of the alcohol column as the temperature drops, but when the temperature rises the marker remains at the lowest position reached. Like the maximum thermometer, the minimum thermometer is normally held in a nearly horizontal position; it is reset by tilting down to allow the marker to return to the top of

the alcohol column. Maximum and minimum temperatures during a period of weather observations may also be recorded by a *thermograph,* Fig. 31–2, which makes a written record. This instrument employs a heat-sensitive bimetallic strip instead of a liquid-filled tube to indicate temperature changes. It is less accurate than a liquid-filled thermometer, but has the advantage of providing a continuous record of the temperature variations over a period of time.

If temperature readings are to be compared, the instruments must be protected from exposure to sunlight. A standard instrument shelter is generally used, consisting of a large box with

sloping roof, closed bottom, and lou-
vered sides. The box is usually raised
about 4 feet off the ground.

Measurement of atmospheric pressure.
The instruments used to measure atmospheric pressure have been described in
Chapter 28. However, the units in which
pressure measurements are expressed in
weather observations are different from
those already given. In weather reporting and forecasting the pressure readings
are expressed in *millibars* (mb). These
are units of pressure in an international
system of weather observation. A millibar is equal to a pressure of about 0.03
inches of mercury. The table at the right
shows the relationship between pressure
readings in millibars and inches of mercury, within the normal range.

ATMOSPHERIC PRESSURE

Inches of Mercury	Millibars
27.00	914.3
28.00	948.2
28.50	965.1
29.00	982.1
29.50	999.0
29.75	1007.5
29.92	1013.2
30.00	1015.9
30.25	1024.4

Atmospheric pressure seldom varies
more than 50 millibars above or below
the normal sea level pressure of 1013.25
millibars at the earth's surface. However, the slight pressure changes that do
occur are extremely important in detecting the passage of highs and lows.

FIG. 31–3. Devices to measure precipitation. Left, a tipping bucket rain
gauge. Right, a weighing rain gauge which continuously records the amount
of precipitation. (*Bendix Aviation Corporation*)

FIG. 31–4. An anemometer. (*Bendix Aviation Corporation*)

Measurement of precipitation. The *rain gauge* consists of a wide-mouthed funnel which catches the rain and empties it into a cylindrical container below. The mouth of the funnel is exactly ten times larger in diameter than the container underneath, so that $\frac{1}{10}$ inch of rain will fill the container to a depth of 1 inch. This magnification of the actual rainfall makes it possible to measure the fall very accurately with a marked stick which is dipped into the container.

Another type of rain gauge has a small divided bucket which catches the water from the funnel, fills on one side, then tips, dumping the water and allowing the other half of the small bucket to fill. Each time one side of the tipping bucket fills with exactly $\frac{1}{100}$ inch of rain, it tips and activates an electrical device that records the amount. The rainwater dumped from the tipping bucket is collected and weighed as a means of checking the accuracy of the record. Another type of rain gauge catches the water in a large bucket which is weighed continuously, the weight being recorded directly on a graph as inches of rain. See Fig. 31–3.

Rain gauges can also be used to measure snowfall. The collected snow is melted and the water is weighed to determine its rain equivalent. A light fluffy snow may yield 1 inch of rain for every 15 inches of snow; a dense well-packed fall may produce 1 inch of rain for every 6 inches of snow.

Measurement of wind speed and direction. To measure wind velocity, an instrument called an *anemometer* (an-uh-*mom*-uh-ter) is used. The most common type of anemometer consists of small cups attached by spokes to a shaft that is free to rotate, as shown in Fig. 31–4. The instrument is mounted on a pole so that the cups will catch the wind and spin the wheel at a rate proportional to the wind speed. The rotation of the wheel is usually converted into an electrical signal which registers the correct wind speed on a dial in some convenient location.

Wind speeds may be recorded in miles per hour, although official weather reports use knots (1.15 miles per hour).

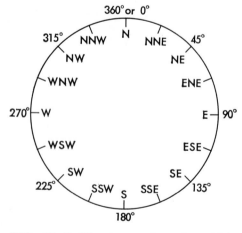

FIG. 31–5. The two systems by which wind directions are given.

Wind velocity may also be expressed by use of the Beaufort scale worked out in 1806 by Admiral Beaufort of the British Navy. The table below relates wind velocities on the Beaufort scale with miles per hour.

A *wind vane* is used to determine wind direction. Usually a wind vane consists only of a free-moving arrow-shaped pointer mounted on top of a pole so that the wind will catch the tail of the arrow and swing the point of the arrow to the direction from which the wind blows. Both the wind vane and anemometer may be combined in a small device that resembles a wingless airplane.

Winds are named according to the direction from which they come. Thus a wind from the west, blowing toward the east, is called a west wind. In some weather reports, more exact directions for winds may be designated by the 32 points of the compass. For certain purposes, where even greater precision is necessary, directions are given in degrees, starting with 0° north and moving clockwise to 360° at north again. These two systems of giving wind direction are shown in Fig. 31–5.

WIND VELOCITY

Terms used in U. S. Weather Bureau Forecasts	Miles Per Hour	Beaufort Number	Wind Effects Observed on Land
			Calm; smoke rises vertically
Light	1– 3	1	Direction of wind shown by smoke drift; but not by wind vanes
	4– 7	2	Wind felt on face; leaves rustle; ordinary vane moved by wind
Gentle	8–12	3	Leaves and small twigs in constant motion; wind extends light flag
Moderate	13–18	4	Raises dust, loose paper; small branches are moved
Fresh	19–24	5	Small trees in leaf begin to sway; whitecaps form on inland waters
Strong	25–31	6	Large branches in motion; whistling heard in telegraph wires; umbrellas used with difficulty
Gale	32–38	7	Whole trees in motion; inconvenience felt walking against wind
	39–46	8	Breaks twigs off trees; generally impedes progress
	47–54	9	Slight structural damage occurs
	55–63	10	Seldom experienced inland; trees uprooted; considerable structural damage occurs
Whole gale	64–74	11	Very rarely experienced; accompanied by widespread damage
Hurricane	75–136	12–17	Very rarely experienced; accompanied by widespread damage

FIG. 31–6. The man at the left is holding a radiosonde which will be carried aloft when the balloon is released. (*United Nations*)

Electronic weather instruments. Observations of conditions at ground level give only a part of the complete picture needed for studying and forecasting the weather. The conditions at upper levels of the atmosphere must also be known. The usual means of investigating the weather of the upper atmosphere is a *radiosonde*, shown in Fig. 31–6. This instrument consists of a small set of measuring devices which record temperature, pressure, and humidity. The instruments are coupled with a miniature radio transmitter and mounted in a small box which is carried aloft by a helium-filled balloon. Special receiving sets record the information as it is automatically sent out by the transmitter. The radiosonde may rise to an altitude of 100,000 feet before the balloon bursts and the instruments fall back to earth by means of a small parachute.

Another valuable electronic weather instrument is *radar.* Because particles of water in the form of cloud droplets or precipitation reflect the radar waves, weather disturbances can be seen on a radar screen. Furthermore, radar gives the precise location and extent of storms, since the reflected echoes indicate distance and direction from the transmitter. On a radar scope an observer can watch the origin and growth of a storm system and track it as it moves across the land.

Radar is particularly useful in tracking hurricanes. Spiral bands of rain clouds winding into the center of the hurricane can be seen on radar 200 to 350 miles away. The appearance of a hurricane on a radar scope is shown in Fig. 31–7. The eye of the storm can be located accurately, and this information can then be used to determine the probable path of the hurricane. Tornadoes can also be tracked by radar so that warnings can be issued to communities in their paths. Lightweight radar sets are carried by commercial airliners to locate and avoid storms and dangerous weather conditions.

Radar also can be used to measure the speed of high altitude winds. A balloon carrying a special radar reflector is released into the air. As it rises and drifts with the wind, its position is recorded by radar at frequent intervals so that simple calculations will give the wind speeds at various levels. Such measurements can be made day or night, in all weather conditions and at great altitudes. They are now a routine part of daily observations at many weather stations.

Recent advances in space science have given meteorologists still another electronic device to use in weather observations. Space satellites, of a type called Tiros, (Fig. 5–5) are built to relay photographs of the earth taken from altitudes of 400 to 500 miles by means of television cameras. These pictures, taken at intervals of about one minute, show the cloud cover of the various areas over which the satellite passes.

By superimposing a sequence of such photographs, weathermen are able to get a picture of atmospheric conditions over a wide area. From such composite photographs they can gain a clearer understanding of weather conditions over a considerable portion of the earth's surface. Further use of meteorological satellites will undoubtedly increase our knowledge of the earth's atmosphere and result in improved weather forecasting.

THE WEATHER MAP

Observing weather conditions. All over the world, every six hours at 1 and 7 P.M. and 1 and 7 A.M. Eastern Stand-

ard Time, observers report weather conditions at their location. Barometers are read and corrected to the corresponding pressure at sea level so that all reports will show pressure on the same basis, despite differences in elevation; wind speed and direction are noted; precipitation for the previous six hours is measured; temperature is read and humidity determined; the extent of clouds covering the sky is noted and height to cloud bases is measured; visibility and any other weather conditions are recorded. The information is then put into an international code, sent to collection centers within each country, and exchanged internationally. In this country, the information is collected and analyzed by the U. S. Weather Bureau.

At the centers receiving the coded weather information, where weather maps are to be prepared, the messages are decoded and the conditions reported are translated into figures and symbols. These are grouped around a small circle

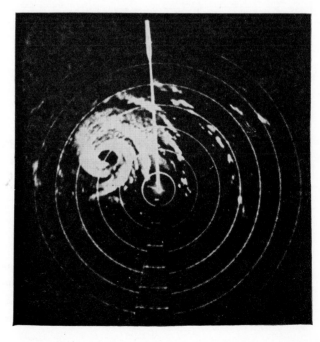

FIG. 31–7. A hurricane as seen on the radar screen of an airplane used for weather observations. (*U. S. Navy*)

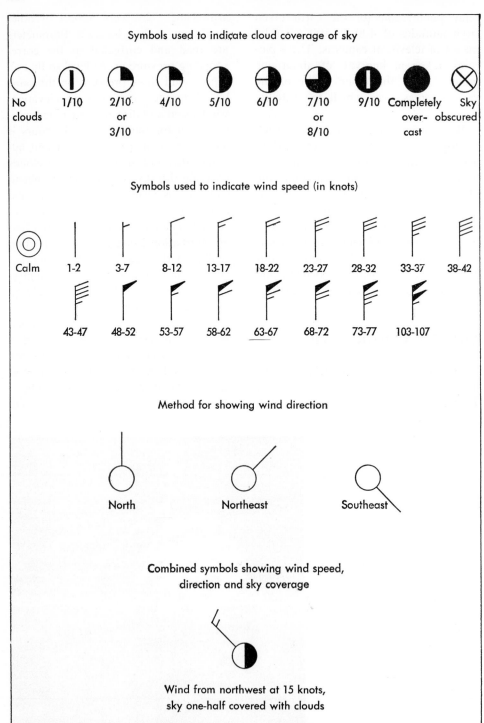

FIG. 31–8. Symbols used in the construction of station models.

KEY

1. Figures showing force of wind in knots (each ½ barb = 5 knots).
2. Arrow showing direction of middle cloud movement.
3. Symbol showing type of middle cloud (thick stratus).
4. Figures showing barometric pressure at sea level (1024.7 millibars—9 or 10 omitted).
5. Figures showing net amount of barometric change in past 3 hours (in tenths of millibars—2.8 millibars).
6. Symbol showing barometric tendency in past 3 hours (rising, then steady).
7. + or − sign showing pressure higher or lower than 3 hours ago.
8. Code figure showing time precipitation began or ended (in this case ended since present and past weather are of different types).
9. Past weather during 6 hours preceding observation (rain).
10. Figures showing amount of precipitation in last 6 hours (.45″).
11. Coverage of lower clouds in tenths.
12. Height of base of clouds in hundreds of feet.

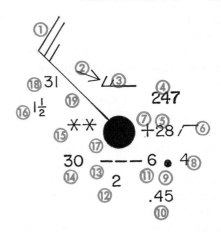

13. Symbol showing type of low cloud (stratus).
14. Figures showing dew point in degrees Fahrenheit.
15. Symbol showing present state of weather (snow).
16. Visibility in miles and fractions.
17. Symbol showing amount of total sky covered by clouds.
18. Figures showing temperature in degrees Fahrenheit.
19. Arrow shaft showing direction of wind (from northwest).

FIG. 31–9. The interpretation of a station model.

drawn on a map at the position of the particular station reporting the information. The circle on the map, along with the figures and symbols describing the weather conditions at that location, is called a *station model.* The method of construction of a station model and an interpretation of its information are shown in Figure 31–9.

Making a weather map. When station models have been recorded on the weather map, the next step is the drawing of lines which connect points of equal pressure. Such lines are called *isobars* and serve to mark positions of fronts and regions of high and low pressure. Figure 31–10 is a weather map

with isobars. The relative spacing of isobars gives some indication of probable wind speed. Closely spaced isobars mean rapid change of pressure and consequently higher wind velocities. Widely separated isobars generally mean light winds. Isobars in rough circles enclose centers of high or low pressure; such centers are usually marked with a large *H* or *L*. Since air tends to move toward regions of low pressure, the general wind direction would always be toward the low pressure areas if it were not for the earth's rotation. Because the Coriolis force also affects winds, they will tend to flow parallel to the isobars. The resulting actual wind direction is thus a kind of compromise between these two effects.

Fronts are indicated on the weather map by means of colored lines or symbols. On colored maps a cold front is a heavy blue line; a warm front is a red line and an occluded front is a purple line. Maps done entirely in black and white use the symbols in Figure 31–10. Air masses are identified on the maps by use of the standard letters describing the type: mP, mT, cP, or cT.

To make accurate forecasts it is necessary to know the pattern of air movement at upper levels as well as at the surface. This information is provided by separate maps with isobars drawn for selected altitudes above 2000 feet.

A complete set of weather maps is issued by the U. S. Weather Bureau every six hours and made available to all who need weather information. Many newspapers publish simplified versions of the official Weather Bureau maps.

WEATHER FORECASTING

Principles of weather forecasting. The atmosphere consists of 5 billion cubic miles of air flowing in constantly changing patterns of weather. The meteorologist's job is to apply scientific knowledge of the physical laws known to control air movements, to weigh previous knowledge of weather in similar situations, and finally to attempt to predict coming weather.

The basic tool of the forecaster is the weather map. From the information shown on the weather maps, the forecaster tries to predict the formation of weather systems and determine the probable path of the disturbances already in existence. One of the fundamental principles which guide the forecaster is the knowledge that in the middle latitudes the upper air moves in a general easterly direction, carrying the low-level weather along with it. The majority of cyclonic

FIG. 31–10. A simplified weather map usually shows isobars, highs and lows, and fronts. It may also indicate other conditions, such as wind directions, temperatures, and precipitation. Front symbols: triangle—cold front; half-circle—warm front; both on opposite sides—stationary front; both on same side—occluded front. (*Adapted from U. S. Weather Bureau*)

storms or lows that affect the United States enter in the northwestern part of the country, move eastward along the northern part over the Great Lakes region and pass out to sea off the North Atlantic coast.

In addition to their general easterly movement, low pressure systems tend to move toward areas of falling pressure and away from regions of rising pressure. The speed with which a weather disturbance moves is determined largely by the amount of difference between the falling pressure of the region ahead of the storm and the rising pressure behind the system. Although there is great variability, the average rate of movement of storms across the United States is about 20 miles per hour in summer and about 30 miles per hour in winter. The slower movement in summer is due to the weaker westerly winds at higher altitudes during warmer periods of the year.

In determining the speed and direction of travel of a storm center, the forecaster relies upon charts showing pressures and winds aloft. For his estimate of the future path of the disturbance, he notes upper air currents, pressures, and previous rates and direction of movement of the system. To determine other features of the coming weather, such as the temperature, humidity, and cloudiness, he must have other information. Some conclusions about these conditions can be reached from knowledge of the steepness of the frontal surfaces connected with the weather system. The degree of slope of the front determines whether the lifting of air will be sufficient to cause condensation of moisture and produce cloudiness and precipitation.

Extended periods of little weather change occur when air masses remain over a large part of the country for several days or even a week or more. The movement of air masses is determined by prevailing wind conditions and the over-all pressure situation. General mapping of the atmospheric conditions throughout the northern hemisphere makes it possible to predict air mass movements up to about five days in advance with fair accuracy. A five-day forecast, however, can only predict the general weather conditions. More specific forecasts cannot be made beyond 48 hours.

U. S. Weather Bureau. In 1870 Congress gave the Army Signal Corps the responsibility for providing weather information and advance warning of storms. As the need for more detailed and accurate weather information grew, the government weather service was transferred about twenty years later to the Department of Agriculture and finally in 1940 to the Department of Commerce in order to serve the growing needs of aviation for weather information. Now the Weather Bureau operates a network of more than 400 full-time stations and receives information from 2000 additional stations in Europe, Asia, North Africa, and northern South America, giving a view of weather over the entire hemisphere.

The principal services provided by the Weather Bureau include detailed 24-hour forecasts and general five-day forecasts for the general public. For aviation it provides a number of specialized services including charts of high level winds and high altitude forecasts needed by pilots flying jet aircraft. It also provides special severe-storm, tornado, and hurricane warnings; flood forecasts; frost warnings for agriculture; special forecasts for ships; and many other services in cooperation with other agencies.

SUMMARY

WEATHER is the condition of the atmosphere at a certain place and time. In the middle latitudes the basic problem in weather prediction is the interpretation of highs and lows moved by the prevailing westerlies.

Basic equipment for weather forecasting consists of some type of maximum-minimum thermometer, barometer, anemometer, wind vane, and rain gauge. Other specialized equipment includes radar and the radiosonde.

Every six hours widely distributed stations send their observations to a collection center. The information is plotted on a map at a point corresponding to the location of the reporting station. A complete plot for a reporting area is called a station model. After all station models are recorded, points of equal pressure are connected on the plot by isobars.

Detailed 24-hour or general 5-day forecasts are made up from interpretation of weather maps, using experience of similar conditions and understanding of laws governing air movement.

VOCABULARY REVIEW

Match the phrase in the left column with the correct word or phrase in the right column. *Do not write in this book.*

1. Measures precipitation
2. Electronic instrument that records and broadcasts temperature, pressure, and humidity
3. Measures temperature
4. Unit of air pressure
5. Connects places of equal atmospheric pressure
6. Measures wind velocity
7. Locates and tracks storms
8. Records temperature
9. Science of the atmosphere

a. radar
b. isobar
c. thermograph
d. rain gauge
e. station model
f. millibar
g. meteorology
h. radiosonde
i. anemometer
j. thermometer

QUESTIONS · GROUP A

Decide whether these statements are true or false. Reword the false statements to make them true. *Do not write in this book.*

1. The Fahrenheit scale is used to measure temperature in the United States.
2. A thermograph keeps a written record of precipitation.
3. The liquid in a minimum thermometer is mercury.
4. Precipitation of 0.4 of an inch would fill a rain gauge to a depth of 4 inches.
5. A wind velocity of 14 knots is equal to a speed of 18.5 miles per hour.

6. A recorded fluffy snowfall of 30 inches would be equal to about 12 inches of rain.
7. A wind direction of 225° would indicate a northwest wind.
8. The accuracy of specific weather forecasts is limited to about 48 hours.
9. The Weather Bureau is under the control of the Department of Commerce.
10. International weather observations are taken every 6 hours.
11. A meteorologist identifies and locates meteors.

GROUP B

1. Construct a station model with the following information: (*a*) sky, overcast (*b*) southwest wind, 16 knots (*c*) temperature, 67° F (*d*) dew point, 47° F (*e*) pressure, 1026.3 millibars (*f*) barometric tendency last three hours, rise of 3.8 millibars (*g*) visibility, 2 miles (*h*) present weather, drizzle (*i*) cloud type, stratus (*j*) ceiling, 8000 feet (*k*) past weather, showers (*l*) precipitation, began 3 to 4 hours ago (*m*) precipitation last 6 hours, 0.73 inches.
2. Convert the following Centigrade readings to Fahrenheit: (*a*) 45° (*b*) 32° (*c*) 74° (*d*) −4°
3. Convert the following Fahrenheit readings to Centigrade: (*a*) 22° (*b*) 80° (*c*) −12° (*d*) 55°
4. Describe the operation of a maximum-minimum thermometer.
5. Convert the following millibar readings into inches of mercury: (*a*) 984.5 (*b*) 952.6 (*c*) 1008.2 (*d*) 1020.0
6. Convert the following pressure readings in inches of mercury to millibars: (*a*) 27.82 (*b*) 30.05 (*c*) 28.36 (*d*) 29.68
7. Describe the operation of two types of rain gauges.
8. What is the function of the radiosonde? How are the instruments recovered after use?
9. What are the steps in the construction of a weather map?
10. How are isobars interpreted?
11. What is the general direction of highs and lows in the United States?
12. Why is a knowledge of the conditions at high altitudes needed for accurate forecasting?

UNIT REVIEW QUESTIONS

1. List the names and symbols of all the gases that are normally present in the atmosphere.
2. List all the variable substances in the atmosphere. Why are these substances called variable?
3. Discuss how our present atmosphere probably evolved.
4. What factors lead to the pollution of air? What steps may be taken to reduce air pollution?
5. How do liquids and solids differ from gases in molecular distribution?

6. Where is the ozone layer located? How does it aid life on earth?

7. Compare and contrast the gravitational attraction on gas molecules in each layer of the atmosphere.

8. With the aid of a diagram discuss the greenhouse effect.

9. As altitude increases why does sky color change from blue to black?

10. By means of diagrams, explain the formation of rainbows, inferior mirages, and superior mirages.

11. Compare and contrast aneroid and mercurial barometers as to function, construction, and relative advantages and disadvantages.

12. How is the atmosphere heated by radiation and conduction?

13. Why are deserts in some regions of the earth extremely hot during the day and very cool at night?

14. Construct a bar graph to show the percent of the sun's energy absorbed by different surfaces.

15. If the earth ceased to rotate, what would be the effect on winds?

16. With the aid of diagrams, explain the causes of land, sea, mountain, and valley breezes.

17. If the capacity of a sample of air is 14.7 grains of water vapor per cubic foot, with an absolute humidity of 3.0 grains per cubic foot, determine the relative humidity. Show all calculations.

18. Explain the operating principle of two types of hygrometer.

19. Why is the moist adiabatic lapse rate rather than the dry adiabatic rate normally used to estimate drop in rising air temperature?

20. What is the function of the condensation nuclei in the formation of clouds?

21. What is meant by the process of coalescence?

22. Describe the methods of artificial rainmaking.

23. Why do hailstorms occur most frequently during the summer?

24. What is an air mass? Describe the characteristics of an air mass.

25. Compare and contrast the seven source regions of North American air masses and their summer and winter characteristics.

26. Is it possible to have air masses of types cTk and cPw? Explain the reason for your answer.

27. Describe how cold, warm, occluded, and stationary fronts develop. Write the symbol for each type of front.

28. Compare and contrast the movements of cold and warm fronts.

29. How do tornadoes form and move?

30. Why is the eye of a hurricane relatively calm?

31. What causes lightning?

32. What is the advantage of a thermograph over a maximum-minimum thermometer?

33. Do you believe that the Centigrade scale has any advantage over the Fahrenheit scale? Explain the reason for your answer.

34. Why is it more accurate to express pressure in millibars than in inches or centimeters of mercury?

35. List several valuable services of the weather bureau.

36. How has radar reduced the hazard of commercial and military flights?

ACTIVITIES

1. Establish a school weather observation station. Equipment can be purchased from any scientific supply house, and some can be homemade. Keep accurate records and publish weather forecasts in the school paper or have them given over the public address system. Compare the accuracy of your forecasts with those given over radio and television or printed in the newspaper.
2. Make a graph to show the relationship of air pressure to temperature.
3. Try to determine the height of buildings, hills, towers, or other high points with a barometer.
4. Write a report on the possibilities of using satellites for weather forecasting.
5. Prepare a report on the properties of the rare gases in the atmosphere.
6. Construct models out of such materials as plastic, glass, cotton, and cardboard to illustrate the different fronts.
7. Determine the percentages of nitrogen and oxygen in the air. Consult a chemistry text or workbook for the method. Check with your instructor before performing any experiments.
8. Prepare oxygen and carbon dioxide. Consult a chemistry text or workbook for the methods and check with your instructor before performing any experiments.
9. On the same day, determine the relative humidity in different places such as the cellar, attic, kitchen, gymnasium, furnace room, lockers, swamps, forest, and city streets. Explain why there are differences in humidity in these places.
10. Fill a shiny metal container with water and add ice cubes, then put in a thermometer. When condensation collects on the outside, read the thermometer to determine the dew point.
11. Photograph various cloud formations. An inexpensive filter may help. See your local photograph supply house.
12. Report on the smogs of California, Pennsylvania, or England.
13. Prepare a report on the history, theory, and technique of rainmaking.
14. Prepare a report on one of the destructive hurricanes along the East Coast during the last ten years.

FURTHER READING

CANOPY OF AIR. L. Barnett, 1953. *Time, Inc., New York.*

WEATHER ELEMENTS. T. A. Blair, 1957. *Prentice-Hall, Inc., Englewood Cliffs, New Jersey.*

WEATHER GLOSSARY. *Superintendent of Documents, Washington 25, D. C.*

PILOT'S WEATHER HANDBOOK. *Superintendent of Documents, Washington 25, D. C.*

WEATHER FOR A HOBBY. R. F. Yates, 1946. *Dodd, Mead and Co., New York.*

WEATHER AND THE OCEAN OF AIR. W. H. Wenstrom, 1942. *Houghton Mifflin Company, Boston, Mass.*

EVERYDAY WEATHER AND HOW IT WORKS. H. Schneider, 1951. *McGraw-Hill Book Co., New York.*

HOW ABOUT THE WEATHER. R. M. Fisher, 1951. *Harper & Brothers, New York.*

THE history of the earth's climates actually began at that distant time when the atmosphere and the oceans first developed their complex exchanges of heat and moisture. However, the study of climate usually passes over those first few billion years.

Climate is generally understood to be the sum of the weather conditions that now exist in a region. It includes the yearly cycles of cold, heat, rain, and snow that are characteristic of each particular place. The exact climate we experience determines what we wear, how we work, and how we spend our leisure. It is made up of a related series of changes that together form the pattern of environment for every one of us. In this concluding unit, some of the forces that mold climate will be considered, and a general survey will be made of the almost infinite variety of climates that result from these influences.

UNIT 9

THE CLIMATES
OF THE EARTH

CHAPTER 32

ELEMENTS OF CLIMATE

THE day-to-day changes in the weather are part of a greater pattern of fluctuation in solar energy, wind, and moisture—the pattern called climate. The word *climate* comes from a Greek word meaning "slope," from the belief of the ancient Greeks that the earth sloped toward the north pole and that differences in climate depended upon this factor. The Greeks were shrewd observers of the causes of climate when they ranked position between the poles and the equator as first in importance.

Nevertheless, climate, which is the average weather in a locality over a number of years, is the result of many influences. Places on the same latitude around the globe may have widely different climates because of local conditions that alter the temperature or modify moisture-bearing winds. Thus the surface of the earth is subject to a countless variety of climates that blend and form every possible environment between the extremes of hot, humid tropics and cold, dry polar regions.

Basic to all climates are the forces that govern the weather. The causes of climate lie in these actions of heat, moisture, and air movements, all making up the daily conditions of weather. In this chapter the influences of the sun, the winds, and the moisture of the air will be examined to discover their role in climate.

TEMPERATURE OVER THE EARTH

Insolation. As we know, energy from the sun reaches the earth in the form of

VOCABULARY

Insolation. The total energy received by the earth from the sun's radiations.

Isotherm. A line on a map joining places that record the same temperature.

Monsoons. Seasonal winds that are more pronounced over large continental areas near the equator.

Heat equator. A line on a map joining places on the earth that have the highest average temperature.

570

solar radiations. The total energy received by the earth as these radiations fall upon its surface is called *insolation.* At any particular location on the earth the amount of insolation is determined mainly by two factors: (1) The angle at which the sun's rays strike the earth, and (2) the length of time the sun shines during a day. Both factors are governed by the latitude of the particular location.

The inclination of the earth's axis and the progress of the seasons were discussed in Chapter 8. From Figs. 8–2 and 8–3, it is evident that near the equator the sun's rays are almost always vertical and the period of daylight does not vary much throughout the year. Thus the equatorial regions of the earth receive more insolation than any other part of the world. A line on a map connecting the locations with the highest average temperature at a given time is called the *heat equator.* It roughly follows the actual equator, as shown in

Latitude	Longest Night
0°	12 hours
17°	13 hours
41°	15 hours
49°	16 hours
63°	20 hours
66½°	24 hours
67°21′	1 month
69°51′	2 months
78°11′	4 months
90°	6 months

Fig. 32–1. Toward the poles, in the higher latitudes, where solar rays are more slanted, temperatures are lower, particularly during the winter when nights are long. The table above shows the increase in the length of the longest night as the latitude increases.

It should be remembered that the length of the longest night as shown in the table is also the length of the longest daylight period in summer. During the summer the high latitudes enjoy very long daylight periods and the sun's rays

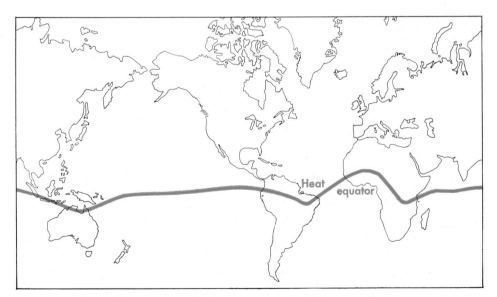

FIG. 32–1. The heat equator roughly follows the geographic equator. Can you explain why the heat equator is not a straight line?

Latitude	Length of Daylight Period (Average, June 21)
27½°	13 hr 53 min
30°	14 hr 5 min
32½°	14 hr 17 min
35°	14 hr 31 min
37½°	14 hr 45 min
40°	15 hr 1 min
42½°	15 hr 17 min
45°	15 hr 37 min
47½°	16 hr

....

are then more nearly vertical, giving these regions summer temperatures very much higher than the winter readings. The table above gives the length of the longest daylight period of the year at various latitudes in the United States.

Other factors affecting temperature. If latitude were the only factor determining the amount of heat received at a particular place, all locations at the same latitude would have the same temperature conditions. In Fig. 32–2 the distribution of temperature over the earth is shown by means of *isotherms,* lines connecting points of equal average temperature. It can be seen that the isotherms do not follow uniformly the parallels of latitude. This indicates that insolation as determined primarily by latitude is not the only factor that regulates the temperature of a location. These are some of the other principal influences on the average temperature at a specific place:

1. Land and water differences. It was pointed out in the discussion of land and sea breezes that the same amount of insolation on land and on water heats the land faster and to a higher temperature than the water surface. One reason for this difference in heating is that water near the surface is mixed by the motion of waves and currents. The surface water warmed by the sun is thus contin-uously replaced by cooler water from below. This condition slows down the heating process. Water surfaces also cool much more slowly than land because convection currents are set up: cool water tends to sink and is replaced by warmer water from below.

Another reason why the same amount of insolation heats the land faster than the water is that land and water have different capacities for absorbing and liberating heat. The *specific heat* of water is higher than that of land; that is, water requires more heat than land does to increase its temperature the same number of degrees. Thus water, having a higher specific heat, warms up more slowly than land. Conversely, water also cools off more slowly than land because it retains its heat longer.

Still another reason for the unequal heating of water and land is the fact that some of the insolation falling on water is used in the evaporation of water. This heat obviously does not warm the water. The land is not similarly affected, since little evaporation of water takes place from land surfaces. Furthermore, some of the heat used in vaporizing water is released in the air masses over the land when water vapor condenses to form clouds, as described in Chapter 29.

The result of the difference in heating between land and water can be traced in the bending of the isotherms in Fig. 32–2 as they pass across land and water areas. The difference is responsible for the extremes of high and low temperatures in inland climates and the relatively moderate temperature variations of coastal climates.

2. Altitude. Air temperature in the troposphere normally decreases with altitude at an average rate of 3.5° F per 1000 feet rise (see Chapter 27). This means that in regions of high altitude

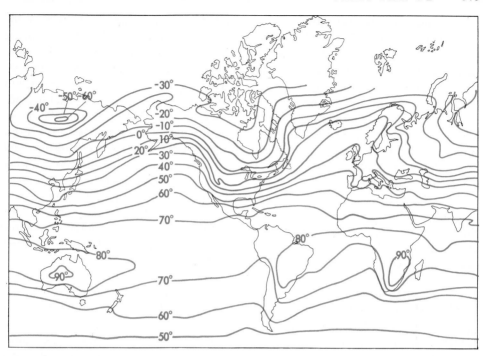

FIG. 32–2. Isotherms of average temperature: above, in January; and below, in July. Why are differences much more pronounced in the northern hemisphere than in the southern hemisphere?

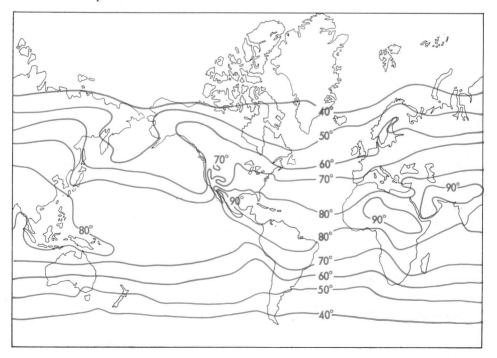

average temperatures are always lower because the surrounding air is cooler. Even in the hot equatorial lands mountains may be so high that their tops are cool enough to be covered with snow.

Examples of all the climate zones found on the earth from latitude zero to the poles can be encountered on the slopes of an Andean peak. As one ascends, he notes that soon the tropical palms are replaced by the deciduous trees of the temperate zones, which are succeeded in turn by cone-bearing trees that are dwarfed and twisted by the wind at the upper limits of the timber line. Above this is an area of grassy meadows that thin out near the lichen-covered, rocky areas that lead to the icecap at the summit. The timber line and the snow line mark a rather irregular area which is higher on the sunny sides than it is on the shaded sides.

3. Ocean currents. Oceans may also strongly influence temperatures if currents passing close to land masses differ in temperature from the land. Such currents have most effect on the land temperatures if winds consistently blow toward the coast. The temperature of northwestern Europe is unusually high for its latitude because of the combined effect of a warm current, the North Atlantic Drift, and the prevailing westerly winds. On the other hand, the warm Gulf Stream current along the east coast of the United States has little effect on its climate because winds come more often from the west, blowing away from the coast.

WIND AND MOISTURE

Seasonal wind changes. The patterns of circulation of the atmosphere have been discussed in Chapter 28. For the most part, the general direction of the wind in a particular place is determined by its location in one of the wind belts (Fig. 28–4). Storms and local weather tend to disturb and mask this effect, but in most places there is a general tendency for the wind to blow in the direction usual in the wind belt. However, some places experience two distinct and directly opposite wind directions during a year. This is caused by the difference in heating between large land masses and oceans. During the summer, the land is heated more than the sea. A low pressure center develops over the land and the air tends to move from the water to the land. During the winter, the land becomes colder than the water and the wind direction is reversed, as air flows out to the oceans. Such seasonal winds are called *monsoons* and are most pronounced over the larger continental land regions near the equator.

Eastern and southern Asia experience some of the world's most extreme monsoon wind shifts. In southern Asia, for example, the Indian monsoons originate from the heating and cooling of the land area in northern India. In summer a low pressure region exists in the north Indian peninsula, causing air to move in from the south over the Indian Ocean. The southerly winds are turned to the right, becoming southwest winds which bring heavy rainfall as they carry moisture from the ocean. In winter, the north portion of the peninsula becomes cold, causing a movement of air toward the water and producing a dry northeast wind. See Fig. 32–3.

Monsoon wind conditions are most prominent over southern and eastern Asia because of the effect of the heating and cooling of the large land area of the Asian continent. The monsoon effect is also more pronounced in this region be-

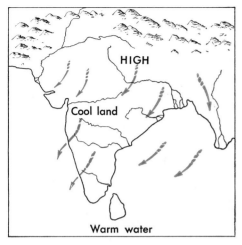 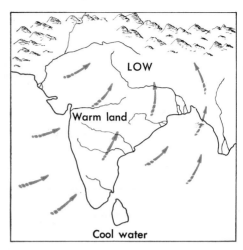

FIG. 32–3. Monsoons are seasonal winds. Why are they more pronounced over large land masses near the equator?

cause the high mountain ranges in northern India shield the southern areas from the effects of the winds from northern Asia. However, monsoon winds also occur in many other regions in the low latitudes where a long stretch of coastline faces toward the equator. The southeastern part of the United States, particularly the Gulf Coast region, experiences a kind of monsoon reversal of wind direction between summer and winter. In summer the moisture-bearing winds come from the south, bringing rain. In winter the wind shifts to the north and is generally dry and cold except for the cyclonic storms which pass.

Pressure belts and precipitation. Most of the precipitation falling upon the earth results from the condensation of moisture in rising air. Within the world's belts of low pressure, the doldrums and the subpolar lows, there is a continuous lifting of air. As a result, the regions of the earth covered by these low pressure belts experience generally heavy precipitation. The most abundant rainfall of the entire earth occurs in the belt around the equator, where the very moist, rising

warm air produces a yearly average rainfall of 70 to 80 inches. From the equator toward the poles, the amount of rainfall steadily decreases and reaches a minimum of 32 to 36 inches per year at around 20° to 30° latitude in the region of the descending air of the horse latitudes. Closer to the poles, at the subpolar lows around 45° to 55° latitude, there is another belt of high precipitation where warm air is lifted by the polar air masses. Yearly average precipitation in the region of the subpolar lows is 40 to 50 inches of rain per year. Above latitudes 50° to 55°, precipitation decreases rapidly to a yearly average of less than 10 inches of rain in the polar regions. (Remember that snowfall is measured as rain for comparative purposes.)

As the pressure belts shift with the seasons, the belts of precipitation associated with them also change their positions. Very near the equator, the sun is nearly overhead all year and the constant heating of the air produces abundant rain all year with no dry season. From about 10° to 20° latitude, the sun has a much stronger heating

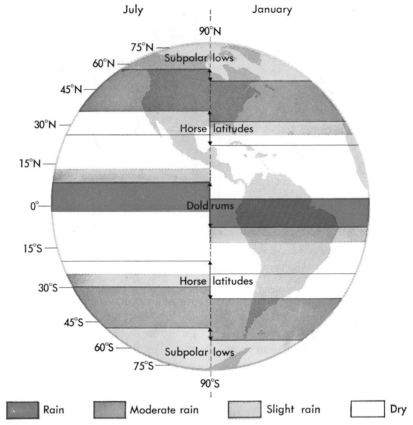

FIG. 32–4. The general rainfall pattern over the earth at two different seasons. Note that this pattern shifts with seasonal shifts in the planetary wind belts and pressure areas.

effect in summer than in winter. Thus in these latitudes the summers are likely to be wet and the winters drier. The zone of the horse latitudes from about 20° to 30° latitude is relatively dry all year. Within the belt of the subpolar lows, precipitation tends to be spread throughout the year as a result of storms generated by the meeting of cold polar air and warm equatorial air. In the lower latitudes of the subpolar low pressure belt, and into the belt of westerly winds, winters tend to be wetter than summers since the storm-producing cold air masses move farther toward the equator

during the winter. Polar regions above latitude 75° have almost no seasonal variation, with little precipitation all year. In Fig. 32–4 the rainfall pattern over the earth is summarized. The results of the seasonal movements of the pressure belts are shown here.

Effect of wind direction on precipitation. The general pattern of precipitation over the world, as determined by the pressure belts, is often altered in a particular location by the direction of its prevailing winds. The effect of winds on precipitation is particularly noticed along the coastlines of continents if the prevailing winds carry moist air from the sea over the land surface. In the dry regions between latitudes 20° to 30°, the eastern coasts of land areas are usually rainy and humid. The prevailing winds here are the easterly trade winds, which bring moist air from the sea. In these same latitudes, the continental interiors and the west coasts are likely to be dry. Land areas in the belt of the westerlies, from about 40° to 60° latitude, tend to have abundant rainfall on the west coasts as a result of moist air brought in by the prevailing westerly winds. Interiors of continents in the latitudes of the westerlies are generally dry, but the east coasts may also be humid even though the westerlies blow from the dry interior. The rainfall on the east coasts in these latitudes is caused by the monsoon reversal of winds during the summer and by the winter storms which originate in the high latitudes and move in an easterly direction, thus tending to

pass over the east coasts of the continents.

Precipitation and mountains. Air forced to rise over mountains or highlands produces precipitation, as ascending air always does. Mountainous regions, therefore, are almost always regions of heavier precipitation. However, the degree to which mountains may affect precipitation is determined largely by the nature of the air that blows against them. Cold winds are deficient in moisture and are not likely to produce much precipitation even if they are forced over high mountains. The heaviest rainfall in the world occurs on mountain slopes which lift warm, moist air from oceans near the equator.

Precipitation always tends to be much more abundant on the windward side of mountains where the air is first lifted. On the sheltered or leeward side, the climate is likely to be dry since the air has lost most of its moisture.

SUMMARY

CLIMATE is the average weather of a particular locality. The factors that control weather are also responsible for climate.

Insolation is the primary factor in the control of climate. It is governed mainly by latitude, which determines the angle of the sun's rays and the length of day at a particular place. The effects of insolation on temperature are modified by the type of surface, by altitude, and by ocean currents.

Migration of the vertical rays of the sun produces seasonal wind changes called monsoons. Most of the earth's precipitation occurs in the low pressure belts. A shift in pressure belts is accompanied by a shift of the rain belts.

Total precipitation in a locality is related to topography and the prevailing winds. Land masses covered by the westerlies tend to have most of their precipitation on the windward sides of mountains and on the west coast, while the interiors tend to aridness and the east coasts to humid climates.

VOCABULARY REVIEW

Match the phrase in the left column with the correct word or phrase in the right column. *Do not write in this book.*

1. Migrating seasonal wind
2. Connects places of equal temperature
3. Energy received from the sun
4. Average weather in a locality
5. Capacity for absorbing and releasing heat
6. Joins places having the highest average temperature

a. specific heat
b. heat equator
c. vaporization
d. insolation
e. isotherm
f. monsoon
g. climate

QUESTIONS · GROUP A

Decide whether these statements are true or false. Reword the false statements to make them true. *Do not write in this book.*

1. At the equator the period of daylight is always about 12 hours.
2. Evaporation is a cooling process.
3. During the summer the prevailing winds in India are from the northeast.
4. The horse latitudes tend to be dry during most of the year.
5. During the winter, the temperature over the oceans is usually warmer than it is over adjacent continents.
6. During certain times of the year the poles may receive greater insolation than the equatorial regions.
7. The greater the latitude, the greater the difference in yearly fluctuation between dark and daylight periods.
8. The specific heat of water is less than that of solid substances.
9. During the summer, isotherms tend to bend poleward.
10. The temperature at the equator never falls below 45° F.

GROUP B

1. What two factors determine the amount of insolation received by a particular locality? How are these factors governed?
2. How is the size of a continent related to the occurrence of monsoons?
3. Compare and contrast the climate on the east and west sides of the Sierra Nevada Mountains.
4. Explain why isotherms are not parallel to lines of latitude.
5. Explain the cause and effect of convection currents.
6. How is climate related to altitude?
7. Chicago and Rome have about the same latitude, but different climates. Why?
8. Discuss the rainfall pattern over the earth as related to prevailing winds and the pressure belts.
9. Explain why the warm Gulf Stream current has more effect on the climate of Europe than it does on that of the east coast of the United States.

CHAPTER 33

CLIMATIC REGIONS

THE earth is a planet of many contrasts. Its surface is divided by the continents and the oceans into opposing regions of land and sea. The land areas are further differentiated as the provinces of mountains, plains and plateaus; these in turn are not uniform, but show a variety of lesser features. Spread over the land, intensifying its contrasts, is a cover of vegetation. Forests, deserts, and grasslands blend into one another, creating a vast pattern.

The areas of different types of vegetation are visible evidence of the subtle but powerful influence of climate differences. Each group of plants responds to the temperature and moisture of its particular location. Thus the plants of a region become the emblems of the climate of that locality. One basis for a division of the earth into zones of climate might be the presence or absence

of certain plants that thrive only in a particular range of temperature or rainfall conditions. However, scientific classification of climates must be founded on something more than the distribution of plants. The primary elements of climate —temperature and precipitation—must be the foundation for a meaningful description of the climates of the world.

CLASSIFICATION OF CLIMATES

Basis for climatic classification. On the basis of temperature alone, the surface of the earth has often been divided into three distinct zones. Around the region of the equator is the *torrid zone,* where temperature is high the entire year, the winter season being completely lacking. At the opposite extreme are the

VOCABULARY

Tropical climate. A climate with an average annual temperature above 68° F.

Middle latitude climate. A climate with an average annual temperature below 68° F., and with an average temperature above 50° F. for at least one month.

Polar climate. A climate with an average temperature below 50° F. even during the warmest month.

579

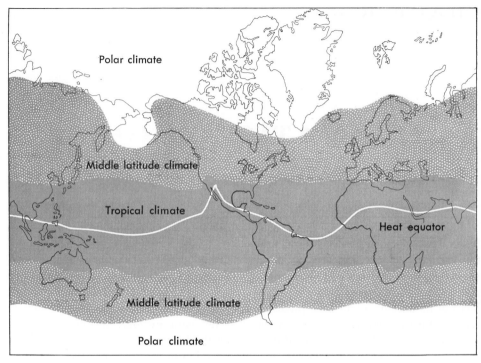

FIG. 33–1. The general boundaries of the major zones of climate.

polar regions, referred to as the *frigid zones,* where temperature is always low and the summer season is greatly reduced. The area between the two extremes of the poles and the equator is described as the *temperate zone.* It is anything but temperate, however, since the difference between winter and summer temperatures is likely to be very great. This simple classification of the earth into climatic zones does not describe temperature conditions very precisely. It also fails completely to take into account the equally important climatic factor of precipitation.

Many more complicated systems of climate classification have been devised, based on temperature and moisture as well as many other factors that contribute to the total climate. Most of these systems are very technical, and no single system has been found to be completely satisfactory. It is unlikely that a system of classification for climate can ever be developed so as to permit definite boundaries to be established, clearly marking the place where one climate changes to another. With very few exceptions, the world's climates blend into each other and their exact point of separation is vague. Also, climates shift their positions somewhat from season to season and year to year, so that a dividing line cannot be permanent.

The system of classification used in this chapter is a simplified version of a plan commonly used in the study of climates. This system divides the earth into temperature zones, but has a more scientific basis than the classification into tropic, frigid, and temperate. The warm zone immediately around the equator is designated as the zone of *tropical climates.* To be classed as tropical, a region must have an average temperature of more than 68° F for the year. The zone between the equatorial and polar regions is described as the zone of *middle latitude climates.* To be classed as middle latitude climate, a region must have for at least one month an average temperature above 50° F. The average temperature for the coldest months in the middle latitudes varies, but in most cases is below 32° F. Close to the north and south poles are the zones of *polar climates,* which have an average temperature of less than 50° F during their warmest month. The general boundaries of these three temperature zones are shown in Fig. 33–1.

Within each of the temperature zones, there is a variety of types of climates, distinguished mainly by differences in precipitation. On this basis, each of the large temperature zones is further divided into smaller regions, which can be described more precisely.

The tropical group of climates. Within about 30° of latitude on both sides of the equator lies the tropical temperature zone, where the sun is nearly always directly overhead at noon. This is where the earth receives maximum insolation, making the tropical climates the warmest of all those found over the world. On and very near the equator, in the belt of the doldrums, rain is abundant all year and the climate is warm and humid. Farther north and south of the equator, in the belts of the trade winds, the climates become warm and dry.

1. The humid climate in the regions close to the equator is called the *tropical rain forest* climate, referring to the dense growth of plants that is invariably found

FIG. 33–2. Dense jungles are characteristic of some tropical rain forests. (*U. S. Forest Service*)

FIG. 33–3. Typical vegetation in the savanna type of climate. (*Bernheim-Conant Expedition of the American Museum of Natural History*)

there. The tropical rain forests consist of a mixture of thousands of kinds of plants. These include tall trees that form a dense shade umbrella beneath which there is only low underbrush. Where some sunlight penetrates, there is a heavy carpet of underbrush, vines, and smaller plants—the *jungle*. See Fig. 33–2. Clearings made in the jungle growth quickly fill in again and leave little trace, due to the extremely rapid growth of the smaller plants. The tropical rain forests are possible because there is no winter season to slow down the plant growth and because the rainfall is extremely heavy (about 100 inches per year). The rainfall may be even higher in a particular rain forest area that is located on the windward side of mountain slopes. The rising air deposits extraordinary amounts of rain. One of the most famous of such locations is Cherrapunji, in northeast India, which has an average annual rainfall of 426 inches. Another is on the island of Kauai in Hawaii, where the average rainfall is 450 inches per year. Regions

of the world in which the tropical rain forest type of climate is found include the Congo area of Africa, the Amazon Basin of South America, parts of Central America, the East Indies, and the Malay peninsula.

2. Within the zone of tropical climates there are dry climates as well as moist ones. One type of tropical dry climate is called the *savanna climate*. It results from the seasonal movement of the doldrums as the sun's vertical rays shift to the north and south of the equator during the year. Regions of tropical climate located between 5° to 20° latitude have the heavy rainfall of the doldrums for a part of the year; then, with the seasonal shifting, they fall under the influence of the trade winds for the remainder of the year. Savanna climates are found in these latitudes; the year is made up of a wet and a dry season. During the wet season, which becomes shorter as distance from the equator increases, rainfall averages between 5 and 10 inches per month and the temperature is warm day and night. The dry

season brings months of almost no rainfall, with very hot days and cool nights. The savanna climate takes its name from the characteristic type of vegetation: a covering of coarse grass with scattered trees or shrubs. See Fig. 33–3. Principal areas with savanna climates include the Sudan of North Africa, the veld of South Africa, the llanos of Venezuela, the campos of Brazil, and northern Australia. India, Burma, Thailand, and Indochina also have savanna regions produced by the seasonal shift of the monsoon winds.

3. Also located within the tropical climatic zone are the world's driest lands, the *tropical deserts*. These deserts lie in the vicinity of 20° to 25° latitude, within the belt of the trade winds. Usually the deserts are in the western half of the continent or on the west side of mountain ranges where the easterly trade winds are unable to bring in moisture from the sea. Because of the extreme lack of atmospheric moisture, the difference between day and night temperatures is likely to be very great on the tropical deserts. During the hottest part of the year daytime temperatures may reach 120° F, yet will drop to 50° F or below during the night. The highest official temperature ever recorded, 136.4° F, was registered in the tropical desert of Tripoli in Africa. The driest desert is in northern Chile, where about 0.5 inches of rain is recorded in five years. Desert vegetation is limited to a few hardy plants; in many areas plants are completely lacking, and there is a bare surface of pebbly rocks or drifting sand. See Fig. 33–4. The chief tropical deserts of the world are the Sahara of northern Africa, the Kalahari of southern Africa, Arabia, the interior of Australia, the Sonora desert of northern Merico and the southwestern United States, and the coast of Peru and northern Chile.

4. Bordering the tropical deserts and extending into the middle latitudes are regions of slightly higher rainfall called *steppes*. The areas of steppe climate usually form a belt around the desert areas of the tropical zone, except on the drier western sides. The climate of the steppes differs from the desert primarily in the slightly greater amount of moisture. Steppes support more plant life than the deserts, principally in the form of low grasses and widely scattered shrubs.

The middle latitude climates. Since they are in the belt of the westerlies and close to the sources of the cyclonic storms that come from along the polar fronts, the middle latitudes are subject to many varieties of weather. Change of the weather from day to day and between the seasons is the most characteristic feature of these climates. Within the zone of the middle latitudes, there is at least one month with an average temperature above 50° F during the

FIG. 33–4. Tropical deserts are the world's driest areas. This is Saudi Arabia, near Nedj. (*Standard Oil Co. of New Jersey*)

summer. However, this gives no indication of the wide range of temperatures found in these climates, and there is similar variability in precipitation. The large continental land masses are one of the major factors producing the variety of climates of the middle latitudes. Most of the continents are in the middle latitudes, particularly in the northern hemisphere: Europe, Asia, and North America are all approximately midway between the equator and the pole. Since the westerlies are the prevailing winds of the middle latitudes, the climates of the western margins of the continents are likely to be moist, the winds bringing in moisture from the sea. The westerlies lose their moisture, however, as they blow inland, so the interiors of the continents tend to be dry. The eastern margins of the land masses have a variety of climates, often with distinct wet and dry seasons produced by monsoon winds.

1. The west coasts of the continents between 30° and 40° latitude lie on the edges of the belt of descending air of the horse latitudes and do not extend very deeply into the belt of westerlies. The seasonal shifts of these wind and pressure belts determine the climates of these regions. During the summer there is the unchanging warm sunny weather of the dry tropical climates. The winter brings the changeability of the middle latitudes. This is the *Mediterranean* climate. The warm, dry summers have temperatures averaging between 70° and 80° F, and relatively steady trade winds. Winters are mild, the average of the coldest month being around 40° to 50° F. Almost all the rain, which averages 15 to 25 inches annually, is received during the winter months when the seasonal shifting of the westerlies toward the equator brings cyclonic storms to these regions. Abundant sunshine is the rule in the Mediterranean climates; even during the rainy months it is seldom cloudy for long periods. The climate is excellent for fruit growing; olives and grapes for wine are widely cultivated, as well as a variety of other fruit and nuts. Some of the important land areas having Mediterranean climates are the shores of the Mediterranean Sea, the southernmost portion of South Africa, central Chile, central and southern California and southern Australia.

2. A climate very similar to the Mediterranean type is found in the same latitudes along the eastern sides of the continents. It is called the *humid subtropical* climate and differs from the Mediterranean type in having greater rainfall (30 to 65 inches annually) which is spread more or less evenly throughout the year. The two climates are similar in range of temperatures, but the summers are uncomfortably warm in the humid subtropical regions because of the excessive humidity. Climatic conditions of warmth and ample rainfall here favor the growth of plants, and in this climate, the land is usually covered with forests or tall grasses. The humid subtropical climate includes eastern and southern Asia and Japan, northern Argentina, Uruguay, and southern Brazil, and southeastern United States.

3. Along the western margins of the continents in the middle latitudes, from about 40° latitude to the edges of the polar regions, the *marine west coast* climate is typical. This climate is produced mainly by the continuous inflow of cool moist air as the prevailing westerlies blow inland from the sea. Since these regions remain within the belt of the westerlies the entire year, precipitation is abundant throughout the year. Average annual precipitation in a marine west

FIG. 33–5. Dense forests of conifers are characteristic of the marine west coast type of climate. This view shows giant Douglas firs in the Mount Baker National Forest, Washington. (*U. S. Forest Service*)

coast climate is 20 to 30 inches, although unusually heavy rainfall of 100 to 150 inches per year may occur where mountains block the eastward movement of the prevailing winds, as in some parts of Washington and Oregon. Most regions with marine west coast climates are covered with forests of hardwood trees or conifers as shown in Fig. 33–5. Areas of the world that have this type of climate are the northwest coast of the United States, the west coast of British Columbia, southern Chile, northwestern Europe and the British Isles, western Australia, and New Zealand.

4. Toward the interior of the land masses in the middle latitudes, the climates become much drier. Within the interiors of the continents are the most arid of all the middle latitude climates, the *middle latitude deserts*. Asia, the largest land mass of the earth, has the driest of these interior deserts; North America is next. The dryness of the middle latitude deserts parallels that of the tropical deserts, but there is a definite difference in the temperature conditions. The cold winter season of the continental interior is lacking in the tropical deserts. It is difficult to describe typical temperature conditions in the deserts of the middle latitudes because some areas are in much higher latitudes and at greater altitudes than others, and thus much colder. Nevertheless, it can be said that summers are warm to hot and winters are very cold and severe. Precipitation is quite low, usually less than 10 inches per year. As might be expected in a region of so little moisture, plant life is very sparse and generally consists of only hardy plants and cacti. See Fig. 33–6. Middle latitude deserts are located in the interior of Asia, in western United States, and in western Argentina.

Like the tropical deserts, the middle latitude deserts merge into semiarid *steppes* where the rainfall is sufficient to support a heavy growth of low grasses. Such areas include the pampas of Argentina, the drier grasslands of our midwestern states, and the famous steppes of Russia.

5. Along the eastern side of the continents in the middle latitudes, climate is influenced mainly by the west-to-east movement of storms carried by the west-

FIG. 33–6. Middle latitude deserts are not usually as dry as tropical deserts. This photograph, taken in Arizona, shows cacti and other resistant plants which grow in such desert climates. (*National Park Service*)

erlies. Since the resulting climate is fairly moist and is controlled by air that has traveled over land surfaces, it is called the *humid continental climate*. The yearly average rainfall of at least 30 inches in this type of climate comes, to a large extent, from the winter cyclonic storms. In many locations summer thunderstorms also contribute a sizable share of the total. A monsoon wind shift may bring heavy summer rains, particularly along the eastern coast of Asia. The outstanding feature of the humid continental type of climate is the wide difference between summer and winter temperatures. Summer temperatures usually average more than 80° F, but during the winter the cold air from the continental interiors drives the temperature down to an average of 30° F or less. In general, the inland regions experience the coldest winters, since they are removed from the moderating influence of the sea. Inland areas also tend to be less humid than the coastal parts. Deciduous and evergreen trees are found in the more moist areas. The less humid parts are usually covered with tall grasses. Humid continental climates are found only in the large continental land masses of the northern hemisphere since there are no land areas in the southern hemisphere large enough for this type of climate. Eastern Europe, eastern Asia and the eastern half of North America are the principal regions with a humid continental climate.

6. The remaining type of middle latitude climate occurs around latitude 50° to 65°. Because these latitudes are approaching the poles, this climate is called *subarctic*. It has a very short

summer which may be surprisingly warm due to the very long periods of daylight at these high latitudes. The winters are extremely cold, however, the average temperatures for the coldest month being −30° F and lower. Precipitation is slight, usually less than 15 inches per year. The lands with subarctic climates are covered with a kind of thin forest of stunted pines, spruce, and similar conifers. This sparse forest is called *taiga* (*ty*-ga), the Russian word used to describe it in Siberia. See Fig. 33–7. The subarctic climate is found in Europe and Asia from Sweden and Finland across northern Siberia to the Pacific and in North America across Canada from Alaska to Labrador.

The polar climates. Just as the tropical regions of the earth lack a winter season, the polar regions are without a summer. Close to the poles the sun is out of sight during the winter for a period up to six months in length. In the summer, when the sun does come into view, its rays are so slanting that they give little heat. The polar regions are also areas of little precipitation, primarily because the air is too cold to hold much moisture. In addition, the general descending motion of the cold air is not favorable to precipitation.

1. The extremely cold, dry climate of the polar ice fields does not begin abruptly in the high latitudes. There is a zone of gradual change between the subarctic climate of the middle latitudes and the perpetual snows of the icecaps. This zone of transition has a *tundra* climate. This is a cold climate; the average temperature of the warmest month lies between 32° and 50° F while the average of the coldest month is about −40° F. Annual precipitation is 10 to 12 inches, occurring mostly during the short summer season in the form of rain. Plant life in the tundra climate consists of a carpet of mosses and related plants with a few scattered small shrubs. See Fig. 33–8. The tundra climate is confined to the northern hemisphere since no land areas lie around the margins of the Antarctic icecap. The most northern parts of the continents of North Amer-

FIG. 33–7. Taiga in Labrador, Canada. The rocks in the foreground and the mountains in the distance are covered with lichen. (*Geographic Branch, Ottawa*)

ica, Europe and Asia have tundra climates.

2. In the immediate neighborhood of the poles the temperature never rises above freezing. Precipitation remains on the surface as snow and ice. The climate of the surface of the ice fields resulting from long accumulation is referred to as the *icecap climate*. Average yearly temperatures for most locations on the icecaps is probably between −10° and −30° F. The lowest temperature ever recorded on earth, −125° F, was measured on the Antarctic icecap. The continental glacier which nearly covers Greenland gives this region an icecap climate.

Local climates. Classification of climates, as we have seen, is based on the effects of position on the earth's surface (latitude) and major differences between various parts of the earth's surface (such as land and water). It is clear that separating the various parts of the earth into regions based on major climatic influences brings some order into the description of climatic conditions, with their confusion of detail.

However, the climate at any particular place, though determined by the major influences, is at the same time affected by a number of minor influences. As a result there exist within the major climate categories already described a great number of small local climates.

The most common examples of local climates occur as a result of modification of the general climate by mountainous or highland areas. The very pronounced effect of altitude on climate has been pointed out in Chapter 32: temperature decreases rapidly with increasing elevation, giving highlands generally lower temperatures than surrounding lowlands. Also, the thin air at higher altitudes retains less heat at night, so that the difference between day and night temperatures is greater. Mountains create local climate effects through their various exposures to the prevailing winds. Mountain slopes facing the wind have more precipitation than the leeward slopes or the surrounding lowlands. However, the factors of temperature and exposure do not create any particular type of mountain or highland climate.

FIG. 33–8. Tundra, showing frozen earth beneath the thin cover of vegetation. (*U. S. Geological Survey*)

CLIMATES OF THE WORLD

	Rainfall	Temperature	Typical Vegetation
Tropical Climates			
Tropical Rain Forest	heavy all year	hot	heavy growth
Savanna	varies with wet and dry seasons	hot	grasslands with trees
Tropical Desert	almost none	hot	none or a few hardy plants
Tropical Steppe	light	hot	grass, few shrubs
Middle Latitude Climates			
Mediterranean	summer moderate winter light	summer warm	variety of trees and other plants
Humid Subtropical	moderate through-out year	summer warm winter mild	forests and grasslands
Marine West Coast	moderate	cool	hardwood and conifer forest
Middle Latitude Desert	very light	summer warm to hot winter very cold	few hardy plants and cacti
Middle Latitude Steppe	light	summer warm to hot winter very cold	grasses
Humid Continental	moderate	summer hot winter cold	forests and grasslands
Subarctic	very light	summer short, hot winter long, very cold	taiga
Polar Climates			
Tundra	very light	cold	mosses, lichens, and shrubs
Icecap	very light	very cold	none

Rather, a mountainous region is likely to have a variety of local climates as altitude and direction of slope change from one part to another. As a result of their patchwork of climate types, highlands do not fit well into any scheme of climate classification.

Local climates are also created by lakes which tend to produce more moderate temperatures and higher precipitation along their leeward shores, as on the eastern shore of Lake Michigan. Forests affect local climatic conditions by reducing wind speed and increasing relative humidity as compared with nearby open land. Even cities create their own climates by reducing wind speed and generating haze and smog, which cause slightly higher temperatures by reducing heat loss.

CLIMATES OF
THE UNITED STATES

The climates of the United States include almost every type that can be found on earth. Even if we exclude Alaska, with its predominantly subarctic and tundra climates, and Hawaii, with its tropical rain forest and savanna climates, the United States still has a very representative sampling of the world's climates. The description in the following sections of the climatic regions of the United States begins with those on the West Coast, where prevailing westerly winds are a major element of climate. The maps, Figs. 33–9 and 33–10, will help to make clear the extent of these climatic regions. As stated earlier, areas of highlands or mountains do not fit into the broad classification of climatic regions. Although all such areas are shown in the map by the same pattern, they actually have a variety of local climates, depending on altitude and other factors.

Marine West Coast climate. This rainy, cool climate is typical of the northern portion of the West Coast, including the coastal areas of Oregon and Washington and the southern coastal extension of Alaska. There is the characteristically abundant rainfall, concentrated mostly in the winter months. The region experiences an unusually heavy average rainfall even for marine west coast climates because mountains near the coasts wring most of the moisture out of the marine air brought in by the westerlies. Heavy stands of timber thrive in the moist climate and form the basis of a large lumbering industry.

Mediterranean climate. The southern part of the West Coast, central and southern California, has the dry summers and very mild temperatures of the Mediterranean climate. Locations actually on the coast have cool summers with much fog; farther inland the summers are hot. Winters are mild in all locations and almost completely free of frost. Rain occurs almost exclusively during the winter months, from cyclonic storms coming from the north. This is a rich agricultural region that produces all kinds of crops, but irrigation is necessary during the long dry summers.

Desert climate. On the leeward side to the east of the coastal mountain ranges and the Sierra Nevada mountains lie the deserts. Very hot summers but mild winters with warm days are characteristic of most locations with desert climate. In spite of the low rainfall, most parts of the deserts support a large variety of native plants and those parts of the desert which can be irrigated produce large crop yields.

Steppes climate. Bordering the western deserts on the east and extending

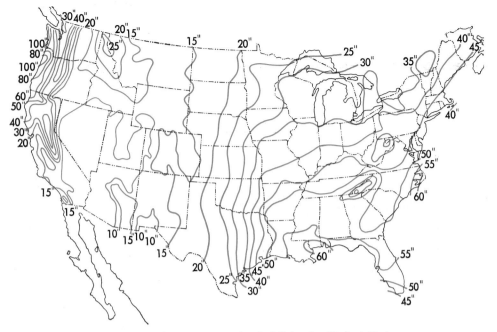

FIG. 33–9. Average annual rainfall in the United States.

FIG. 33–10. The major climatic regions of the United States. What relationships can you find between this map and the one above?

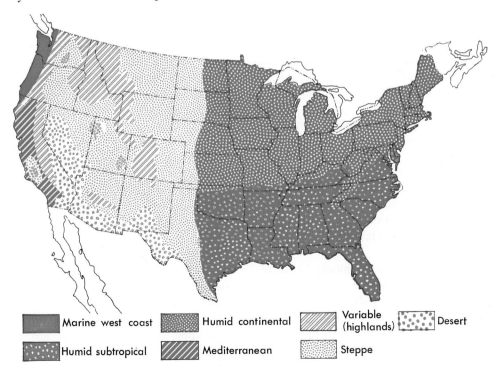

Marine west coast   Humid continental   Variable (highlands)   Desert

Humid subtropical   Mediterranean   Steppe

into the northwest behind the coastal mountains are the semiarid lands of the steppes. This includes the Great Plains, which illustrate the heavy cover of low grasses most characteristic of the steppes. Farming in the steppes is uncertain because of the unpredictable rainfall, but it is the richest grazing land in the world.

Humid subtropical climate. The entire southeastern part of the United States has the humid subtropical climate except for the southern tip of Florida which has a tropical rain forest climate. The southeast is characterized by warm, humid summers and usually mild winters. The humid subtropical regions of the United States differ from similar climates in the rest of the world in being subject to occasional periods of very cold weather during the winter. These cold spells are caused by the invasion of cold polar air far to the south of its usual limits. The polar air masses are able occasionally to penetrate so far south because of the open nature of the land in the midwestern part of the country. The lack of obstructions to the north also allows cyclonic storms to move southward and give the inland states of the southeast abundant rain in the winter. The south Atlantic and Gulf coastal states receive their maximum rainfall in the summer when cool moist air from the sea is brought in over the warmer land surfaces. The warm temperatures and abundant rain of this type of climate encourages rapid plant growth and supports extensive agriculture in this region.

Humid continental climate. North of the humid subtropical southeast and east of the semiarid steppes of the west is a large area of the United States which has the severe winters and warm summers of the continental type of climate. This general region can be subdivided into two very similar climate types, designated as "warm-summer" and "cool-summer," on the basis of the somewhat less severe temperatures of the southern part. The warm-summer subdivision includes a block of states extending from Kansas and Nebraska on the west to the Atlantic coast on the east. In this zone, summers are long, warm, and humid as a result of the influence of maritime tropical air masses that move up from the south. Winter temperatures alternate between the relatively mild readings produced by warmer air from the south and severe cold waves caused by invasions of polar air from the north. Rainfall is likely to be spread throughout the year coming from thunderstorm type disturbances in the summer and from cyclonic storms in the winter. This type of climate is often spoken of as corn-belt climate because it favors the growth of tall grain crops such as corn.

The cool-summer type of humid continental climate has, in spite of its name, fairly warm summers. However, the heat waves are likely to be shorter and less severe than in the warm-summer climate. It is the winter temperatures of this climate that are extreme. The winters are colder and somewhat longer than in the humid continental climate more to the south. The western parts of this climatic area tend to have moist summers and relatively dry winters. The eastern part, however, particularly the New England region, has almost as much precipitation in the winter as in the summer because of the converging of the eastward moving cyclonic storms of this part of the country. The cool-summer type of humid continental climate favors the growth of grains, particularly wheat.

SUMMARY

THE major consideration in climatic classification is temperature. The three main zones are the tropical, middle latitude, and polar climates. Based on the amount of precipitation, each zone is divided into regions.

The rain forest of the tropical zone is hot and humid and supports heavy vegetation. There is little change in monthly temperature, and rainfall averages 100 inches per year. Wet and dry seasons mark the coarse grassed savannas. Within the trade wind belts the tropical deserts have daily extremes in temperature and very little moisture. Bordering the tropical deserts are the steppes, which support more vegetation because they receive greater precipitation.

Located in the westerly wind belts, the middle latitudes have the greatest variety and extremes of weather. Mediterranean climates during the summer are warm and sunny, winters are mild and rainy. The humid subtropical has greater rainfall and higher humidity. Marine west coast climates are marked by precipitation throughout the year. Middle latitude deserts range from hot and dry summers to cold severe winters. Movement of the westerlies exerts the greatest influence on the east coast of continents, producing humid continental climates. General characteristics are possible monsoon wind shifts, wide range between summer and winter temperatures, and summer thunderstorms. The subarctic has short summers, long cold winters, and slight precipitation.

Polar climates are the transitional tundra and the icecap climate.

VOCABULARY REVIEW

Match the phrase in the left column with the correct word or phrase in the right column. *Do not write in this book.*

1. Carpet of mosses and related plants
2. Average annual temperature above 68° F
3. Climate affecting a small area
4. Belt around tropical deserts
5. Average annual temperature below 68° F
6. Coarse grasses with some trees and shrubs
7. Sparse subarctic forest

a. monsoon
b. middle latitude climate
c. savanna
d. local climate
e. taiga
f. tundra
g. steppe
h. tropical climate

QUESTIONS · GROUP A

In some of the following groups of terms, three are related in some way and one is not. Select the unrelated term and give a reason why you believe it is not related.

1. (*a*) rainy (*b*) cool (*c*) lack of vegetation (*d*) Oregon
2. (*a*) low crop yield (*b*) valley of California (*c*) windward side of Sierra Nevada Mountains (*d*) mild winters

3. (*a*) Great Plains (*b*) Sahara (*c*) pampas (*d*) steppes
4. (*a*) Florida (*b*) warm humid summers (*c*) low grasses (*d*) southern Brazil
5. (*a*) Cherrapunji (*b*) Sonora desert (*c*) Kauai (*d*) maximum insolation
6. (*a*) little daily temperature change (*b*) Kalahari (*c*) northern Chile (*d*) few hardy plants
7. (*a*) torrid (*b*) frigid (*c*) moderate (*d*) temperature
8. (*a*) tundra (*b*) cold temperature (*c*) Antarctic (*d*) northern Asia
9. (*a*) cornbelt of the United States (*b*) steppes climate (*c*) humid continental climate (*d*) cyclonic storms during the winter
10. (*a*) jungle (*b*) tropical rain forest (*c*) no winter season (*d*) high pressure belt

Decide whether these statements are true or false. Reword the false statements to make them true. *Do not write in this book.*

11. The Sahara is an example of a middle latitude desert.
12. Cone-bearing trees are found above the timber line.
13. Most of the United States is located in the middle latitude climatic belt.
14. The types of vegetation characteristic of a steppe region are lichens and other similar plants.
15. The greatest yearly temperature ranges occur in the polar climates.
16. The pampas have very definite wet and dry seasons.
17. The westerlies are the prevailing winds of the polar climates.
18. Rains of the tropical forests result from the descent of cold air from higher elevations.
19. Mediterranean climates are restricted to the coast of Italy.
20. Yearly precipitation in continental United States is greatest in Florida.

GROUP B

1. Compare and contrast the daily temperature with the annual temperature range in tropical rain forests.
2. Describe each of the climatic regions in the United States.
3. Why is temperature a poor basis for climatic classification?
4. Why are strong winds dangerous to farm lands in the Great Plains?
5. Account for the heavy rainfall in Cherrapunji.
6. Contrast the amount of rainfall on the leeward and windward sides on the Sierra Nevadas. Explain why this is so.
7. What is taiga? Name some areas with this type of climate and vegetation.
8. Explain the occurrence of local climates within larger climatic regions.
9. Give several examples to show how climate affects the activities, occupations, housing, and general characteristics of people in various parts of the world.
10. Explain why the driest desert in the world is in northern Chile.

UNIT REVIEW QUESTIONS

1. Why is rain more frequent in the doldrums than in the horse latitudes?
2. Why do the ocean currents in the Pacific have more effect on the climate of the west coast of the United States than the Gulf Stream has on the east coast?
3. What are the differences between weather and climate?

4. Compare and contrast the summer and winter monsoons in India.
5. What is the relationship of latitude to length of daylight?
6. Differentiate between an isotherm and the heat equator.
7. How are the specific heats of water and land related to climate?
8. Why is evaporation a cooling process?
9. How does vegetation change as altitude increases?
10. Compare the three major climatic zones on the basis of temperature.
11. Using an outline form, list the major characteristics of each of the climatic regions of the continental United States.
12. Why are the tundra and taiga found only in the northern hemisphere?
13. Compare the warm-summer and cool-summer divisions of the humid continental climate in the United States. Explain any differences.
14. Account for the lack of heavy precipitation in the polar regions.
15. Account for the large difference between daytime and nighttime temperatures in the tropical deserts.

ACTIVITIES

1. On outline maps of the world show by using color codes the distribution of climatic zones and average annual rainfall.
2. On an outline map of the United States use a color code to show the distribution of climatic regions.
3. Choose one of the climatic regions discussed in this unit and write a detailed report on that region.
4. Write a report on the great deserts of the world.
5. Construct dioramas to illustrate the environments of different climatic regions.
6. Draw a large map of the United States and attach to it samples of products representative of the different climatic regions.
7. Construct a model to show the effect of the Sierra Nevadas on the climate of California.
8. On a large graph, plot rainfall and temperature data for different parts of the world. A good basis would be monthly averages.

FURTHER READING

CLIMATOLOGY. T A. Blair, 1942. *Prentice-Hall, Inc., Englewood Cliffs, New Jersey.*

CLIMATE IN EVERYDAY LIFE. C. E. P. Brooks, 1951. *Philosophical Library Inc., New York.*

CLIMATE AND MAN. Department of Agriculture Yearbook, 1941. *Government Printing Office, Washington 25, D. C.*

CLIMATE, VEGETATION AND MAN. L. Hadlow, 1953. *Philosophical Library, Inc., New York.*

DESERTS. G. B. Pickwell, 1939. *McGraw-Hill Book Company, Inc., New York.*

AN INTRODUCTION TO CLIMATE. G. T. Trewartha, 1954. *McGraw-Hill Book Company, Inc., New York.*

APPENDIX

A. THE PHYSIOGRAPHIC PROVINCES OF THE UNITED STATES

1. The Laurentian Upland Province. An elevated region of ancient igneous and metamorphic rocks, with a covering of glacial debris. Most of this province lies in Canada, but its southern extensions enter New York, Minnesota, Wisconsin, and Michigan.

2. The New England Province. Also a region of igneous and metamorphic rocks, mostly glaciated, but having a great variety of features. The southern part is less rugged than the northern. The province includes parts of Canada, a strip of eastern New York, and nearly all of the New England states. Two small projections extend into New Jersey and Pennsylvania.

3. The Older Appalachians. A region of complex rocks. It is composed of two sections, the mountainous Blue Ridge and a rolling upland, the Piedmont. This province was not covered by glaciers and therefore lacks glacial deposits. It extends from Pennsylvania to Georgia and Alabama.

4. The Triassic Lowland. A small province with underlying weak sedimentary rocks, lying between the two extensions of the New England Province. It has a low and gently rolling landscape, with a few ridges due to igneous rock outcrops. It extends diagonally across New Jersey, Pennsylvania, and Maryland into Virginia.

5. The Coastal Plain. A region of sedimentary rock beds which are part of the continental shelf that has recently emerged from the ocean. A rolling landscape near the Piedmont grades into flat topography without any sharp dividing line. Varying in width, the coastal plain extends from Long Island to Texas.

6. The Newer or Folded Appalachians. A region of sedimentary rocks of varying resistance, strongly folded and faulted. Long ridges of the harder beds alternate with fertile lowlands developed on weaker rocks. The province stretches from Lake Champlain in New York south to Alabama.

7. The Appalachian Plateaus. An elevated area of almost horizontal sedimentary beds, of the same types as in the Newer Appalachians. The surface features are flat, rounded, or rugged, depending on how deeply streams have cut through the beds. The province includes parts of New York, Pennsylvania, Ohio, West Virginia, Kentucky, Tennessee, and Alabama.

8. The Interior Lowlands. A plains region of sedimentary rocks, with glacial deposits in the northern part. Gently rolling prairies are broken by occasional highlands made up of glacial deposits or resistant rock formations. The province extends from Canada south to northern Texas.

9. The Ozark Plateaus and **10. The Ouachita Mountains.** Provinces similar to the Appalachian Plateau and the Newer Appalachians, respectively. They extend through parts of Missouri, Arkansas, and Oklahoma.

596

1. The Laurentian Upland; 2. The New England Province; 3. The Older Appalachians; 4. The Triassic Lowland; 5. The Coastal Plain; 6. The Newer or Folded Appalachians; 7. The Appalachian Plateaus; 8. The Interior Lowlands; 9. The Ozark Plateaus; 10. The Ouachita Mountains; 11. The Great Plains; 12. The Northern Rockies; 13. The Southern Rockies; 14. The Columbia Plateau; 15. The Basin and Range Province; 16. The Colorado Plateau; 17. The Pacific Ranges.

11. The Great Plains. A region of horizontal beds like the Interior Lowlands but with much less rainfall and a higher elevation. It is flat, with long cliffs marking the edges of the beds, and many isolated rock remnants, the result of erosion in a dry climate. The province extends through the western states east of the Rocky Mountains, from Canada to Texas.

12. The Northern Rockies. This province includes a number of mountain ranges of varying complex structure and surface appearance. It extends through parts of Montana, Idaho, Wyoming, and Utah.

13. The Southern Rockies. This area includes the series of long ranges extending from Wyoming to northern New Mexico.

14. The Columbia Plateau. A region of horizontal lava beds covering old, worn-down mountains. Its flat topography is deeply cut by a few large rivers. In places, isolated peaks, groups of the old mountains, and a few volcanic cones stand out above the plateau. This province covers parts of Idaho, Washington, and Oregon.

15. The Basin and Range Province. A region of complex rocks in many small mountain ranges, with sedimentary beds in the basins between the ranges. The ranges extend roughly north and south. The province includes western Utah, all of Nevada, and portions of Oregon, California, Arizona, New Mexico, and Texas.

16. The Colorado Plateau. An elevated semiarid region of more or less horizontal sedimentary beds of varying resistance. Rivers have cut deep canyons into the layers, while the more resistant beds stand out as prominent cliffs. Volcanic features also break the flatness of the topography. The province includes sections of Colorado, New Mexico, Utah, and Arizona.

17. The Pacific Ranges. This province consists of two chains of mountains, with a lowland trough between them, extending from Mexico to the Alaska Peninsula. It includes some desert lands, and the mountain ranges are of various types and origins. The province includes the western parts of the states that border the Pacific: Washington, Oregon, and California.

B. KEY FOR
IDENTIFICATION OF MINERALS

The identification of particular mineral specimens is made simpler if a series of tables, or *key,* is used. The key in this book consists of 11 tables in which a number of the more important minerals are arranged systematically according to their characteristics.

Before attempting to use the key for identification of minerals, the student should thoroughly review the text material in Chapter 11 dealing with the characteristic properties of minerals (pages 151–162). In the key, the first step in arrangement of minerals is a division into two groups: those having metallic luster and those without metallic luster. The metallic luster group is further divided according to color; the nonmetallic luster group is divided according to the color of the streak. The mineral species which fall into these groups are then arranged according to hardness.

The procedure in using the tables is a step-by-step determination of the properties of the specimen to be identified. First examine the mineral and determine its luster, color and streak, and hardness. Turn to the general classification list, page 601, and find the number of the table which applies. Then read carefully across the appropriate column of the table, and examine the mineral, making any required tests, to determine its properties as described there.

To illustrate the use of the tables, assume that we have a specimen of galenite. By examination, we see that it has metallic luster, which places it in the left column of the classification list, page 601. Next, we see that it is gray, which places it in the last group of the column. Now we determine the hardness and find that it is very soft. Turning to Table 2 as directed in the list, we find a detailed analysis of four minerals in the section labeled *gray, very soft.* In the righthand section of the *Key* column, distinctive features of each mineral are given as a help in distinguishing among the members of a small group. We determine that our sample does not have the low specific gravity of molybdenite and pyrolusite, nor is it sectile, like argentite. Galenite remains, and by elimination, we find that our sample is most likely to be this mineral. A check of the other characteristics listed, including testing for fusibility, helps to make the identification more certain.

Some additional information on the arrangement and terminology used in the tables will be helpful.

Luster. The presence of metallic luster is the first basis of classification in the key. Therefore it is of great importance to determine the luster of a mineral specimen. It is helpful to note that minerals with metallic luster are opaque; that is, they do not allow light to pass through them. However, some dark, nonmetallic minerals appear opaque, and so some of these have been included in both the metallic and nonmetallic tables in the key. Metallic luster is common to all true metals. In some minerals, the luster is indistinctly metallic, ranging between metallic and nonmetallic: this is called *submetallic.* The luster of minerals composed mostly of nonmetallic elements may be described as follows: *adamantine,* exceedingly brilliant; *vitreous,* glassy; *resinous,* with appearance of resin; *pearly,* with appear-

599

ance of mother-of-pearl; *greasy or waxy,* with appearance of oiled or waxed surface; *silky,* similar to pearly, found in finely fibrous minerals; *dull,* without bright or shiny surface, earthy. A particularly bright luster may be referred to as *splendent.*

Color, Streak, Hardness and Specific Gravity. The methods and scales used in determining these properties as given in Chapter 11 are referred to in the tables.

Cleavage and Fracture. Cleavage, the breaking of a mineral along the faces of its crystal planes, may be described in geometrical terms. A few of the more common terms used in the table are *cubic,* in the form of a cube; *rhombohedral,* in a form having six faces intersecting at angles other than 90°; *octahedral,* in a form having eight faces; *basal,* cleaving parallel to the base of the crystal; *clinopinacoidal,* in monoclinic crystals, cleaving parallel to the oblique and the vertical axes; *prismatic,* cleaving in forms with faces parallel to the vertical axis.

Most of the terms describing fracture are self-explanatory. Many minerals show *conchoidal* fracture: they break in smooth, curving surfaces resembling the inside of a shell; in *hackly* fracture, the mineral breaks with thin points that catch the skin as one scrapes a finger across the surface.

Fusibility. The fusibility of a mineral is an important aid to identification. The temperature of fusion is not accurately known except for a few species. The approximate fusing points of different minerals, that is, their relative fusing points, can be determined by comparison. A small fragment of the mineral is heated with the oxidizing flame in the forceps or on a charcoal block. Seven species of minerals have been chosen as a scale of fusibility. Beginning with the most easily melted, they are stibnite—1; natrolite—2; garnet—3; actinolite—4; orthoclase—5; bronzite—6; quartz—7. If the specimen to be identified fuses as readily as stibnite, it has a fusibility of 1; if it cannot be rounded on the thinnest edges, like quartz, it is 7, and so on.

Other Characteristics. The table uses standard terms to indicate the ability of a mineral to transmit light: *opaque,* no light transmitted even through thin edges or layers; *translucent,* some light transmitted but objects appear indistinctly through the substance; *transparent,* objects distinctly seen through the substance. The **tenacity** of a mineral, that is, its behavior when an attempt is made to break, cut, hammer, or similarly alter it, is described as *brittle,* breaks under distortion; *sectile,* can be cut without crumbling; *malleable,* can be hammered into thin sheets; *flexible,* can be bent visibly without breaking; *elastic,* thin layers can be bent and spring back when released. Some brittle minerals are very rigid and strong and break with great difficulty. These are said to be *tough.*

The external forms and internal structures of minerals are described in the tables by a variety of terms. Some types of crystalline or amorphous masses are *acicular,* needlelike crystals; *botryoidal,* closely joined, small rounded masses, like grapes; *fibrous,* very thin crystals or filaments; *foliated,* plates or leaves which are easily separated; *granular,* grains, closely packed; *nodular,* round masses of irregular shape; *pisolitic,* small masses about the size of peas; *scaly,* thin scales or plates; *sheaflike,* crystals resembling a sheaf of wheat. Many similar terms are in general use in describing minerals. Further discussion of this subject may be found in any standard textbook of mineralogy.

The last column of each table in the key includes, as well as the name of the mineral species, its chemical formula and a roman numeral indicating the system in which the mineral crystallizes. The crystal systems are I, Isometric; II, Tetragonal; III, Hexagonal; IV, Orthorhombic; V, Monoclinic; and VI, Triclinic. See page 155. If no system number is given, the mineral is amorphous.

CLASSIFICATION OF MINERALS

Minerals with metallic luster	
Color red or brown	*Table*
Very soft	1
Hard	1
Color yellow	
Very soft	1
Soft	1
Hard	1
Color white or silver	
Very soft	1
Hard	1
Color gray	
Very soft	2
Hard	2
Color gray to black	
Very soft	2
Soft	2
Hard	2
Very hard	2

Minerals without metallic luster	
Streak reddish	*Table*
Very soft	3
Soft	3
Hard	3
Streak brown	
Very soft	3
Soft	3,4
Hard	4
Very hard	4
Streak yellow	
Very soft	4
Soft	4
Hard	4,5
Very hard	5
Streak blue or green	
Very soft	5
Soft	5
Hard	5
Streak black	
Very soft	5
Soft	5
Hard	5
Streak gray or white	
Very soft	6,7
Soft	6,7
Hard	6
Very hard	6,7
Streak white	
Soft	8
Hard	9
Very hard	9,10,11
Adamantine	10,11

MINERALS WITH METALLIC LUSTER

TABLE 1 (Color group)	Hardness	KEY	LUSTER	COLOR	STREAK	HARDNESS, S.G., AND CLEAVAGE	CHARACTERISTICS	SPECIES
COLOR RED OR BROWN	VERY SOFT	STREAK WHITE	Pearly to metallic on cleavage	Light to dark brown	White	2.5 to 3 / 2.75 / Basal, perfect	Infusible. Yields a little water in closed tube. Decomposes in strong sulfuric acid. Transparent to opaque. Sectile, elastic. Foliated	MICA Phlogopite complex silicate V
	HARD	STREAK RED MALLEABLE	Metallic	Copper red, tarnishes black	Copper red	2.5 to 3 / 8.8 to 8.9 / None. Fracture hackly	Fuses at 780 C. Gives green solution in nitric acid, then blue in ammonia (DANGER). Malleable. Sometimes cubic; rounded branches	NATIVE COPPER Cu I
		STREAK DEEP RED	Submetallic to dull	Reddish black	Red	4 to 6 / 4.3 to 4.7 / None. Fracture uneven	Infusible; becomes magnetic on charcoal. Yields water in closed tube. Soluble in hydrochloric acid. Opaque. Brittle. Massive, botryoidal	TURGITE $2Fe_2O_3 + H_2O$
		COMPARE S.G.	Metallic	Reddish brown	Reddish brown	4 to 6 / 4.9 to 5.3 / Basal. Fracture uneven	Infusible. Yields no water in a closed tube. Sometimes magnetic. Opaque. Brittle. Massive, botryoidal	HEMATITE Red Ocher Fe_2O_3 III
		S.G. 6.4 TO 9.7	Submetallic to greasy	Gray, green, brown to black	Brownish black to olive green or grayish	5.5 to 6 / 6.4 to 9.7 / None. Fracture uneven or conchoidal	Infusible. Gives coating of lead oxide with soda on charcoal. Soluble in acids. Nitric acid leaves fluorescent spot. Opaque. Brittle. Massive, botryoidal	URANINITE UO_2 I
COLOR YELLOW	VERY SOFT	DOES NOT TARNISH MALLEABLE	Metallic	Rich yellow to silvery yellow	Gold yellow	2.5 to 3 / 19.3 / None	Fuses readily. Soluble only in aqua regia. Does not tarnish. Very malleable. Grains or nuggets	NATIVE GOLD Au I
	SOFT	IRIDESCENT TARNISH	Metallic	Bronze yellow (brass)	Dark greenish black	3.5 to 4 / 4.1 to 4.3 / One poor. Fracture uneven	Gives copper on charcoal. Yields sulfur in test tube. Produces green solution with nitric acid. Often tarnished; iridescent	CHALCOPYRITE $CuFeS_2$ II
		BROWN TARNISH	Metallic	Bronze yellow	Dark grayish black	3.5 to 4.5 / 4.4 to 4.7 / Basal. Fracture uneven	Fuses to black, magnetic mass. Dissolves in hydrochloric acid to form H_2S. Often has dark brown tarnish. Opaque. Massive, granular	PYRRHOTITE $Fe_{1-x}S$ or Fe_7S_8 III
	HARD	BRASS YELLOW COLOR	Metallic	Pale brass yellow	Brownish black to greenish black	6 to 6.5 / 4.8 to 5.2 / Indistinct. Fracture uneven	Fuses easily, leaving magnetic residue. Yields sulfur in a closed tube. Opaque. Massive or in cubes	PYRITE FeS I
		GRAYISH YELLOW COLOR	Metallic	Pale grayish yellow	Dark brownish black	6 to 6.5 / 4.9 to 5 / Indistinct. Fracture uneven	Fuses easily, leaving magnetic residue. Yields sulfur in a closed tube. Brittle. Massive, fibrous, or crystalline	MARCASITE FeS_2 IV
WHITE OR SILVER	VERY SOFT TO HARD	COMPARE S.G.	Metallic (mirrorlike)	Silvery or steel gray	Red	1 to 6 / 4.9 to 5.3 / None. Fracture uneven	Infusible. No cracking when heated. Soluble in hydrochloric acid. Opaque. Brittle	HEMATITE Specular Fe_2O_3 III
		COMPARE S.G.	Metallic	Silver white. Bright white. Black if tarnished	White	2.5 to 6 / 10 to 11 / None. Fracture hackly	Fuses readily. Dissolves in nitric acid. Malleable. Opaque. Cubic crystals	NATIVE SILVER Ag I
	HARD	S.G. 6 OR ABOVE	Metallic	Silver white to steel gray	Dark gray to black	5.5 to 6 / 6 to 6.4 / Prismatic, distinct. Fracture uneven	Fuses easily, leaving magnetic residue and arsenic coating. Tarnishes yellowish. Gives garlic smell after hammer blow. Opaque. Massive, wedgelike crystals	ARSENOPYRITE FeAsS IV

MINERALS WITH METALLIC LUSTER

TABLE 2

	KEY	LUSTER	COLOR	STREAK	HARDNESS, S.G., AND CLEAVAGE	CHARACTERISTICS	SPECIES
COLOR GRAY — VERY SOFT — S.G. BELOW 5	SECTILE	Metallic	Lead gray	Blackish lead gray with bluish tinge	1 to 1.5 4.7 to 4.8 Basal, perfect	Infusible. Yields sulfur fumes in oxidizing flame. Opaque. Sectile. Usually foliated. Hexagonal crystals; greasy, flexible plates.	MOLYBDENITE MoS_2 III
COLOR GRAY — VERY SOFT — S.G. BELOW 5	BRITTLE	Metallic	Iron black to steel gray	Black	2.5* 4.8 Two cleavages. Prismatic. Fracture uneven, splintery	Infusible. Yields chlorine with hydrochloric acid. Gives amethyst bead with borax. Opaque. Brittle. Radiating fibers or massive	PYROLUSITE MnO_2 II
COLOR GRAY — VERY SOFT — S.G. ABOVE 7	SECTILE	Metallic	Blackish lead gray	Blackish lead gray	2.5 7.3 Poor cubic and dodecahedral. Fracture uneven or subconchoidal	Fuses to form silver button in oxidizing flame. Reacts to test for sulfur. Yields silver with soda. Tarnishes dull black. Sectile. Cubic crystals.	ARGENTITE Ag_2S I
COLOR GRAY — VERY SOFT — S.G. ABOVE 7	NOT SECTILE	Metallic (Dull if coated)	Dark lead gray	Dark lead gray to black	2.5 to 2.75 7.4 to 7.6 Cubic, perfect	Fuses readily, producing lead and sulfur fumes. Opaque. Brittle. Cubic crystals	GALENITE PbS I
COLOR GRAY TO BLACK — HARD — VERY SOFT	MAGNETIC	Metallic	Dark gray to iron black	Black	5.5 5 Octahedral parting. Fracture conchoidal, uneven	Infusible. Soluble in hydrochloric acid. Magnetic. Striated. Granular	MAGNETITE Fe_3O_4 I
COLOR GRAY TO BLACK — VERY SOFT	GREASY	Metallic	Black	Black	1 to 2 2 to 2.3 Basal, perfect. Flexible scales	Infusible. Insoluble. Greasy feel. Opaque. Sectile. Hexagonal crystals, fibrous	GRAPHITE C III
COLOR GRAY TO BLACK — SOFT — S.G. 4 TO 5	NOT MAGNETIC	Submetallic	Iron black to steel gray	Reddish brown and black	4 4.2 to 4.4 Prismatic and basal poor; perfect side. Fracture uneven	Infusible. Gives amethyst bead with borax. Yields water in closed tube. Yields chlorine with hydrochloric acid. Translucent. Brittle. Striated prisms	MANGANITE $MnO(OH)$ IV
COLOR GRAY TO BLACK — HARD — S.G. 4 TO 5	STREAK BROWNISH RED AND BLACK WEAKLY MAGNETIC	Submetallic to metallic	Iron black to brownish black	Brownish red and black	5 to 6 4.1 to 5 None. Fracture conchoidal	Infusible. Pale yellow when held in hot oxidizing flame, turning to colorless or white when cooled. Weakly magnetic. Opaque. Brittle. Granular	ILMENITE Menaccanite $FeTiO_3$ III
COLOR GRAY TO BLACK — HARD — S.G. 4 TO 5	STREAK LIGHT GRAYISH BROWN SLIGHTLY MAGNETIC	Submetallic	Iron black	Light grayish brown	5.5 4.3 to 4.6 None. Fracture uneven	Infusible. Becomes magnetic when heated. Gives green bead in borax after cooling. May be slightly magnetic. Opaque. Brittle. Massive or octahedral crystals	CHROMITE $FeCr_2O_4$ I
COLOR GRAY TO BLACK — VERY HARD	S.G. 9 TO 9.5 (IF PURE)	Metallic	Steel black	Gray to brown to black	5.5 9 to 9.5† None. Fracture uneven or conchoidal	Infusible. Gives coating of lead oxide with soda on charcoal. Soluble in acids. Opaque. Brittle. Massive, fibrous, botryoidal	URANINITE Pitchblende UO_2 I
COLOR GRAY TO BLACK — VERY HARD	S.G. 4.2	Metallic to adamantine	Black, reddish brown or red	Gray to light yellow brown	6 to 6.5 4.2 Prismatic. Fracture uneven	Infusible. Insoluble. Opaque. Brittle. Crystals or massive	RUTILE TiO_2 II

* Crystal hardness 6 to 6.5   † If pure

MINERALS WITHOUT METALLIC LUSTER

TABLE 3

KEY	SPECIES	CHARACTERISTICS	HARDNESS, S.G., AND CLEAVAGE	STREAK	COLOR	LUSTER
STREAK REDDISH						
S.G. LESS THAN 3 (VERY SOFT)	BAUXITE $Al_2O_3 + 2H_2O$	Infusible. Insoluble. Colors blue in cobalt nitrate test. Opaque. Brittle. Usually massive like hard clay; pisolitic	1 to 3 — 2.0 to 2.6 — None — Fracture earthy	Red	Red	Dull
BRITTLE (S.G. 3 OR MORE, SOFT)	TURGITE Red Ocher $2Fe_2O_3 + H_2O$	Infusible. Becomes black and magnetic on charcoal. Yields water in closed tube. Soluble in hydrochloric acid. Opaque. Brittle. Massive or botryoidal	1 to 2.5 — 3 to 4 — None — Fracture earthy	Red	Red	Dull
SECTILE	REALGAR AsS V	Volatile, combustible—burns with blue flame. Gives arsenic (garlic) odor. Transparent to translucent. Often has yellow spots. Sectile	1.5 to 2 — 3.5 — Basal and clinopinacoidal Fracture conchoidal	Red to orange	Red and orange	Resinous
COMPARE S.G.	CUPRITE Cu_2O I	Fuses readily, yielding copper. Colors flame green; blue with hydrochloric acid. Translucent to opaque. Brittle. Often has green or blue spots	3.5 to 4 — 5.8 to 6.1 — Octahedral Fracture uneven	Red to brown	Red to brown	Adamantine to dull
COMPARE S.G.	CINNABAR HgS III	Volatile. Yields sulfur fumes and mercury droplets. Transparent to opaque. Brittle to sectile. Hexagonal crystals, massive, granular, acicular	4 — 8 to 8.2 — Prismatic, perfect Fracture uneven	Scarlet	Red to brownish red	Adamantine to dull
STREAK ORANGE, S.G. ABOVE 5 (HARD)	ZINCITE ZnO III	Infusible—turns black. Soluble in acid. Translucent to opaque. Brittle. Pyramidal crystals rare, granular, foliated	4 to 4.5 — 5.4 to 5.7 — None — Fracture conchoidal	Orange	Red to orange	Subadamantine
YIELDS WATER IN CLOSED TUBE	TURGITE $2Fe_2O_3 + H_2O$	Infusible. Becomes black and magnetic on charcoal. Yields water in closed tube. Soluble in hydrochloric acid. Opaque. Brittle. Massive or botryoidal	4 to 6 — 4.3 to 4.7 — None — Fracture uneven	Red	Reddish black	Submetallic to dull
STREAK BROWN						
FLUORESCES GREEN	WILLEMITE Zn_2SiO_4 III	Fuses with difficulty. Yields zinc oxide with soda on charcoal. Gelatinizes with HCl. Fluoresces green. Translucent to opaque. Brittle. Massive	5.5 — 3.9 to 4.2 — Imperfect Fracture uneven	Reddish and brownish	Yellowish, greenish, brownish	Vitreous-resinous
S.G. 2.6 (VERY SOFT)	KAOLINITE $Al_2Si_2O_5(OH)_4$ IV	Infusible. Yields water in closed tube. Insoluble. Colors blue in cobalt nitrate test. Opaque. Brittle (clay)	1 — 2.6 — Basal Fracture earthy	Brown	Yellow	Dull
S.G. 3.6 TO 4	LIMONITE Yellow Ocher $2Fe_2O_3 \cdot 3H_2O$	Infusible. Turns black and magnetic on charcoal. Yields water in a closed tube. Opaque	1 to 2.5 — 3.6 to 4 — None — Fracture earthy	Brown	Brown	Dull
S.G. 2 TO 2.5	BAUXITE $Al_2O_3 + 2H_2O$	Infusible. Insoluble. Colors blue in cobalt nitrate test. Opaque. Brittle. Usually massive like hard clay; pisolitic	1 to 3 — 2.0 to 2.5 — None — Fracture earthy	Brown	Brown	Dull
BECOMES MAGNETIC ON CHARCOAL (SOFT)	SIDERITE $FeCO_3$ III	Infusible. Turns black and magnetic on charcoal. Effervesces in hot acid. Translucent to near opaque. Brittle. Curved crystals	3.5 to 4 — 3.8 — Rhombohedral, perfect Fracture conchoidal	Brown	Dark brown to gray	Dull to vitreous
REMAINS NONMAGNETIC AFTER HEATING	SPHALERITE ZnS I	Infusible. Reacts to test for sulfur. Remains nonmagnetic after heating. Effervesces in hot acid, giving H_2S	3.5 to 4 — 3.9 to 4.1 — Perfect. Six cleavages Fracture uneven	Brown	Yellow to brown	Resinous

MINERALS WITHOUT METALLIC LUSTER

TABLE 4	KEY	SPECIES	CHARACTERISTICS	HARDNESS, S.G., AND CLEAVAGE	STREAK	COLOR	LUSTER
STREAK BROWN — SOFT	COLORS FLAME GREEN, FUSES READILY	CUPRITE Cu_2O I	Fuses readily, yielding copper. Colors flame green; blue with hydrochloric acid. Translucent to opaque. Brittle. Often has green or blue spots	3.5 to 4 5.8 to 6.1 Octahedral Fracture uneven	Brown	Red to brown	Dull to adamantine
STREAK BROWN — HARD	BECOMES MAGNETIC WHEN HEATED	CHROMITE $FeCr_2O_4$ I	Infusible. Becomes magnetic when heated. Gives green bead in borax after cooling. May be slightly magnetic. Opaque. Brittle. Massive or octahedral crystals	5.5 4.3 to 4.6 None Fracture uneven	Brown	Iron black	Submetallic
STREAK BROWN — VERY HARD	NOT MAGNETIC S.G. 4.2	RUTILE TiO_2 II	Infusible. Insoluble. Opaque. Brittle. Crystals or massive	6 to 6.5 4.2 Prismatic Fracture uneven	Light brown	Reddish brown	Adamantine
STREAK BROWN — VERY HARD	NOT MAGNETIC S.G. 6.8	CASSITERITE SnO_2 II	Infusible. Yields metallic tin with soda on charcoal. Not magnetic. Translucent to opaque. Brittle. Prismatic crystals; granular; fibrous	6.5 6.8 Imperfect Fracture uneven	Light brown	Brown to black	Adamantine to greasy
STREAK YELLOW — VERY SOFT	COMPARE S.G	OPAL $SiO_2 + H_2O$	Infusible. Yields water in closed tube. Insoluble in acid. Transparent to opaque. Brittle. Massive, botryoidal. Earthy variety, diatomite	0.5 to 1.5 1.5 Fracture conchoidal	Yellow	White to yellow or gray	Dull to vitreous
STREAK YELLOW — VERY SOFT	COMPARE S.G	KAOLINITE $Al_2Si_2O_5(OH)_4$ IV	Infusible. Yields water in closed tube. Insoluble. Colors blue in cobalt nitrate test. Opaque. Brittle (yellow clay)	1 to 2.5 2.6 Basal Fracture earthy	Yellow	Yellow	Dull
STREAK YELLOW — VERY SOFT	COMPARE S.G	LIMONITE Yellow Ocher $2Fe_2O_3 \cdot 3H_2O$	Infusible. Turns black and magnetic on charcoal. Yields water in a closed tube. Opaque	1 to 2.5 3.6 to 4 None Fracture earthy	Yellow to brown	Yellow to brown	Dull
STREAK YELLOW — VERY SOFT	COMPARE S.G	CARNOTITE $K_2(UO_2)(VO_4)_2$ $3H_2O$ IV	Infusible. Cold borax bead is fluorescent green. Powder turns red brown in boiling nitric acid and dissolves to green solution. Opaque. Sectile. Scaly powder	1 to 2 4.1 to 5.0 Basal, perfect Fracture earthy	Yellow	Bright yellow	Dull
STREAK YELLOW — VERY SOFT	COMPARE S.G	ORPIMENT As_2S_3 IV	Reacts to tests for arsenic and sulfur. Translucent. Slightly sectile; flexible plates. Massive, foliated, botryoidal	1.5 to 2 3.5 Perfect	Yellow	Yellow often with orange spots	Resinous to pearly
STREAK YELLOW — VERY SOFT	COMPARE S.G.	NATIVE SULFUR S IV	Burns with blue flame and odor of sulfur. Translucent. Brittle. Orthorhombic crystals, massive	1.5 to 2.5 2.0 to 2.1 Prismatic, basal, imperfect Fracture conchoidal	Yellow to white	Light yellow to brown	Resinous
STREAK YELLOW — SOFT	COMPARE S.G.	SIDERITE $FeCO_3$ III	Infusible. Turns black and magnetic on charcoal. Effervesces in hot acid. Translucent to near opaque. Brittle. Curved crystals	3.5 to 4 3.8 Rhombohedral, perfect Fracture conchoidal	Gray to yellow and brown	Gray to dark brown	Dull to vitreous
STREAK YELLOW — SOFT	COMPARE S.G.	SPHALERITE ZnS I	Infusible. Reacts to test for sulfur. Remains nonmagnetic after heating. Effervesces in hot acid, giving H_2S	3.5 to 4 3.9 to 4.1 Perfect. Six cleavages	Light yellow to brown	Yellow to brown	Resinous
STREAK YELLOW — HARD	COLOR BROWN TO BLACK	LIMONITE Goethite $2Fe_2O_3 \cdot 3H_2O$ IV	Infusible. Turns black and magnetic on charcoal. Yields water in a closed tube. Opaque. Dark and light bands. Stalactitic; radiating plates	5.0 to 5.5 4 to 4.4 Prismatic, perfect Fracture conchoidal	Yellow	Brown to black	Dull to adamantine

MINERALS WITHOUT METALLIC LUSTER

TABLE 5

STREAK		KEY	LUSTER	COLOR	STREAK	HARDNESS, S.G., AND CLEAVAGE	CHARACTERISTICS	SPECIES
STREAK YELLOW	HARD	COLOR OCHER YELLOW	Submetallic	Ocher yellow	Ocher yellow	5 to 6 4.1 to 5 None Fracture conchoidal	Infusible. Pale yellow when held in hot oxidizing flame, turning to colorless or white when cooled. Weakly magnetic. Opaque. Brittle. Granular.	ILMENITE Menaccanite $FeTiO_2$ III
	VERY HARD	S.G. 2.6	Nearly dull	Brown to yellow	Light yellow	7 2.6 None Fracture conchoidal	Infusible. Insoluble. Translucent to opaque. Brittle to tough. Crystals six-sided with striations. Often with inclusions.	QUARTZ Jasper $SiO_2 + Fe_2O_3$ III
STREAK BLUE OR GREEN	SOFT	COLOR BLUE	Dull to vitreous	Blue	Pale blue	3.5 to 4 3.8 Perfect Fracture conchoidal	Fuses readily. Colors flame green. Yields copper. Yields water in closed tube. Effervesces in acid. Translucent to opaque. Brittle, often velvety	AZURITE $Cu_3(OH)_2(CO_3)_2$ V
	VERY SOFT	S.G. 2.6 TO 3	Pearly to dull	White to dark green, black, brown, rose, yellow	Lighter green	1 to 2.5 2.6 to 3.0 Basal, perfect Fracture scaly, earthy	Fuses with difficulty. Yields water in closed tube. Translucent to opaque. Tough to brittle. Somewhat sectile. Usually finely foliated to massive	CHLORITE $MgFeAlSi_3 \cdot H_2O$ V
	SOFT	S.G. 3.9 TO 4	Adamantine, silky or dull to vitreous	Green	Pale green	3.5 to 4 3.9 to 4 Basal, perfect Fracture conchoidal	Fuses readily, coloring flame green. Leaves copper on charcoal. Yields water in closed tube. Effervesces in acid. Translucent to opaque; often banded. Brittle	MALACHITE $CuCO_3 + Cu(OH)_2$ V
	HARD	COMPARE S.G.	Vitreous	Greenish black	Grayish green	5 to 6 3.2 to 3.6 Prismatic, perfect; two cleavages, often one parting	Fusible at 2.5–5. Insoluble. Translucent to opaque. Brittle. Massive, granular	AUGITE Pyroxene complex silicate V
	HARD	COMPARE S.G.	Submetallic to greasy	Gray, green, brown, black	Olive green	5.5 to 6 6.4 to 9.7 None Fracture uneven or conchoidal	Infusible. Gives coating of lead oxide with soda on charcoal. Soluble in acids. Opaque. Brittle. Massive, fibrous, botryoidal	URANINITE Pitchblende UO_2 I
STREAK BLACK	VERY SOFT	S.G. 2.6	Dull	Red or reddish brown to black or white	Black	1 to 2.5 2.6 Micaceous Fracture earthy	Infusible. Yields water in closed tube. Insoluble. Colors blue in cobalt nitrate test. Opaque. Brittle.	KAOLINITE $Al_2Si_2O_5(OH)_4$ IV
	SOFT	S.G. 4.2 TO 4.4	Submetallic	Iron black	Black	4 4.2 to 4.4 Prismatic and basal poor, side perfect. Fracture uneven	Infusible. Gives amethyst bead with borax. Yields water in closed tube. Yields chlorine with hydrochloric acid. Translucent. Brittle. Striated prisms	MANGANITE $MnO(OH)$ IV
	HARD		Submetallic to metallic	Iron black to brownish black	Black	5 to 6 4.1 to 5 None Fracture conchoidal	Infusible. Pale yellow when held in hot oxidizing flame, turning to colorless or white when cooled. Weakly magnetic. Opaque. Brittle. Granular.	ILMENITE Menaccanite $FeTiO_2$ III
	HARD	COMPARE S.G.	Submetallic to greasy	Gray, green, brown to black	Brownish black to grayish	5.5 to 6 6.4 to 9.7 None Fracture uneven or conchoidal	Infusible. Gives coating of lead oxide with soda on charcoal. Soluble in acids. Opaque. Brittle. Massive, fibrous, botryoidal	URANINITE Pitchblende UO_2 I

MINERALS WITHOUT METALLIC LUSTER
STREAK GRAY OR WHITE

TABLE 6		KEY	LUSTER	COLOR	STREAK	HARDNESS, S.G., AND CLEAVAGE	CHARACTERISTICS	SPECIES
VERY SOFT		S.G. 2 TO 2.6 COLOR GRAY	Dull	Gray, red, white, brown	Gray	1 to 3 — None — Fracture earthy	Infusible. Insoluble. Colors blue in cobalt nitrate test. Opaque. Brittle. Usually massive like hard clay; pisolitic	BAUXITE $Al_2O_3 + 2H_2O$
HARD		STREAK GRAYISH BROWN	Submetallic	Iron-black	Light grayish brown	5.5 — 4.3 to 4.6 — None — Fracture uneven	Infusible. Becomes magnetic when heated. Gives green bead in borax after cooling. May be slightly magnetic. Opaque. Brittle. Octahedral crystals, massive	CHROMITE $FeCr_2O_4$ I
VERY SOFT		COLOR DARK GRAY	Dull	Gray or brown to black	Dark gray	1 — 2.6 — Basal — Fracture earthy	Infusible. Yields water in closed tube. Insoluble. Colors blue in cobalt nitrate test. Opaque. Brittle (clay)	KAOLINITE $Al_2Si_2O_5(OH)_4$
HARD TO VERY HARD		COMPARE HARDNESS	Adamantine	Brown to black	Gray	6.5 — 6.8 — Imperfect — Fracture uneven	Infusible. Yields metallic tin with soda on charcoal. Not magnetic. Translucent to opaque. Brittle. Prismatic crystals; granular; fibrous	CASSITERITE SnO_2 II
			Submetallic to greasy	Gray, green, brown to black	Grayish	5.5 to 6 — 6.4 to 9.7 — None — Fracture uneven or conchoidal	Infusible. Gives coating of lead oxide with soda on charcoal. Soluble in acids. Opaque. Brittle. Massive, fibrous, botryoidal	URANINITE UO_2 I
SOFT		COMPARE S.G.	Vitreous	Yellow green	Gray	6 to 7 — 3.25 to 3.5 — One basal — Fracture uneven	Fuses at 3–3.5 to a magnetic mass. Yields water when strongly heated. Opaque. Brittle. Crystals darker with parallel striations	EPIDOTE $HCa_2(Al,Fe)_3Si_3O_{13}$ V
		COMPARE S.G.	Vitreous to dull	Gray to dark brown	Gray	3.5 to 4 — 3.8 — Perfect, rhombohedral — Fracture conchoidal	Infusible. Turns black and magnetic on charcoal. Effervesces in hot acid. Translucent to near opaque. Brittle. Curved crystals	SIDERITE $FeCO_3$ III
		S.G. 1.5	Dull	Gray	Gray	.05 to 1.5 — 1.5 — — Fracture conchoidal	Infusible. Yields water in closed tube. Insoluble in acid. Transparent to opaque. Brittle. Massive, botryoidal. Earthy variety, diatomite	OPAL $SiO_2 + H_2O$
VERY SOFT		STRONG DOUBLE REFRACTION	Vitreous	White when pure	Gray to white	2 to 3 — 2.7 — Rhombohedral, perfect — Fracture conchoidal	Infusible. Effervesces in dilute, cold hydrochloric acid. Fluoresces red, pink, yellow. Strong double refraction. Transparent. Brittle	CALCITE Iceland Spar $CaCO_3$ III
		OFTEN TINTED OR DARKENED	Vitreous to dull or pearly	White when pure	Gray to white	2 to 3 — 2.7 — Rhombohedral, perfect — Fracture conchoidal	Infusible. Effervesces in dilute, cold hydrochloric acid. Transparent to nearly opaque. Often tinted or darkened. Brittle	CALCITE $CaCO_3$ III
HARD		CONCHOIDAL FRACTURE	Vitreous	Black to dark gray, red	Gray to white	6 — 2.2 to 2.8 — — Fracture conchoidal	Fuses at 3.5–4 with intumescence. Insoluble in acids. Brittle, with sharp edges	OBSIDIAN complex silicate
		PRISMATIC CRYSTALS YIELDS WATER IN CLOSED TUBE	Vitreous	Black	Gray to white	5 to 6 — 2 to 3.4 — Cleavage angle 56° and 124° — Fracture subconchoidal to uneven	Fusible with difficulty. Yields water in a closed tube. Translucent to opaque. Brittle. Prismatic crystals, fibrous, granular, massive	AMPHIBOLE Hornblende complex silicate V
VERY HARD		S.G. 3.15 TO 4.3	Vitreous to resinous	Red, brown, yellow, green, black, white	Gray to white	6.5 to 7.5 — 3.15 to 4.3 — None — Fracture uneven	Fuses at 3–3.5. Gelatinizes with HCl after fusing. Insoluble. Translucent to opaque. Brittle. Crystals 4, 6 or 8-sided, granular, massive	GARNET Pyrope complex silicate I

MINERALS WITHOUT METALLIC LUSTER
STREAK GRAY OR WHITE

TABLE 7	KEY	SPECIES	CHARACTERISTICS	HARDNESS, S.G., AND CLEAVAGE	STREAK	COLOR	LUSTER
VERY HARD	USUALLY MORE BRITTLE WITH IMPURITIES	QUARTZ Chert SiO_2 III	Infusible. Insoluble. Flake held in flame breaks up. Translucent. Brittle. Massive, botryoidal, nodular	7; None; Conchoidal fracture; 2.6 to 2.7	Gray to white	Gray, brown, black	Waxy to dull
	USUALLY DARKER IN COLOR THAN CHERT	QUARTZ Flint SiO_2 III	See above.	7; None; Conchoidal fracture; 2.6 to 2.7	Gray to white	Gray, brown, black	Waxy to dull
	S.G. 2.9 TO 3.2	TOURMALINE complex silicate III	Mostly infusible. Gelatinizes with HCl after fusion. Insoluble. Transparent to opaque. Often zoned with bands. Very brittle. Prismatic crystals, often striated	7 to 7.5; None; Fracture uneven or conchoidal; 2.9 to 3.2	Gray to white	Black, red, green, pink	Vitreous
VERY SOFT		TALC $Mg_3(OH)_2Si_4O_{10}$ V	Infusible. Insoluble. Swells, turns white, and gives violet color in cobalt nitrate test. Opaque to transparent. Sectile; plates flexible.	1 to 1.5; Basal, perfect (micaceous); Fracture uneven; 2.7 to 2.8	White	Apple green to white, gray, etc.	Pearly to dull or greasy
	COMPARE S.G.	CALCITE Chalk $CaCO_3$ III	Infusible. Effervesces in dilute, cold hydrochloric acid. Transparent to nearly opaque. Brittle	0.5 to 1.5; Fracture earthy; 2.6	White	White	Dull
		GYPSUM $CaSO_4 + H_2O$ V	Fuses at 3. Yields water in closed tube. Phosphorescent. Fluorescent yellow. Transparent to opaque. Brittle, plates flexible. Varied crystal forms, fibrous	1.5 to 2; Clinopinacoidal, perfect, two; Fracture conchoidal; 2.3	White	White, gray, brown	Pearly, silky, dull, glassy
	COLOR YELLOW	NATIVE SULFUR S IV	Burns with blue flame and odor of sulfur. Translucent. Brittle. Orthorhombic crystals, massive	1.5 to 2.5; Prismatic, basal, imperfect. Conchoidal fracture; 2.0 to 2.1	White	Yellow	Resinous
	COMPARE S.G.	BAUXITE $Al_2O_3 + 2H_2O$	Infusible. Insoluble. Colors blue in cobalt nitrate test. Opaque. Brittle. Usually massive like hard clay; pisolitic	1 to 3; None; Fracture earthy; 2.0 to 2.6	White	White, gray, red, brown	Dull
		MICA Muscovite complex silicate V	Infusible. Insoluble. Gives little water in closed tube. Transparent to translucent. Flexible, elastic plates or sheets	2 to 2.5; Basal, perfect; 2.75 to 3	White	White, light yellow, brown, pale green	Vitreous to pearly
VERY SOFT TO SOFT	TRANSPARENT SHOWS STRONG DOUBLE REFRACTION	CALCITE Iceland Spar $CaCO_3$ III	Infusible. Effervesces in dilute, cold hydrochloric acid. Fluoresces red, pink, yellow. Strong double refraction. Transparent. Brittle	2 to 3; Rhombohedral, perfect; Fracture conchoidal; 2.7	White	White when pure	Vitreous
	OFTEN TINTED OR DARKENED	CALCITE $CaCO_3$ III	Infusible. Effervesces in dilute, cold hydrochloric acid. Transparent to nearly opaque. Often tinted or darkened. Brittle	2 to 3; Rhombohedral, perfect; Fracture conchoidal; 2.7	White	White when pure	Vitreous to dull or pearly
	SOLUBLE IN WATER TASTES SALTY	HALITE NaCl I	Fuses readily. Colors flame deep yellow. Soluble in water. Tastes salty. Transparent to translucent. Brittle	2.5; Cubic, perfect; Fracture conchoidal; 2.1 to 2.6	White	White to gray or brown	Vitreous, dull when moist
	FUSES READILY COLORS FLAME YELLOW	CRYOLITE Na_3AlF_6 V	Fuses very readily, coloring flame yellow. Transparent to translucent. Almost invisible in water. Brittle	2.5; Imperfect; Fracture uneven; 3	White	White to brown	Vitreous or greasy

MINERALS WITHOUT METALLIC LUSTER
STREAK WHITE   SOFT

TABLE 8 / KEY	LUSTER	COLOR	STREAK	HARDNESS, S.G., AND CLEAVAGE	CHARACTERISTICS	SPECIES
FLEXIBLE, ELASTIC SHEETS → DARKER COLOR	Vitreous, pearly, splendent	Dark brown to black	White	2.5 to 3 — 2.7 to 3.4; Basal, perfect	Fuses on thin edges. Decomposes in hot, strong sulfuric acid. Transparent to translucent. Flexible, elastic plates or sheets	MICA Biotite complex silicate V
TRANSPARENT	Pearly to metallic on cleavage surface	Light to dark brown	White	2.5 to 3 — 2.75; Basal, perfect	Fuses with difficulty. Decomposes in hot, strong sulfuric acid. Transparent to translucent. Flexible, elastic plates or sheets	MICA Phlogopite complex silicate V
COLORS FLAME YELLOWISH GREEN INSOLUBLE IN ACIDS	Vitreous	White to bluish or brownish or reddish	White	2.5 to 3.5 — 4.3 to 4.6; Basal, prismatic, perfect (diamond shaped cleavage). Fracture uneven	Fuses at 3. Colors flame yellow green. Insoluble in acid. Reacts to sulfur test with soda. May fluoresce orange after heating. Translucent. Brittle	BARITE $BaSO_4$ IV
GREENISH COLOR FIBROUS	Silky or greasy	Green to yellow green	White	2.5 to 4 — 2.2 to 2.6; None. Fracture fibrous	Yields water in closed tube. Decomposed by hydrochloric acid. Yellow variety fluoresces cream yellow. Opaque to translucent. Flexible to sectile	ASBESTOS Chrysotile $MgSi_2O_5(OH)_4$ V
COLORS FLAME PURPLE RED	Pearly	Gray green, rose red and violet to white or pale yellow	White	2.5 to 4 — 2.7 to 3.3; Basal, perfect (micaceous). Fracture scaly	Fuses and expands. Colors flame purple red. Yields little water in closed tube. Translucent to transparent. Tough	LEPIDOLITE complex silicate V
REACTS LIKE BORAX UNDER BLOWPIPE HARDNESS 3 S.G. 1.9	Vitreous to dull	Colorless or white upon exposure to air	White	3 — 1.9; Basal, perfect. Produces long splinters. Fracture conchoidal	Reacts like borax under blowpipe but with less swelling. Surface often chalky. Transparent to translucent. Brittle	KERNITE $Na_2B_4O_7 + 4H_2O$ V
COLORS FLAME RED, CRACKLES WHEN HEATED	Vitreous	White to bluish	White	3 to 3.5 — 4; Basal, prismatic, perfect (diamond shaped cleavage). Fracture uneven	Fuses with difficulty. Colors flame red. Cracks when heated. After heating fluoresces bright green. Transparent to translucent. Brittle	CELESTITE $SrSO_4$ IV
FUSES, YIELDING METALLIC LEAD. BUBBLES IN ACID	Vitreous to adamantine	White to gray	White	3 to 3.5 — 6.5; Prismatic, imperfect. Fracture conchoidal	Fuses readily yielding metallic lead with soda on charcoal. Bubbles in acid. Transparent to translucent. Brittle	CERUSSITE $PbCO_3$ IV
FALLS TO PIECES WHEN HEATED WITH A BLOWPIPE ON CHARCOAL	Vitreous to dull	White to gray	White	3 to 4 — 2.9 to 3; Prismatic, imperfect. Fracture conchoidal	Falls to pieces when heated with a blowpipe on charcoal. Bubbles in acid. Transparent to translucent. Brittle. Fibrous	ARAGONITE $CaCO_3$ IV
FUSES EASILY YIELDS WATER IN CLOSED TUBE	Vitreous or pearly on cleavage surface	White to yellow and red	White	3.5 to 4 — 2.1 to 2.2; Perfect, one. Fracture uneven	Fuses at 2.5. Yields water in closed tube. Swells, writhes in wormlike manner when heated. Transparent to translucent. Brittle. Sheaflike crystals	STILBITE Zeolite complex silicate V
DOES NOT EFFERVESCE IN COLD, DILUTE ACID	Vitreous to dull or pearly	White to gray	White	3.5 to 4 — *2.8 to 2.9; Rhombohedral, perfect. Fracture conchoidal	Infusible. Does not effervesce in cold dilute acid. Not fluorescent. Transparent to translucent. Curved surfaces when broken. Brittle	DOLOMITE $MgCa(CO_3)_2$ III
DECREPITATES PHOSPHORESCENT WHEN GENTLY HEATED	Vitreous	White, green, violet, blue, brown, yellow	White	4 — 3 to 3.25; Octahedral, perfect	Fuses at 3. Phosphorescent when gently heated. Decrepitates. Transparent to nearly opaque. Brittle	FLUORITE CaF_2 I

* When pure

MINERALS WITHOUT METALLIC LUSTER

STREAK WHITE   VERY HARD TO HARD

TABLE 9 KEY	LUSTER	COLOR	STREAK	HARDNESS, S.G., AND CLEAVAGE	CHARACTERISTICS	SPECIES
TURNS FLAME RED YELLOW (Ca)	Vitreous to almost resinous	Green, brown, yellow, white	White	5; 3.2; Basal, imperfect. Fracture conchoidal	Infusible. Soluble in acid. Turns flame reddish yellow. Fluoresces orange when heated. Opaque. Brittle. Prismatic crystals, granular, massive	APATITE $Ca_5(Cl,F)\cdot(PO_4)_3$ III
FUSES IN CANDLE FLAME	Vitreous	White	White	5 to 5.5; 2.2; Prismatic, perfect, two cleavages. Fracture uneven across the prism	Fuses in candle flame. Yields water in a closed tube. May fluoresce orange or blue to greenish white when heated. Transparent to translucent. Brittle	NATROLITE $Na_2Al_2Si_3O_{10}+2H_2O$ IV
FUSES WITH DIFFICULTY CLEAVAGE ANGLES 56° AND 124°	Vitreous	Black	White	5 to 6; 2 to 3.4; Prismatic, 56° and 124°. Fracture subconchoidal to uneven	Fuses with difficulty. Yields water in closed tube. Translucent to opaque. Brittle. Prismatic crystals, fibrous, granular, massive	HORNBLENDE Amphibole complex silicate V
S.G. 2.71 TWIN STRIATIONS	Vitreous to pearly	Gray to greenish and reddish	White	5 to 6; 2.71; Basal, perfect. Fracture uneven	Fuses at 3.5. Translucent to near opaque. Often has bluish iridescence. Brittle	LABRADORITE Feldspar $(Na,Ca)AlSi_3O_{10}$ VI
YIELDS WATER IN CLOSED TUBE	Vitreous	White, light green to dark green	White	5 to 6; 2.9 to 3.4; Prismatic, perfect. Two cleavages	Fuses to black or white glass. Yields water in closed tube. Insoluble in acid. Transparent to opaque. Massive. One of two jade minerals	NEPHRITE Actinolite, Amphibole complex silicate V
POWDER GELATINIZES WITH HCl	Vitreous, resinous	Yellowish greenish, brownish	White	5.5; 3.9 to 4.2; Imperfect. Fracture uneven	Fuses with difficulty. Yields zinc oxide with soda on charcoal. Gelatinizes with hydrochloric acid. Fluoresces green. Translucent to opaque. Brittle. Massive	WILLEMITE Zn_2SiO_4 III
FUSES AT 2.5 AND BLACKENS	Vitreous	Red and brown to gray	White	5.5 to 6.5; 3.4 to 3.7; Prismatic, perfect with two cleavages. Fracture uneven	Fuses at 2.5. Gives amethyst bead with borax. Insoluble. Blackens on exposure. Transparent to opaque. Tough, crystals brittle. Often with brown or black spots	RHODONITE $MnSiO_3$ VI
FUSES WITH INTUMESCENCE. GLASSY	Vitreous	Black to dark gray or red	White	6; 2.2 to 2.8; Fracture conchoidal	Fuses at 3.5 to 4 with intumescence. Insoluble in acids. Brittle, with sharp edges	OBSIDIAN complex silicate
LACKS TWIN STRIATIONS ON CRYSTAL FACES	Vitreous	White, red, green, flesh color	White	6 to 6.5; 2.55; Basal, perfect. Blocky. Fracture conchoidal	Fuses at 5. Not affected by acids. Translucent to transparent. Brittle. Often very large crystals	MICROCLINE Feldspar $KAlSi_3O_8$ VII
WHEN PURE, S.G. 2.63, TWIN STRIATIONS	Vitreous to pearly	White to gray, red, green	White	6 to 6.5; *2.63; Basal, perfect. Fracture conchoidal	Fuses with difficulty (4–5). Insoluble. Transparent to translucent. Brittle. Sometimes in thin, flat crystals	ALBITE Feldspar $NaAlSi_3O_{16}$ VI
BLOCKY CLEAVAGES TWO AT 90°, ONE GOOD	Vitreous to pearly	White to gray, red, green, etc.	White	6 to 6.5; 2.5 to 2.65; Basal, perfect. Blocky at 90°. Fracture conchoidal	Fuses with difficulty. Insoluble. Not fluorescent after blowpiping. Transparent to opaque. Brittle. Short prismatic crystals	ORTHOCLASE Feldspar $KAlSi_3O_8$ VI
S.G. 2.76 TWIN STRIATIONS	Vitreous	White, gray, red, brown, green	White	6 to 6.5; *2.76; Basal, perfect, two at right angles. Fracture conchoidal	Fuses at 5. Insoluble. Transparent to translucent. Brittle. Rare	ANORTHITE Feldspar $CaAl_2Si_2O_8$ V
S.G. ABOVE 3 PURPLISH RED FLAME	Vitreous to pearly	White to gray and buff, green	White	6.5 to 7; 3.1 to 3.2; Perfect, prismatic 87° and 93°. Splinters. Fracture uneven * When pure	Fuses at 3.5 with red purple flame. Insoluble. Fluoresces orange. Transparent to opaque. Brittle. Long, striated crystals	SPODUMENE Pyroxene $LiAlSi_2O_6$ V

COMPARE S.G.

FUSES WITH DIFFICULTY

TABLE 10

MINERALS WITHOUT METALLIC LUSTER
STREAK WHITE — VERY HARD TO ADAMANTINE

KEY	LUSTER	COLOR	STREAK	HARDNESS, S.G. AND CLEAVAGE	CHARACTERISTICS	SPECIES
FUSES, NOT AFFECTED BY ACIDS	Subvitreous to silky	Green to white; often spotty or patterned	White	6.5 to 7 3.3 to 3.5 — Prismatic. Two cleavages. Fracture splintery	Fuses readily. Not affected by acids. Colors sodium flame yellow. Tough. Massive, fibrous, granular	JADEITE Jade $NaAlSi_2O_6$
INFUSIBLE GREEN CRYSTALLINE GRAINS	Vitreous	Green	White	6.5 to 7 3.3 to 3.4 — One fair, one poor. Fracture conchoidal	Infusible. Gelatinizes with hydrochloric acid. May be magnetic. Transparent to translucent. Brittle	OLIVINE Chrysolite $(MgFe)_2SiO_4$ IV
FUSES GELATINIZES WITH HCl AFTER FUSION	Vitreous to resinous	Red, brown, yellow, green, black, white	White	6.5 to 7.5 3.15 to 4.3 — None. Fracture uneven	Fuses at 3–3.5. Gelatinizes with HCl after fusing. Insoluble. Translucent to opaque. Brittle. Crystals 4, 6, or 8-sided, granular, massive	GARNET Pyrope complex silicate I
S.G. ABOVE 4, SQUARE PRISMS AND PYRAMIDS RARELY IRREGULAR GRAINS	Adamantine	Colorless, brown, gray, blue, violet, reddish, green	Colorless	6.5 to 7.5 4.2 to 4.8 — Two cleavages poor. Fracture conchoidal to uneven	Infusible. Insoluble. Colors whiten when heated and glow briefly only once. Fluorescent yellow orange. Transparent to opaque. Brittle	ZIRCON SiO_2 II
MICROSCOPIC CRYSTALS ARRANGED IN SLENDER, BANDED, PARALLEL FIBERS	Waxy	White, red, green, blue, brown, gray, black	White	7 2.6 to 2.65 — None. Fracture conchoidal	Infusible. Insoluble. Flake held in flame breaks up. Dissolves with effervescence with soda on platinum wire. Translucent. Brittle	QUARTZ Chalcedony SiO_2 III
WITH WAVY COLOR BANDS	Waxy or vitreous	Red, brown, white, blue, yellow, gray, green	White	7 2.6 to 2.65 — None. Fracture conchoidal	See above	QUARTZ Agate SiO_2 III
WITH STRAIGHT COLOR BANDS	Waxy or vitreous	White, gray, brown, red, green	White	7 2.6 to 2.65 — None. Fracture conchoidal	See above	QUARTZ Onyx SiO_2 III
TRANSPARENT SIX-SIDED CRYSTALS	Vitreous	Colorless	White	7 2.65 to 2.7 — None. Fracture conchoidal	See above	QUARTZ Rock Crystal SiO_2 III
PURPLE OR VIOLET COLOR	Vitreous	Purple color due to traces of manganese or iron	White	7 2.65 to 2.7 — None. Fracture conchoidal	See above	QUARTZ Amethyst SiO_2 III

S.G. NOT ABOVE 2.7

HARDNESS NOT BELOW 7

MINERALS WITHOUT METALLIC LUSTER
STREAK WHITE

TABLE 11	KEY	LUSTER	COLOR	STREAK	HARDNESS, S.G., AND CLEAVAGE	CHARACTERISTICS	SPECIES
VERY HARD / S.G. NOT ABOVE 2.7	LIKE GLASS	Vitreous	Gray, black, brownish	White	7 · None · Fracture conchoidal · 2.65 to 2.7	Infusible. Insoluble. Flake held in flame breaks up. Dissolves with effervescence with soda on platinum wire. Translucent. Brittle	QUARTZ Smoky SiO_2 III
WAXY TO DULL	MORE BRITTLE OFTEN WITH IMPURITIES	Waxy to dull	Gray, black, brown	White	7 · None · Fracture conchoidal · 2.6 to 2.7	See above	QUARTZ Chert SiO_2 III
	USUALLY DARKER IN COLOR THAN CHERT, COMPACT	Waxy to dull	Gray, black, brown	White	7 · None · Fracture conchoidal · 2.6 to 2.7	See above	QUARTZ Flint SiO_2 III
	STRIATED PRISMS, PYROELECTRIC, SHOWS DICHROISM, S.G. 2.9-3.2	Vitreous	Black, red, pink, green, brown	White	7 to 7.5 · None · Fracture uneven or conchoidal · 2.9 to 3.2	Mostly infusible. Insoluble. Gelatinizes with HCl after fusion. Transparent to opaque. Often zoned with bands. Very brittle. Prismatic crystals	TOURMALINE Complex silicate III
	S.G. BELOW 3	Vitreous	Greenish to bluish and yellow green	White	7.5 to 8 · Basal, poor · Fracture conchoidal · 2.6 to 2.8	Infusible. Does not decrepitate violently. Insoluble. Transparent to translucent. Brittle. Large, long, prismatic crystals, striated	BERYL $Be_3Al_2(SiO_6)_3$ III
HARDNESS ADAMANTINE	CRYSTALS PRISMS, CLEAVAGE BASAL, PERFECT	Vitreous	Yellow, white, blue, red, green	White	8 · Basal, perfect, one cleavage · Fracture conchoidal, uneven · 3.4 to 3.65	Infusible. Insoluble. Gives blue color in cobalt nitrate test. Transparent to opaque. Brittle	TOPAZ $Al_2SiO_4F_2$ IV
	HARDNESS 9, S.G. ABOUT 4	Vitreous to adamantine	Gray, brown, red, yellow, blue, black, pink	White	9 · Basal, rhombic parting · Fracture conchoidal · 3.95 to 4.1	Infusible. Insoluble. Powder gives blue color in cobalt nitrate test. Transparent to opaque. Brittle to tough	CORUNDUM Al_2O_3 III
	HARDNESS 10—SCRATCHES CORUNDUM	Adamantine	White, colorless, gray, blue, pink, black	White	10 · Octahedral, perfect · Fracture conchoidal · 3.5	Infusible. Insoluble. Often fluorescent. Translucent to opaque. Brittle. Crystals, grains, pebbles	DIAMOND C I

GLOSSARY

aa. Block lava.

absolute humidity. The weight of water vapor actually contained in a given quantity of air.

accretion. The growth of nonliving things by the addition of molecules around a center.

acids. Compounds which contain hydrogen and which turn blue litmus paper red.

adiabatic change. A temperature change that takes place without the addition or loss of heat to or from the surroundings.

advection fog. A fog produced by the horizontal movement of air over a cool surface.

agonic line. A line connecting locations of zero magnetic variation.

air mass. A large body of air that has about the same temperature and humidity throughout.

algae. Green water-dwelling thallophytes (a potential source of oxygen in space vehicles).

alluvial plain. A plain formed by the deposition of materials from rivers and streams.

altimeter. An instrument used to measure altitude.

amber. Fossil resin.

amorphous. Not crystalline; having no orderly arrangement of the molecules.

anemometer. An instrument to measure wind velocity.

aneroid barometer. A type of barometer which operates without the use of liquids.

angular unconformity. An unconformity in which the lower rock layers are tilted, folded, or faulted and the upper rock layers are horizontal.

annular eclipse. A type of partial eclipse of the sun in which a ring of light is seen around the edge of the moon.

anticline. The crest or upfold of a rock fold.

anticyclone. A large mass of high-pressure air, with winds moving out from it in a clockwise whirl; a high.

aphelion. The point on the earth's orbit farthest from the sun.

apogee. The point in a satellite's orbit farthest from the object around which it revolves.

apparent solar time. Time as determined by the apparent position of the sun.

aquifer. A water-bearing layer of porous rock.

arête. A sharp, narrow ridge separating two cirques or glacial valleys.

artesian well. A well penetrating through impervious rock to a water-bearing layer.

artifacts. Structures or implements made by man.

asteroid. One of the many tiny planets between the orbits of Mars and Jupiter.

astronautics. The scientific exploration of space.

atoll. A roughly circular coral reef which encloses a lagoon.

atom. The smallest subdivision of an element that has all the properties of that element.

aurora. Streamers of glowing ionized gases in the earth's atmosphere.

axes of a crystal. Imaginary lines running from the center of a crystal face to the center of the opposite face.

axis of fold. An imaginary line running along the top of an anticline or along the bottom of a syncline.

barchan. A crescent-shaped dune.

barograph. A recording barometer.

barometer. An instrument to measure air pressure.

barrier reef. A long narrow coral reef some distance from the shore.

base level. The level of the body of water into which a stream flows.

basement complex. The earliest rocks of the earth.

bases. Compounds which contain a combination of one atom of oxygen and one atom of hydrogen, called the hydroxide (OH) group; they turn red litmus blue.

batholith. A large mass of intrusive igneous rock, whose lower limit is unknown.

bead test. A color test in which a borax bead formed on a platinum wire loop is used to determine the chemical makeup of minerals.

613

bedding planes. Surfaces along which rock layers part readily, by which one layer may be distinguished from another.

bedrock. The unweathered solid rock of the earth's crust.

binary stars. Pairs of stars rotating around a common center.

binomial nomenclature. A system of naming living things using two Latin terms, the genus and species.

block mountains. Mountains that result from faulting.

body waves. Earthquake waves that travel through the body of the earth; primary and secondary waves.

braided stream. A stream whose channel is filled with deposits that split it into many small channels.

Brunton pocket transit. An instrument used to measure dip, strike, etc. in rock outcrops.

butte. A flat-topped, steep-walled hill, usually a remnant of horizontal beds, smaller and narrower than a mesa.

calcareous. Composed of calcium carbonate.

caldera. A basinlike depression formed by the destruction of a volcanic cone.

carbonation. The chemical combination of substances with carbon dioxide.

carbon dioxide cycle. A series of processes by which the balance of carbon dioxide and oxygen in the atmosphere is maintained.

carbonization. A process in which remains of living things are partly decomposed, leaving a residue of carbon.

carnivore. A flesh-eating animal.

celestial navigation. The determination of direction and location by observation of celestial objects.

celestial north pole. That point in the sky directly over the earth's north pole.

Celsius. See centigrade.

centigrade. A temperature scale on which water boils at 100° and freezes at 0°. Also called Celsius.

Cepheid variable. A type of variable star whose distance from the earth can be determined.

chemical compound. A substance formed by the combination of two or more different elements in a definite weight relationship.

chromosphere. The sun's surface atmosphere, made up of glowing gases.

chronometer. An extremely accurate clock generally used for navigational purposes.

cinder cone. Cone formed by the explosive type of volcanic eruption; it has a narrow base and steep, symmetrical slopes of interlocking, angular cinders.

circumpolar whirl. High-altitude winds moving around the earth from west to east.

cirque. A bowl-shaped depression in a mountainside, formed at the head of a valley glacier.

cirrus clouds. A family of high-altitude clouds.

cleavage. The breaking of a mineral so that it yields definite flat surfaces.

clinometer. A pendulum or mounted level that shows the degree of tilt from the horizontal.

cloud seeding. Methods of artificially producing precipitation from clouds.

coastal plain. An exposed part of the sea floor, usually consisting of stream- or wave-deposited sediments.

cold front. A front at which a colder air mass thrusts under a warmer air mass.

comet. A member of the solar system, composed of rocks and frozen gases and having a very eccentric orbit.

complex mountains. Mountains that result from a combination of faulting, folding, and volcanic action.

composite cone. Cone formed by intermediate type of volcanic eruption, consisting of alternate layers of cinders and lava.

conchoidal fracture. Shell-like surface produced by breaking certain minerals.

condensation nucleus. A center around which a cloud droplet is formed.

conic projection. A map based on projection of the globe on the surface of a cone.

connate water. Water bound within tiny cavities in sedimentary rock.

constellation. An apparent grouping of stars in a recognizable pattern.

constructional landforms. Landforms that have been built up by forces acting beneath the earth's surface.

continental shelf. Relatively shallow ocean floor bordering a continental land mass.

continental slope. A zone of rapidly increasing depth in the sea between the edge of the continental shelf and the deeper ocean basin.

contour interval. The difference in elevation between two successive contour lines.

contour lines. Lines on a map joining points on the earth having the same elevation.

coprolites. Fossil excrement.

cordillera. A belt of mountain systems.

core. The very dense interior part of the earth.

Coriolis effect. The tendency of moving objects to veer to the right in the northern hemisphere and to the left in the southern hemisphere.

corona. A halo of faintly glowing gases outside the chromosphere of the sun; usually visible only during a solar eclipse.

crest. The ridge of a wave, elevated above the surrounding water.

crevasse. A deep crack in a glacier.

crystal. A mineral form caused by the arrangement of atoms, ions, or molecules in definite geometric patterns.

crust. The outer layer of the solid earth.

cumulus clouds. A family of clouds that resemble balls of wool, usually having flat bases.

cyclone. A large mass of low-pressure air, with winds moving into it in a counterclockwise whirl; a low.

dead reckoning. A method of navigation depending mainly upon determination of speed and direction.

decomposition. The breaking down of a compound into elements or simpler compounds.

deflation. Blowing away of loose soil and rock particles by wind.

deformation. The result of diastrophism as shown in the tilting, bending, or breaking of rock layers.

delta. A triangular deposit at the mouth of a stream.

density. The weight per unit volume of any material.

density current. A current caused by the sinking of water as it increases in density.

desert pavement. A layer of close-fitting larger stones left on the desert floor after the lighter material has blown away.

dessicated. Dried out, mummified.

dew point. The temperature at which a given quantity of air reaches 100 percent relative humidity.

diastrophism. Movement of the solid parts of the earth.

diatoms. Algae with cell walls of silica.

dike. Solidified magma in vertical cracks or fissures.

dip. The angle of inclination of a rock bed or a fault surface, measured in degrees.

disconformity. Parallel horizontal rock layers separated by an erosional surface.

dissected. Cut up by agents of erosion.

distributaries. The small streams by which a main stream empties across a delta.

divide. The ridges or regions of high ground that separate the drainage basins of streams.

doldrums. Belt of calm air under lower pressure near the equator.

dome mountains. Mountains that form when sedimentary beds are uplifted into broad, circular domes.

Doppler effect. The apparent effect on a train of waves if there is relative motion between the source and the receiver.

double replacement. The exchange of parts of two compounds to form two new compounds.

drift. A general term for the material deposited by a glacier or by glacial meltwater.

drumlin. A long, low mound of till, rounded at one end and pointed at the other.

dune. A hill or ridge of wind-blown sand.

earthshine. Illumination of the darker portion of the moon by reflection of light from the earth.

eclipse. The cutting off of light from one celestial body by another.

electrons. Electrically negative parts of atoms.

element. A substance that cannot be changed by ordinary means into a simpler substance.

ephemeris. A type of almanac useful in determining positions of celestial bodies.

epicenter. The point or line on the earth's surface directly above the center of origin of an earthquake.

equation of time. The difference between apparent solar time and mean solar time on any particular date.

equinox. A time when the sun is directly overhead at noon on the equator.

erosion. The removal of soil and rock fragments by natural agents.

erosional unconformity. A disconformity.

erratic. A large boulder, deposited by glacial action, whose composition is different from that of the native bedrock.

escape velocity. The speed a rocket must reach in order to leave the earth's immediate gravitational field.

esker. A winding ridge of stratified drift deposited by streams running under or through glacial ice.

estuary. A shallow bay extending inland; a drowned river valley.

exfoliation. The splitting off of scales or flakes of rock as a result of weathering.

exosphere. The layer of atmosphere, above the ionosphere, that blends off into outer space.

extrusive rocks. Igneous rocks formed when magma flows out over the earth's surface.

fall line. Region where a coastal plain adjoins the oldland, characterized by numerous waterfalls.

fault. A fracture in a rock surface, along which there is displacement of the broken surfaces.

faulting. The movement of rock layers along a break.

fault scarp. A cliff formed at the surface of a fault.

fauna. The forms of animal life of a particular region or time period.

Ferrel's Law. The mathematical statement of the Coriolis effect.

fetch. The extent of open water across which a wind blows.

fiord. A drowned glacial valley.

fissure. An open fracture in a rock surface.

floe. A drifting section of arctic ice.

flood plain. The part of a stream valley which is covered with water during flood stage.

flora. The forms of plant life of a particular region or time period.

fluorescence. A luminescence given off by substances that are irradiated by ultraviolet or x-rays.

focus. The spot in the earth which is the center of origin of an earthquake; the source of the earthquake.

folded mountains. Mountains that result from the folding of rocks.

foliation. In minerals, structure showing thin leaves or layers; arrangement of minerals within a rock in bands or layers.

foot wall. The underside rock wall of an inclined fault.

fossil. Preserved evidences of ancient life on the earth.

fracture. The way in which a mineral breaks when it does not yield along a cleavage or parting surface.

fringing reef. A coral reef closely attached to the shore.

front. The boundary between two air masses.

frost wedging. Prying off of fragments of rock by expansion of freezing water in crevices.

fumaroles. Fissures or holes in volcanic regions, from which steam and other volcanic gases are emitted.

galaxy. An astronomical system composed of billions of stars.

gangue. Waste minerals of little commercial value.

gastroliths. Fossil gizzard stones of reptiles.

geanticline. Very broad upfold in the earth's crust, extending for hundreds of miles.

geode. A hollow stone, usually lined or filled with mineral matter, formed by deposition in a rock cavity.

geologic revolutions. Periods of marked crustal movement separating one geologic era from another.

geosyncline. Very broad downfold in the earth's crust, extending for hundreds of miles.

geyser. A hot spring which periodically erupts steam and hot water.

gnomonic projection. A map based on projection of the globe on a plane surface.

graben. A trough developed when parallel faults allow the blocks between them to sink, forming broad valleys flanked on each side by steep fault scarps. Also called *rift valley*.

gradient. The difference in elevation between the head and mouth of a stream.

gravity fault. A normal fault.

great circle. Any circle drawn on the earth's surface that divides the sphere in half.

greenhouse effect. The process by which the atmosphere traps the sun's radiations.

Greenwich time. Time as measured on the prime meridian, used to determine longitude.

ground water. Water which penetrates into spaces within the rocks of the earth's crust.

gullying. A type of erosion in which deep channels form as water flows down a slope.

gyrocompass. A type of compass in which direction is determined by the gyroscopic action of a spinning wheel.

hachures. A method of indicating relief on a map; short straight lines drawn in the direction that water would take in flowing down the slopes.

hail. Ice pellets formed by the successive freezing of layers of water.

half-life. The time interval during which half of a given amount of radioactive material disintegrates.

hanging valley. The valley of a tributary which enters the main valley from a considerable height above the main stream bed.

hanging wall. The topside rock wall of an inclined fault.

hardness (H). The resistance of a mineral to scratching.

heat equator. A line on a map joining places on the earth that have the highest average temperature.

hook. A curved spit.

horse latitudes. A belt of calm air under greater pressure, about 30° north and south of the equator.

horst. An elevated area formed between parallel faults by uplift.

humidity. Water vapor in the air.

humus. The organic matter in the soil, produced by decomposition of plant and animal materials.

hurricane. A destructive tropical storm over the Atlantic Ocean; such storms over the Pacific Ocean are called *typhoons*.

hydration. The chemical combination of substances with water.

hydrologic cycle. The continuous process by which water is evaporated from the sea, precipitated over the land, and eventually returned to the sea.

hydrosphere. The earth's envelope of water.

hygrometer. An instrument to measure humidity.

igneous rocks. Rocks formed by the solidification of magma.

inclination. The tilting of a planet's axis in relation to its orbit around the sun.

index fossils. Fossils that are found only in rocks of one particular period of geologic time; guide fossils.

index of refraction. A measure of a substance's ability to bend or refract light rays.

inertial guidance. A completely self-contained system of electronic navigation.

inferior mirage. A type of mirage in which the observer seems to be above the image in the mirage.

insolation. The total energy received by the earth from the sun's radiations.

international date line. An imaginary line at about 180° longitude; when it is crossed, standard time changes by 24 hours forward or backward.

intrusive rocks. Rocks formed when magma solidifies among other rocks below the earth's surface; also called *plutonic rocks*.

invertebrates. Animals without backbones.

ion. An atom or radical that carries an electric charge.

ionosphere. The layer of the atmosphere above the stratosphere, containing molecules of ionized gases.

island arc. Chains of islands lying close to the edges of continents.

isobar. A line drawn on a weather map connecting locations with the same atmospheric pressure.

isogonic line. A line connecting locations of equal magnetic variation.

isoseismal. Lines connecting equal points of earthquake wave intensity. They are concentric to the epicenter.

isostasy. The state of balance of the earth's crust.

isotherm. A line on a map joining places that record the same temperature.

isotopes. Atoms of the same element which differ from each other in atomic weight.

jet streams. Swift, high-altitude winds at the edges of the circumpolar whirls.

Jolly balance. A spiral spring balance used to determine specific gravity of minerals.

joint. A fracture in a rock surface.

kame. A mound of stratified drift deposited by streams running off a glacier.

karst topography. A type of landscape characteristic of some limestone regions, in which drainage is mostly by means of underground streams in caverns.

kettle. A depression remaining after the melting of large blocks of ice buried in glacial drift.

laccolith. A domed mass of igneous rock formed by intrusion beneath other rocks.

lacustrine plains. Lake plains, formed by the emergence of a lake floor by either uplift or drainage.

lagoon. The body of water between an offshore bar and the mainland.

lapilli. Small fragments of volcanic rock thrown out during an eruption.

latitude. Location measured in degrees north and south of the equator.

lava. Liquid rock material that flows out on the surface of the earth from sources below.

leaching. Removal of minerals from soil and rock by solution as water seeps down from the surface.

levee. The raised bank of a stream.

light year. The distance that light travels in one year.

limb. The darker outer edge of the sun.

lithosphere. The solid part of the earth.

lode. A system of veins that is rich enough in mineral ores to be profitably mined.

loess. An extensive deposit of wind-blown silt.

longitude. Location measured in degrees east or west of the prime meridian.

longitudinal waves. Surface earthquake waves; long waves.

Loran. A system of electronic navigation.

luster (L). The appearance of the surface of a mineral in reflected light.

magma. Molten rock materials below the earth's surface.

magmatic water. Water released from rock by the heat of volcanic activity.

magnetic variation. The difference, measured in degrees, between true north and magnetic north; also called *declination*.

magnitude. The apparent brightness of a star in comparison with other stars.

mantle. The thicker, more dense part of the earth beneath the crust.

mantle rock. The layers of loose weathered rock lying over solid bedrock.

map projection. A representation of the globe, or a portion of it, on a flat surface.

massive. In masses without definite form.

massive rocks. Rocks which are unstratified.

mass-wasting. Erosional processes caused chiefly by gravity.

meanders. Wide curves typical of well-developed streams.

mean solar time. Time as measured by the average position of the sun.

Mercator projection. A map projection of the globe on a cylinder.

meridian. An imaginary line from pole to pole, crossing the equator at a right angle.

mesa. A large, wide, flat-topped hill, usually a remnant of horizontal beds.

metal. An element whose oxide unites with water to form a base.

metalloid. An element that has some of the properties of both metals and nonmetals.

metamorphic rocks. Rocks that have been changed from their original form by great heat and pressure.

meteor. A rocklike particle in space; one of the smallest members of the solar system.

meteoric water. That part of the ground water resulting from rain and snow.

meteorite. A meteor which actually strikes the earth's surface.

meteorology. The science of the atmosphere.

mid-ocean ridges. A series of underwater mountain ranges in the ocean basins.

millibar. A unit of air pressure used in international weather observations.

mineral. Chemical compounds or uncombined elements found in rocks.

mirage. An optical illusion caused by refraction of light as it passes through air layers of varying densities.

Mohorovicic discontinuity (Moho). The zone of contact between the crust and the mantle.

Mohs' scale. A numerical scale of hardness represented by ten minerals, ranging in hardness from 1 (talc) to 10 (diamond).

molecule. The smallest particle of a substance that can exist and still show the properties of the substance.

monadnocks. Isolated hills or mountains of resistant rocks rising above the general level of a peneplane.

monoclinal ridge. A ridge formed by a simple, steplike bend in horizontal beds of rock.

monsoon. Seasonal wind that is more pronounced over large continental areas near the equator.

moraine. A ridge or mound of boulders, gravel, sand, and clay carried on or deposited by a glacier.

mudflow. The movement of a large mass of mud and rock debris down a valley as a result of heavy rains.

mud torrents. Thick streams of mud formed when condensed water vapor mixes with volcanic ash and dust.

nautical mile. A distance equal to one minute of latitude; about 1.15 statute miles.

neap tides. Lower than usual tides produced when the sun and moon are at right angles.

nebula. A cloud of gases or dust in space.

neutrons. The electrically neutral parts of atoms.

névé. Granular ice formed from accumulated snow which later becomes glacial ice.

nimbus clouds. A family of clouds, usually producing precipitation.

nitrogen cycle. The complex series of actions by which the nitrogen content of the atmosphere is maintained.

nonmetal. An element whose oxide unites with water to form an acid.

normal fault. A fault with a hanging wall that has dropped down in relation to the footwall because of tension; the surface is lengthened. Also called *gravity fault*.

normal lapse rate. The usual rate of temperature decrease with altitude in the troposphere.

nova. A star which suddenly becomes many times brighter than normal.

nuclear fission. A nuclear reaction in which heavy atoms split to form lighter nuclei.

nuclear fusion. A nuclear reaction in which lighter-weight particles combine to form heavier nuclei.

nucleus (of an atom). The central part of the atom, containing most of the mass of the atom.

occluded front. A type of weather front created when an advancing cold front overtakes a warm front.

oceanography. The scientific study of the sea and its characteristics.

offset. Displaced. (In vertical faulting, the layers on one side of the fault are displaced (offset) so that they are no longer continuous with those on the other side.)

offshore bar. A sand bar more or less parallel to the mainland.

ore. A mixture of minerals containing at least one substance which can be profitably recovered.

outwash plains. Plains formed by the deposition of materials washed out from the edges of a glacier.

oxbow lake. A lake formed by the isolation of a meander from the main stream.

oxidation. The chemical combination of substances with oxygen.

oxide. A compound which consists of an element combined with oxygen alone.

ozone layer. A region in the lower part of the ionosphere containing large amounts of ozone.

pahoehoe lava. Lava that has solidified with a smooth, ropy, or billowy appearance.

paleontology. The science which deals with the study of fossils.

parallel of latitude. An imaginary line drawn on the earth's surface parallel to the equator.

parasitic cones. Volcanic cones developed at openings some distance below the main vent.

peneplane. The flat surface that remains after the wearing down of landforms by the agents of weathering and erosion.

penumbra. The lighter outer part of a shadow.

perigee. The point of a satellite's orbit nearest to the object around which it revolves.

perihelion. The point on the earth's orbit nearest the sun.

permeability. The degree to which water can penetrate and pass through rock.

petrifaction. A process in which the original substance of a fossil is replaced by mineral matter.

petrology. The scientific study of rocks.

phosphorescence. The continued giving off of light rays from certain minerals after exposure to ultraviolet light.

photosphere. A layer of brilliantly glowing gases beneath the chromosphere, source of most of the radiant energy from the sun.

physiography. The branch of geology that deals with the earth's surface features.

pillow lava. A basaltic lava that develops a structure resembling a pile of pillows when it solidifies under water.

pitch. The angle between the axis of a fold and the horizontal plane.

pitching fold. Folds whose axes slant downward at each end.

placer deposit. Deposits of minerals in the gravels of stream beds.

plain. A region of horizontal rock layers which has low relief due to a comparatively low elevation.

planetary circulation. The movement of the atmosphere over the entire earth.

planetesimal theory. The theory that the planets of the solar system were formed by the clumping together of smaller bodies.

plastic deformation. The folding or flowing of solid rock under conditions of great heat and pressure.

plateau. A region of horizontal rock layers which has high relief due to higher elevation.

plutonic rocks. See *intrusive rocks.*

polar easterlies. Weak easterly planetary winds near the poles.

Polaris. The star very near to the celestial north pole.

polarized light. Light that vibrates in one plane rather than in all planes.

porphyry. A mineral texture of fairly large crystals set in a mass of very fine crystals.

pothole. A rounded depression in the rock of a stream bed.

precipitation. Moisture that condenses and falls from the air. Also, separation of an insoluble substance from a solution.

primary ore deposits. Mineral deposits that develop by crystallization of elements and compounds in magma.

primary waves. The first waves of an earthquake, having a speed of 3.4 to 8.5 miles per second; one of two body waves.

prime meridian. The 0° longitude line passing through Greenwich.

protons. The electrically positive parts of atoms.

pseudofossils. Rock structures superficially resembling fossils but not made by prehistoric organisms.

psychrometer. A hygrometer that uses a wet-and-dry bulb thermometer.

radar. A short-wave radio device that can be used to locate and track storms.

radial symmetry. A body plan like a star or wheel.

radiation. The process by which energy is given off in the form of rays.

radiation fog. A fog formed as a result of radiation heat loss by the earth. Also called *ground fog.*

radical. A group of atoms which act as a single atom in a reaction.

radioactivity. The spontaneous breakdown of uranium and certain other elements to produce invisible radiations.

radiolarians. Protozoans which secrete silicious shells of intricate design.

radiosonde. A set of electronic instruments that record and broadcast temperature, pressure, and humidity conditions at high altitudes.

radio telescope. An electronic device that focuses radio waves from outer space.

red shift. A shift in the spectral lines in the light from distant galaxies, caused by their receding motion.

refraction. The bending of a water wave when it approaches the shore at an angle, caused by the slowing down of the part that reaches shallow water first.

rejuvenation. Any action which tends to increase the gradient of a stream.

relative humidity. The ratio between water vapor actually in the air and the maximum possible amount at a given temperature.

relief. The irregularity in elevation of parts of the earth's surface.

replacement. The formation of mineral replicas of organic remains by the exchange of minerals for cell contents.

residual boulders. Large rock fragments formed in place by weathering of the solid bedrock.

residual soil. Decomposed bedrock material remaining on the surface in the area where it was formed.

resin. A sticky liquid that flows from wounds in trees and hardens in air.

reverse fault. A fault with a hanging wall that has been pushed up over the foot wall by compression; the surface is shortened. Also called *thrust fault*.

revolution. The movement of a celestial body in its orbit. See also *geologic revolution*.

rift valley. See *graben*.

rip currents. Swift currents running away from the shore through lines of breakers.

rock glacier. An accumulation of rocky material moving slowly down a valley in the manner of a glacier.

roche moutonée. A rounded and smoothed rock projection, shaped by glacial action.

rotation. The turning of a celestial body on its axis.

salts. Compounds which contain a metal and a nonmetal or a nonmetallic group. Most are neutral to litmus paper.

satellite. Any celestial object that revolves around a larger object; a natural or artificial moon.

scale. The mathematical comparison between actual distance and distance on a particular map.

seamount. An underwater volcanic peak.

secondary ore deposits. Mineral deposits composed of materials derived from rocks that have been broken down by weathering.

secondary waves. The second type of earthquake wave, having a speed of 2 to 2.5 miles per second; one of two body waves.

sedimentary rocks. Rocks formed in layers from materials deposited by water, wind, ice, or other agents.

seismogram. The graphic record of earthquake waves which indicates the time, length, distance, direction, and intensity of an earthquake.

seismograph. An instrument to detect and measure movements of the earth's crust.

sextant. An instrument used to determine elevation of celestial bodies above the horizon.

shadow zone. A region on the earth's surface where a particular earthquake wave cannot easily be detected.

sheet wash. A type of erosion in which water strips away exposed topsoil slowly and evenly on a slope.

shield cone. Cone with a broad base and gentle slope, formed by the quiet type of volcanic eruption and composed of successive layers of lava. Also called *lava dome*.

sidereal time. Time based on the actual rotation period of the earth.

sidereal year. The time required for the earth to complete one revolution with respect to the stars.

silica. Silicon dioxide, quartz.

sill. Solidified magma in horizontal rock formations.

silt. Soil particles intermediate in size between clay particles and sand grains.

sink. A depression in the earth's surface formed by the collapse of the roof of an underground cavern.

sleet. Ice pellets formed when rain falls through a layer of freezing air.

slumping. A minor landslide involving only a small amount of loose mantle material.

soil creep. Slow movement of a mass of soil down a slope, caused by the soil's own weight.

solar flare. An unusually bright cloud of gases erupting from the sun, lasting for a few hours.

solar prominence. A streamer of glowing gas extending thousands of miles into the sun's atmosphere.

solar system. The sun and the celestial objects that revolve around it.

solstice. A time when the sun seems to reverse its apparent movement north or south of the equator.

solution. A type of mixture in which two or more substances are so thoroughly mixed that the particles of each substance are the smallest that can exist freely.

spatter cones. Small cones that form in lava fields away from the main vent. Lava is spattered out of them through holes in a thin crust.

specific gravity (SG). A number that compares the density of a substance with that of water.

spectrograph. A type of spectroscope which makes a photograph record of the spectrum of an object viewed through a telescope.

spectroscope. An instrument that separates a beam of light into its various component colors.

spectrum. The band of colors seen when light is separated by a prism.

spit. A sand bar extending outward from the shore.

spring tides. Higher than usual tides produced when the moon and sun are in line.

squall line. A long line of heavy thunderstorms often advancing just ahead of a fast-moving cold front.

stack. An isolated column of rock left standing as waves erode a shoreline.

stalactite. A stony projection from the roof of a cavern, formed of minerals deposited from dripping water.

stalagmite. A raised deposit on the floor of a cavern, formed by minerals deposited from dripping water.

standard time. Time determined by division of the earth's surface into 24 time zones, whose centers are approximately 15 degrees apart in longitude.

station model. A group of symbols on a weather map describing the weather conditions at a particular location.

steppes. Regions bordering the tropical deserts, often extending into the middle latitudes.

strata. Rock layers or beds.

stratified rocks. Rocks which occur in parallel layers.

stratigraphy. The study of rock layers.

stratopause. The top boundary of the stratosphere.

stratosphere. The layer of the atmosphere above the troposphere, in which the temperature remains fairly constant.

stratovolcanoes. Volcanoes having cones of alternate layers of lava and solid fragments.

stratus clouds. A family of clouds that form in layers.

streak. The color of a thin layer of the finely powdered mineral.

stream piracy. The diversion of water of one stream into another.

striae. Scratches on the surface of rocks resulting from the movement of glacial ice.

strike. The direction of a line along the edge of an inclined bed where it meets the horizontal plane. The strike is always at right angles to the dip.

structural geology. The study of rocks and their relationships.

subpolar low. A belt of lower air pressure at about 60° north and south latitudes.

subsidence. Sinking of the earth's crust.

subsoil. A layer of weathered rock lying below the topsoil and lacking in organic matter.

substitution. The replacement of one element by another in a compound; single replacement.

superior mirage. A type of mirage in which the observer seems to be below the image in the mirage. Also called *looming*.

syncline. The trough or downfold of a rock fold.

synthesis. The formation of a compound by a combination of elements or more simple compounds.

taiga. A type of vegetation characteristic of subarctic climates.

talus. A mass of rock debris at the base of a steep mountain or cliff.

tarn. A lake formed in a glacial cirque.

tectonic earthquakes. Earthquakes that are the result of crustal movements such as faulting.

temperature inversion. An unusual condition in which the layer of air at the surface is colder than the layer above it.

tension. A stress on rocks caused by the pulling apart of the rock masses of the earth.

thermocline. A zone of rapid temperature change usually found near the surface of bodies of water.

thermograph. A recording thermometer.

thermonuclear reaction. A nuclear fusion reaction taking place at high temperature.

thrust. Horizontal movement of the earth's crust.

thrust fault. See *reverse fault.*

tidal bore. A wave which passes up a river from the sea as the tide rises.

tidal oscillations. Very slow rocking motions in parts of the oceans, occurring in response to the tidal bulges.

till. Glacial deposits which have not been stratified or sorted by water action.

topographic map. A map showing surface features of a portion of the earth.

topography. The physical features of a region.

tornado. A relatively small, destructive middle-latitude storm, usually originating over the land.

trade winds. Planetary winds blowing generally toward the equator in tropical areas.

traprock. General term for various volcanic rocks useful for building roads.

trenches. Deep fissure on the ocean floor, caused by faulting.

tributary. A stream which flows into a larger one.

tropical year. The time from one vernal equinox to the next.

tropopause. The upper boundary of the troposphere.

troposphere. The layer of the atmosphere closest to the earth's surface, in which most weather activities occur.

trough. The depression on either side of a wave crest.

tsunami. A giant wave produced by disturbances on the sea floor; commonly called a "tidal wave."

tundra. A type of climate in the zone of transition between the subarctic regions and the icecaps.

turbidity currents. Strong currents produced by material sliding down the continental slopes.

umbra. The darker inner part of a shadow.

unconformity. An eroded bedrock area which is covered by younger sedimentary rocks.

undertow. A constant current running beneath a line of breakers as water from the breaking waves escapes back to deeper water.

upslope fog. A fog produced by the adiabatic cooling of air as it moves up a slope.

upwelling. Movement of deeper sea water to the surface.

uranium lead. Lead produced by the decomposition of uranium through radioactivity.

valley train. The deposit of rock material carried down by a stream originating from a glacier confined in a narrow valley.

variable star. Any star whose brightness appears to change from time to time.

varves. Annual double layers of fine sediments.

vein. A more or less vertical sheetlike deposit of minerals formed from solutions rather than from magma.

ventifact. A stone that has been smoothed by wind abrasion.

vertebrates. Animals with backbones.

vertical fault. A fault formed by the raising of the blocks of rock evenly so that the layers remain in their original horizontal position.

volcanic neck. A rock plug formed in the passageway of a volcano when magma slowly cools and solidifies there.

volcanism. A general term including all types of activity due to movement of magma.

volcano. The vent from which molten rock materials reach the surface, together with the accumulations of volcanic materials deposited around the vent.

warm front. A front at which a warmer air mass overrides a colder air mass.

warping. The bending of sedimentary beds of rock into broad, low domes and shallow basins.

water gap. A valley that cuts across a mountain ridge, through which the stream still flows.

water table. The upper boundary of the ground water, below which all spaces within the rock are completely filled with water.

wave-built terrace. A seaward extension of a wave-cut terrace, produced by debris from wave action.

wave-cut terrace. A level surface of rock under the water along the shore, formed as waves cut back the shoreline.

weathering. The natural disintegration and decomposition of rocks and minerals.

weightlessness. A condition that occurs when there is no accelerating force acting upon an object.

wind gap. An abandoned stream valley cutting across a ridge.

yazoo stream. A tributary which drains the flood plain of a large stream.

INDEX

Page·references for illustrations are printed in **boldface** type.